Penguin Education X57

# Managerial Economics

Penguin Modern Economic Readings

*General Editor*

B. J. McCormick

*Advisory Board*

K. J. W. Alexander
R. W. Clower
J. Spraos
H. Townsend

# Managerial Economics

## Selected Readings

Edited by G. P. E. Clarkson

Penguin Books

Penguin Books Ltd, Harmondsworth,
Middlesex, England
Penguin Books Inc., 7110 Ambassador Road
Baltimore, Md 21207, U.S.A.
Penguin Books (Australia) Ltd, Ringwood,
Victoria, Australia

First published 1968

This selection © G. P. E. Clarkson, 1968
Introduction and notes © G. P. E. Clarkson, 1968

Made and printed in Great Britain by
Richard Clay (The Chaucer Press Ltd), Bungay, Suffolk
Set in Monotype Times Roman

11728

# Contents

## Part Five **Mathematical Programming**

# Introduction

Managerial economics takes as its domain the economic aspects of management decisions. It is concerned with all decisions that have an economic content irrespective of the level within the enterprise at which they are made. For management is a decision-making activity, and to manage well is to control the decision process so that the resulting behaviour is in keeping with stated objectives.

Traditionally, major emphasis was placed upon the financial decisions such as capital budgeting, equipment replacement, and the analysis of investment opportunities. These questions are of central importance to a firm, and economic analysis was applied to determine the criteria by which such decisions should be judged. More recently, the development of numerous mathematical techniques for analysing decision situations has led to the growth of an activity called operations research. These techniques are being applied to an ever increasing range of managerial problems. Since operations research is devoted to the task of improving decision behaviour, the scope of managerial economics can only be viewed as including these activities and techniques.

In a single volume of readings one is faced with the certainty of having to omit many aspects of varying relevance and importance. A choice must be made between selecting papers on theoretical developments or empirical applications. In either case one must also decide whether it would be more valuable to include contributions closely allied to economic theory or to present those that evolved as a consequence of close inspection of actual operations. In addition there is the level of mathematical difficulty to be considered. An otherwise excellent paper may be rendered unusable by a reader's innumeracy. One must also resolve the dilemma posed by articles which summarize and those that describe special developments or applications in great detail. Finally, there is the question of using a number of approaches to a subject, which implies choosing between a selection of excerpts, or letting one paper speak for all.

These issues are resolved in the following way. First, it cannot be stressed too emphatically that a manager's job is to make and take decisions. Accordingly, the theory and practice of decision-making are the primary subjects of this volume. Second, theoretical developments are more readily evaluated and understood when incorporated in empirical applications. The majority of the readings, therefore, are examples of the use to which particular techniques or models can be put. Third, the important aspects of many decision techniques are most succinctly stated in mathematical form. To assist the reader two types of mathematical papers are included. The first, such as are found in Part Two, contain an explanation of the mathematics employed as part of the exposition. The second type, only to be found in Part Five, incorporates complete descriptions of the techniques concerned. Although they give examples of applications, they are included to provide sufficient information on these techniques so that the remaining papers can be fully understood. With respect to the final two questions both readings that summarize and those that describe an application in detail are included. Excerpts, however, are eschewed. The subject in question is treated in one paper, presented to the reader as an outstanding member of its class.

The readings are divided into five sections. Part One is devoted to a comprehensive exposition of decision theories and their relevance to the managerial decision process. Part Two illustrates the applicability of simple mathematical models to a variety of decision situations – diversification, consumer behaviour, and control of accounts. Two of these papers employ Markov Chains. It should be noted once again that the mathematics employed is explained in the text. Part Three covers the more familiar ground of investment and capital budgeting. Both selections summarize the developments in their respective fields, and both employ mathematical analysis to explicate derivations and results. Readers unfamiliar with mathematical programming should turn to Part Five where a lucid exposition of these techniques is available. Part Four is concerned with the analysis, planning, and control of scheduling production and inventory systems. The mathematics employed is either explained in the text or a discussion of same is available in Part Five. The last section is to be viewed, in part, as a mathematical appendix. It contains an extensive treatment of linear and dynamic programming.

The five sections comprise an outline of the activity encompassed by managerial economics. Any selection of a dozen papers perforce excludes a number of important topics. The serious student is invited to avail himself of the references provided in each of the readings. Care has been taken to include papers that refer widely to the available literature.

# Part One Economic Theory and Business Behaviour

Theories of the managerial decision process are of great importance to the managerial economist. Historically, the manager has been represented as a member of the genus *homo economicus*. His objective has been to maximize net revenue and his decision behaviour was presumed to be guided by the precepts of utility maximization. More recently, the decision process itself has come under close scrutiny by a variety of behavioural scientists. Theoretical descriptions have been compared with test data and new theories have been developed to cope with the inadequacies of the old.

The paper by Simon presents a detailed analysis and survey of the major developments in decision theory. He includes theories of utility, conflict, bargaining, and uncertainty and ends with a discussion of an information processing theory of human problem solving.

Clarkson's paper is concerned with the application of information processing theories to managerial decision problems. He singles out the concept of satisficing and the technique of heuristic programming and discusses how these two contributions are likely to affect future developments in economic theory.

# 1 H. A. Simon

Theories of Decision-making in Economics and
Behavioral Science

H. A. Simon (1959), 'Theories of decision-making in economics and behavioral science', *American Economic Review*, **49**, 253–83.

Recent years have seen important new explorations along the
boundaries between economics and psychology. For the economist, the immediate question about these developments is whether
they include new advances in psychology that can fruitfully be
applied to economics. But the psychologist will also raise the
converse question – whether there are developments in economic
theory and observation that have implications for the central core
of psychology. If economics is able to find verifiable and verified
generalizations about human economic behavior, then these
generalizations must have a place in the more general theories of
human behavior to which psychology and sociology aspire. Influence will run both ways.[1]

## I How Much Psychology Does Economics Need?

How have psychology and economics gotten along with little
relation in the past? The explanation rests on an understanding
of the goals toward which economics, viewed as a science and a
discipline, has usually aimed.

Broadly speaking, economics can be defined as the science that
describes and predicts the behavior of several kinds of economic
man – notably the consumer and the entrepreneur. While perhaps
literally correct, this definition does not reflect the principal focus
in the literature of economics. We usually classify work in economics along two dimensions: (a) whether it is concerned with

1. The influence of economics upon recent work in the psychology of
higher mental processes is well illustrated by Bruner, Goodnow, and Austin
[14, Ch. 3 and 4]. In this work, game theory is used to throw light on the
processes of concept formation.

industries and the whole economy (macroeconomics) or with individual economic actors (microeconomics); and (b) whether it strives to describe and explain economic behavior (descriptive economics), or to guide decisions either at the level of public policy (normative macroeconomics) or at the level of the individual consumer or businessman (normative microeconomics).

The profession and literature of economics have been largely preoccupied with normative macroeconomics. Although descriptive macroeconomics provides the scientific base for policy prescription, research emphases have been determined in large part by relevance to policy (e.g. business cycle theory). Normative microeconomics, carried forward under such labels as 'management science', 'engineering economics', and 'operations research', is now a flourishing area of work having an uneasy and ill-defined relation with the profession of economics, traditionally defined. Much of the work is being done by mathematicians, statisticians, engineers, and physical scientists (although many mathematical economists have also been active in it).[2]

This new area, like the old, is normative in orientation. Economists have been relatively uninterested in descriptive microeconomics – understanding the behaviour of individual economic agents – except as this is necessary to provide a foundation for macroeconomics. The normative microeconomist 'obviously' doesn't need a theory of human behavior: he wants to know how people *ought* to behave, not how they *do* behave. On the other hand, the macroeconomist's lack of concern with individual behavior stems from different considerations. First, he assumes that the economic actor is rational, and hence he makes strong predictions about human behavior without performing the hard work of observing people. Second, he often assumes competition, which carries with it the implication that only the rational survive. Thus, the classical economic theory of markets with perfect competition and rational agents is deductive theory that requires almost no contact with empirical data once its assumptions are accepted.[3]

2. The models of rational decision-making employed in operations research are surveyed in Churchman, Ackoff, and Arnoff [16]; Bowman and Fetter [11]; and Vazsonyi [69].

3. As an example of what passes for empirical 'evidence' in this literature,

Undoubtedly there is an area of human behavior that fits these assumptions to a reasonable approximation, where the classical theory with its assumptions of rationality is a powerful and useful tool. Without denying the existence of this area, or its importance, I may observe that it fails to include some of the central problems of conflict and dynamics with which economics has become more and more concerned. A metaphor will help to show the reason for this failure.

Suppose we were pouring some viscous liquid – molasses – into a bowl of very irregular shape. What would we need in order to make a theory of the form the molasses would take in the bowl? How much would we have to know about the properties of molasses to predict its behavior under the circumstances? If the bowl were held motionless, and if we wanted only to predict behavior in equilibrium, we would have to know little, indeed, about molasses. The single essential assumption would be that the molasses, under the force of gravity, would minimize the height of its center of gravity. With this assumption, which would apply as well to any other liquid, and a complete knowledge of the environment – in this case the shape of the bowl – the equilibrium is completely determined. Just so, the equilibrium behavior of a perfectly adapting organism depends only on its goal and its environment; it is otherwise completely independent of the internal properties of the organism.

If the bowl into which we were pouring the molasses were jiggled rapidly, or if we wanted to know about the behavior before equilibrium was reached, prediction would require much more information. It would require, in particular, more information about the properties of molasses: its viscosity, the rapidity with which it 'adapted' itself to the containing vessel and moved toward its 'goal' of lowering its center of gravity. Likewise, to predict the short-run behavior of an adaptive organism, or its behavior in a complex and rapidly changing environment, it is not enough to know its goals. We must know also a great deal

---

I cite pp. 22–3 of Friedman's *Essays in positive economics* [27], which will amaze anyone brought up in the empirical tradition of psychology and sociology, although it has apparently excited little adverse comment among economists.

about its internal structure and particularly its mechanisms of adaptation.

If, to carry the metaphor a step farther, new forces, in addition to gravitational force, were brought to bear on the liquid, we would have to know still more about it even to predict behavior in equilibrium. Now its tendency to lower its center of gravity might be countered by a force to minimize an electrical or magnetic potential operating in some lateral direction. We would have to know its relative susceptibility to gravitational and electrical or magnetic force to determine its equilibrium position. Similarly, in an organism having a multiplicity of goals, or afflicted with some kind of internal goal conflict, behavior could be predicted only from information about the relative strengths of the several goals and the ways in which the adaptive processes responded to them.

Economics has been moving steadily into new areas where the power of the classical equilibrium model has never been demonstrated, and where its adequacy must be considered anew. Labor economics is such an area, oligopoly or imperfect competition theory another, decision-making under uncertainty a third, and the theory of economic development a fourth. In all of these areas the complexity and instability of his environment becomes a central feature of the choices that economic man faces. To explain his behavior in the face of this complexity, the theory must describe him as something more than a featureless, adaptive organism; it must incorporate at least some description of the processes and mechanisms through which the adaptation takes place. Let us list a little more concretely some specific problems of this kind:

(a) The classical theory postulates that the consumer maximizes utility. Recent advances in the theory of rational consumer choice have shown that the existence of a utility function, and its characteristics, if it exists, can be studied empirically.

(b) The growing separation between ownership and management has directed attention to the motivations of managers and the adequacy of the profit-maximization assumption for business firms. So-called human relations research has raised a variety of issues about the motivation of both executives and employees.

(c) When, in extending the classical theory, the assumptions of perfect competition were removed, even the definition of rationality became ambiguous. New definitions had to be constructed, by no means as 'obvious' intuitively as simple maximization, to extend the theory of rational behavior to bilateral monopoly and to other bargaining and outguessing situations.

(d) When the assumptions of perfect foresight were removed, to handle uncertainty about the environment, the definition of rationality had to be extended in another direction to take into account prediction and the formation of expectations.

(e) Broadening the definition of rationality to encompass goal conflict and uncertainty made it hard to ignore the distinction between the objective environment in which the economic actor 'really' lives and the subjective environment that he perceives and to which he responds. When this distinction is made, we can no longer predict his behavior – even if he behaves rationally – from the characteristics of the objective environment; we also need to know something about his perceptual and cognitive processes.

We shall use these five problem areas as a basis for sorting out some recent explorations in theory, model building, and empirical testing. In Section II, we will examine developments in the theory of utility and consumer choice. In Section III, we will consider somewhat parallel issues relating to the motivation of managers. In Section IV, we will deal with conflict of goals and the phenomena of bargaining. In Section V, we will survey some of the work that has been done on uncertainty and the formation of expectations. In Section VI, we will explore recent developments in the theory of human problem-solving and other higher mental processes, and see what implications these have for economic decision-making.

## II The Utility Function

The story of the re-establishment of cardinal utility, as a consequence of the introduction of uncertainty into the theory of choice, is well known.[4] When Pareto and Slutsky had shown that

4. Ward Edwards [23] provides an account of these developments from the psychologist's point of view; Chapter 2 of Luce and Raiffa [43] is an excellent introduction to the 'new' utility theory. Arrow [5] contains a nonmathematical survey of this and related topics.

the theory of consumer demand could be derived from the properties of indifference curves, without postulating a cardinal utility function underlying these curves, it became fashionable to regard utility as an ordinal measure – a ranking of alternatives by preference. Indeed, it could be shown that only ordinal utility had operational status – that the experiments that had been proposed, and even tried in a couple of instances, to measure an individual's utilities by asking him to choose among alternatives could never distinguish between two cardinal utility functions that were ordinally equivalent – that differed only by stretchings and contractions of the unit of measurement.

It was shown by von Neumann and Morgenstern, as a by-product of their development of the theory of games, that if the choice situation were extended to include choices among uncertain prospects – among lottery tickets, say – cardinal utilities could be assigned to the outcomes in an unequivocal way.[5] Under these conditions, if the subject's behavior was consistent, it was possible to measure cardinally the utilities that different outcomes had for him.

A person who behaved in a manner consistent with the axioms of choice of von Neumann and Morgenstern would act so as to maximize the expected value – the average, weighted by the probabilities of the alternative outcomes of a choice – of his utility. The theory could be tested empirically, however, only on the assumption that the probabilities assigned to the alternatives by the subject were identical with the 'objective' probabilities of these events as known to the experimenter. For example, if a subject believed in the gamblers' fallacy, that after a run of heads an unbiased coin would be more likely to fall tails, his choices might appear inconsistent with his utility function, while the real difficulty would lie in his method of assigning probabilities. This difficulty of 'subjective' versus 'objective' probability soon came to light when attempts were made to test experimentally whether people behaved in accordance with the predictions of the new utility theory. At the same time, it was discovered that the problem had been raised and solved thirty years earlier by the

5. The second edition of von Neumann and Morgenstern [50] contains the first rigorous axiomatic demonstration of this point.

English philosopher and mathematician Frank Ramsey.[6] Ramsey
had shown that, by an appropriate series of experiments, the
utilities and subjective probabilities assigned by a subject to a
set of uncertain alternatives could be measured simultaneously.

*Empirical studies*

The new axiomatic foundations of the theory of utility, which
show that it is possible at least in principle to determine empirically whether people 'have' utility functions of the appropriate
kind, have led to a rash of choice experiments. An experimenter
who wants to measure utilities, not merely in principle but in
fact, faces innumerable difficulties. Because of these difficulties,
most experiments have been limited to confronting the subjects
with alternative lottery tickets, at various odds, for small amounts
of money. The weight of evidence is that, under these conditions,
most persons choose in a way that is reasonably consistent with
the axioms of the theory – they behave as though they were maximizing the expected value of utility and as though the utilities of
the several alternatives can be measured.[7]

When these experiments are extended to more 'realistic' choices
– choices that are more obviously relevant to real-life situations –
difficulties multiply. In the few extensions that have been made,
it is not at all clear that the subjects behave in accordance with
the utility axioms. There is some indication that when the situation is very simple and transparent, so that the subject can easily
see and remember when he is being consistent, he behaves like a
utility maximizer. But as the choices become a little more complicated – choices, for example, among phonograph records instead of sums of money – he becomes much less consistent.[8]

We can interpret these results in either of two ways. We can say

6. Ramsey's important essay [57] was sufficiently obscure that it was overlooked until the ideas were rediscovered independently by de Finetti [26].
Valuable notes on the history of the topic together with a thorough formal
treatment will be found in the first five chapters of Savage [58].
7. Some of the empirical evidence is reviewed in [23]. A series of more recent empirical studies is reported in Davidson and Suppes [21].
8. Some more recent experiments [57a], show a relatively high degree of
transitivity. A. G. Papandreou, in a publication I have not yet seen (University of California Publications in Economics) also reports a high degree of
transitivity. See also [21, Ch. 3] and [47].

that consumers 'want' to maximize utility, and that if we present them with clear and simple choices that they understand they will do so. Or we can say that the real world is so complicated that the theory of utility maximization has little relevance to real choices. The former interpretation has generally appeared more attractive to economists trained in classical utility theory and to management scientists seeking rules of behavior for normative microeconomics; the latter to behavioral scientists interested in the description of behavior.

## Normative applications

The new utility theory has provided the formal framework for much recent work in mathematical statistics – i.e. statistical decision theory.[9] Similarly (it would be accurate to say 'synonymously'), this framework provides the basis for most of the normative models of management science and operations research designed for actual application to the decision-making problems of the firm.[10] Except for some very recent developments, linear programming has been limited to decision-making under certainty, but there have been far-reaching developments of dynamic programming dealing with the maximization of expected values of outcomes (usually monetary outcomes) in situations where future events can be predicted only in terms of probability distributions.[11]

Again, there are at least two distinct interpretations that can be placed on these developments. On the one hand, it can be argued: 'Firms would like to maximize profits if they could. They have been limited in doing so by the conceptual and computational difficulties of finding the optimal courses of action. By providing powerful new mathematical tools and computing machines, we

9. The systematic development of statistics as decision theory is due largely to A. Wald [70] on the basis of the earlier work of J. Neyman and E. Pearson. Savage [58] carries the development farther, erecting the foundations of statistics solidly on utility and probability theory.

10. This work relates, of course, to profit maximization and cost minimization rather than utility maximization, but it is convenient to mention it at this point. See [11], [16], and [69].

11. Arrow, Harris, and Marschak [3] were among the first to treat inventory decisions dynamically. A general treatment of the theory of dynamic programming will be found in Bellman [9].

now enable them to behave in the manner predicted by Alfred Marshall, even if they haven't been able to in the past.' Nature will imitate art and economic man will become as real (and as artificial) as radios and atomic piles.

The alternative interpretation rests on the observation that, even with the powerful new tools and machines, most real-life choices still lie beyond the reach of maximizing techniques – unless the situations are heroically simplified by drastic approximations. If man, according to this interpretation, makes decisions and choices that have some appearance of rationality, rationality in real life must involve something simpler than maximization of utility or profit. In Section VI, we will see where this alternative interpretation leads.

## The binary choice experiment

Much recent discussion about utility has centered around a particularly simple choice experiment. This experiment, in numerous variants, has been used by both economists and psychologists to test the most diverse kinds of hypotheses. We will describe it so that we can use it as a common standard of comparison for a whole range of theories and empirical studies.[12]

We will call the situation we are about to describe the *binary choice* experiment. It is better known to most game theorists – particularly those located not far from Nevada – as a two-armed bandit; and to most psychologists as a partial reinforcement experiment. The subject is required, in each of a series of trials, to choose one or the other of two symbols – say, plus or minus. When he has chosen, he is told whether his choice was 'right' or 'wrong', and he may also receive a reward (in psychologist's language, a reinforcement) for 'right' choices. The experimenter can arrange the schedule of correct responses in a variety of ways. There may be a definite pattern, or they may be randomized. It is not essential that one and only one response be correct on a given trial: the experimenter may determine that both or neither

12. My understanding of the implications of the binary choice experiment owes much to conversations with Julian Feldman, and to his unpublished work on the experiment.* See also, Bush and Mosteller [15] particularly Chapter 13.

* Now available in Feigenbaum and Feldman [72].

will be correct. In the latter case the subject may or may not be informed whether the response he did not choose would have been correct.

How would a utility-maximizing subject behave in the binary choice experiment? Suppose that the experimenter rewarded 'plus' on one-third of the trials, determined at random, and 'minus' on the remaining two-thirds. Then a subject, provided that he believed the sequence was random and observed that minus was rewarded twice as often as plus, should always, rationally, choose minus. He would find the correct answer two-thirds of the time, and more often than with any other strategy.

Unfortunately for the classical theory of utility in its simplest form, few subjects behave in this way. The most commonly observed behavior is what is called *event matching*.[13] The subject chooses the two alternatives (not necessarily at random) with relative frequencies roughly proportional to the relative frequencies with which they are rewarded. Thus, in the example given, two-thirds of the time he would choose minus, and as a result would make a correct response, on the average, in 5 trials out of 9 (on two-thirds of the trials in which he chooses minus, and one-third of those in which he chooses plus).[14]

All sorts of explanations have been offered for the event-matching behavior. The simplest is that the subject just doesn't understand what strategy would maximize his expected utility; but with adult subjects in a situation as transparent as this one, this explanation seems far-fetched. The alternative explanations imply either that the subject regards himself as being engaged in a competitive game with the experimenter (or with 'nature' if he accepts the experimenter's explanation that the stimulus is random), or that his responses are the outcome of certain kinds of learning processes. We will examine these two types of explanation further in Sections IV and V respectively. The important

13. An example of data consistent with event-matching behavior is given on p. 283 of [15].

14. Subjects tend to choose the more highly rewarded alternative slightly more frequently than is called for by event matching. Hence, the actual behavior tends to be some kind of average between event matching and the optimal behavior. See [15, Ch. 13].

conclusion at this point is that even in an extremely simple situation, subjects do not behave in the way predicted by a straight-forward application of utility theory.

## Probabilistic preferences

Before we leave the subject of utility, we should mention one recent important development. In the formalizations mentioned up to this point, probabilities enter only into the estimation of the consequences that will follow one alternative or another. Given any two alternatives, the first is definitely preferable to the second (in terms of expected utility), or the second to the first, or they are strictly indifferent. If the same pair of alternatives is presented to the subject more than once, he should always prefer the same member of the pair.

One might think this requirement too strict – that, particularly if the utility attached to one alternative were only slightly greater or less than that attached to the other, the subject might vacillate in his choice. An empirical precedent for such vacillation comes not only from casual observation of indecision but from analogous phenomena in the psycho-physical laboratory. When subjects are asked to decide which of two weights is heavier, the objectively heavier one is chosen more often than the lighter one, but the relative frequency of choosing the heavier approaches one-half as the two weights approach equality. The probability that a subject will choose the objectively heavier weight depends, in general, on the ratio of the two weights.

Following several earlier attempts, a rigorous and complete axiom system for a utility theory incorporating probabilistic preferences has been constructed recently by Duncan Luce[15]. Although the theory weakens the requirements of consistency in preference, it is empirically testable, at least in principle. Conceptually, it provides a more plausible interpretation of the notion of 'indifference' than does the classical theory.

## III The Goals of Firms

Just as the central assumption in the theory of consumption is that the consumer strives to maximize his utility, so the crucial

15. cf. [43, App. 1].

assumption in the theory of the firm is that the entrepreneur strives to maximize his residual share – his profit. Attacks on this hypothesis have been frequent.[16] We may classify the most important of these as follows:

(a) The theory leaves ambiguous whether it is short-run or long-run profit that is to be maximized.

(b) The entrepreneur may obtain all kinds of 'psychic income' from the firm, quite apart from monetary rewards. If he is to maximize his utility, then he will sometimes balance a loss of profits against an increase in psychic income. But if we allow 'psychic income', the criterion of profit maximization loses all of its definiteness.

(c) The entrepreneur may not care to maximize, but may simply want to earn a return that he regards as satisfactory. By sophistry and adept use of the concept of psychic income, the notion of seeking a satisfactory return can be translated into utility maximizing but not in any operational way. We shall see in a moment that 'satisfactory profits' is a concept more meaningfully related to the psychological notion of aspiration levels than to maximization.

(d) It is often observed that under modern conditions the equity owners and the active managers of an enterprise are separate and distinct groups of people, so that the latter may not be motivated to maximize profits.

(e) Where there is imperfect competition among firms, maximizing is an ambiguous goal, for what action is optimal for one firm depends on the actions of the other firms.

In the present section we shall deal only with the third of these five issues. The fifth will be treated in the following section; the first, second, and fourth are purely empirical questions that have been discussed at length in the literature; they will be considered here only for their bearing on the question of satisfactory profits.

### Satisficing versus maximizing

The notion of satiation plays no role in classical economic theory, while it enters rather prominently into the treatment of motiva-

16. For a survey of recent discussions see Papandreou [55].

tion in psychology. In most psychological theories the motive to act stems from *drives*, and action terminates when the drive is satisfied. Moreover, the conditions for satisfying a drive are not necessarily fixed, but may be specified by an aspiration level that itself adjusts upward or downward on the basis of experience.

If we seek to explain business behavior in the terms of this theory, we must expect the firm's goals to be not maximizing profits, but attaining a certain level or rate of profit, holding a certain share of the market or a certain level of sales. Firms would try to 'satisfice' rather than to maximize.[17]

It has sometimes been argued that the distinction between satisficing and maximizing is not important to economic theory. For in the first place, the psychological evidence on individual behavior shows that aspirations tend to adjust to the attainable. Hence in the long run, the argument goes, the level of aspiration and the attainable maximum will be very close together. Second, even if some firms satisficed, they would gradually lose out to the maximizing firms, which would make larger profits and grow more rapidly than the others.

These are, of course, precisely the arguments of our molasses metaphor, and we may answer them in the same way that we answered them earlier. The economic environment of the firm is complex, and it changes rapidly; there is no *a priori* reason to assume the attainment of long-run equilibrium. Indeed, the empirical evidence on the distribution of firms by size suggests that the observed regularities in size distribution stem from the statistical equilibrium of a population of adaptive systems rather than the static equilibrium of a population of maximizers.[18]

Models of satisficing behavior are richer than models of maximizing behavior, because they treat not only of equilibrium but of the method of reaching it as well. Psychological studies of the

17. A comparison of satisficing with maximizing models of decision-making can be found in [64, Ch. 14]. Katona [40] has independently made similar comparisons of economic and psychological theories of decision.

18. Simon and Bonini [66] have constructed a stochastic model that explains the observed data on the size distributions of business firms.

formation and change of aspiration levels support propositions of the following kinds:[19]

(a) When performance falls short of the level of aspiration, search behavior (particularly search for new alternatives of action) is induced.

(b) At the same time, the level of aspiration begins to adjust itself downward until goals reach levels that are practically attainable.

(c) If the two mechanisms just listed operate too slowly to adapt aspirations to performance, emotional behavior – apathy or aggression, for example – will replace rational adaptive behavior.

The aspiration level defines a natural zero point in the scale of utility – whereas in most classical theories the zero point is arbitrary. When the firm has alternatives open to it that are at or above its aspiration level, the theory predicts that it will choose the best of those known to be available. When none of the available alternatives satisfies current aspirations, the theory predicts qualitatively different behavior: in the short run, search behavior and the revision of targets; in the longer run, what we have called above emotional behavior, and what the psychologist would be inclined to call neurosis.[20]

### Studies of business behavior

There is some empirical evidence that business goals are, in fact, stated in satisficing terms.[21] First, there is the series of studies stemming from the pioneering work of Hall and Hitch that

19. A standard psychological reference on aspiration levels is [42]. For applications to economics, see [61] and [45] (in the latter, consult the index under 'aspiration levels').

20. Lest this last term appear fanciful I should like to call attention to the phenomena of panic and broken morale, which are well known to observers of the stock market and of organizations but which have no reasonable interpretation in classical utility theory. I may also mention that psychologists use the theory described here in a straightforward way to produce experimental neurosis in animal and human subjects.

21. A comprehensive bibliography of empirical work prior to 1950 will be found in [37]. Some of the more recent works is [19], [24], and [39, Ch. 11].

indicates that businessmen often set prices by applying a standard markup to costs. Some economists have sought to refute this fact, others to reconcile it – if it is a fact – with marginalist principles. The study of Earley[22] belongs to the former category, but its evidence is suspect because the questions asked of businessmen are leading ones – no one likes to admit that he would accept less profit if he could have more. Earley did not ask his respondents how they determined marginal costs and marginal revenue, how, for example, they estimated demand elasticities.

Another series of studies derived from the debate over the Keynesian doctrine that the amount of investment was insensitive to changes in the rate of interest. The general finding in these studies has been that the rate of interest is not an important factor in investment decisions.[23]

More recently, my colleagues Cyert and March, have attempted to test the satisficing model in a more direct way [19]. They found in one industry some evidence that firms with a declining share of market strove more vigorously to increase their sales than firms whose shares of the market were steady or increasing.

### Aspirations in the binary choice experiment

Although to my knowledge this has not been done, it would be easy to look for aspiration-level phenomena in the binary choice experiment. By changing the probabilities of reward in different ways for different groups of subjects we could measure the effects of these changes on search behavior – where amount of search would be measured by changes in the pattern of responses.

### Economic implications

It has sometimes been argued that, however unrealistic the classical theory of the firm as a profit maximizer, it is an adequate theory for purposes of normative macroeconomics. Mason, for example, in commenting on Papandreou's essay on 'Problems in the theory of the firm'[24] says 'The writer of this critique must confess a lack of confidence in the marked superiority, *for purposes of economic analysis*, of this newer concept of the firm over the older conception of the entrepreneur.' The italics are Mason's.

22. Cf. [22a, pp. 44–70].
23. Cf. [24], [39, Ch. 11], and [71].
24. [55, pp. 183–222].

The theory of the firm is important for welfare economics – e.g. for determining under what circumstances the behavior of the firm will lead to efficient allocation of resources. The satisficing model vitiates all the conclusions about resource allocation and are derivable from the maximizing model when perfect competition is assumed. Similarly, a dynamic theory of firm sizes, like that mentioned above, has quite different implications for public policies dealing with concentration than a theory that assumes firms to be in static equilibrium. Hence, welfare economists are justified in adhering to the classical theory only if: (a) the theory is empirically correct as a description of the decision-making process; or (b) it is safe to assume that the system operates in the neighborhood of the static equilibrium. What evidence we have mostly contradicts both assumptions.

## IV  Conflict of Interest

Leaving aside the problem of the motivations of hired managers, conflict of interest among economic actors creates no difficulty for classical economic theory – indeed, it lies at the very core of the theory – so long as each actor treats the other actors as parts of his 'given' environment, and doesn't try to predict their behavior and anticipate it. But when this restriction is removed, when it is assumed that a seller takes into account the reactions of buyers to his actions, or that each manufacturer predicts the behaviors of his competitors – all the familiar difficulties of imperfect competition and oligopoly arise.[25]

The very assumptions of omniscient rationality that provide the basis for deductive prediction in economics when competition is present lead to ambiguity when they are applied to competition among the few. The central difficulty is that rationality requires one to outguess one's opponents, but not to be outguessed by them, and this is clearly not a consistent requirement if applied to all the actors.

25. There is by now a voluminous literature on the problem. The difficulties in defining rationality in competitive situations are well stated in the first chapter of von Neumann and Morgenstern [50].

## Game theory

Modern game theory is a vigorous and extensive exploration of ways of extending the concept of rational behavior to situations involving struggle, outguessing, and bargaining. Since Luce and Raiffa [43] have recently provided us with an excellent survey and evaluation of game theory, I shall not cover the same ground here.[26] I concur in their general evaluation that, while game theory has greatly clarified the issues involved, it has not provided satisfactory solutions. Not only does it leave the definition of rational conduct ambiguous in all cases save the zero-sum two-person game, but it requires of economic man even more fantastic reasoning powers than does classical economic theory.[27]

## Power and bargaining.

A number of exploratory proposals have been put forth as alternatives to game theory – among them Galbraith's notion of countervailing power [30] and Schelling's bargaining theory [59, 60]. These analyses draw at least as heavily upon theories of power and bargaining developed initially to explain political phenomena as upon economic theory. They do not lead to any more specific predictions of behavior than do game-theoretic approaches, but place a greater emphasis upon description and actual observation, and are modest in their attempt to derive predictions by deductive reasoning from a few 'plausible' premises about human behavior.

At least four important areas of social science and social policy, two of them in economics and two more closely related to political science, have as their central concern the phenomena of power and the processes of bargaining: the theory of political parties, labor-management relations, international politics, and oligopoly theory. Any progress in the basic theory applicable to one of these is certain to be of almost equal importance to the others. A growing recognition of their common concern is

26. Chapters 5 and 6 of [43] provide an excellent survey of the attempts that have been made to extend the theory of games to the kinds of situations most relevant to economics.

27. In a forthcoming volume on *Strategy and market structure*, Martin Shubik approaches the topics of imperfect competition and oligopoly from the standpoint of the theory of games.

evidenced by the initiation of a new cross-disciplinary journal, *Journal of Conflict Resolution*.

## Games against nature

While the binary choice experiment is basically a one-person game, it is possible to interpret it as a 'game against nature', and hence to try to explain it in game-theoretic terms. According to game theory, the subject, if he believes in a malevolent nature that manipulates the dice against him, should minimax his expected utility instead of maximizing it. That is, he should adopt the course of action that will maximize his expected utility under the assumption that nature will do her worst to him.

Minimaxing expected utility would lead the subject to call plus or minus at random and with equal probability, regardless of what the history of rewards has been. This is something that subjects demonstrably do not do.

However, it has been suggested by Savage [58] and others that people are not as interested in maximizing utility as they are in minimizing regret. 'Regret' means the difference between the reward actually obtained and the reward that could have been obtained with perfect foresight (actually, with perfect hindsight!). It turns out that minimaxing regret in the binary choice experiment leads to event-matching behavior.[28] Hence, the empirical evidence is at least crudely consistent with the hypothesis that people play against nature by minimaxing regret. We shall see, however, that event-matching is also consistent with a number of other rules of behavior that seem more plausible on their face; hence we need not take the present explanation too seriously – at least I am not inclined to do so.

## V The Formation of Expectations

While the future cannot enter into the determination of the present, expectations about the future can and do. In trying to gain an understanding of the saving, spending, and investment behavior of both consumers and firms, and to make short-term predictions of this behavior for purposes of policy-making,

28. Cf. [64, Ch. 16].

economists have done substantial empirical work as well as theorizing on the formation of expectations.

*Empirical studies*

A considerable body of data has been accumulated on consumer's plans and expectations from the Survey of Consumer Finances, conducted for the Board of Governors of the Federal Reserve System by the Survey Research Center of the University of Michigan.[29] These data, and similar data obtained by others, begin to give us some information on the expectations of consumers about their own incomes, and the predictive value of their expenditure plans for their actual subsequent behavior. Some large-scale attempts have been made, notably by Modigliani and Brumberg[30] and, a little later, by Friedman [28] to relate these empirical findings to classical utility theory. The current empirical research on businessmen's expectations is of two main kinds:

1. Surveys of businessmen's own forecasts of business and business conditions in the economy and in their own industries[31] These are obtained by straightforward questionnaire methods that assume, implicitly, that businessmen can and do make such forecasts. In some uses to which the data are put, it is also assumed that the forecasts are used as one basis for businessmen's actions.

2. Studies of business decisions and the role of expectations in these decisions – particularly investment and pricing decisions. We have already referred to studies of business decisions in our discussion of the goals of the firm.[32]

*Expectations and probability*

The classical way to incorporate expectations into economic theory is to assume that the decision-maker estimates the joint probability distribution of future events.[33] He can then act so as to maximize the expected value of utility or profit, as the case may be. However satisfying this approach may be conceptually,

29. Cf. [39, Ch. 5].
30. Cf. [48, pp. 383–436].
31. Cf. [24, pp. 165–88] and [29, pp. 189–98].
32. See the references cited [12, p. 160].
33. A general survey of approaches to decision-making under uncertainty will be found in [2] and in [43, Ch. 13].

it poses awkward problems when we ask how the decision-maker actually estimates the parameters of the joint probability distribution. Common sense tells us that people don't make such estimates, nor can we find evidence that they do by examining actual business forecasting methods. The surveys of businessmen's expectations have never attempted to secure such estimates, but have contented themselves with asking for point predictions – which, at best, might be interpreted as predictions of the means of the distributions.

It has been shown that under certain special circumstances the mean of the probability distribution is the only parameter that is relevant for decision – that even if the variance and higher moments were known to the rational decision-maker, he would have no use for them.[34] In these cases, the arithmetic mean is actually a certainty equivalent, the optimal decision turns out to be the same as if the future were known with certainty. But the situations where the mean is a certainty equivalent are, as we have said, very special ones, and there is no indication that businessmen ever ask whether the necessary conditions for this equivalence are actually met in practice. They somehow make forecasts in the form of point predictions and act upon them in one way or another.

The 'somehow' poses questions that are important for business cycle theory, and perhaps for other problems in economics. The way in which expectations are formed may affect the dynamic stability of the economy, and the extent to which cycles will be amplified or damped. Some light, both empirical and theoretical, has recently been cast on these questions. On the empirical side, attempts have been made: (a) to compare businessmen's forecasts with various 'naïve' models that assume the future will be some simple function of the recent past, and (b) to use such naïve models themselves as forecasting devices.

The simplest naïve model is one that assumes the next period will be exactly like the present. Another assumes that the change from present to next period will equal the change from last period to present; a third, somewhat more general, assumes that the

34. The special case in which mean expectations constitute a certainty equivalent is treated in [62]. An alternative derivation, and fuller discussion is given by Theil [67, Ch. 8, sect. 6].

next period will be a weighted average of recent past periods. The term 'naïve model' has been applied loosely to various forecasting formulae of these general kinds. There is some affirmative evidence that business forecasts fit such models. There is also evidence that elaboration of the models beyond the first few steps of refinement does not much improve prediction.[35] Arrow and his colleagues [4] have explored some of the conditions under which forecasting formulas will, and will not, introduce dynamic instability into an economic system that is otherwise stable. They have shown, for example, that if a system of multiple markets is stable under static expectations, it is stable when expectations are based on a moving average of past values.

The work on the formation of expectations represents a significant extension of classical theory. For, instead of taking the environment as a 'given', known to the economic decision-maker, it incorporates in the theory the processes of acquiring knowledge about that environment. In doing so, it forces us to include in our model of economic man some of his properties as a learning, estimating, searching, information-processing organism [65].

## The cost of information

There is one way in which the formation of expectations might be reincorporated in the body of economic theory: by treating information-gathering as one of the processes of production, so to speak, and applying to it the usual rules of marginal analysis. Information, says price theory, should be gathered up to the point where the incremental cost of additional information is equal to the incremental profit that can be earned by having it. Such an approach can lead to propositions about optimal amounts of information-gathering activity and about the relative merits of alternative information-gathering and estimating schemes.[36]

This line of investigation has, in fact, been followed in statistical decision theory. In sampling theory we are concerned with the

35. Cf., e.g. [20].
36. Fundamental and applied research are examples of economically significant information-gathering activities. Griliches [34] has recently made an attempt to estimate the economic return from research on hybrid corn.

optimal size of sample (and in the special and ingenious case of sequential sampling theory, with knowing when to stop sampling), and we wish to evaluate the efficiencies of alternative sampling procedures. The latter problem is the simpler, since it is possible to compare the relative costs of alternative schemes that have the same sampling error, and hence to avoid estimating the value of the information.[37] However, some progress has been made also toward estimating the value of improved forecast accuracy in situations where the forecasts are to be used in applying formal decision rules to choice situations.[38]

The theory of teams developed by Marschak and Radner is concerned with the same problem.[39] It considers situations involving decentralized and interdependent decision-making by two or more persons who share a common goal and who, at a cost, can transmit information to each other about their own actions or about the parts of the environment with which they are in contact. The problem then is to discover the optimal communication strategy under specified assumptions about communication costs and payoffs.

The cost of communication in the theory of teams, like the cost of observations in sampling theory, is a parameter that characterizes the economic actor, or the relation of the actor to his environment. Hence, while these theories retain, in one sense, a classical picture of economic man as a maximizer, they clearly require considerable information about the characteristics of the actor, and not merely about his environment. They take a long stride toward bridging the gap between the traditional concerns of economics and the concerns of psychology.

*Expectations in the binary choice experiment*

I should like to return again to the binary choice experiment, to see what light it casts on the formation of expectations. If the subject is told by the experimenter that the rewards are assigned at random, if he is told what the odds are for each alternative,

37. Modern treatments of sampling theory, like Cochran [17] are based on the idea of minimizing the cost of obtaining a fixed amount of information.

38. For the theory and an application to macroeconomics, see Theil [67, Ch. 8, sects. 5 and 6].

39. Cf. e.g. [46].

*and if he believes the experimenter*, the situation poses no fore-casting problem. We have seen, however, that the behavior of most subjects is not consistent with these assumptions.

How would sequential sampling theory handle the problem? Each choice the subject makes now has two consequences: the immediate reward he obtains from it, and the increment of in-formation it provides for predicting the future rewards. If he thinks only of the latter consequences, he is faced with the classical problem of induction: to estimate the probability that an event will occur in the future on the basis of its frequency of occurrence in the past. Almost any rule of induction would require a rational (maximizing) subject to behave in the following general manner: to sample the two alternatives in some proportion to estimate the probability of reward associated with each; after the error of estimate had been reduced below some bound, always to choose the alternative with the higher probability of reward. Unfortu-nately, this does not appear to be what most subjects do.

If we give up the idea of maximization, we can make the weaker assumption that the subject is adaptive – or learns – but not necessarily in any optimal fashion. What do we mean by adapta-tion or learning? We mean, gradually and on the basis of experi-ence responding more frequently with the choice that, in the past, has been most frequently rewarded. There is a whole host of rules of behavior possessing this characteristic. Postulate, for example, that at each trial the subject has a certain probability of responding 'plus', and the complementary probability of re-sponding 'minus'. Postulate further that when he makes a parti-cular response the probability of making the same response on the next trial is increased if the response is rewarded and decreased if the response is not rewarded. The amount of increment in the response probability is a parameter characterizing the learning rate of the particular subject. Almost all schemes of this kind produce asymptotic behaviors, as the number of trials increases, that are approximately event-matching in character.

Stochastic learning models, as the processes just described are usually called, were introduced into psychology in the early 1950s by W. K. Estes and Bush and Mosteller [15] and have been investigated extensively since that time. The models fit some of the gross features of the observed behaviors – most strikingly the asymptotic probabilities – but do not explain very satisfactorily the fine structure of the observations.

Observations of subjects in the binary choice experiment reveals that usually they not only refuse to believe that (or even to act as if) the reward series were random, but in fact persist over many trials in searching for systematic patterns in the series. To account for such behavior, we might again postulate a learning model, but in this case a model in which the subject does not react probabilistically to his environment, but forms and tests definite hypotheses about systematic patterns in it. Man, in this view, is not only a learning animal; he is a pattern-finding and concept-forming animal. Julian Feldman [25] has constructed theories of this kind to explain the behavior of subjects in the binary choice experiment, and while the tests of the theories are not yet completed, his findings look exceedingly promising.

As we move from maximizing theories, through simple stochastic learning theories, to theories involving pattern recognition our model of the expectation-forming processes and the organism that performs it increases in complexity. If we follow this route, we reach a point where a theory of behavior requires a rather elaborate and detailed picture of the rational actor's cognitive processes.

## VI  Human Cognition and Economics

All the developments we have examined in the preceding four sections have a common theme: they all involve important modifications in the concept of economic man and, for the reasons we have stated, modifications in the direction of providing a fuller description of his characteristics. The classical theory is a theory of a man choosing among fixed and known alternatives, to each of which is attached known consequences. But when perception and cognition intervene between the decision-maker and his objective environment, this model no longer proves adequate. We need a description of the choice process that recognizes that alternatives are not given but must be sought; and a description that takes into account the arduous task of determining what consequences will follow on each alternative.[40]

40. Cf. [63, Ch. 5], [64, part 4], and [14].

The decision-maker's information about his environment is much less than an approximation to the real environment. The term 'approximation' implies that the subjective world of the decision-maker resembles the external environment closely, but lacks, perhaps, some fineness of detail. In actual fact the perceived world is fantastically different from the 'real' world. The differences involve both omissions and distortions, and arise in both perception and inference. The sins of omission in perception are more important than the sins of commission. The decision-maker's model of the world encompasses only a minute fraction of all the relevant characteristics of the real environment, and his inferences extract only a minute fraction of all the information that is present even in his model.

Perception is sometimes referred to as a 'filter'. This term is as misleading as 'approximation', and for the same reason: it implies that what comes through into the central nervous system is really quite a bit like what is 'out there'. In fact, the filtering is not merely a passive selection of some part of a presented whole, but an active process involving attention to a very small part of the whole and exclusion, from the outset, of almost all that is not within the scope of attention.

Every human organism lives in an environment that generates millions of bits of new information each second, but the bottle neck of the perceptual apparatus certainly does not admit more than 1,000 bits per second, and probably much less. Equally significant omissions occur in the processing that takes place when information reaches the brain. As every mathematician knows, it is one thing to have a set of differential equations, and another thing to have their solutions. Yet the solutions are logically implied by the equations – they are 'all there', if we only knew how to get to them! By the same token, there are hosts of inferences that *might* be drawn from the information stored in the brain that are not in fact drawn. The consequences implied by information in the memory become known only through active information-processing, and hence through active selection of particular problem-solving paths from the myriad that might have been followed.

In this section we shall examine some theories of decision-making that take the limitations of the decision-maker and the complexity of the environment as central concerns. These theories incorporate some mechanisms we have already discussed – for example, aspiration levels and forecasting processes – but go beyond them in providing a detailed picture of the choice process.

A real-life decision involves some goals or values, some facts about the environment, and some inferences drawn from the values and facts. The goals and values may be simple or complex, consistent or contradictory; the facts may be real or supposed, based on observation or the reports of others; the inferences may be valid or spurious. The whole process may be viewed, metaphorically, as a process of 'reasoning', where the values and facts serve as premises, and the decision that is finally reached is inferred from these premises [63]. The resemblance of decision-making to logical reasoning is only metaphorical, because there are quite different rules in the two cases to determine what constitute 'valid' premises and admissible modes of inference. The metaphor is useful because it leads us to take the individual *decision premise* as the unit of description, hence to deal with the whole interwoven fabric of influences that bear on a single decision – but without being bound by the assumptions of rationality that limit the classical theory of choice.

### Rational behavior and role theory

We can find common ground to relate the economist's theory of decision-making with that of the social psychologist. The latter is particularly interested, of course, in social influences on choice, which determine the *role* of the actor. In our present terms, a role is a social prescription of some, but not all, of the premises that enter into an individual's choices of behavior. Any particular concrete behavior is the resultant of a large number of premises, only some of which are prescribed by the role. In addition to role premises there will be premises about the state of the environment based directly on perception, premises representing beliefs and knowledge, and idiosyncratic premises that characterize the personality. Within this framework we can accommodate both the rational elements in choice, so much emphasized by economics, and the nonrational elements to which psychologists and sociologists often prefer to call attention.

## Decision premises and computer programs

The analysis of choice in terms of decision premises gives us a conceptual framework for describing and explaining the process of deciding. But so complex is the process that our explanations of it would have remained schematic and hypothetical for a long time to come had not the modern digital computer appeared on the scene. The notion of decision premise can be translated into computer terminology, and when this translation has been accomplished, the digital computer provides us with an instrument for simulating human decision processes – even very complex ones – and hence for testing empirically our explanations of those processes [53].

A fanciful (but only slightly fanciful) example will illustrate how this might be done. Some actual examples will be cited presently. Suppose we were to construct a robot incorporating a modern digital computer, and to program (i.e. to instruct) the robot to take the role of a business executive in a specified company. What would the program look like? Since no one has yet done this, we cannot say with certainty, but several points are fairly clear. The program would not consist of a list of prescribed and proscribed behaviors, since what an executive does is highly contingent on information about a wide variety of circumstances. Instead, the program would consist of a large number of *criteria* to be applied to possible and proposed courses of action, of routines for *generating* possible courses of action, of computational procedures for *assessing* the state of the environment and its implications for action, and the like. Hence, the program – in fact, a role prescription – would interact with information to produce concrete behavior adapted to the situation. The elements of such a program take the form of what we have called decision premises, and what the computer specialists would call instructions.

The promise of constructing actual detailed descriptions of concrete roles and decision processes is no longer, with the computer, a mere prospectus to be realized at some undefined future date. We can already provide actual examples, some of them in the area of economics.

1. *Management science*. In the paragraphs on normative applications in Section II, we have already referred to the use of such

mathematical techniques as linear programming and dynamic programming to construct formal decision processes for actual situations. The relevance of these decision models to the present discussion is that they are not merely abstract 'theories' of the firm, but actual decision-making devices. We can think of any such device as a simulation of the corresponding human decision-maker, in which the equations and other assumptions that enter into the formal decision-making procedure correspond to the decision premises – including the role prescription – of the decision-maker.

The actual application of such models to concrete business situations brings to light the information-processing tasks that are concealed in the assumptions of the more abstract classical models:[41]

(a) The models must be formulated so as to require for their application only data that are obtainable. If one of the penalties, for example, of holding too small inventories is the loss of sales, a decision model that proposes to determine optimal inventory levels must incorporate a procedure for putting a dollar value on this loss.

(b) The models must call only for practicable computations. For example, several proposals for applying linear programming to certain factory scheduling problems have been shown to be impracticable because, even with computers, the computation time is too great. The task of decision theory (whether normative or descriptive) is to find alternative techniques – probably only approximate – that demand much less computation.

(c) The models must not demand unobtainable forecast information. A procedure that would require a sales department to estimate the third moment of next month's sales distribution would not have wide application, as either description or prescription, to business decision-making.

These models, then, provide us with concrete examples of roles for a decision-maker described in terms of the premises he is expected to apply to the decision – the data and the rules of computation.

41. Cf. [65, pp. 51–2].

2. *Engineering design.* Computers have been used for some years to carry out some of the analytic computations required in engineering design – computing the stresses, for example, in a proposed bridge design. Within the past two years, ways have been found to program computers to carry out synthesis as well as analysis – to evolve the design itself.[42] A number of companies in the electrical industry now use computers to design electric motors, transformers, and generators, going from customer specifications to factory design without human intervention. The significance of this for our purpose here is that the synthesis programs appear to simulate rather closely the processes that had previously been used by college-trained engineers in the same design work. It has proved possible to write down the engineers' decision premises and inference processes in sufficient detail to produce workable computer programs.

3. *Human problem solving.* The management science and engineering design programs already provide examples of simulation of human decision-making by computer. It may be thought that, since in both instances the processes are highly arithmetical, these examples are relevant to only a very narrow range of human problem-solving activity. We generally think of a digital computer as a device which, if instructed in painful detail by its operator, can be induced to perform rather complicated and tedious arithmetical operations. More recent developments require us to revise these conceptions of the computer, for they enable it to carry out tasks that, if performed by humans, we would certainly call 'thinking' and 'learning'.

Discovering the proof of a theorem of Euclid – a task we all remember from our high school geometry course – requires thinking and usually insight and imagination. A computer is now being programmed to perform this task (in a manner closely simulating the human geometer), and another computer has been successfully performing a highly similar task in symbolic logic for the past two years.[43] The latter computer is programmed to learn – that is to improve its performance on the basis of successful

42. A nontechnical description of such a program will be found in [33].
43. The program for proving theorems in logic is discussed in [51] and [52], Gelernter and Rochester's geometry program in [31].

problem-solving experience – to use something akin to imagery or metaphor in planning its proofs, and to transfer some of its skills to other tasks – for example, solving trigonometric identities – involving completely distinct subject matter. These programs, it should be observed, do not involve the computer in rapid arithmetic – or any arithmetic for that matter. They are basically non-numerical, involving the manipulation of all kinds of symbolic material, including words.

Still other computer programs have been written to enable a computer to play chess.[44] Not all of these programs, or those previously mentioned, are close simulations of the processes humans use. However, in some direct attempts to investigate the human processes by thinking-aloud techniques and to reproduce in computer programs the processes observed in human subjects, several striking simulations have been achieved.[45] These experiments have been described elsewhere and can't be reviewed here in detail.

4. *Business games.* Business games, like those developed by the American Management Association, International Business Machines Corporation, and several universities, represent a parallel development.[46] In the business game, the decisions of the business firms are still made by the human players, but the economic environment of these first, including their markets, are represented by computer programs that calculate the environment's responses to the actions of the players. As the games develop in detail and realism, their programs will represent more and more concrete descriptions of the decision processes of various economic actors – for example, consumers.

The games that have been developed so far are restricted to numerical magnitudes like prices and quantities of goods, and hence resemble the management science and engineering design programs more closely than they do those we have described under the heading of human problem solving. There is no reason, however, to expect this restriction to remain very long.

44. A survey of computer chess programs can be found in [54].
45. Much of this work is still unpublished, but see [53] [54], and [72].
46. Two business games are described by Andlinger [1].

*Implications for economics*

Apart from normative applications (e.g. substituting computers for humans in certain decision-making tasks) we are not interested so much in the detailed descriptions of roles as in broader questions:

(a) What general characteristics do the roles of economic actors have?

(b) How do roles come to be structured in the particular ways they do?

(c) What bearing does this version of role theory have for macroeconomics and other large-scale social phenomena?

*Characterizing role structure.* Here we are concerned with generalizations about thought processes, particularly those generalizations that are relatively independent of the substantive content of the role. A classical example is Dewey's description of stages in the problem-solving process. Another example, of particular interest to economics, is the hypothesis we have already discussed at length: that economic man is a *satisficing* animal whose problem solving is based on search activity to meet certain aspiration levels rather than a *maximizing* animal whose problem solving involves finding the best alternatives in terms of specified criteria [64]. A third hypothesis is that operative goals (those associated with an observable criterion of success, and relatively definite means of attainment) play a much larger part in governing choice than nonoperative goals (those lacking a concrete measure of success or a program for attainment).[47]

*Understanding how roles emerge.* Within almost any single business firm, certain characteristic types of roles will be represented: selling roles, production roles, accounting roles, and so on [22]. Partly, this consistency may be explained in functional terms – that a model that views the firm as producing a product, selling it, and accounting for its assets and liabilities is an effective simplification of the real world, and provides the members of the organization with a workable frame of reference. Imitation within the culture provides an alternative explanation. It is exceedingly

47. Cf. [45, p. 156].

difficult to test hypotheses as to the origins and causal conditions for roles as universal in the society as these, but the underlying mechanisms could probably be explored effectively by the study of less common roles – safety director, quality control inspector, or the like – that are to be found in some firms, but not in all.

With our present definition of role, we can also speak meaningfully of the role of an entire business firm – of decision premises that underlie its basic policies. In a particular industry we find some firms that specialize in adapting the product to individual customers' specifications; others that specialize in product innovation. The common interest of economics and psychology includes not only the study of individual roles, but also the explanation of organizational roles of these sorts.

*Tracing the implications for macroeconomics.* If basic professional goals remain as they are, the interest of the psychologist and the economist in role theory will stem from somewhat different ultimate aims. The former will use various economic and organizational phenomena as data for the study of the structure and determinants of roles; the latter will be primarily interested in the implications of role theory for the model of economic man, and indirectly, for macroeconomics.

The first applications will be to those topics in economics where the assumption of static equilibrium is least tenable. Innovation, technological change, and economic development are examples of areas to which a good empirically tested theory of the processes of human adaptation and problem solving could make a major contribution. For instance, we know very little at present about how the rate of innovation depends on the amounts of resources allocated to various kinds of research and development activity [34]. Nor do we understand very well the nature of 'know how', the costs of transferring technology from one firm or economy to another, or the effects of various kinds and amounts of education upon national product. These are difficult questions to answer from aggregative data and gross observation, with the result that our views have been formed more by arm-chair theorizing than by testing hypotheses with solid facts.

## VII Conclusion

In exploring the areas in which economics has common interests with the other behavioral sciences, we have been guided by the metaphor we elaborated in Section I. In simple, slow-moving situations, where the actor has a single, operational goal, the assumption of maximization relieves us of any need to construct a detailed picture of economic man or his processes of adaptation. As the complexity of the environment increases, or its speed of change, we need to know more and more about the mechanisms and processes that economic man uses to relate himself to that environment and achieve his goals.

How closely we wish to interweave economics with psychology depends, then, both on the range of questions we wish to answer and on our assessment of how far we may trust the assumptions of static equilibrium as approximations. In considerable part, the demand for a fuller picture of economic man has been coming from the profession of economics itself, as new areas of theory and application have emerged in which complexity and change are central facts. The revived interest in the theory of utility, and its application to choice under uncertainty, and to consumer saving and spending is one such area. The needs of normative macroeconomics and management science for a fuller theory of the firm have led to a number of attempts to understand the actual processes of making business decisions. In both these areas, notions of adaptive and satisficing behavior, drawn largely from psychology, are challenging sharply the classical picture of the maximizing entrepreneur.

The area of imperfect competition and oligopoly has been equally active, although the activity has thus far perhaps raised more problems than it has solved. On the positive side, it has revealed a community of interest among a variety of social scientists concerned with bargaining as a part of political and economic processes. Prediction of the future is another element common to many decision processes, and particularly important to explaining business cycle phenomena. Psychologists and economists have been applying a wide variety of approaches, empirical and theoretical, to the study of the formation of expectations. Surveys of consumer and business behavior, theories of statistical induction, stochastic learning theories, and theories of concept formation have all been converging on this problem area.

The very complexity that has made a theory of the decision-making process essential has made its construction exceedingly difficult. Most approaches have been piecemeal – now focused on the criteria of choice, now on conflict of interest, now on the formation of expectations. It seemed almost utopian to suppose that we could put together a model of adaptive man that would compare in completeness with the simple model of classical economic man. The sketchiness and incompleteness of the newer proposals has been urged as a compelling reason for clinging to the older theories, however inadequate they are admitted to be.

The modern digital computer has changed the situation radically. It provides us with a tool of research – for formulating and testing theories – whose power is commensurate with the complexity of the phenomena we seek to understand. Although the use of computers to build theories of human behavior is very recent, it has already led to concrete results in the simulation of higher mental processes. As economics finds it more and more necessary to understand and explain disequilibrium as well as equilibrium, it will find an increasing use for this new tool and for communication with its sister sciences of psychology and sociology.

*References*

1. ANDLINGER, G. R. (1958) 'Business games – play one', *Harvard Bus. Rev.*, **36**, 115–25.
2. ARROW, K. J. (1951) 'Alternative approaches to the theory of choice in risk-taking situations', *Econometrica*, **19**, 404–37.
3. ARROW, K. J., HARRIS, T. E. and MARSCHAK, J. (1951) 'Optimal inventory policy', *Econometrica*, **19**, 250–72.
4. ARROW, K. J. and NERLOVE, M. (1958) 'A note on expectations and stability', *Econometrica*, **26**, 297–305.
5. ARROW, K. J. (1958) 'Utilities, attitudes, choices', *Econometrica*, **26**, 1–23.
6. BAKAN, D. (1953) 'Learning and the principle of inverse probability', *Psych. Rev.*, **60**, 360–70.
7. A. BAVELAS, (1948) 'A mathematical model for group structures', *Applied Anthropology*, **7**, 16–30.
8. BECKMANN, M. (1958) 'Decision and team problems in airline reservations', *Econometrica*, **26**, 134–45.

9. BELLMAN, R. (1957) *Dynamic programming*. Princeton.

10. BOWEN, H. R. (1955) *The business enterprise as a subject for research*. New York.

11. BOWMAN, E. H. and FETTER, R. B. (1957) *Analysis for Production Management*. Homewood, Ill.

12. BOWMAN, M. J. ed. (1958) *Expectations, uncertainty, and business behavior*. New York.

13. BREMS, H. 'Response lags and nonprice competition', in Bowman [12, Ch. 10, pp. 134–43].

14. BRUNNER, J. GOODNOW, J. J. and AUSTIN, G. A. (1956) *A study of thinking*. New York.

15. BUSH, R. R. and MOSTELLER, F. (1955) *Stochastic models for learning*. New York.

16. CHURCHMAN, C. W., ACKOFF, R. L. and ARNOFF, E. L. (1957) *Introduction to operations research*. New York.

17. COCHRAN, W. G. (1953) *Sampling techniques*. New York.

18. CYERT, R. M. and MARCH, J. G. (1955) 'Organizational structure and pricing behavior in an oligopolistic market', *Am. Econ. Rev.*, **45**, 129–39.

19. CYERT, R. M. and MARCH, J. G. (1956) 'Organizational factors in the theory of oligopoly', *Quart. Jour. Econ.*, **70**, 44–64.

20. DARCOVICH, W. 'Evaluation of some naïve expectations models for agricultural yields and prices', in Bowman [12, Ch. 14, pp. 199–202].

21. DAVIDSON, D. and SUPPES, P. (1957) *Decision making: an experimental approach*. Stanford.

22. DEARBORN, D. C. and SIMON (1958) 'Selective perception: A note on the departmental identification of executives', *Sociometry*, **21**, 140–4.

22a. EARLEY, J. S. (1956) 'Marginal policies of "Excellently managed" companies', *Am. Econ. Rev.*, **66**, 44–70.

23. EDWARDS, W. (1954) 'The theory of decision making', *Psych. Bull.*, **51**, 380–417.

24. EISNER, R. 'Expectations, plans, and capital expenditures', in Bowman [12, Ch. 12, 165–88].

25. FELDMAN, J. (1958) 'A theory of binary choice behavior', Carnegie Inst. of Tech., Grad. Sch. Indus. Admin., Complex Information Processing Working Paper No. 12, rev. Unpublished ditto.

26. FINETTI, B. DE (1937) 'La prevision: ses lois logiques, ses sources subjectives', *Annales Inst. Henri Poincare*, **7**, 1–68.

27. FRIEDMAN, M. (1953) *Essays in positive economics*. Chicago.

28. FRIEDMAN, M. (1956) *A Theory of the consumption function*. New York.

29. FRIEND, I. 'Critical evaluation of surveys of expectations, plans, and investment behavior', in Bowman [12, Ch. 13, pp. 189–98].

30. GALBRAITH, J. K. (1952) *American capitalism: the concept of countervailing power*. Boston.

31. GELERNTER, H. L. and ROCHESTER, N. (1958) 'Intelligent behavior in problem-solving machines', *IBM J. Research and Develop.*, **2**, 336–45.

32. GEORGESCU-ROEGEN, N. 'The nature of expectation and uncertainty' in Bowman [12, Ch. 1, pp. 11–29].

33. GODWIN, G. L. (1958) 'Digital computers tap out designs for large motors – fast', *Power*.

34. GRILICHES, Z. (1957) 'Hybrid corn: an Exploration in the economics of technological change', *Econometrica*, **25**, 501–22.

35. GUETZKOW and SIMON, H. A. (1955) 'The impact of certain communication nets in task oriented groups', *Management Sci.*, **1**, 233–50.

36. HALEY, B. F. ed. (1952) *A survey of contemporary economics*, Vol. II. Homewood, Ill.

37. HAYES, S. P. (1950) 'Some psychological problems of economics', *Psych. Bull.*, **47**, 289–330.

38. HOLT, C. C., MODIGLIANI, F. and SIMON, H. A. (1955) 'A linear decision rule for production and employment scheduling', *Management Sci.*, **2**, 1–30.

39. KATONA, G. (1951) *Psychological analysis of economic behavior*. New York.

40. KATONA, G. (1953) 'Rational behavior and economic behavior', *Psych. Rev.*, **60**, 307–18.

41. LEAVITT, H. J. (1951) 'Some effects of certain communication patterns on group performance', *J. Abnormal and Soc. Psych.*, **46**, 38–50.

42. LEWIN, K. and others, (1944) 'Level of aspiration', in J. McV. Hunt, *Personality and the behavior disorders* pp. 333–78, New York.

43. LUCE, R. D. and RAIFFA, H. (1957) *Games and decisions*. New York.

44. MACK, R. 'Business expectations and the buying of materials', in Bowman [12, Ch. 8, pp. 106–18].

45. MARCH, J. G. and SIMON, H. A. (1958) *Organizations*. New York.

46. MARSCHAK, J. (1955) 'Elements for a theory of teams', *Management Sci.*, **1**, 127–37.

47. MAY, K. O. (1954) 'Intransitivity, utility, and the aggregation of preference patterns', *Econometrica*, **22**, 1–13.

48. MODIGLIANI, F. and BRUMBERG, R. E. (1954) 'Utility analysis and the consumption function', in K. K. Kurihara, *Post keynesian Economics*, pp. 388–436, New Brunswick, N.J.

49. MOSTELLER, F. and NOGEE, P. (1951) 'An experimental measurement of utility', *J. Pol. Econ.* **59**, 371–404.

50. NEUMANN, J. VON and MORGENSTERN, O. (1947) *Theory of games and Economic behavior*. Princeton.

51. NEWELL, A. and SIMON, H. A. (1956) 'The logic theory machine', *IRE Transactions of information theory*, IT-**2**, 61–79.

52. NEWELL, A. SHAW, J. C. and SIMON, H. A. (1957) 'Empirical explorations of the logic theory machine', *Proceedings of the Western Joint Computer Conference, Feb. 26–28, 1957*, pp. 218–30.

53. NEWELL, A., SHAW, J. C. and SIMON, H. A. (1958) 'Elements of a theory of human problem solving', *Psych. Rev.* 65, 151–66.

54. NEWELL, A., SHAW, J. C. and SIMON, H. A. (1958) 'Chess-playing programs and the problem of complexity', *IBM J. Research and Develop.*, 2, 320–35.

55. PAPANDREOU, A. G. 'Some basic problems in the theory of the firm', in Haley [36, Ch. 5, pp. 183–222].

56. PECK, M. J. 'Marginal analysis and the explanation of business behavior under uncertainty', in Bowman [12, Ch. 9, pp. 119–33].

57. RAMSEY, F. P. (1931) 'Truth and probability', in the *Foundations of mathematics and other logical essays* pp. 156–98, London.

57a. ROSE, A. M. (1957) 'A study of irrational judgments', *J. Pol. Econ.*, 65, 394–402.

58. SAVAGE, L. J. (1954) *The foundations of statistics.* New York.

59. SCHELLING, T. C. (1957) 'Bargaining, communication, and limited war', *J. Conflict Resolution*, 1, 19–36.

60. SCHELLING, T. C. (1956) 'An Essay on Bargaining', *Am. Econ. Rev.*, 46, 281–306.

61. SIEGEL, S. (1957) 'Level of aspiration and decision making', *Psych. Rev.*, 64, 253–62.

62. SIMON, H. A. (1956) 'Dynamic programming under uncertainty with a quadratic criterion function', *Econometrica*, 24 ,74–81.

63. SIMON, H. A. (1957) *Administrative behavior.* New York.

64. SIMON, H. A. (1957) *Models of man.* New York.

65. SIMON, H. A. 'The role of expectations in an adaptive or behavioristic model', in Bowman [12, Ch. 3, pp. 49–58].

66. SIMON, H. A. and BONINI, C. P. (1958) 'The size distribution of business firms', *Am. Econ. Rev.*, 48, 607–17.

67. THEIL, H. (1958) *Economic forecasts and policy.* Amsterdam.

68. THURSTONE, L. L. (1931) 'The indifference function', *J. Soc. Psych.* 2, 139–67.

69. VAZSONYI, A. (1958) *Scientific programming in business and industry.* New York.

70. WALD, A. (1950) *Statistical decision functions.* New York.

71. WILSON, T. and ANDREWS, P. W. S. (1951) *Oxford studies in the Price Mechanism.* Oxford.

72. FEIGENBAUM, E. A. and FELDMAN, J. (1963) *Computers and thought.* New York.

# 2 G. P. E. Clarkson

Interactions of Economic Theory and Operations
Research

G. P. E. Clarkson (1963) 'Interactions of economic theory and operations
research', in A. R. Oxenfeldt (ed.), *Models of markets*, Columbia University
Press, pp. 339–61.

In the last few years an increasing amount of attention has been
paid to the theoretical and technical developments that have
evolved from the interaction of economic theory and operations
research. During this period a number of papers have appeared
which review the advances in economic theory as well as in the
techniques of operations research.[1] Some of these papers have
been directly concerned with the interplay between these two
bodies of knowledge.[2] It would be redundant to devote this paper
to retracing developments that have already been well noted and
discussed. Hence, I shall not present a complete history of these
interactions but, instead, I shall focus upon two important innovations that have occurred as a direct consequence of the activity
of economic theorists and operation researchers. The first of these
innovations is the modified concept of rational behavior known
as 'satisficing'; and the second is the technique of theory and
model construction known as 'heuristic programming'. Customarily these two notions are presented and discussed independently. But it is the combination of these two ideas that has led to
what I am going to take the liberty of calling one of the major
advances in our knowledge of organizational and individual
decision-making behavior. In order to point out the effects that
these two concepts have had both on the economic theory of the

1. See, for example, the excellent review articles of H. A. Simon (1959)
'Theories of decision-making in economics', *Am. Econ. Rev.*, **49**, 253–83;
and R. Dorfman (1960) 'Operations research', *Am. Econ. Rev.*, **50**, 575–623.
2. See the papers presented by W. W. Cooper, W. J. Baumol, and C. J.
Hitch and R. N. McKean (1961) for the symposium, 'Managerial economics: a new frontier?' to be found in the *Papers and Proc. of the AEA*,
*Am. Econ. Rev.*, **51**, 131–55.

firm and on the practice of operations research, this paper is divided into three main sections. The first part is devoted to a brief description of some of the important changes in the theory of the firm that have been brought about by the introduction of the satisficing concept of behavior. The second contains a brief description of the development of heuristic programming, as well as an actual example in which the satisficing concept and the technique of heuristic programming are conjoined in the solution of a complex business problem. And the third section is devoted to an attempt to assess the implications of these two innovations both for general economic theory and its policy considerations as well as the practice of operations research.

## Developments in the Theory of the Firm

To be able to trace a change or development in a theory, one must have a point at which to begin. For our purpose, the starting point will be the classical or conventional theory of the firm. Unfortunately, there is considerable disagreement among economists as to precisely what is the 'Theory of the Firm'. Since no one theory has been graced with this title for any length of time, I shall present what I consider represents a reasonable consensus of opinion.

### Classical theory[3]

The classical theory of the firm is a theory of market behavior. It is concerned with explaining, at a general and aggregated level, the allocative process of the market place. In particular, the theory takes as its objective the explanation of the behavior of firms and, consequently, the allocation of resources among firms under varying market conditions, e.g. pure competition, oligopoly, and monopoly. The firm, in this theory, is an entity whose objective is to maximize its net revenue (profits). The firm sets out to accomplish this objective by taking the prices of its inputs (labor, materials, equipment, and capital) as being given to it by the market place. It then examines its production function which

3. For a more detailed and extensive description of the classical theory of the firm see J. M. Henderson and R. E. Quandt (1958) *Microeconomic theory*, especially pp. 42–84. New York, McGraw-Hill.

is taken to be determined by the current state of technology. To maximize its net revenue, the firm decides upon the particular combination of inputs and outputs that is optimal with respect to the given prices and the production function.

In the market condition known as pure competition the firm is allowed to sell at a given price whatever quantity of finished product it produces. In this situation the theory is concerned with specifying the conditions under which such an optimum can be attained. In particular, when we are dealing with firms that only produce one product, the theory states the optimum position will be reached if the output of each firm is adjusted so that the marginal cost of producing this number of items is exactly equal to the marginal revenue derived from their sale. The theory also extends to multiproduct firms and specifies the optimal procedures whereby these firms can decide how much of each good it should produce. After specifying the conditions under which firms engaging in pure competition can maximize their net revenue, the theory then explains the effects of changes in the prices of products and factors of production which result from alterations in the equilibrium position of the total market.

Because all markets do not meet the conditions of perfect competition, the theory extends to meet cases where the market for the factors of production is imperfect, or the market for final products is imperfect, or both. One case in particular has received a considerable amount of attention. This is the market condition called oligopoly, where a small number of producers effectively dominate the market for a product or a specific set of products. In this case there are a number of contending theories whose primary objective is to specify the manner in which, for example, firm A takes into account the pricing and output decisions of firms B and C.[4] However, in all these extensions to different market conditions the theory retains the same internal decision-making process – namely, it is the object of each firm to maximize its profit. Thus, while the classical theory of the firm has been extended to meet various market situations, its primary purpose has remained unchanged. Its objective is to specify

4. For a survey of some recent theories of oligopoly see: Franco Modigliani (1958) 'New developments on the oligopoly front', *J. Pol. Econ.*, **46**, 215–32.

the mechanisms by which resources are allocated in the market place.

Lately, this theory, or collection of theories, has come under attack from a number of quarters. Some critics have argued that firms do not decide how much to produce by equating marginal cost with marginal revenue. As evidence, they point to the difference between the economic concept of cost found in the theory as against the accounting concept of cost used in actual business firms.[5] Other critics have noted that the theory does not view the firm as an organization and ignores the existence of such items as management planning, budgets, standard operating procedures, and the host of other components which they argue should be included in a theory of a firm's decision-making process.[6] These and many other criticisms reflect the central fact that the classical theory of the firm was constructed to explain, at a general level, the behavior of firms within a given market, and not the behavior of individuals within a particular firm. Consequently, these criticisms not only reflect the disparity between the behavior of actual firms and the firms of the theory, but also the directions in which the theory ought to be revised if it is to become a vehicle for explaining and predicting the variety of behavior exhibited in the market place, as well as inside the firm.

## Recent revisions

As noted above, the many critiques are not so much comments on the inadequacy of classical theory to meet its stated goals as they are suggestions to guide the development of a new microtheory of the firm. That is to say, the majority of suggestions pertain to the construction of a theory that describes and predicts the internal decision-making process of a firm. Most of these suggestions have come from economists who, while engaged in consulting and operations research capacities, found that the classical theory was not suited to their needs. For example, to

5. See, for example: R. L. Hall and C. J. Hitch (1951) 'Price theory and business behavior', in T. Wilson and P. W. S. Andrews (eds.), *Oxford studies in the price mechanism*, 107–38, Oxford Univ. Press.

6. A. Papandreou 'Some basic problems in the theory of the firm', in B. F. Haley (ed.), *A survey of contemporary economics*, vol. 2, 183–219. Homewood, Ill.

quote a leading economist: 'I can say quite categorically that I have never encountered a business problem in which my investigation was helped by any specific economic theorem.'[7] As one might expect, the disparity between theory and observable practices has stimulated economists to propose several new theories. And we shall now examine two of the principal classes of revisions that have taken place.

*Market theories.* The first major revision was proposed by Professor Baumol. From his observations of business behavior Baumol arrived at the conclusion that firms do not devote all their energies to maximizing profits, but rather, that as long as a 'satisfactory level' of profit is maintained, a company will seek to maximize its sales revenue. This theory, which is worked out in some detail,[8] differs sharply in some respects from the classical theory out of which it grew. One obvious difference is that total sales revenue has been substituted for profits. But what is much more important is that the theory includes two decision criteria or objectives – namely, a satisfactory level of profit and the highest sales possible. In other words, the firm is no longer viewed as working toward one objective alone. Instead, it is portrayed as having to balance two competing and not necessarily consistent goals.

From this principal hypothesis Baumol draws several important conclusions, which are more consistent with observed behavior than the conclusions drawn from conventional theory. The first of these is that firms faced with an increase in fixed costs will either pass these costs directly to the consumer in the form of higher prices or will try to reduce an expense over which they have some control, e.g. advertising expenditures. Conventional theory, on the other hand, asserts that changes in fixed costs (overhead) should not lead a firm to alter either its output or its prices. A second and rather important conclusion that Baumol draws is: 'Sales maximization makes far greater the presumption that businessmen will consider *non*price competition to be the more advantageous alternative.'[9] Classical theory asserts that

7. W. J. Baumol, 'What can economic theory contribute to managerial economics?' *Papers and Proc. Am. Econ. Assoc.*, 144.

8. W. J. Baumol (1959) *Business behavior, value and growth*, especially pp. 45–53. Macmillan, New York.

9. W. J. Baumol, *Business behavior*, p. 76.

businessmen will consider price cuts or increases as the primary mechanism for increasing profits, but observations of business behavior do not support this dictum. On the contrary, firms appear to go to great lengths to set their prices at the same levels as their competitors, while devoting their competitive energies toward advertising, product distribution, servicing, and the like.

While Baumol's theory is clearly more consistent with observed behavior, its primary focus is upon the behavior of firms in the market place. The theory does not describe in any detail the decision procedures whereby firms are able to maximize their sales subject to their satisfactory-level-of-profit constraint. That is to say, even though a firm may wish to maximize its sales, if it is not aware of the particular set of decisions and procedures that will lead it to this goal, then it is unlikely to succeed. Skepticism with respect to this and other basic premises of the decision-making process in these market theories stimulated a second major type of revision.

*Behavioral theories.* Even though operations researchers have not been concerned with conducting large surveys of business practice, their exertions have produced samples of data on business decision making which are strikingly at variance with the decision processes postulated in classical market theories. This divergence between theory and data has led some economists to abandon nomative formulations – that is, rules by which price output decisions should be made – and concentrate on developing a body of theory that describes and predicts the actual decision processes found in business firms. Instead of focusing on market mechanisms these theorists consider the firm as the basic unit. Their objective is the analysis and prediction of a firm's decision-making behavior on price, output, internal resource allocation, and so on. To create such a theory, however, requires a knowledge of the major classes and attributes of business decisions. It is easy to see how these researchers have been led, from such a research commitment, to investigate the variety of alternatives facing business decision makers as well as the processes by which choices are made. In brief, the object of this research is to discover how organizational objectives are formed, how decision strategies are developed, and how, on the basis of these strategies, conflicts are reduced and decisions made.[10]

The minute one abandons the classical notion that all firms have a single, universal goal, to maximize net revenue, and substitutes for it the notion that firms have a variety of goals, then a decision mechanism must be introduced that permits conflicts between objectives to be resolved. As noted above, Baumol retained the principle of maximization in his market theory but made the pursuit of maximum sales revenue contingent upon the firm's realizing, at the same time, an acceptable level of profit. But for a theory that intends to describe as well as predict the internal decision behavior of firms it is not sufficient merely to name a decision mechanism, e.g. maximize sales subject to a profit constraint. If the object is to describe decision behavior, then the processes included in the theory must be defined in sufficient detail to allow the relevant decisions to be traced through the organization and tested against observable behavior. Mechanisms must be introduced that account for the processes by which a search for new information is initiated, the order in which alternatives are considered, and the order in which decisions are made.

The inclusion of these and other, similar decision processes into a theory of firm behavior has led to the development of what has been entitled the Behavioral Theory of the Firm.[11] This is a theory of how an organization makes decisions on the basis of the information that is available at any given point in time. It is a theory of decision-making behavior which has substituted the notion of a satisfactory level of performance for the classical principle of maximization.

By abandoning the classical principle of maximizing for the behavioral principle of satisficing, the theorist can add to his

10. For examples of the literature on this research, see: R. M. Cyert and J. G. March (1956) 'Organizational factors in a theory of oligopoly', *Quart. J. Econ.* **70**, 44–64; R. M. Cyert, W. R. Dill, and J. G. March (1958). 'The role of expectations in business decision-making', *Admin. Sci. Quart.*, **3**, 307–40; and R. M. Cyert and J. G. March (1959) 'Introduction to a behavioral theory of organizational objectives', in M. Haire (ed.), *Modern organization theory*. New York.

11. For a complete statement of the theory and of the empirical research that has been conducted so far, see R. M. Cyert and J. G. March (1963) *The behavioral theory of the firm*. Prentice-Hall.

theory as many goals or objectives as are consistent with observed behavior. Each goal now enters the theory as a single constraint, and current performance on each goal is evaluated with respect to past and expected performance. Hence, the total number of objectives defines a set of satisfactory performance figures. A satisfactory level of performance on sales, for example, represents a level of aspiration with respect to sales which the firm will use to evaluate alternative decisions. The level of aspiration can rise or fall over time, but in the short run it performs the task of measuring the success of present performance. Current results are either satisfactory or they are unsatisfactory. And each goal enters the decision-making process with one or the other of these values.[12]

For example, consider the decision mechanisms included in a model that was designed to describe and predict the behavior of a firm entering a market previously dominated by one major producer.[13] In this duopoly model, Cyert, Feigenbaum, and March outline the decision-making procedures used by each firm. The decision process consists of a sequence of individual decisions which finally result in each firm setting its output for the coming period. The output decision is made by first considering the competitor's reactions to any proposed changes in output over the previous period. Estimates of the demand for and the costs of producing this output are made, and the estimated profits are calculated to make sure that this profit is at an acceptable level. If a satisfactory level of profit is not obtained, then the firm searches for ways of reducing costs, revises its estimates of the demand for its product, and if necessary, lowers the profit goal so that it is consistent with the revised cost and output figures. Although this model was not developed to reproduce the behavior of any particular firm, it was tested against the recorded history of the tin can industry. By specifying parameter values for the

12. For a more extensive discussion of the need for, as well as the characteristics of a satisfying decision mechanism, see: J. Margolis (1958) 'The analysis of the firm: rationalism, conventionalism, and behaviorism', *J. Business*, **31**, 187–99; H. A. Simon (1952) 'A behavioral model of rational choice', *Quart. J. Econ.* **59**, 99–118.

13. R. M. Cyert, E. A. Feigenbaum, and J. G. March (1959) 'Models in a behavioral theory of the firm', *Behavioral Sci.* **4**, 81–95.

model, a stream of behavior was generated that closely paralleled some of the notable features of the behavior of the Continental Can Company from the time it entered the market as a competitor of the American Can Company.[14] Since a classical model of duopoly does not exist that can generate roughly comparable outputs on the basis of roughly comparable inputs, it is not possible to compare the performance of a classical model with this behavioral one. But it is possible to compare, at a fairly general level, the behavior of this model with the behavior of two specific, existing business firms. Whether this advance could have been made without the introduction of a satisficing mechanism is difficult to determine. That it was made with its inclusion is, of course, a matter of historical fact.

## The Development of Heuristic Programming

At the same time that these revisions were taking place in the economic theory of the firm, advances were being made by operations researchers in the application of such techniques as linear and dynamic programming to business problems. Many production, scheduling, and inventory problems are now being tackled and solved by the application of these and other mathematical tools.[15] But a significant proportion of management's problems – namely, those whose structure is elusive and whose importance requires special treatment by middle and top management – are too complex to be successfully handled by current operations research techniques. Even though heroic simplifications can always be made there are a striking number of decision problems which are simply not amenable to current mathematical treatment. The answer appears to lie in the theory and technique of heuristic programming. To understand what is meant and implied by this technique we must first briefly examine the theory of human problem solving from which this technique has evolved.

14. Op. cit., Figs. I and II, pp. 91 and 92.
15. These techniques are discussed and many applications are noted in C. W. Churchman, R. L. Ackoff, and E. L. Arnoff (1957) *Introduction to operations research*. Wiley.

G. P. E. Clarkson

## A theory of human problem solving

The theory of human problem solving that we shall consider was developed by Newell, Shaw, and Simon,[16] to explain and predict the decision-making behaviour of humans engaged in solving specified tasks. The object of the theory is to explain the problem solving process by identifying the types of decision processes that people use as well as the various decision mechanisms that permit these processes to be employed. A basic assumption of the theory is that thinking processes can be isolated as well as identified, and that they can be represented by a series of straightforward mechanical operations. This is not to say that thought processes are simple or easy to represent, but rather that they can be broken down into their elemental parts that, in turn, consist of collections of simple mechanisms. When these operations are recorded as a set of statements (decision rules) which describe the behavior under investigation, that behavior is said to have been 'programmed'.

Programs, however, can contain a wide variety of decision rules. When operations researchers apply their mathematical techniques to a business problem the programs they construct to produce a solution almost invariably employ algorithmic decision rules. These decision rules describe a set of procedures and calculations which guarantee that the required minimum or maximum will be found.

Humans, on the other hand, when engaged in solving complex problems, do not employ these algorithmic techniques. Instead they use 'rules of thumb', or heuristics, to guide them in their search for solutions. For example, in a game of chess a good player may look three or four moves ahead on a number of possible plays. And by evaluating the consequences of these possibilities he will decide on his next move. If, however, algorithmic decision rules were employed to search for the 'best' move he would now have to examine every possible move and its consequences before coming to a decision. If there were thirty possible moves that he could make and he examined each alternative for two moves ahead, then he would need to examine $30^4$, or roughly 800,000 possibilities before he could be sure that he

16. A Newell, J. C. Shaw, and H. A. Simon (1958) The elements of a theory of human problem solving, *Psychological Rev.* **65**, 151–66.

had found the best move.[17] Clearly, chess players, like other human beings, are unable to consider 800,000 possibilities in a few minutes. Thus, the importance of rules of thumb or heuristics is that they frequently lead us to solutions which we would otherwise reach much more expensively, if at all, by algorithmic and other analytic techniques.

When a program is constructed that attempts to reproduce the decision processes of a human problem solver the decision rules are in the form of heuristics. These programs are called heuristic programs and have two important characteristics. The first is the ability to determine, at any point in the decision process, its subsequent action by making choices between the alternatives that are available to it at that particular point in time. This property, called branching, or conditional transfer, allows a program to adapt itself to changes in the alternatives. Hence, heuristic programs can follow strategies. The second important characteristic is the capacity to use any set or sets of operations repetitively and recursively. In other words, a specific operation can be employed over and over again to perform the same function on a stream of inputs; or a decision rule can be applied to itself, to form a hierarchy of the same operations to be applied to a specific set or sets of inputs. In this manner a heuristic program can use the same decision mechanisms to process different pieces of information or to solve quite different sets of problems.

Heuristic programming, then, is an attempt to incorporate into the theoretical structure of a model the selective, rule of thumb processes that humans employ in solving complex problems. It is a technique that has been used to reproduce parts of the thinking or problem-solving process.[18] And more recently it has begun to be used as an aid in management decision making.[19]

17. For an excellent discussion of existing chess programs as well as the problems involved in constructing a heuristic chess program, see A. Newell, J. C. Shaw, and H. A. Simon (1958) 'Chess-playing and the problems of complexity', *IBM J. Res. and Develop.*, **2**, 320–35.

18. For an excellent example of the growing literature of this subject, see A. Newell and H. A. Simon (1959) 'The simulation of human thought', W. Dennis (ed.), *Current Trends in psychological theory*, pp. 152–79. Univ. Pittsburgh Press, 1959.

19. See, for example, H. A. Simon (1960) *The new science of management decision.* Harper and Brothers.

G. P. E. Clarkson

*Heuristic programming: an example*

To illustrate these remarks let us consider for a moment a heuristic program which was developed to solve assembly-line balancing problems.[20] Although no direct attempt was made to simulate a particular, human assembly-line balance, this program was modeled on the decision processes used by skilled human schedulers. The object of the program is to schedule, or balance, an assembly line.

The problem of scheduling an assembly line is similar to many other types of industrial scheduling problems, e.g. the scheduling of orders in a job shop, the routing of travelling salesmen, and the assigning of a given number of men to a given number of machines. The essence of these tasks is a combinatorial problem in which the elements of a set (the pieces that go to make up the final article, the orders in a job shop, and the like) are ordered or grouped on the basis of one or more criteria. While some of these problems have been tackled by standard operations research techniques,[21] they are frequently too large and complex to be solved by algorithmic procedures. For example, if the product to be assembled contains one hundred parts and we are looking for the most efficient way to assemble them, then to be certain we had located the best way we might have to inspect each of $100! = 9.3 \times 10^{157}$ possible arrangements. Now, if we employed a high-speed computer and inspected $10^6$ orderings each second it would take $3 \times 10^{114}$ years to cover them all. Clearly, blind-search techniques of this sort are simply not feasible methods for solving combinatorial problems of any size.

The task of scheduling an assembly line consists of assigning the components making up the total assembly to work stations along the line. In order to consider an actual problem, Tonge's program assumes that the speed of the conveyer belt is fixed, e.g. there is constant production rate, and that the time required to assemble each component part is known. The goal of the program

20. F. M. Tonge (1961) *A heuristic program for assembly-line balancing.* Prentice-Hall.

21. For an excellent discussion of the application of linear programming to many of these problems, see A. Charnes and W. W. Cooper (1961) *Management models and industrial applications of linear programming.* Wiley.

is to discover the minimum number of workmen that are needed to keep up with the given production rate and to meet the partial ordering constraints imposed on the assembly operation. Heuristics are employed to sufficiently simplify the task so that it can finally be solved by straightforward methods.

The program consists of three main phases. The first is concerned with ordering the elemental tasks into fairly large subassemblies. Each of these subassemblies contains its own partial orderings between its elements, and each requires a certain amount of operating time. Hence, at the end of phase one, the program has constructed a hierarchy of subassemblies. The second phase takes these subassemblies and assigns to them the required number of workmen. It then treats each subassembly as a separate scheduling problem and assigns the workmen to the various components of each subassembly. After this rough scheduling of men and component parts is completed, phase three is employed. This phase consists of a 'smoothing' operation. It adjusts the components and the men among the work stations set up by the first two phases until the distribution of assigned time per worker is as even as possible.

Since this program was not designed to reproduce a specific scheduler's behavior, it is somewhat difficult to directly compare its performance with that of an industrial scheduler. However, the program was tested on a 70-element problem that was roughly similar to a particular industrial assembly line. Even though the industrial engineer had to contend with a few extra constraints, the program's performance compared very favorably with that of the engineer's. For the 70-element problem the heuristic program required 23 men to complete the assembly operation, as against the 26 men assigned to the task by the industrial scheduler. While this result by no means demonstrates the superiority of the heuristic program it is striking evidence of the power and versatility of this technique.

## Implications of These Innovations for Economic Theory and Operations Research

From the foregoing discussion it should be readily apparent that the introduction of the concept of satisficing and the technique of heuristic programming have already had a significant impact on the fundamental research conducted in the economic theory of the firm and in operations research. It should be clear that the chief object of this research is to be able to explain, as well as improve, the decision-making behavior of individuals and organizations. Although most of this research is of very recent origin, sufficient progress has been made to tempt me to try and outline some of the implications this research should have on the development of economic theory and on the guiding of business decisions.

*Economic theory*

It is my belief that the principal effect of the researches in decision-making behavior will be noticed in economic theory itself. For example, in the first section it was noted that the empirical investigation of business decision procedures has led some economists to propose extensive revisions in the classical theory of the firm. These revisions were stimulated by the manifest disparity between classical theory and observed practice. One of the more notable of these differences is exemplified by the way the pricing mechanism is employed. In the classical theory, firms are supposed to maximize their profit. And the pricing mechanism is declared to be the most efficient method of allocating resources in the market place. But if, as in Baumol's theory, firms only maximize sales revenue subject to a satisfactory-profit constraint, or if, as in the Behavioral Theory of the Firm, firms no longer maximize any criterion function, then the classical assertions about the efficacy of the pricing mechanism may also require revision.

As a further example, consider the assumptions, contained in classical theories, that have been called into question by these researches into decision-making behavior. In particular, consider the assumption that firms, or individuals, make decisions by maximizing a clearly defined decision function. All the evidence collected so far by these investigators supports the hypothesis that individuals and organizations make decisions by paying attention to a limited number of objectives, and by doing what they can to see that they meet these goals most of the time.[22] The objectives,

22. For an extensive and stimulating discussion of organizational decision-making behavior, see J. G. March and H. A. Simon (1958) *Organizations*. Wiley.

however, are not stated as clearly defined decision functions. On the contrary, they are usually stated in terms of past behavior, and current performance either is or is not up to these fairly flexible standards or objectives. If this is a reasonably accurate statement of the case, then the setting of prices for, example, can only be one of a number of organizational objectives. As a result, a firm will only consider the altering of prices as one of the possible alternatives facing it at any point in time.

A corollary of this conclusion is that changes in the prices of a firm's inputs will also not have the effects on their decision processes that are asserted by classical theory. Firms do not equate marginal cost with marginal revenue. And even if they had some idea of how to make these calculations, the pressure of satisfying competing goals would probably prevent them from carrying out and making use of such calculations.

It is apparent, therefore, that as behavioral theories are developed and tested, the conflict between the classical and the new will probably sharpen. And as I am reasonably convinced that the evidence will support the behavioral theories, I would expect to see some rather large and basic revisions being made in many branches of economic theory. These changes will not be induced because the revised theories are simpler or more elegant than classical ones. On the contrary, theories of individual and organizational decision-making behavior are almost certain to be more complex and less esthetically pleasing than their classical counterparts. But what will cause the changes to occur is the simple fact that as more is learned about decision processes, theories will be constructed which will explain and predict a large part of many decision procedures.

As evidence for this claim and as an example of the manner in which these revisions may take place, consider the following example of a behavioral theory of the trust investment process.[23] The object of this research was to construct a theory that would describe and predict the portfolio selections of a particular trust investor. The theory was built by observing and incorporating the decision processes of the trust investor into a program for computer simulation. The theory was tested for its ability to

23. G. P. E. Clarkson (1962) *Portfolio selection: a simulation of trust investment.* Prentice-Hall.

predict the actual behavior of the trust officer by requiring it to select a series of portfolios for an actual set of trust accounts. These accounts were processed both by the trust officer and the theory during the first and third quarters of 1960. The portfolios chosen by the theory compared very favorably with those chosen by the trust investor. As a further test, the decision processes by which the theory generated its portfolios were compared with the trust officer's recorded decision behavior. Even though it is not possible to say that the theory completely reproduces the recorded behavior, the evidence from these tests strongly supports the hypothesis that the theory explains a considerable portion of the trust investment process.[24]

A theory that describes and predicts one trust investor's portfolio selection process is still a long way from becoming a general theory of trust investment. But the evidence is there that theories can be built that explain and predict, to a considerable level of detail, the decision processes of human decision makers. Hence, if the success in building theories of individual behavior can be translated into theories of organizational and market behavior, then many branches of economic theory will undergo substantial alterations.[25]

So far, I have been discussing the changes that may take place in the theories of various economic units, e.g. the firm. But if my prognoses are correct, then revisions that are made in the theory of the firm, for example, must also be reflected in the aggregate theories of market behavior. That is to say, if the firm is no longer to be pictured as a static, profit-maximizing entity, then the theory that accounts for the aggregate behavior of firms must undergo some change. Clearly, if firms are more accurately represented as complex organizations confronted with the task of satisfying many competing goals, the theory that accounts for their aggregate behavior will have to take account of this fact.

As yet there is not a sufficient amount of data to suggest in any

24. For an extensive analysis of the results obtained from these tests, *see* ibid., Chs. 6, 7.

25. For a detailed examination of the way in which the economic theory of consumer behavior might be revised to accommodate a behavioral theory of consumer behavior, see G. P. E. Clarkson (1963) *The Theory of Consumer demand: a critical appraisal.* Prentice-Hall.

detail how such a revised market theory should be constructed. However, one component it would have to include is the apparent lack of interest on the part of large corporations in engaging in price competition. For example, Baumol has already observed that oligopolists will consider nonprice competition to be the more advantageous alternative. Also, the behavioral theory of the firm suggests that large firms, whether oligopolists or not, prefer to have a stable environment to work with. And one way to keep the environment stable is to avoid price competition. Hence, whatever form the revised theory finally takes, it no longer is likely to represent the market as a place where firms struggle fiercely to meet price competition. Instead, the theory should provide us with a more accurate picture of the nature of competitive markets and of the forces that influence the behavior of individual firms.

## Economic policy

If we accept, for the moment, the supposition that the evidence will largely support the behavioral theories, then what will be the effect of these theoretical revisions on policy considerations? In particular, can we say anything about the amendments that may have to be made to our conception of how pricing policies should be regulated?

Classical theory, as mentioned earlier, asserts that competitive pricing is the most efficient way to keep the prices of finished products, e.g. consumer prices, as low as possible. Consequently, when competitive pricing appears to have vanished and one or two companies dominate an industry, antitrust measures are invoked with the intent of restoring competitive pricing to that particular market. But if, as investigations of business behavior suggest,[26] the pricing decision is only one of a firm's decision problems, then increasing the number of firms in the market may not have the desired effect. In other words, unless it can be shown that the number of firms in the industry has a direct effect on the prices that are set, it does not make much sense to invoke anti-

26. For further discussion of this point, see H. A. Simon (1962) 'New developments in the theory of the firm', *Papers and Proc. of the AEA, Amer. Econ. Rev.* **52**, 1–15.

trust measures whose purpose is to increase the number of competing firms.

For example, it has been observed in a number of cases that increases in internal administrative costs frequently lead firms to centralize their allocative processes.[27] In effect, these firms replace internal pricing mechanisms with central planning. Departments no longer maintain their own profit and loss figures, but instead work from allocated budgets and set prices. A further stimulant to centralize decision making has been provided by the high-speed computer, and it is clear that many firms are making full use of their data-processing abilities. If most prices and budgets of large corporations are set by a central plan, this plan will not be sensitive to external changes. The vast amount of coordination required by central planning precludes the possibility of its being very sensitive to external disturbances. Hence, if prices within an industry are judged to be too high and antitrust measures are invoked, then for these measures to be effective they must somehow directly affect some of the principal components of a firm's internal plan. Unfortunately, not enough is yet known about the planning process to suggest effective procedures for inducing the desired change. But the evidence is sufficient to call into question many of the traditional beliefs about the efficacy of market mechanisms in controlling prices.

As a further example of how policy conclusions may have to be revised, consider the traditional conception of a firm's reaction to various tax policies. In particular, let us examine the effect of levying a lump-sum or poll tax on all corporations.

Under classical theory, the assessing of a lump-sum tax is supposed to be one of the most effective ways of taxing a corporation without having the cost of this tax passed on to the consumer. This conclusion is supported by the classical assertion, referred to earlier, that changes in fixed costs should be ignored when setting prices and output. But observations of business behavior do not support this assertion. On the contrary, firms have been observed to raise prices to compensate for increases in overhead costs. And, in Baumol's analysis, increases in overhead costs,

27. For example, see J. G. March and H. A. Simon (1958) *Organizations*, Wiley, especially, Ch. 7; H. A. Simon, *The New science of management decision*, Ch. 5.

such as a poll tax, will be shifted, at least in part, to the consumer, because 'when they are levied on him, the oligopolist will raise his prices and reduce his selling costs to a point where his profit constraint is once again satisfied. . . . Since no one seems to deny that businessmen do, in fact, often raise prices when their overheads increase this point must be accepted by someone who questions the sales maximization hypothesis.'[28]

If the classical conclusion concerning the poll tax is in error, it is reasonable to suppose that other conclusions about tax policies may also be erroneous. And if our conclusions about the efficacy of the price mechanism are also substantially correct, then it would appear that many of the standard notions about appropriate policies are also in need of re-examination. Manifestly, it would be pleasant to be able to point to all the errors and indicate the necessary corrections. But until a great deal more is learned about organizational behavior such a procedure is simply not feasible. The best that can be done is to point toward a few of the most likely candidates and hope, by this approach, to generate an attitude of healthy suspicion toward the remaining, unexplored conclusions.

## Business decision making

If it is possible to point out the likely revisions in economic theory and its policy conclusions, then it is pertinent to inquire into the effects these changes may have on the business decision maker. If and when our understanding of decision processes reaches the point where the 'best' procedures can be prescribed, then the advances in economic theory will be of great importance to the businessman. But until the requisite knowledge has been acquired, it is perhaps more fruitful to examine the implications of current research for operations research. In other words, it seems more reasonable to examine the effects of recent research on the techniques of decision making rather than on the process itself.

When operations researchers first tried to employ traditional economic models to solve business problems, they discovered that important changes had to be made. Out of this search for new analytical techniques, innovations like linear programming,

28. W. J. Baumol, *Business behavior, value and growth*, p. 78.

game theory, and statistical decision theory evolved. These techniques have been successfully applied to a large number of business problems, and the application of operations research techniques has become an established tool in management's decision process.

The advent of heuristic programming, however, opens up an important new class of problems. It will allow operations researchers to tackle problems that previously were far too complex and ill structured to be solved by standard techniques. For example, one of the earliest uses of this technique was in the analysis and synthesis of electric motor design. Ten years ago, in one company, engineers worked out the designs for standard and special order electric motors. Today, a computer, programmed with a relatively simple heuristic program, takes customers' orders for many types of electric motors, generators, and transformers, and sends the design specifications to the factory floor.[29] Earlier, we described Tonge's line balancing program which, by combining heuristics and some simple mathematical techniques, was able to schedule assembly operations as well as, if not more efficiently than, skilled industrial engineers. Indeed the technique of heuristic programming has made it possible to develop programs which will solve many of the problems that traditionally have been the concern of middle management.

The fact that it is now technically possible to begin replacing managers with heuristic programs does not imply that it is yet economically desirable to do so.[30] For example, consider the case of the trust officer at a bank. The evidence gathered so far suggests that his job of selecting portfolios for trust accounts could be taken over by a suitably programmed computer. The evidence also suggests that the computer can be programmed to select its portfolios for the same reasons as the human investor. Presumably, the computer could even be taught how to improve upon its performance. But, before a computer will ever replace a trust

29. G. L. Goodwin (1958) 'Digital computers tap out designs for large motors fast', *Power* (April 1958), 102–4, 190–2.

30. For an extremely interesting analysis of the future role of computers in management decision making, see H. A. Simon (1960) 'The corporation: will it be managed by machines?' in M. Anshen and G. L. Bach (eds.), *Management and corporations 1985*. McGraw-Hill.

investor, it must be demonstrated that it is either more efficient or cheaper to employ a computer instead of the trust investor. As yet the evidence on this point is far from clear. And the flexibility of the human problem solver is still orders of magnitude greater than that of current computer programs. But, as our programming abilities develop and our understanding of problem solving behavior grows, I am convinced that heuristic programming will become one of the primary tools in management's decision-making apparatus.

## Conclusion

In the last few pages I have made a number of strong statements about the current state of economic theory. I have also pointed out some of the effects that the proposed revisions of economic theory may have on government policy and business practice. And I have noted that the current state of our knowledge is insufficient to identify and assess these changes with any significant degree of accuracy. However, the reason for this state of affairs is easy to identify. Economists have an abundance of theories but a dearth of facts. Until this situation is corrected the best we can do is point to the difficulties and hope for the best.

Consequently, if we are to understand decision processes, and if we are to use this knowledge to assist in public and private decision procedures, a large amount of effort must be devoted to empirical research. This research will have to focus on the decision-making processes of individuals and organizations, and unlike a good deal of previous research, it will have to be conducted in a reasonably systematic way.

For example, most of the information we have about business behavior is derived from economist's and operations researchers' anecdotes, and sample surveys of business behavior. Neither are very reliable sources of information. The former are subject to bias by the observer's preconceptions. And the latter often contain scanty pieces of ill-supported and unverified data. As a result, whether we are satisfied or not with classical theories, there is no solid foundation of data from which to develop and test.

However, the scarcity of reliable data is not a result of a paucity of ways for collecting it. On the contrary, intensive interviews, detailed observations, and the techniques employed in simulation studies are all useful methods for gathering and sorting data. Since the number of untested hypotheses far exceeds the available data it is toward this objective that the emphasis on empirical research should be placed.

# Part Two Some Managerial Decision Models

An important characteristic of a managerial economist is the ability to use mathematical models to analyse decision situations. Though the range of possible situations is enormous, problems can be classified according to the applicability of specific analytic tools.

In the first paper, Ansoff formulates a model by which a company can compare and evaluate alternative diversification decisions. The model combines qualitative and quantitative procedures. It exemplifies the process by which a model can reduce the apparent complexities of such decisions to a sequence of simple evaluations.

The Harary–Lipstein and Cyert–Davidson–Thompson papers illustrate how a given method of analysis, Markov Chains, can be applied to the purchasing behaviour of consumers on the one hand and to the estimation of doubtful accounts receivable on the other. Readers who are unfamiliar with Markov Chains are reminded that an exposition is provided in the text by Harary–Lipstein, while examples are worked out in the Appendix of the Cyert–Davidson–Thompson paper.

# 3  H. I. Ansoff

A Model for Diversification

H. I. Ansoff (1958) 'A model for diversification', *Management Science*, 4, 392–414.

## 1. Purpose of the Paper

The purpose of this paper is to construct a model describing a business phenomenon commonly known as diversification. It is generally recognized that a variety of very different models can be constructed to describe any given real-life situation. The models will differ depending on the skill and knowledge of the analyst, as well as on the particular purpose of the analysis. A recent paper by J. Sayer Minas [13] describes an inherent conflict between comprehensiveness and accuracy with which the real-life situation is covered on one hand and the precision and mathematical completeness of the model on the other. The resolution of this conflict can be likened to a kind of 'Heisenberg principle': The closer a model is made to mirror reality, the lower the precision of measurements which can be made with the aid of the model.

The model presented in this paper is oriented toward the specific purpose of providing top management of a large corporation with a tool for making intelligent diversification decisions. Our purpose will be to make it a reasonably comprehensive and accurate mirror of reality without attempting, for the time being, to provide an algorithm for selection of 'optimum strategies'. The purpose will be to identify the variables which have a first-order influence on diversification decisions and to identify important structural relations among them. In the language of classical physics we appear to be dealing with a step which is intermediate between a 'description' and a 'model'. If this effort is successful, the results should provide management with a means for making informed diversification decisions through a combination of computation and judgment.

## 2 Product-market Strategies

Many different definitions can be found for the term 'diversification'. For the purpose of this paper we will define it in terms of a particular kind of change in the product-market makeup of a company.

Let the *product line* of a manufacturing company be described by two sets of statements:

(a) Statement of the physical characteristics of the individual products (for example, size, weight, materials, tolerances, etc.) which is sufficiently complete for the purpose of setting up a manufacturing operation;

(b) The performance characteristics of the products (for example, in the case of an airplane, its performance in terms of speed, range, altitude, pay-load, etc.) which endow them with competitive characteristics on the markets on which they are sold.

For a definition of the 'market' we can borrow a concept commonly used by the military – the concept of a mission. Let a *product mission* be a description of the job which the product is intended to perform.[1]

To borrow another example from the airplane industry, one of the missions to which Lockheed Aircraft Corporation caters is commercial air transportation of passengers; another is provision of airborne early warning for the Air Defense Command; a third is performance of air-to-air combat.

In each of these examples the mission can be described in specific quantitative terms and performance of competing products can be evaluated quantitatively. In many other types of business which have less well defined product missions, such as 'cleansing of the teeth and prevention of tooth decay', job specification and hence measurement of competitive performance is a great deal more difficult.[2]

1. For our purposes, the concept of a mission is more useful in describing market alternatives than would be the concept of a 'customer', since a customer usually has many different missions, each requiring a different product.

2. One is tempted to enunciate an appropriate Parkinson's Law to the effect that advertising budget spent on a product is in an inverse ratio to the precision with which its mission can be specified.

Using the concepts of product line and product mission, we can now define a *product-market strategy* as a joint statement of a product line and the corresponding set of missions which the products are designed to fulfill. Thus, if we let $\pi_i$ represent the product line and $\mu_j$ the corresponding set of missions, then the pair $\sigma_{ij}:(\pi_i, \mu_j)$ is a product-market strategy.

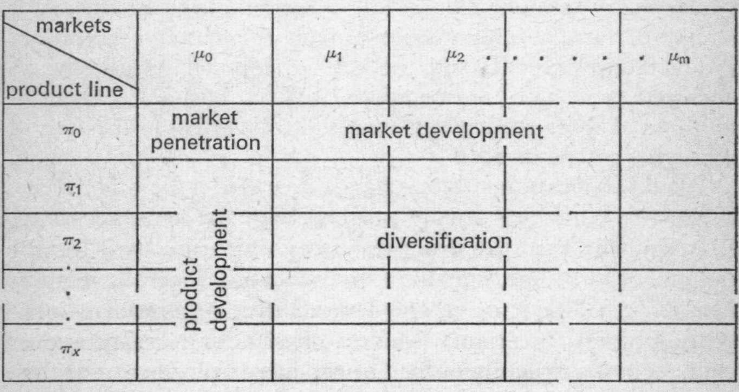

| markets / product line | $\mu_0$ | $\mu_1$ | $\mu_2$ . . . . . . $\mu_m$ |  |  |
|---|---|---|---|---|---|
| $\pi_0$ | market penetration | market development |  |  |  |
| $\pi_1$ |  |  |  |  |  |
| $\pi_2$ | product development |  | diversification |  |  |
| . |  |  |  |  |  |
| . |  |  |  |  |  |
| . |  |  |  |  |  |
| $\pi_x$ |  |  |  |  |  |

a product-market strategy $\sigma_{ij} : (\pi_i, \mu_j)$
overall company product-marketing strategy $\sigma_k \equiv \{\sigma_{ij}\}$

Figure 1.

Four commonly recognized business growth alternatives can now be identified as different product-market strategies. Thus, *market penetration* (see Fig. 1) is an effort to increase company sales without departing from an original product-market strategy. The company seeks to improve business performance either by increasing the volume of sales to its present customers or by finding new customers who have mission requirement $\mu_0$. *Market development* can be identified as a strategy in which the company attempts to adapt its present product line (generally with some modification in the product characteristics) to new missions. For example, an airplane company which adapts and sells its passenger transport for the mission of cargo transportation engages in market development.

A *product development* strategy, on the other hand, retains the

77

present mission and pursues development of products with new and different characteristics which will improve the performance of the mission. *Diversification* is the final alternative. It calls for a simultaneous departure from the present product line and the present market structure.

Each of the above strategies describes a distinct path which a business can take toward future growth. In most actual situations a business will simultaneously follow several of these paths. As a matter of fact, a simultaneous pursuit of market penetration, product development, and market development is usually recognized as a sign of a progressive, well-run business. Pursuit of all three of these strategies is essential to survival in the face of economic competition.

The diversification strategy stands apart from the other three. While the latter are usually pursued with the same technical, financial, and merchandising resources which are used for the original product line, pursuit of diversification generally requires new skills, new techniques, and new facilities. As a result, diversification almost invariably leads to physical and organizational changes in the structure of the business which represent a distinct break with past business experience. In view of these differences, it is logical to inquire into the conditions under which pursuit of a diversification strategy becomes necessary or desirable for a company.

The question can be put in the following form. We can think of market penetration, market development, and product development as component strategies of the *overall company product strategy* and ask whether this overall strategy should be broadened to include diversification.

## 3 Why Companies Diversify

A study of business literature and of company histories reveals many different reasons for diversification. Companies diversify to compensate for technological obsolescence, to distribute risk, to utilize excess productive capacity, to re-invest earnings, to obtain top management, etc., etc. One study of diversification [16] lists a total of 43 reasons for diversification. Fortunately, all of these reasons can be interpreted in terms of a relatively small number of typical expected patterns of business activity for a given company.

A standard method used to analyze future company growth prospects is through the means of long-range sales forecasts. Preparation of such forecasts involves simultaneous consideration of world-wide business trends alongside the trends in the particular industry to which the company belongs. Among the major factors considered are:

(a) General economic trends.

(b) Political and international trends.

(c) Trends peculiar to the industry. (For example, forecasts prepared in the airplane industry must take account of the following major prospects:

    i. A changeover, which is taking place within the military establishment, from manned aircraft to missiles.

    ii. Trends in government expenditures for the military establishment.

    iii. Trends in demand for commercial air transportation.

    iv. Prospective changes in the government 'mobilization base' concept and consequent changes toward the aircraft industry.

    v. Rising expenditures required for research and development.)

(d) Estimates of the company's competitive strength as compared to other members of the industry.

(e) Estimates of improvements in company performance which can be achieved through market penetration, product development, and market development.

(f) Trends in the manufacturing costs.

Such forecasts usually assume that company management will be aggressive and that management policies will be such as to take full advantage of the opportunities offered by the environmental trends. Thus, a long-range forecast of this type can be taken as an estimate of the best possible results the business can hope to achieve short of diversification.

The results fall into three typical trends which are illustrated in Fig. 2. These trends are compared to a growth curve for the national economy (GNP), as well as to a hypothetical growth curve for the industry to which the company belongs.

One of the curves illustrates a sales forecast which declines with time. This may be the result of an expected contraction of demand, obsolescence of manufacturing techniques, emergence of new products better suited to the mission to which the company

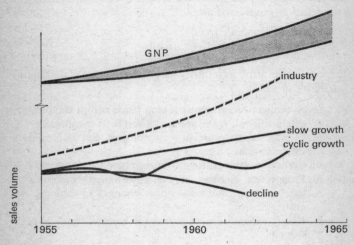

Figure 2.

caters, etc. Another typical pattern is one of cyclic sales activity. One common cause of this is seasonal variations of demand. Less apparent, but more important, are slower cyclic changes, such as, for example, peace–war variation in demand in the aircraft industry.

If the most optimistic sales estimates (which can be attained short of diversification) fall in either of the preceding cases, diversification is strongly indicated. However, a company may choose to diversify even if its prospects may, on the whole, appear favorable. This is illustrated by the 'slow growth curve'. As drawn in Fig. 2, the curve indicates rising sales which, in fact, grow faster than the economy as a whole. Nevertheless, the particular company may belong to one of the so-called 'growth industries' which as a whole is surging ahead. A company may diversify because it feels that its prospective growth rate is not satisfactory by comparison to the industry.

Preparation of trend forecasts is far from a precise science. There is always uncertainty about the likelihood of the basic environmental trends, as well as about the effect of these trends on the industry. Furthermore, there is additional uncertainty about the ability of a particular business organization to perform in the new environment. Consequently, any realistic company forecast would include several different trend forecasts, each with an (explicitly or implicitly) assigned probability. As an alternative, the trend forecast may be represented by a widening spread between two extremes, similar to that shown for GNP in Fig. 2.

In addition to trends, long-range plans must also take account of another class of events. These are certain environmental conditions which, if they occurred, would have a recognizable effect on sales; however, their occurrence cannot be predicted with certainty – they may be called *contingent* (or catastrophic) events.

For example, in the aircraft industry catastrophic forecasts may be based on the following environmental discontinuities:

(a) A major technological discontinuity (popularly described as a 'break-through') whose characteristics can be foreseen, but timing cannot at present be determined. This would occur, for example, if a new manufacturing process were discovered for manufacture of high strength, thermally resistant aircraft bodies.

(b) An economic recession which would lead to loss of orders for commercial aircraft and would change the pattern of spending for military aircraft.

(c) A limited war which would sharply increase the demand for goods produced by the air industry.

(d) Sudden cessation of cold war (which was a subject of considerable interest a year ago [i.e., 1957]).

(e) A major economic depression.

The two types of sales forecast are illustrated on Fig. 3 for a hypothetical company. Sales curves $S_1$ and $S_2$ represent a spread of trend forecasts and $S_3$ and $S_4$, two contingent forecasts. The difference between the two types lies in the degree of uncertainty associated with each.

## Some Managerial Decision Models

In the case of trend forecasts we can trace a crude time history of sales based on events which we fully expect to happen. Our uncertainty arises from not knowing when they will take place and the way they will interact with the business activity. In the case of contingency forecasts we can again trace a crude time history. However, our uncertainty is greater. We lack precise

$$P_1 = P_1(t_0) \; ; \; P_2 = P_2(t_0) \; ; \; P_3 = P_3(t_0, T) \; ; \; P_4 = P_4(t_0, T)$$

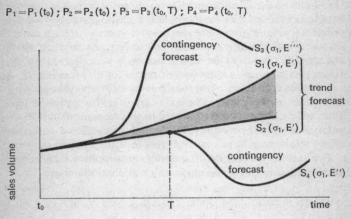

Figure 3.

knowledge of not only *when* they will occur, but also of *whether* they will occur. In describing trend forecasts, we can assign to each a probability $p = p(t_0)$, whereas for contingency forecasts, the best we can do is to express its probability with $p = p(t_0, T)$, where $T$ is the time at which the catastrophic event occurs. In going from a trend to a contingency forecast we advance, so to speak, one notch up the scale of ignorance.

In considering the relative weight which should be given to contingent events in diversification planning, it is necessary to take account not only of the magnitude of the effect it would produce on sales, but also the relative probability of its occurrence. For example, if a deep economic depression were to occur, its effect on many industries would be devastating. However, many companies feel safe in neglecting it in their planning because it is generally felt that the likelihood of a deep depression is very small, at least for the near future.

It appears to be a common business practice to put primary emphasis on trend forecasts. In fact, in many cases long range planning is devoted exclusively to this. Potential corporate instability in the light of contingency is frequently viewed either as 'something one cannot plan for' or as a second-order correction to be applied only after the trends have been taken into account. The emphasis is on 'planning for growth' and planning for contingencies is viewed as an 'insurance policy' against reversals.

People familiar with planning problems in the military establishment will note here an interesting difference between the military and the business attitudes. While business planning emphasizes trends, military planning emphasizes contingencies. To use a crude analogy, a business planner is concerned with planning for continuous, successful, day-after-day operation of a supermarket. If he is progressive, he also buys an insurance policy against fire, but he spends relatively little time in planning for fires. The military is more like the fire engine company. The fire is the thing. Day-to-day operations are of interest only insofar as they can be utilized to improve readiness and fire-fighting techniques. It appears that in some important respects the business planning problem is the easier one of the two.

## 4 Sales Objectives

Analysis of forecasts is useful, not only for determining the desirability of diversification, it also indicates two basic goals toward which diversification action should contribute. These goals may be referred to as *long range sales objectives*. They are illustrated on Fig. 4.

The solid lines describe the performance of a hypothetical company before diversification (when its overall product strategy was $\sigma_1$) under a general trend, which is represented by the sales curve market $S_1(\sigma_1, E')$, and in a contingency represented by $S_1(\sigma_1, E'')$, where $E'$ and $E''$ describe the respective environmental conditions. The dashed lines show the improved performance as a result of diversification when the overall product-market strategy becomes $\sigma_2$.

The first diversification effect was to improve the growth pattern of the company. The corresponding *growth objective* can be stated in the form:[3]

$$\dot{S}_1(\sigma_2, E') - \dot{S}_1(\sigma_1, E') \geqq \delta(t)$$

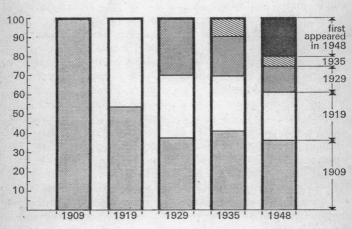

Figure 4.

The second effect desired of diversification is improvement in company stability under contingent conditions. Not only should diversification prevent sales from dropping as low as they might have before diversification, but the *percentage drop* should also be lower. The second sales objective is thus a *stability objective*:

$$\frac{S_1(\sigma_1, E') - S_2(\sigma_1, E'')}{S_1(\sigma_1, E')} - \frac{S_1(\sigma_2, E') - S_2(\sigma_2, E'')}{S_1(\sigma_2, E')} \geqq \rho(t)$$

As will be seen later, the two sales objectives can be viewed as constraints on the choice of the preferred diversification strategy.

3. Some companies (particularly in the growth industries) fix an annual rate of growth which they wish to attain. Every year this rate of growth is compared to the actual growth during the past year. A decision with respect to diversification action for the coming year is then based on the extent of the disparity between the objective and the actual rate of growth.

## 5 Unforeseeable Contingencies

So far our discussion has dealt with reasons and objectives for diversification which can be inferred from market forecasts. These objectives are based on what may be called *foreseeable* market conditions – conditions which can be interpreted in terms of time-phased sales curves. We have dealt with forecasts on two levels of ignorance: trend forecasts for which complete time histories can be traced and contingent forecasts, the occurrence of which is described by probability distribution. In problems dealing with planning under uncertainty, it is often assumed that trends and contingencies, taken together, exhaust all possible alternatives. In other words, if $p_0 \ldots p_n$ are the respective probabilities of occurrence assigned to the respective alternatives, the assumption is made that

$$\sum_{i=0}^{n} p_i = 1$$

Since this assumption leads to a neat and manageable conceptual framework, there is a tendency to disregard the fact that it is indeed not true, that the sum of the probabilities of the events for which we can draw time histories is less than one, and that there is a recognizable class of events to which we can assign a probability of occurrence, but which otherwise is not specifiable in our present state of knowledge. One must move another notch up the scale of ignorance before the possibilities can be exhausted.

Among analysts one runs into a variety of justifications for neglecting this last step. One simple-minded argument is that, since no information is available about these unforeseeable contingencies, one might as well devote his time and energy to planning for the foreseeable circumstances. Another somewhat more sophisticated rationale is that in a very general sense, planning for the foreseeable also prepares one for the unforeseeable contingencies.

One finds a very different attitude among experienced military and business people. They are very well aware of the importance and relative probability of unforeseeable events. They point to this fact and ask why one should go through an elaborate mockery of specific planning steps for the foreseeable events while neglecting the really important possibilities. Their substitute for such planning is contained in practical maxims for conducting one's business – be solvent, be light on your feet, be flexible. Unfortunately, it is not always clear (even to the people who preach it) what this flexibility means.

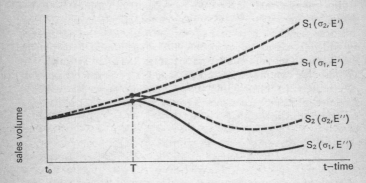

growth objective: $S_1(\sigma_2, E') - S_1(\sigma_1, E') \geqq \delta(t)$

stability objective: $\dfrac{S_1(\sigma_1, E') - S_2(\sigma_2, E'')}{S_1(\sigma_1, E')} - \dfrac{S_1(\sigma_1, E') - S_2(\sigma_2, E'')}{S_1(\sigma_2, E')} \geqq \rho(t)$

Figure 5.

An example of the importance of the unforeseeable class of events to business can be found in a very interesting study by the Brookings Institution [10]. A part of this study examined the historical ranking of 100 largest ranking corporations over the period of the last 50 years. An example of the mobility among the 100 largest is given in Fig. 5. It is seen that of the 100 on the 1909 list, only 36 were among the 100 largest in 1948. A majority of the giants of yesteryear have dropped behind in a relatively short span of time.

The lesson to be drawn from this illustration is that if most of the companies which dropped from the 1909 list had made forecasts of the foreseeable type at that time (some of them undoubtedly did so), they would have very likely found the future growth prospects to be excellent. A majority of the events that hurt them could not at the time be specifically foreseen. Railroads, which loomed as the primary means of transportation, have given way to the automobile and the airplane. The textile industry, which appeared to have a built-in demand in an expanding world population, was challenged and dominated by synthetics. Radio, radar, television created means of communication unforeseeable in significance and scope in 1909.

But the lessons of the past 50 years appear fully applicable today. The pace of economic and technological change is so rapid as to make it virtually certain that major breakthroughs comparable to those of the last 50 years, and yet not foreseeable in scope and character, will profoundly change the structure of the national economy.

This problem which, by comparison to planning under uncertainty, may be called the problem of planning under ignorance, deserves serious attention. A natural question at this point is, 'Can any lessons be drawn from the preceding example with respect to the specific problem of diversification?' An indication of the answer is provided by the Brookings study:

The majority of the companies included among the 100 largest of our day have attained their positions within the last two decades. They are companies that have started new industries or have transformed old ones to create or meet consumer preferences. The companies that have not only grown in absolute terms but have gained an improved position in their own industry may be identified as companies that are notable for drastic changes made in their product mix and methods, generating or responding to new competition. There are two outstanding cases in which the industry leader of 1909 had by 1948 risen in position relative to its own industry group and also in rank among the 100 largest – one in chemicals and the other in electrical equipment. These two (General Electric and DuPont) are hardly recognizable as the same companies they were in 1909 except for retention of the name; for in each case the product mix of 1948 is vastly different from what it was in the earlier year, and the markets in which the companies meet competition are incomparably broader than those that accounted for their earlier place at the top of their industries. They exemplify the flux in the market positions of the most successful industrial giants during the past four decades and a general growth rather than a consolidation of supremacy in a circumscribed line.

This suggests that existence of specific undesirable trends is a sufficient, but not a necessary, condition in order to commend diversification to a company. An examination of the foreseeable alternatives should be accompanied by an analysis of how well the overall company product-market strategy covers the so-called growth areas of technology – areas which appear fraught with potential discoveries. If such analysis shows that the company's product line is too narrow and that its chances of taking advantage of important discoveries are limited, such company is well advised to diversify, even if its definable horizons appear bright.


## 6 Diversification Objectives

As formulated in Section 4, long range objectives have the advantage of generality; they serve as a common yardstick to any new product-market strategy which a company may contemplate. The price for this generality is a lack of specificity; the objectives provide no indication of where a company should look for diversification opportunities in the broad product-market field of the national economy. Nor do they provide a means for a final evaluation of the respective merits of different opportunities which compete for company attention. The objectives are mainly useful as minimal goals which must be attained in order to give a company desirable growth characteristics. As we shall see later, they operate as constraints in the final evaluation processes: only strategies which meet the long range sales objectives are admitted to the final test of the probable business success of the competing diversification strategies.

To complete the formulation of our problem, it remains to specify two things: a means of reducing a very large field of possibilities to a particular set of diversification strategies which deserve close scrutiny by a diversifying company, and a means for evaluating the merits of the respective strategies within this set.

Business literature employs a variety of terms to describe alternative directions which a diversification program can follow. A commonly encountered breakdown is into vertical, horizontal, and lateral diversification directions.

Each product manufactured by a company is made up of functional components, parts, and basic materials which go into the final assembly. It is usual for a manufacturing concern to buy a large fraction of these from outside suppliers. One way to diversify is to branch out into production of components, parts, and materials. This is commonly known as *vertical diversification* (or sometimes as vertical integration). Perhaps the most outstanding example of vertical diversification is afforded by the Ford empire in the days of Henry Ford, Sr.[4]

*Horizontal diversification* can be described as introduction of new products which, while they do not contribute to the present product line in any way, cater to missions which lie within the industry of which the company is a member. The term 'industry' is taken here to mean an area of economic activity to which the present activities of the company have a substantial carry-over of know-how and experience by virtue of its past experience in technical, financial, and marketing areas.[5]

*Lateral diversification* can be described as a move beyond the confines of the industry to which a company belongs. This obviously opens a great many possibilities, from operating banana boats to building atomic reactors. It can be seen that while definitions of vertical and horizontal diversification are restrictive, in the sense that they de-limit the field of interest, lateral diversification is permissive. Adoption of a lateral diversification policy is merely an announcement of intent of the company to range far afield from its present market structure.

How does a company choose among these diversification

4. At first glance it would appear that vertical diversification is inconsistent with our definition of a diversification strategy (see Section 2). It should be recognized, however, that the respective missions which components, parts, and materials are designed to perform are distinct and different from the mission of the overall product. Furthermore, the technology in fabrication and manufacture of these is again likely to be very different from the technology of manufacturing the final product. Thus, vertical diversification does imply both catering to new missions and introduction of new products.

5. As is well known, the term 'industry' is commonly used in several senses. Sometimes it is taken to mean a set of missions which have a basic underlying characteristic in common, such as, for example, the air industry, the automotive industry, etc. Sometimes the unifying notion is a common area of technology, such as electronics industry, chemical industry, steel industry, etc.

directions? In part the answer depends on the reasons which prompt diversification action. If a company is diversifying because its sales trend shows a declining volume of demand, it would be unwise to consider vertical diversification, since this would be at best a temporary device to stave off an eventual decline of business. On the other hand, if the trend forecast indicates 'slow growth' in an otherwise healthy and growing industry, then both vertical and horizontal diversification would be desirable for strengthening the position of the company in a field in which its knowledge and experience are concentrated.

If the major concern is with stability under a contingent forecast, chances are that both horizontal and vertical diversification could not provide a sufficient stabilizing influence and that lateral action is indicated. Finally, if the concern is with the narrowness of the technological base in the face of what we have called unforeseeable contingencies, then lateral diversification into new areas of technology would be clearly called for.

An analysis of the sales trends impelling diversification can thus be used to formulate conditions which diversification possibilities must meet in order to fit the company requirements. These conditions can be termed as *diversification objectives*. In contrast to sales objectives which set forth general growth requirements, diversification objectives specify types of diversification strategies which will improve the product-market balance of the company.

For example, in the light of the trends described for the aircraft industry, an aircraft company may formulate the following diversification objectives:

In order to meet long-range sales objectives through diversification the company needs the following moves:

(a) a vertical diversification move to contribute to the technological progress of the present product line;

(b) a horizontal move to improve the coverage of the military market;

(c) a horizontal move to increase the percentage of commercial sales in the overall sales program;

(d) a lateral move to stabilize sales against a recession;

(e) a lateral move to broaden company's technological base.

Some of the diversification objectives apply to characteristics of the product, some to those of the product missions. Each objective is designed to improve some aspect of the balance between the overall product-market strategy and the expected environment. Thus, objectives (a), (b), and (c) are designed to improve the balance under the trend conditions, objectives (c) and (d) under foreseeable contingencies, and objective (e) to strengthen the company against unforeseeable contingencies.

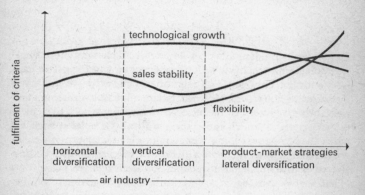

Figure 6.

It is apparent that a diversification strategy which is highly desirable for one of the objectives is likely to be less desirable for others. A schematic graphical illustration of this is presented in Fig. 6. The horizontal axis represents alternative diversification strategies in a decreasing order of affinity with respect to the present market structure (including both technological and business characteristics). In the air industry, which is going through a period of rapid technological change, the best promise for taking advantage of the growth trend seems to lie in the fields of vertical diversification into major system components or lateral diversification in adjacent areas of technology, such as electronics. The problem of sales stability could probably be best met through lateral diversification. However, horizontal diversification into new types of new products for the air industry is also desirable for this purpose. Finally, if its participation in the technological growth of the national economy is confined to one major area, an airframe company is well advised to diversify laterally as a means of acquiring a flexibility for unforeseen contingencies.

Diversification objectives are useful for determining merits of individual cases. However, they do not provide a central orienting theme which can give shape and a sense of direction to the diversification program. Such theme must be sought in the long range objectives of the company.


## 7 Long Range Company Objectives

So long as a company confines its growth to changes other than diversification, statement of long range company objectives can frequently be confined to generalities: 'growth', 'flexibility', 'financial stability', etc. However, when a break is contemplated with the past pattern of business, it becomes necessary to reduce the objectives to much more specific form. Questions, such as where the company is going, what unifying characteristics it should preserve as it goes through a period of change, should be answered before intelligent diversification decisions are made.

Sales objectives described in Section 4 provide part of the answer. However, they must be supplemented by a statement of the long range product-market policy.

A consistent course of action is to adopt a policy which will preserve a kind of technological coherence among the members of the product line with the focus on the products of the parent company. Thus, a company which is mainly distinguished for a type of engineering and production excellence would continue to select product-market entries which would strengthen and maintain this excellence. Perhaps the best known example of such policy is exemplified by the DuPont slogan, 'Better things for better living through chemistry.'

Another approach is to set long term growth policy in terms of the breadth of market which the company intends to cover. It may choose to confine its diversification to the vertical or horizontal direction, or it may select a type of lateral diversification which is circumscribed by the characteristics of the missions to which the company intends to cater. For example, a company which has its

92

origins in the field of air transportation may expand its interest to all forms of transportation of people and cargo. 'Better transportation for better living through advanced engineering,' while a borrowed slogan, might be descriptive of such long-range policy.

A greatly different policy is to place a primary emphasis on the financial characteristics of the corporation. This method of diversification generally places no limits on engineering and manufacturing characteristics of new products (although in practice, competence and interests of the corporate management will usually provide some orientation for diversification moves). The decisions regarding the desirability of new acquisitions are made exclusively on the basis of financial considerations. Rather than a manufacturing entity, the corporate character is now one of a 'holding company'. The top management delegates a large share of its product planning and administrative functions to the divisions and concerns itself largely with coordination and financial problems of the corporation and with building up a balanced 'portfolio of products' within the corporate structure.

These alternative long-range policies demonstrate the extremes. Most actual diversification case histories have taken a path intermediate between them; furthermore, neither of the extremes can be claimed to offer an intrinsically more promising road to success. The choice of policy rests in large part on the preferences and objectives of the management of the diversifying company, as well as on the skills and training of its people.

The fact that there is more than one successful path to diversification is illustrated by the case of the aircraft industry. Among the major successful airframe manufacturers, Douglas and Boeing have to date limited their growth to horizontal diversification into missiles and new markets for new types of aircraft. Lockheed has carried horizontal diversification further to include aircraft maintenance, aircraft service, and production of ground handling equipment. North American Aviation, on the other hand, appears to have chosen vertical diversification through establishment of its subsidiaries in Atomics International, Autonetics, and Rocketdyne, thus providing a basis for manufacture of complete air vehicles of the future.

Bell appears to have adopted a policy of technological consistency among the members of its product line. It has diversified laterally but primarily into types of products for which it had previous know-how and experience. General Dynamics provides a further interesting contrast. It is a widely laterally diversified company and, among major manufacturers of air vehicles, appears to come closest to the 'holding company' extreme. Its airplane and missile manufacturing operations in Convair are paralleled by production of submarines in the Electric Boat Division, military, industrial, and consumer electronic products in the Stromberg-Carlson Division, and electric motors in the Electro Dynamic Division.

## 8 Qualitative Evaluation

In the preceding sections we have dealt with two basic factors which affect diversification actions. These are the long-range objectives of the company and the more specific diversification objectives.

The problem now is to apply these to evaluation of diversification opportunities. Since the objectives are stated in both quantitative (sales objectives) and qualitative terms (diversification objectives and company product-market policy), it is convenient to construct a two-step evaluation process: first, application of qualitative criteria in order to narrow the field of diversification opportunities; and second, application of numerical criteria to select the preferred strategy (or strategies).

The long-range product-market policy can be applied as a criterion for the first rough cut in the qualitative evaluation. It can be used to order a large field of opportunities (which each company can compile by using commonly available industrial classifications) into classes of diversification moves which are consistent with the basic character of the diversifying company. For example, a company whose policy is to remain a manufacturing concern deriving its competitive strength from technical excellence of its products would eliminate as inconsistent classes of consumer products which are sold on the strength of advertising appeal rather than superior quality.

Each individual diversification opportunity which is consistent with the long-range objectives can next be examined in the light of individual diversification objectives. This process tends to eliminate opportunities which, while consistent with the desired product-market makeup, are nevertheless likely to lead to an unbalance between the company product line and the probable environment. For example, a company which wishes to preserve and expand its technical excellence in, say, design of large highly-stressed machines controlled by feed-back techniques may find consistent product opportunities both inside and outside the industry to which it presently caters. If a major diversification objective of this company is to correct cyclic variations in demand characteristic of the industry, it would choose opportunities which lie outside.

The diversification opportunities which have gone through the two screening steps can be referred to as the 'admissible set'. A member of the set satisfies at least one diversification objective, but very probably it will not satisfy all of them. Therefore, before subjecting them to the quantitative evaluation, it is necessary to group them into several alternative overall company product-market strategies, composed of the original strategy and one or more of the admissible diversification strategies. These alternative overall strategies should be roughly equivalent in meeting all of the diversification objectives.

At this stage it is particularly important to make allowance for the unforeseeable contingencies discussed in Section 5. Since available numerical evaluation techniques are applicable only to trends and foreseeable contingencies, it is important to make sure that the alternatives subjected to the evaluation have a comparable built-in diversified technological base. In practice this process is less formidable than it may appear. For example, a company in the aircraft industry has to take account of the areas of technology in which major discoveries are likely to affect the future of the industry. This would include atomic propulsion, certain areas of electronics, automation of complex processes, etc. In designing alternative overall strategies the company would then make sure that each contains product entries which will give the company a desirable and comparable degree of participation in these areas.

95

A schematic description of the preceding steps looks as follows:

$$\{\text{totality of } \sigma_{ij} \text{ available to company}\} \xrightarrow{\text{Long-range product-market policy}}$$

$$\{\sigma_{ij} \text{ consistent with policy}\} \xrightarrow{\text{Individual diversification objectives}}$$

$$\{\text{admissible } \sigma_{ij}\} \xrightarrow{\text{Diversification objectives as a group}}$$

$$\xrightarrow{\text{Balance for unforeseeable contingencies}}$$

$$\{\text{alternative overall product-market strategies } \sigma_k = \sigma_i + \sigma_{ij}\}$$

## 9 Quantitative Evaluation

So far we have been concerned with establishing a balanced relationship between the company and its business environment. An important remaining question is: 'Given such relationship will the company make money, will its profit structure be more attractive after diversification?'

The measurement we seek might be called the *profit potential* of diversification. It should accomplish two purposes. It should compare the performance of the company before and after a given diversification move; it should also compare the performances of several alternative diversification strategies. In the light of the characteristics of the diversification problem discussed in the preceding sections, the profit potential should have the following properties:

(a) Since diversification is invariably accompanied by a change in the investment structure of the business, profit potential should take account of such changes. It should take explicit account of new capital brought into the business, changes in the rate of capital formation resulting from diversification, as well as the costs of borrowed capital.

(b) Usually the combined performance of the new and the old product-market lines is not a simple sum of their separate performances (another common reason for diversification is to take advantage of this inherent characteristic – to produce a combined performance which exceeds the sum of individual performances). Profit potential should take account of this non-linear characteristic.

(c) Each diversification move is characterized by a transition period during which readustment of the company structure to new operating conditions takes place. The benefits of a diversification move may not be realized fully for some time (in fact, one of the common purposes of diversification into so-called growth industries is to 'start small and grow big'). Therefore, measurement of profit potential should span a sufficient length of time to allow for effects of the transition.

(d) Business performance will vary depending on the particular economic–political environment. Profit potential must provide an overall estimate of the probable effect of alternative environments described earlier in this paper.

(e) The statement of sales objectives in Section 4 specified the general characteristics of growth and stability which are desired. Profit potential function should be compatible with these characteristics.

Unfortunately there is no single yardstick of performance among those commonly used in business practice which possesses all of these characteristics. In fact, the techniques currently used for measurement of business performance constitute, at best, an imprecise art. It is common to measure different aspects of performance through application of different performance tests. Thus, the earning ability of the business is measured through tests of income adequacy; preparedness for contingencies, through tests of debt coverage and liquidity; attractiveness to investors through measurement of shareholders' position; efficiency in the use of money, physical assets and personnel, through tests of sales efficiency and personnel productivity. These tests employ a variety of different performance ratios, such as return on sales, return on net worth, return on assets, turnover of net worth, ratio of assets to liabilities, etc. The total number of ratios may run as high as 20 in a single case.

In the final evaluation of a diversification opportunity which immediately precedes a diversification decision, all of these tests, tempered with business judgment, would normally be applied.

However, for the purpose of preliminary elimination of alternatives, it has become common to use a single test in the form of return on investment, which is a ratio between earnings and the capital invested in producing these earnings.

While the usefulness of return on investment is commonly accepted, there appears to be considerable room for argument regarding its limitations and its practical application [3, 16]. Fundamentally, the difficulty with the concept seems to be that on one hand it fails to provide an absolute measure of business performance applicable to a range of very different industries, and on the other, definition of the term 'investment' is subject to a variety of interpretations.

Since our aim is to use the concept as a measure of *relative* performance of different diversification strategies, we need not be concerned with its failure to provide a yardstick for comparison with other industries, nor even with other companies in the same industry as the parent company. Similarly, so long as a consistent practice is used for defining investment in alternative courses of action, our concern with proper definition of investment can be smaller than in many other cases. Nevertheless, a particular definition of what constitutes profit-producing capital cannot be given in general terms. It would have to be determined in each case in the light of particular business characteristics and practices (such as, for example, the extent of government-owned assets, depreciation practices, inflationary trends, etc.).

For the numerator of our return on investment we shall use net earnings after taxes. A going business concern has standard techniques for estimating its future earnings. These depend on the projected sales volume, tax structure, trends in material and labor costs, productivity, etc. If the diversification opportunity being considered is itself a going concern, its profit projections can be used for estimates of combined future earnings. If the opportunity is a new venture, its profit estimates should be made on the basis of the average performance for the industry.

In the light of earlier discussion, it is important for our purposes to recognize that estimated earnings depend on the overall product-market strategy, the amount of capital to be invested in diversification, the estimated sales volume, and the particular economic-political environment being studied. If we use previously employed notation and let $P$ stand for earnings and $I$ for the capital investment, we can recognize the determining influences on the earnings in the following *profit function*:

$$P = h(I, S, E, \sigma) \qquad (1)$$

As mentioned previously, a diversification move is accompanied by a change in the investment structure of the diversifying company. The type of change used in any given case, as well as the amount of capital involved, will depend on the resources available for diversification purposes, the particular product-market strategy, as well as on the method which the diversifying company selects for expansion of its manufacturing activities. The choice of the particular method of expansion (there are four basic alternatives: use of existing facilities, expansion, acquisition of controlling interest, and merger) is a part of the larger problem of business fit (see Sec. 10). For this reason it will not be discussed in this paper. We will assume that for each product-market entry an appropriate type of expansion can be selected [1].

The source of investment for the new venture may be one of the following:

1. The diversifying company may be in the fortunate position of having excess capital.

2. The company may be in a position to borrow capital at attractive rates.

3. It may be in a position to exchange part of its equity for an equity in another company (for example, through an exchange of stock).

4. It may decide to withdraw some of the capital invested in the present business operation and invest it in diversification.

Let us define the following:

| | |
|---|---|
| $\sigma_l$ | original product-market strategy of the company. |
| $\sigma_k = \sigma_l + \sigma_{ij}$ | overall product-market strategy resulting from the qualitative evaluation (where $\sigma_{ij}$ is the diversification strategy). |
| $I(t)$ | total capital invested in the business in year $t$. |

$i_1(t)$, $i_2(t)$, $i_3(t)$, $i_4(t)$     investments made in $\sigma_{ij}$ in year $t$ from the four respective sources enumerated above.

$r(t)$     prevailing interest rate for capital on the open market.

$k(t)$     dividends paid out in year $t$.

Also let us make the following assumptions:

(a) That the diversification program may be spread over a period of time and that investments in diversification may be made yearly from time $t = 0$ up to $t$.

(b) That all four types of investment described on the preceding page may be made during this period.

(c) That if the company does not diversify, earnings of the company, in excess of paid out dividends, may be divided between additional investments in the company's product-market line and investments in outside ventures.

(d) If the company diversifies, earnings in excess of dividends are all reinvested in the business either in the original product strategy $\sigma_l$ or in the diversification strategy $\sigma_{ij}$.

To simplify notation, select a particular economic-political environment, a diversification strategy, and a specified sales volume so that Expression (1) becomes

$$P = h(I, S, E, \sigma) = h(I)$$

Let $P_0 = h_0(I)$ be profit earned by $\sigma_l$ before diversification.

$P_1 = h_1(I)$ be profit earned by $\sigma_l$ after diversification.

$P_2 = h_2(I)$ be profit earned by $\sigma_{ij}$ after diversification.

Using this notation and the preceding assumptions we can write the *present value* of return on investment in the following form:

If the company does not diversify

$$R(t) = \frac{P(t)(1 + r)^{-(t+1)}}{I_p(t)}, \qquad (2)$$

where $P(t)$ represents earnings for year $t$

$$P(t) = h_0\left[ I(t) - \sum_{\tau=0}^{t} i_1(\tau) \right] + r \sum_{\tau=0}^{t} i_1(\tau), \qquad (3)$$

$I(t)$ is the total capital available to the business in year $t$

$$I(t) = I(0) + \sum_{\tau=1}^{t} P(\tau - 1)[1 - k(\tau)], \qquad (3)$$

and $I_p(t)$ is the present value of the total capital which is in the business in year $t$

$$I_p(t) = I(0) + \sum_{\tau=1}^{t} P(\tau - 1)[1 - k(\tau)](1 + r)^{-\tau} \qquad (3)$$

*If the company does diversify*, the present value of return on investment becomes

$$\bar{R}(t) = \frac{\bar{P}(t)(1 + r)^{-(t+1)}}{\bar{I}_p(t)}, \qquad (4)$$

where $\bar{P}(t)$ represents earnings

$$\bar{P}(t) = h_1 \left[ \bar{I}(t) - \sum_{\tau=0}^{t} \sum_{j=1}^{4} i_j(\tau) \right] + h_2 \left[ \sum_{\tau=0}^{t} \sum_{j=1}^{4} i_j(\tau) \right] - r \sum_{\tau=0}^{t} i_2(\tau) \qquad (5)$$

$\bar{I}(t)$ represents the capital

$$\bar{I}(t) - I(0) + \sum_{\tau=1}^{t} \bar{P}(\tau - 1)[1 - k(\tau)] + \sum_{\tau=0}^{t} [i_2(\tau) + i_3(\tau)], \qquad (5)$$

and $\bar{I}_p(t) = I(0) + \sum_{\tau=1}^{t} \bar{P}(\tau - 1)[1 - k(\tau)](1 + r)^{-\tau}$

$$+ \sum_{\tau=0}^{t} [i_2(\tau) + i_3(\tau)](1 + r)^{-\tau} \qquad (5)$$

Using (2) and (4) we obtain the improvement in return on investment in year $t$ which can be brought about by diversification:

$$\Delta R(t) = \bar{R}(t) - R(t) \qquad (6)$$

For a selected investment policy, $i_1(t)$, $i_2(t)$, $i_3(t)$, and $i_4(t)$ specified for $\tau = 0 \ldots t$, $\Delta R$ can be computed for each year for which forecasted data are available employing information normally provided in such forecasts.

The next step is to consider the return on investment in a time perspective. Completion of a diversification move by a company will normally span a period of time. During this period the return on investment should be expected to vary, and even drop temporarily below pre-diversification levels. In order to assess the full effect of diversification, it is, therefore, desirable to compute an average return over a period which includes the transition to diversifying operations and which extends as far as possible into the future beyond the transition.

In principle it would be desirable to measure the effects of diversification over an indefinite future [18]. In practice this period will be measured by the time span for which long range forecasts are available.

Let $N$ be a period which includes transition and for which forecasted data are available. Further, recall that $\Delta R$ was computed for a particular environment $E$ and that usually several different forecasts will be available in order to take account of several probable environments. Let $E^1 \ldots E^n \ldots E^g$ be the environments considered by the company, each with an associated probability distribution $p^n(T)$ (see Sec. 3).

*Then the expected average improvement in return to be derived from the diversified operations* can be written in the form

$$(\Delta R)_e = \frac{1}{N} \sum_{n=1}^{g} \sum_{t=0}^{N} \sum_{\tau=t}^{N} \Delta R(E^n, \tau) p^n(\tau) \tag{7}$$

$(\Delta R)_e$ meets all of the conditions laid down for profit potential earlier in this section.

Recall that Eq. (7) is computed for a particular overall product-market strategy $\sigma_k = \sigma_l + \sigma_{ij}$, and that in the preceding section the totality of diversification possibilities was reduced to a set of such strategies, say $\{\sigma_k\}_m$.

The final step of selecting the preferred strategy through comparison of their respective prospect potentials can be stated as follows:

For a given increase in investment $\bar{I}_p - I(0)$ over a period from $t = 0$ to $t = N$ and an investment policy $i_1(t), i_2(t), i_3(t), i_4(t)$ for $t = 0 \ldots N$ specified for each $\sigma_k$, we can compute $[\Delta R(\sigma_k)]_e$.

Recall that in Sec. 4 we stated long-range sales objectives which require that certain minimum sales performance be shown for each $E^n$. Since [see Eq. (1) in this section] $(\Delta R)_e$ is a function of sales $S$, the long-range sales objectives can be viewed as a constraint to be applied to $\Delta[R(\sigma_k)]_e$.

Thus, the preferred overall company strategy $\sigma_p$ is such that

$$[\Delta R(\sigma_p)]_e = \max_m [\Delta R(\sigma_k)]_e \qquad (8)$$

subject to the conditions that in the trend environment

$$\dot{S}_l(\sigma_k, E^1) - \dot{S}_l(\sigma_l, E^1) \geqq \delta(t) \qquad (9)$$

and for contingent environments $E^n$, $n = 2 \ldots g$, where $g$ is the number of distinct environments considered in the forecast,

$$\frac{S_1(\sigma_1, E^1) - S_2(\sigma_1, E^n)}{S_1(\sigma_1, E^1)} - \frac{S_1(\sigma_k, E^1) - S_2(\sigma_k, E^n)}{S_1(\sigma_k, E^1)} \geqq \rho^n(t) \qquad (10)$$

## 10 Interpretation of Results

The approach used above in arriving at the desirable diversification strategies is, of course, not rigorous in the mathematical sense of the word. The conceptual model is one of successive elimination of alternatives involving either application of qualitative criteria, or straightforward numerical comparisons. Mathematical notation has served more as a shorthand language than a tool of analysis. While straightforward, the required evaluations may involve some difficult practical problems, such as computation of capital investment or assignment of earnings to the respective members of the product line. Nevertheless, all of the required basic data are normally available in long-range sales and financial forecasts.

The final numerical evaluation is recognizable as a form of the problem of allocation of resources under uncertainty. While expected value is used for the payoff function, the usual danger, implicit in the expected value approach, of unbalanced preparedness for alternative environments is anticipated through the requirement of a minimum performance level in each, as expressed in the sales objectives. Incidentally, since the sales objectives can be computed independently of $(\Delta R)_e$, they are not constraints in the usual sense of the word. They can be applied to the admissible set $\{\sigma_k\}_m$ before $(\Delta R)_e$ are computed. The method for providing against what we have called unforeseeable contingencies is not as satisfactory as it should be in view of the importance of this class of futures. A rationale and an accompanying quantitative evaluation are needed and these should be used to restate the problem of allocation of resources under uncertainty.

One of the reasons why a simplified approach was possible lies in the fact that we have dealt with only a half of the diversification problem. Our concern has been with what might be called *external* aspects of diversification. We have sought to select diversification strategies in the light of the probable economic-political environments and the long-range goals of the company. We have not been concerned with the influence of the internal, organizational, and business characteristics of the company on the diversification decisions.

It happens that business performance of a company is determined both by external characteristics of the product-market strategy and internal fit between the strategy and business resources. The first of these factors is what we have called *profit potential* of the product-market strategy, the second is the *business fit* of the strategy with respect to the diversifying company. Profit potential measures potential earnings as a function of the economic-political environment, characteristics of the demand, and nature of the competition under the assumption that the diversifying company is capable of offering effective competition in the new product-market area.

Business fit tests the validity of this assumption. It is a measure of the company's ability to penetrate the new market. It is determined by the particular strengths and weaknesses which the company brings to the new venture, such as the capabilities and past experience in engineering, production, finance, and merchandising.

Business fit is only one of the important internal aspects of the diversification problem. Other aspects include organization for diversification, development of new product-market ideas, methods of corporate expansion, anti-merger legislation, problems of corporate control, etc. While the external aspects generally deal with the advantages to be derived from diversification, the internal aspects deal with assessment of costs and risks. The overall diversification problem is to balance these against one another.

Unfortunately, quantitative evaluation of internal aspects is even more difficult than for the external ones. Consequently, a usual approach to this part of the problem is to derive qualitative criteria which are added to those discussed in this paper.

An interesting discussion of the internal aspects can be found in [17] and [11]. It is also the subject of [1].

## References

1. ANSOFF, H. IGOR (1957) 'An action program for diversification', Lockheed Aircraft Corp. Calif.
2. AMA CONFERENCE HANDBOOK (1956) *Mergers and acquisitions: for growth and expansion*. AMA Special Finance Conference, New York.
3. DRUCKER, PETER F. (1954) *The practice of management*. Harper & Brothers.
4. FEDERAL TRADE COMMISSION (1955) 'Report on corporate mergers and acquisitions', Government Printing Office, Washington.
5. FINANCIAL MANAGEMENT SERIES 113 (1957) 'Integration policies and problems in mergers and acquisitions', AMA, New York.
6. FINANCIAL MANAGEMENT SERIES 114 (1957) 'Legal, financial, and tax aspects of mergers and acquisitions', AMA, New York.
7. FINANCIAL MANAGEMENT SERIES 115 (1957) 'A case study in corporate acquisition', AMA, New York.
8. HERTZ, DAVID BENDEL (1957) 'Operations research in long-range diversification planning', Special Report No. 17, Operations Research Applied (New Uses and Extensions), Am. Management Assoc.
9. HILL, W. E. (1956) *Planned product diversification*, William E. Hill Co., New York.
10. KAPLAN, A. D. H. (1954) 'Big enterprise in a competitive system', The Brookings Institution, Washington.
11. KLINE, CHARLES H. (1955) 'The strategy of product policy', *Harvard Business Rev.*, July–August.
12. LANGE, HARRY R. (1957) 'Expansion through acquisition', Implementing Long-Range Company Planning, Stanford Research Institute, Calif. (Speech given before Industrial Economics Conference, San Francisco, January 21–22.)
13. MINAS, J. SAYER (1956) 'Formalism, realism and management science', *Management Sci.* 3, 9–14.
14. ROCKWELL, JR, W. F. (1956) 'Planned diversification of industrial concerns', *Advanced Management*, May.

15. SONGER, WESLEY A. 'Organizing for growth and change', General Management Series A M A Pamphlet 171.
16. SCHWARTZ, CHARLES R. (1956) 'The return-on-investment concept as a tool for decision making', General Management Series A M A Pamphlet 183, New York.
17. STAUDT, THOMAS A. (1954) 'Program for product diversification', *Harvard Business Rev.*, November–December.
18. WILLIAMS, JOHN BURR (1956) *The theory of investment value*. North-Holland Publishing Co., Amsterdam.

# 4 F. Harary and B. Lipstein

The Dynamics of Brand Loyalty: a Markovian Approach

F. Harary and B. Lipstein (1962), 'The dynamics of brand loyalty: a Markovian approach', *Operations Research*, **10**, 19–40. (This paper will shortly appear in F. Harary, *Graph Theory in Social Models*, Holden-Day.)

An important step in the progress of probability theory was made by A. A. Markov (1856–1922). He initiated a basic study of sequences of events with a given distribution of initial probabilities, which have the simple property that the probability of the next event in the successive sequence of trials depends only on the present outcome and *not* on the particular occurrence of any of the events before that. There has been a vigorous theoretical study of such situations, now called 'Markov chains'. Modern expositions of Markov chains are contained in the books of Doob [5], Feller [7], and Kemeny and Snell [13]. The initial motivation for the concentration on Markov chains was provided by applications to physics. The particular areas of physics that prove themselves to be eminently suited for mathematical treatment by Markov chains include statistical mechanics, especially Brownian motion; *see* Kac [12]. Shannon formally initiated the area of information theory in his paper [19]. One of his essential hypotheses is that every signal-producing system has an underlying Markov chain.

More recently, there have been many applications of Markov chains as a mathematical model in surprisingly diverse areas. These include the work on learning theory independently developed by Bush and Mosteller [4] and Estes [6]. Anderson [1] has combined Markov chains with elementary statistics for the purpose of studying changes in attitudes. The setting of Markov chains in the study of labor mobility was exploited by Blumen, Kogan, and McCarthy [3]. Marshall and Goldhammer [18] have used Markov chains for the study of epidemiology of mental disease. A study of Lipstein [16] describes a specific application of Markov chains to the phenomena of brand switching and brand loyalty. Kuehn [15] coordinated Markov chains with brand switching and Harary [8] utilized Markov chains in a theoretical investigation of social power.

## Introduction

We first summarize the basic concepts of Markov chains. Directed graphs are then introduced to provide a geometric and structural point of view. This combination of structure with probability has both conceptual and intuitive advantages. We then show that the set of all brands of a particular product category, e.g. cigarettes, coffee, automobiles, etc., can be validly regarded as a concrete case of abstract Markov chains. The implications of this kind of realization and their meaning in terms of marketing processes are also indicated. We then consider an over-simplified situation that is nevertheless sufficiently complicated to indicate the various applications. This is followed by a section in which we describe and discuss real applications, together with related problems and implications.

One of the criteria for judging the utility of a mathematical model for real phenomena is the discovery of new and fruitful concepts, results, and methods. It is possible that the methods developed herein may be appropriate for the further study of the many applications of Markov chains to various other fields.

## Markov Chains

*A finite Markov chain* consists of a collection of *n events* or *states* $E_1, E_2, \ldots, E_n$ that satisfies the following conditions:

1. There is a given distribution of *initial probabilities* $(a_1, a_2, \ldots, a_n)$ where $a_k$ is the probability that the first event is $E_k$.
2. In addition, there is a given *matrix of transition probabilities*:

$$P = \begin{Vmatrix} p_{11} p_{12} \ldots p_{1n} \\ p_{21} p_{22} \ldots p_{2n} \\ \cdots \\ p_{n1} p_{n2} \ldots p_{nn} \end{Vmatrix},$$

where the number $p_{ij}$ is the conditional probability that if the present event is $E_i$, then the next event is $E_j$.

3. In order for the numbers $a_i$ and $p_{ij}$ to have probabilistic validity, it is also necessary to require that:

$$0 \leq a_1 \leq 1 \text{ and } \sum_{i=1}^{i=n} a_i = 1,$$

for any $i = 1$ to $n$. $\quad 0 \leq p_{ij} \leq 1$ and $\sum_{j=1}^{j=n} p_{ij} = 1$.

A Markov chain operates as follows. We may visualize a process that moves from state to state. By means of the initial probability distribution, the process starts at one of the states $E_i$, with probability $a_i$. If at any time it is in state $E_j$, then it moves to state $E_k$ with probability $P_{jk}$, which is of course determined by the probability distribution of the $j$th row of matrix $P$. Thus the entire process is completely described by the initial probability distribution and the transition probability matrix.

This leads to the usual description of a Markov chain as a sequence of states or events in which the next state is completely determined only by the present state and does not depend at all on those states that occurred previously. Strictly speaking, this is a description of the workings of a *stationary Markov chain*. In fact, throughout this paper, by an unqualified Markov chain we shall always mean a stationary Markov chain. However, 'Markov chain' sometimes has a more general meaning in probability theory. Namely, it is sometimes permitted that the transition matrix $P$ be different at each time step.

A *stochastic matrix* is one in which each element is between 0 and 1 inclusive and the sum of the entries in any row is 1. Thus the transition matrix $P$ of any Markov chain is stochastic. It follows at once that $P^2$, the ordinary matrix product of $P$ with itself, is also stochastic. Let $p_{ij}^{(2)}$ be the $i, j$ entry of $P^2$. By definition of matrix multiplication, it follows at once that $p_{ij}^{(2)}$ is the probability of going from $E_i$ to $E_j$ in two steps. In general, the $i, j$ entry of any power $P^m$ is the probability of going from state $E_i$ to state $E_j$ in $m$ steps. Thus the entries of the powers of $P$ are called *higher transition probabilities*.

If we start with a Markov chain whose transition matrix is $P$, we may form the successive powers $P^2$, $P^3$, etc. If these matrices approach a limiting matrix $\bar{P} = \lim_{n \to \infty} P^n$ then $\bar{P}$ contains the expected values of the transition probabilities, which this Markov chain would reach if allowed to remain in operation indefinitely. It is readily seen that if some power $P^r$ of $P$ has only positive entries, the rows of $P$ are identical. This property of the chain is sometimes called the '*steady state*'.

It is very important in the applications of Markov chains to be able to calculate the average time (in terms of the number of steps) during which a chain will stay in a given state. We shall call this the *average staying time* of that state. Other important concepts are that of the *average waiting time* it will take a chain to reach a given state, from its beginning, and the *average transition time* it takes to get from one state to another.

## Directed Graphs

We now develop some concepts from the theory of directed graphs, or more briefly digraphs, to provide a structural view-point toward several concepts in Markov chains. There are two books on graph theory: König [14] and Berge [2]. In addition, there is an elementary monograph by Harary and Norman [10] in which the introductory concepts of graph theory are given. The most recent reference on digraph theory is the book by Harary, Norman, and Cartwright [11], see also Harary [9].

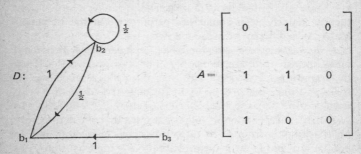

Figure 1 A digraph $D$ and its structure matrix $A$.

A *directed graph* or a *digraph* consists of a finite collection $b_1, b_2, \ldots, b_m$ of *points* together with a collection of ordered pairs $(b_i, b_j)$ of points. These ordered pairs are called the *directed lines* or whenever the context precludes ambiguity, the *lines* of the digraph. In Fig. 1 we show a digraph $D$ with three points and four lines. The line joining $b_2$ with itself is called a *loop*. The two

110

directed lines $(b_1, b_2)$ and $(b_2, b_1)$ constitute a *symmetric pair* of directed lines.

A 1 to 1 correspondence between directed graphs and square binary matrices (whose entries are 0 and 1) may be defined by the following procedure. We write a 1 in the $i, j$ place of the matrix if and only if there is a line from boint $b_i$ to $b_j$. Thus the matrix $A$ corresponds to the digraph $D$ of Fig. 1. We call $A$ the *adjacency matrix* or the *structure matrix* of $D$.

Before developing additional structural concepts relating to digraphs, we exploit Fig. 1 still further by showing the manner in which it may be regarded as representing the matrix $P$ of a Markov chain. Consider the points $b_i$ as states $E_i$. When the number $p_{ij}$ is 0, we do not draw any line in the digraph. However, there is a directed line for each nonzero entry of the transition matrix $P$. To make this example somewhat more concrete, consider the numbers 1 and $\frac{1}{2}$ which are written in Fig. 1 near the four lines of this digraph. The corresponding transition matrix is

$$P = \begin{Vmatrix} 0 & 1 & 0 \\ \frac{1}{2} & \frac{1}{2} & 0 \\ 1 & 0 & 0 \end{Vmatrix}.$$

Since $P$ is a stochastic matrix, it follows that *a digraph with numbers indicated near its lines represents the transition matrix of a Markov chain if and only if the sum of the numbers of the lines leading out from each point is 1*. Such a configuration is called a Markov digraph.

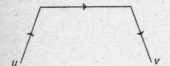

Figure 2a A path from $u$ to $v$.

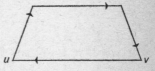

Figure 2b A cycle.

A *directed path* of $D$ consists of a collection of distinct points together with successively directed lines that start from one of these points, $u$, and terminate at another one of these points, $v$. This is called a *path from $u$ to $v$*; see Fig. 2a. Thus no line occurs more than once and there are no loops in any path. A cycle is obtained from a path from $u$ to $v$ when the single directed line $\vec{vu}$ is added; *see* Fig. 2b. If there is a path in $D$ from $u$ to $v$, we say that the point $v$ is *reachable* from point $u$.

A digraph $D$ is *strongly connected* or more briefly *strong* if any two points are mutually reachable. A *strong component* of $D$ is a maximal strong subgraph. In Fig. 3, we show a digraph $D$ having three strong components $S_1$, $S_2$, and $S_3$ as indicated.

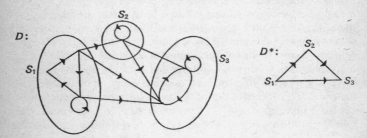

Figure 3 A digraph with three strong components.

Intuitively, a digraph is *weakly connected* or *weak* if on ignoring all the directions of its lines, i.e. the indicated arrows on its lines, the resulting configuration has a connected appearance in that every two points may be joined by an unoriented path. (A precise definition, is given in Harary, Norman, and Cartwright [11].) A *weak component* of $D$ is a maximal weak subgraph. In Fig. 4, we

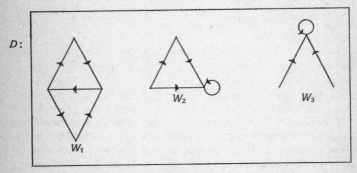

Figure 4 A digraph with three weak components.

112

show a digraph $D$ having three weak components $W_1$, $W_2$, and $W_3$.

A digraph is *disconnected* if it is not even weakly connected. Thus the entire digraph $D$ of Fig. 4 is disconnected.

A *transmitter* of a digraph is a point not reachable from any other point, but it can reach another point. Similarly, a *receiver* is reachable from another point but cannot reach any other point.

The condensation or condensed digraph $D^*$ of a given digraph $D$ is that digraph whose points are the strong components of $D$ and whose directed lines are induced by the directions of the lines between points of the strong components in $D$. In Fig. 3, the digraph $D^*$ is the condensation of the digraph $D$ as shown.

We shall develop other concepts of digraph theory as required for application to Markov chains.

## Graphical Properties of Chains

The purpose of the present section is to tie together the notion of higher transition probabilities in Markov chains with some of the fundamental concepts of digraph theory.

It is very useful to have a classification of the states of a chain in accordance with its structural properties. These are completely determined by the transition matrix $P$, or more intuitively by the directed graph associated with $P$. We follow mainly the terminology of Kemeny and Snell [13] with regard to the classification of states.

We have already seen that a Markov digraph is a digraph together with an assignment of positive real numbers to its directed lines such that the sum of the values on all the lines leaving each point is 1. It follows that each number assigned to a line is positive but does not exceed 1. It is clear that the transition matrix of any Markov chain yields a Markov digraph when the states are regarded as points and the directed lines indicate a positive probability of a direct transition from one state to another. Thus, the Markov digraph associated with the transition matrix of a Markov chain has $n$ points $E_1, E_2, \ldots, E_n$ and there is a line from $E_i$ to $E_j$ if and only if the probability $p_{ij} > 0$. Let $p_{ij}^{(m)}$ be the $i,j$ entry of the matrix $P^m$. In accordance with the definition in the preceding section, we say that a state $E_j$ is *reachable* from state $E_i$

113

if there is a (directed) path in the Markov digraph from $E_i$ to $E_j$. Thus, in matrix terms, $E_j$ is reachable from $E_i$ if for some positive integer $m$ the probability $p_{ij}^{(m)}$ is positive.

We now begin the classification of states. A state of a chain is called an *absorbing state* if no other state is reachable from it. In matrix terms, $E_k$ is an absorbing state if $p_{kk} = 1$ while $p_{kj} = 0$ when $j \neq k$. An *absorbing chain* has at least one absorbing state, and from any state, an absorbing state is reachable. It is possible to characterize absorbing chains in terms of well-known concepts from digraph theory. We have already defined a transmitter and a receiver of a digraph. Obviously *a state of a chain is an absorbing state if and only if it is a receiver in its Markov digraph.*

A *point basis* of a digraph is a minimal collection of points from which all other points are reachable. The directional opposite of this concept is called a point contrabasis. Thus, a *point contrabasis* of a digraph is a minimal collection of points such that from any other point, at least one of these points is reachable. Obviously any transmitter of a digraph is contained in every point basis and every receiver is in every point contrabasis. In this terminology, *an absorbing chain is one whose Markov digraph has a point contrabasis consisting of all its absorbing states.*

The *subgraph generated by a set of points* $v_1$, $v_2$, . . . of $D$ consists of these points together with all directed lines of $D$ between any two of them. In an *ergodic set* of states, any two states are mutually reachable and this set cannot be left once it is entered. Thus, *an ergodic set of states generates a strongly connected subgraph of the Markov digraph $D$, which is a strong component of $D$ such that in the condensation $D^*$, this strong component is a receiver.* An *ergodic state* is any state in an ergodic set. If the lines of $D$ in Fig. 3 have values that make $D$ a Markov digraph then $S_3$ is an ergodic set of states, but $S_1$ is not. Finally, an *ergodic chain* is one whose states form a single ergodic set. Thus *a chain is ergodic if and only if its Markov digraph is strongly connected.*

A *closed set* of states is a collection of states such that no state outside of this set is reachable from any state in the set. Thus, every ergodic set of states is closed, but not conversely.

A *transient set* of states is a set in which any two states are mutually reachable and which can be left. Thus, a transient set of states generates a strong subgraph of the Markov digraph. It is clear that a *maximal transient set* of states generates a strong component of $D$ such that the corresponding point of $D^*$ is *not* a receiver. Thus, we see that *any strong component of the condensation $D^*$ of the Markov digraph $D$ of a chain is either an ergodic set or a maximal transient set*. A *transient state* is any state in a maximal transient set of states. We illustrate these concepts by referring to the digraph $D$ and its condensation $D^*$ shown in Fig. 3. This digraph $D$ can be regarded as the Markov digraph of a chain, once probabilities are assigned to its directed lines in such a way that the sum of the probabilities of all the lines from each of its points is 1. Here $S_1$ and $S_2$ are maximal transient sets of states, while $S_3$ is a maximal ergodic set.

A *cyclic chain* is an ergodic chain in which each state can only be entered at certain periodic intervals. A *regular chain* is an ergodic chain that is not cyclic.

It sometimes happens that a chain has a transition matrix that can be partitioned as follows:

$$P = \left\| \begin{array}{ccc} P_1 & 0 & 0 \\ 0 & P_2 & 0 \\ 0 & 0 & P_3 \end{array} \right\|.$$

In this case there are mutually exclusive subsets of its states each of which by itself constitutes a Markov chain. Clearly each of the square submatrices $P_1, P_2, \ldots$ is itself stochastic. It is then much more convenient to decompose such a chain into smaller chains and study these small chains separately. The weak components $W_1, W_2, \ldots$ of the Markov digraph serve to determine the submatrices $P_1, P_2, \ldots$ of the transition matrix $P$, that result in such a diagonalized partition. If the Markov digraph $D$ is disconnected, then the rows and columns of $P$ can be reordered to obtain such a partitioning by writing all the states in the first weak component, followed by states in the second weak component, etc.

This may be illustrated by the digraph $D$ of Fig. 4. This is the digraph of a chain having 10 states, which lie in 3 weak components. Let $P_i$ be the transition matrix of weak component $W_i$ of Fig. 4. Then the transition matrix of the entire chain is expressible in the above decomposed form. In general, *a chain is decomposable if and only if its digraph is disconnected*.

We have seen in this section that the structural properties of a chain as represented in its digraph enables one to make a complete classification of states, regardless of the particular values of the positive probabilities of the chain.

## Brands as Chains

A brand chain is a Markov chain in which the states are brands and the transition probabilities tell the likelihood of consumers moving from one brand to another.

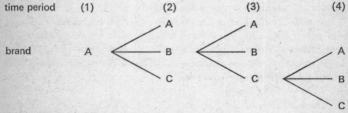

Figure 5 A probability tree.

The observable manifestations of the extent of consumer loyalty are the sequence of consumer purchases. A 'probability tree' as diagrammed in Fig. 5 is an elementary but useful way of looking at the sequence of purchases of a group of consumers. In the diagram, the market consists of three brands identified as A, B, and C. At time period 1, all consumers are in one of three positions; only the position of brand A is shown for this period. In the second time period, consumers in position A have the option of continuing with the same brand or switching to brands B or C. The same is true of consumers who have previously purchased brand B and brand C. The transition from period 1 to 2 is represented by a branching process. There is a similar branching process from period 2 to 3, etc. With a multiplicity of brands even this probability tree quickly exceeds the limits of physical handling.

Fortunately this complex of information can be summarized rather conveniently. Assume that the initial consumer sample is composed of 1,000 respondents who are distributed over the three

116

brands A, B, C. We can associate part of this sample of 1,000 consumers with each of the branches going from time period 1 to 2.

In the example shown in Fig. 6, half of the consumers who

|  | row sum | period 2 A | B | C |
|---|---|---|---|---|
| column sum | 1,000 | 250 | 275 | 475 |
| period 1   A | 250 | 125 | 75 | 50 |
| period 1   B | 250 | 75 | 100 | 75 |
| period 1   C | 500 | 50 | 100 | 350 |

Figure 6 The brand movement matrix.

initially purchased brand A remained with the brand in the second period, 75 went to brand B, and 50 went to brand C. In Fig. 6, the row sums give the number of consumers in period 1 in the three brand positions. The column sums give consumer purchases in period 2. The internal details of the table identify those

|  | A | B | C |
|---|---|---|---|
| A | .5 | .3 | .2 |
| B | .3 | .4 | .3 |
| C | .1 | .2 | .7 |

Figure 7 The brand probability matrix of Figure 6.

consumers who stayed with the same brand and those consumers who switched. Thus in this matrix we have summarized the basic switching pattern and staying pattern of consumers in a two-time-period situation. The efficiency of this matrix representation increases rapidly as the number of brands in a particular marketing situation increase.

Now we can take the next rather simple step. If we divide each element of this matrix by its row sum, then the resulting matrix is stochastic. Thus we are in a position to talk about the probability of a consumer remaining with the same brand or switching to another brand; see Fig. 7.

The entries in the resulting stochastic matrix are the transition probabilities in a finite Markov chain.

periods 2 and 3

|  | | AA | AB | AC | BA | BB | BC | CA | CB | CC |
|---|---|---|---|---|---|---|---|---|---|---|
| | AA | .4 | .3 | .3 | 0 | 0 | 0 | 0 | 0 | 0 |
| | AB | 00 | 0 | 0 | .3 | .5 | .2 | 0 | 0 | 0 |
| | AC | 0 | 0 | 0 | 0 | 0 | 0 | .3 | .2 | .5 |
| periods 1 and 2 | BA | .5 | .3 | .2 | 0 | 0 | 0 | 0 | 0 | 0 |
| | BB | 0 | 0 | 0 | .2 | .5 | .3 | 0 | 0 | 0 |
| | BC | 0 | 0 | 0 | 0 | 0 | 0 | .1 | .3 | .6 |
| | CA | .4 | .3 | .3 | 0 | 0 | 0 | 0 | 0 | 0 |
| | CB | 0 | 0 | 0 | .3 | .4 | .3 | 0 | 0 | 0 |
| | CC | 0 | 0 | 0 | 0 | 0 | 0 | .2 | .3 | .5 |

Figure 8a Second order probability matrix.

A similar approach also serves to represent consumer behavior over more than two periods. The appropriate matrix gives the number of consumers who buy AA in periods 1 and 2 and brands AB in periods 2 and 3, those who buy CA in periods 1 and 2, and AC in periods 2 and 3, etc.; on normalizing this matrix, we obtain the second order probability matrix shown in Fig. 8a.

As shown in Fig. 8b the tabulation problem for higher order matrices with many brands involved takes on a complicated appearance very quickly. It is possible by a very simple device to recast the data contained in any higher order matrix in such a way that the resulting matrix will have a partitioned appearance. This may be accomplished by choosing a different order for the columns than for the rows. We write the pairs of brands in the rows in that order in which we first have all pairs ending in A, then all ending in B, and so forth. For the columns, however, we first write all pairs of brands beginning with A, then all those beginning with B, etc. The resulting matrix has the simple form of Fig. 8b, which is not the transition matrix of a Markov chain, because the rows and columns are not similarly ordered.

periods 2 and 3

|  | AA | AB | AC | BA | BB | BC | CA | CB | CC |
|---|---|---|---|---|---|---|---|---|---|
| AA | .4 | .3 | .3 | | | | | | |
| BA | .5 | .3 | .2 | | | | | | |
| CA | .4 | .3 | .3 | | | | | | |
| AB | | | | .3 | .5 | .2 | | | |
| BB | | | | .2 | .5 | .3 | | | |
| CB | | | | .3 | .4 | .3 | | | |
| AC | | | | | | | .3 | .2 | .5 |
| BC | | | | | | | .1 | .3 | .6 |
| CC | | | | | | | .2 | .3 | .5 |

periods 1 and 2 (label for rows AB, BB, CB)

Figure 8b A partitioned form of Figure 8a.

Each submatrix in this partition has the same order as the number of brands. Therefore, the tabulation problem for higher order matrices does not get out of hand, and all of the information is contained in a collection of matrices each of which is of the same order as the original transition matrix.

We are interested in studying the structural properties of brand switching using transition probabilities. These structural patterns have interesting implications for marketing strategy. We restrict ourselves to a marketing situation that consists of three brands A, B, and C. In Fig. 10 the structure matrix is shown below the related digraph. Even without knowledge of the precise numerical values of the probabilities of brand switching, the graphical structure yields some information on the nature of consumer behavior.

The first case is an example of totally loyal consumers. They continue to buy the same brand in each period. We find nonzero entries only on the main diagonal of the matrix. This might represent a mature and stable product category with satisfied consumers.

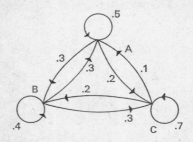

Figure 9 The digraph of the Markov chain whose transition matrix is given in Figure 7.

The second digraph presents the opposite competitive picture in that consumers never remain with the same brand in the next period. In this case we find all the nonzero elements off the main diagonal. For example, after trying chocolate cake, we may be inclined to seek another flavor the next time. Another possible situation might be cosmetic manufacturers who make extravagant claims about their product. Each promises to make the user more beautiful than she realistically can be. Each time the woman uses the product she is somewhat disappointed and hopes that the next manufacturer's product will give better results.

The third digraph shows a situation in which consumers shift from brand B to brands A and C with some interchange between A and C. But once consumers leave brand B, they do not return. Thus brand B corresponds to a transient state of a Markov chain. Strategically, it is very weak. If the same conditions persist, it will be ruined. The product manager for brand B would do well to test his product against competitors, since it appears that once consumers sample A or C they show no tendency to go back to B.

In the same digraph brands A and C exchange customers between themselves but never relinquish customers to any other brand. Thus brands A and C form an ergodic set. A desirable strategy for a manufacturer would be to establish a set of brands

120

within a market that form an ergodic set. The manufacturer always retains the consumer within his company franchise by providing a variety of products. Such a company position is then impregnable, at least until the introduction of significant change into the competitive complex, i.e. as long as the Markov chain remains stationary.

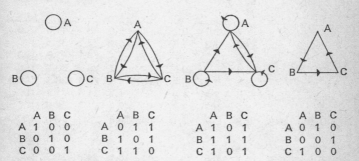

| | A | B | C | | | A | B | C | | | A | B | C | | | A | B | C |
|---|---|---|---|---|---|---|---|---|---|---|---|---|---|---|---|---|---|---|
| A | 1 | 0 | 0 | | A | 0 | 1 | 1 | | A | 1 | 0 | 1 | | A | 0 | 1 | 0 |
| B | 0 | 1 | 0 | | B | 1 | 0 | 1 | | B | 1 | 1 | 1 | | B | 0 | 0 | 1 |
| C | 0 | 0 | 1 | | C | 1 | 1 | 0 | | C | 1 | 0 | 1 | | C | 1 | 0 | 0 |

Figure 10 The graphs of hypothetical brand situations and their structure matrices.

The fourth digraph of Fig. 10 indicates that consumers buy brands A, B, and C in a cyclical pattern. Every third purchase period, they return to the same brand. This situation is called a periodic chain. This might be generated by boredom with the product. All of these hypothetical market situations are oversimplifications. However, they are useful examples of the more complicated real world. As a result of our approach, every theorem on finite Markov chains becomes a true statement for brand situations. In the next section these theorems will be applied and interpreted within the realm of brand switching in the market place.

## Chains in the Marketing Environment

Conventional brand share data (derived from retail store audits) suffer from the same limitations of aggregation as do more global economic series. Such data may give a false impression of stability to most markets. The small monthly percentage changes are often caused by major shifts in consumer buying. Perhaps the

121

single most important contribution of the application of Markov chains to marketing is that it forces a change of focus. While brand share data tell where the consumers are, the chain analysis

**Second Purchase Period Total Market Brands**

| Brands | A | B | C | D | E | F | G | DNB | Total % |
|---|---|---|---|---|---|---|---|---|---|
| A | 22.9 | 1.7 | 2.1 | 0.2 | 2.1 | 6.1 | 23.9 | 41.0 | 100 |
| B | 2.2 | 33.0 | 0.3 | 1.9 | — | 5.3 | 22.1 | 35.2 | 100 |
| C | 5.0 | 1.8 | 13.7 | — | — | 5.4 | 33.1 | 41.0 | 100 |
| D | 0.7 | 5.6 | — | 29.5 | — | 4.2 | 26.7 | 33.3 | 100 |
| E | — | 3.8 | 1.9 | — | 32.9 | 4.8 | 20.4 | 36.2 | 100 |
| F | 2.9 | 2.8 | 2.4 | 1.0 | 0.6 | 21.7 | 21.4 | 47.2 | 100 |
| G | 3.1 | 6.2 | 8.2 | 3.5 | 1.3 | 7.2 | 31.6 | 38.9 | 100 |
| DNB | 6.2 | 7.3 | — | 2.1 | 5.4 | 10.3 | 28.7 | 40.8 | 100 |

**Hard Core Component**

| | A | B | C | D | E | F | G | DNB | Total % |
|---|---|---|---|---|---|---|---|---|---|
| A | 32.4 | 1.1 | 0.6 | — | 1.1 | 3.1 | 24.8 | 36.9 | 100 |
| B | 0.5 | 47.7 | — | — | — | 2.0 | 26.2 | 23.6 | 100 |
| C | 2.3 | 0.8 | 17.0 | — | — | 1.6 | 40.3 | 38.0 | 100 |
| D | — | 0.9 | — | 37.2 | — | 1.8 | 30.7 | 29.4 | 100 |
| E | — | 2.9 | — | — | 50.0 | 5.8 | 22.5 | 18.8 | 100 |
| F | 2.1 | 1.7 | 1.0 | 0.4 | 0.9 | 29.4 | 24.2 | 40.3 | 100 |
| G | 1.8 | 20.3 | 3.4 | 1.2 | — | 10.9 | 35.6 | 26.8 | 100 |
| DNB | 10.4 | 4.2 | 2.5 | 4.6 | 8.3 | — | 20.0 | 50.0 | 100 |

**Switcher Component**

| | A | B | C | D | E | F | G | DNB | Total % |
|---|---|---|---|---|---|---|---|---|---|
| A | 7.3 | 2.8 | 4.6 | 0.5 | 3.7 | 11.0 | 22.4 | 47.7 | 100 |
| B | 5.0 | 8.4 | 0.8 | 5.0 | — | 10.9 | 15.3 | 54.6 | 100 |
| C | 8.6 | 3.2 | 9.1 | — | — | 19.8 | 23.1 | 45.2 | 100 |
| D | 2.9 | 20.0 | — | 5.7 | — | 11.4 | 14.3 | 45.7 | 100 |
| E | — | 5.6 | 5.6 | — | — | 2.8 | 16.6 | 69.4 | 100 |
| F | 4.3 | 4.9 | 5.2 | 2.2 | — | 7.1 | 16.0 | 60.3 | 100 |
| G | 1.7 | 1.4 | 2.6 | 3.2 | 1.0 | — | 32.3 | 57.8 | 100 |
| DNB | 10.4 | 3.3 | 5.7 | 2.3 | — | 10.8 | 22.5 | 45.0 | 100 |

*First Purchase Period*

Figure 11.

concentrates on the process by which consumers reach a particular brand position. It is thus concerned with dynamic aspects of market behavior.

Figures 11 and 12 display actual transition probability matrices for two different product categories. Each figure shows a matrix for the total market and two related matrices; one derived from

**Second Purchase Period Total Market Brands**

| Brands A | | B | C | D | E | F | DNB | G | Total % |
|---|---|---|---|---|---|---|---|---|---|
| A | 43.2 | 3.4 | 2.3 | 1.9 | 0 | 5.7 | 27.9 | 15.6 | 100 |
| B | 0.9 | 39.7 | 4.4 | 6.0 | 0.3 | 10.4 | 27.4 | 10.9 | 100 |
| C | 0.4 | 2.1 | 53.6 | 2.4 | 0.5 | 7.0 | 24.4 | 9.6 | 100 |
| D | 0.9 | 4.1 | 6.7 | 47.7 | 2.2 | 6.6 | 20.2 | 11.6 | 100 |
| E | 0 | 0 | 2.8 | 2.4 | 46.5 | 6.5 | 35.1 | 6.7 | 100 |
| F | 1.2 | 2.3 | 6.7 | 1.9 | 1.1 | 53.2 | 25.7 | 7.9 | 100 |
| DNB | 2.2 | 3.1 | 11.3 | 4.8 | 5.3 | 14.4 | 37.7 | 21.2 | 100 |
| G | 5.0 | 3.0 | 5.3 | 2.7 | 1.6 | 11.4 | 22.3 | 48.7 | 100 |

**Hard Core Component**

| | A | B | C | D | E | F | DNB | G | |
|---|---|---|---|---|---|---|---|---|---|
| A | 54.0 | 2.7 | 1.1 | 0 | 0 | 2.9 | 26.8 | 12.5 | 100 |
| B | 0.5 | 56.4 | 2.1 | 1.4 | 0.5 | 3.0 | 23.9 | 12.2 | 100 |
| C | 0.3 | 0.4 | 64.4 | 0.2 | 0.4 | 2.9 | 21.6 | 9.8 | 100 |
| D | 0.7 | 0.3 | 0.9 | 65.8 | 0.6 | 3.5 | 17.7 | 10.5 | 100 |
| E | 0 | 0 | 0.6 | 2.5 | 52.6 | 3.4 | 34.8 | 6.1 | 100 |
| F | 0.7 | 0.7 | 2.2 | 0.5 | 0.2 | 62.6 | 25.0 | 8.1 | 100 |
| DNB | 2.6 | 3.5 | 15.0 | 5.3 | 8.2 | 20.1 | 22.3 | 23.0 | 100 |
| G | 3.1 | 4.2 | 2.1 | 4.5 | 3.2 | 5.8 | 21.7 | 55.4 | 100 |

**Switcher Component**

| | A | B | C | D | E | F | DNB | G | |
|---|---|---|---|---|---|---|---|---|---|
| A | 17.3 | 5.1 | 5.1 | 6.4 | 0 | 12.2 | 30.8 | 23.1 | 100 |
| B | 1.5 | 12.1 | 8.3 | 13.6 | 0 | 22.7 | 33.3 | 8.5 | 100 |
| C | 0.6 | 7.3 | 20.9 | 8.9 | 0.6 | 19.4 | 32.7 | 9.6 | 100 |
| D | 1.2 | 11.8 | 18.5 | 10.9 | 5.6 | 12.9 | 25.3 | 13.8 | 100 |
| E | 0 | 1.3 | 11.4 | 9.5 | 12.7 | 20.3 | 35.4 | 9.4 | 100 |
| F | 3.0 | 7.4 | 21.8 | 6.6 | 4.1 | 21.5 | 28.5 | 7.1 | 100 |
| DNB | 1.7 | 2.8 | 7.5 | 4.3 | 2.3 | 8.4 | 53.8 | 19.2 | 100 |
| G | 6.6 | 7.3 | 3.8 | 1.2 | 6.3 | 18.7 | 25.2 | 30.9 | 100 |

*First purchase period*

Figure 12.

hard-core consumers and one from consumers typified as switchers. The transition probabilities for the total market for both products are characterized by high probabilities on the main diagonal. With the exception of the DNB (did not buy) brand and product G, which is an all-other brand grouping, the probability of switching to other brands is quite small. As might be expected, different product categories have different levels of loyalty (as reflected by the magnitude of the diagonal entries). The products in Fig. 11 have loyalties that are almost twice as high as those in Fig. 12.

The entries for the related matrices are obtained by classifying consumers as hard-core or switcher types. A family is considered hard core if it devotes 75 per cent or more of its purchases to any single brand in the time period under study. By the nature of the definitions used, the hardcore matrices for both products show higher brand loyalty diagonal entries than is the case with the total market.

There are interesting structural differences between the hardcore and switcher matrices. A transition probability matrix is close to the steady state when each of its rows are reasonably similar to one another. The rows of the switcher matrix in Fig. 11 are more alike than is the case with the hard-core matrix. Thus, the switcher matrix is closer to the steady state than the hard-core matrix. Irrespective of the last brand purchase for the switcher matrix, the probability of going to brand A from any other brand is of the same order of magnitude. Consumers in this group tend to react to most market stimuli. On the other hand, the hard-core matrix represents a more stable component of the market. The outstanding tendency is to remain with the same brand. The matrix of completely loyal buyers is characterized by ones on the main diagonal. Each brand is a closed set and an absorbing brand. Such a chain has no steady state. Consumers remain fixed in their brand positions and there is never any change in brand share. Contrary to our intuition, stability in the market place might best be measured by the degree to which the matrix is removed from the steady state.

Consumer panel data when converted to transition probabilities give rise to ergodic chains. In most situations there is almost always some probability of consumers going from any brand in the market place to any other brand.

The discovery of closed sets in a marketing situation is of obvious importance. One of the most interesting empirical findings is that under normal conditions 'chains-own-brands' buyers tend to make up a closed set since consumers switch among such brands. Hence it is then possible to partition the transition matrix into chains-own-brands and other nationally advertised brands. Equally interesting is the discovery of under what circumstances these closed sets can be disrupted so that consumers will show some tendency to switch from this closed set of brands to other brands in the market.

We must be prepared to accept the fact that in applying this method to actual market data, none of these classifications will fit in the precise sense. These classifications become significant if we regard very small transition probabilities as approximating zero.

We have also found groups of nationally advertised brands within a product category that make a closed set. These brands tend to 'feed' one another. This need not imply that these consumers do not switch to other brands. However, it is important to know that once a consumer is in one of these brands, there is a reduced tendency to go to any other brand in the market. This suggests that the reason for this relation should be investigated and that a company should attempt to create this relation for its own brands. While the Markov chain analysis cannot tell how to accomplish this, it does provide a measure of success in achieving this objective.

The transient state is another important theoretical and practical classification. There are brands that can be viewed as transient states. The probabilities of remaining with a transient brand tend to be materially lower. These brands are characterized by high probabilities of exit. Again the discovery of a transient brand, particularly if it has a sufficient share of the market, is of considerable importance, since it provides basic clues for marketing strategy.

While we have not uncovered absorbing brands, some brands tend to show a greater tendency in this direction. This is reflected in the different magnitudes of probabilities on the diagonal. The stronger brands show higher levels of loyalty and hence retain the consumers who try the brands. The two-period tabulation of panel data that are needed for producing the transition probabilities such as those shown in Figs. 11 and 12 provide another useful source of analysis. All of our studies have given some attention to the source and disposition of business. It is through the study of source and disposition of business that we have uncovered approximations to the various states described earlier.

While it is not known how long people tend to remain hardcore buyers or switchers, we do know that they remain in these categories long enough to be of marketing interest. The empirical findings indicate that each product category generates different proportions of hard-core and switcher-type buyers. Our studies have identified brands with hard-core buyers ranging from 50 per cent of the market to as high as 80 per cent of all consumers. The identification of a product category as a high or low hardcore product class with consequent levels of loyalty have obvious consequences for marketing and advertising plans. The effects of a diminution of advertising on a brand that is characterized by high levels of loyalty will obviously be less than on a brand that is characterized by lower loyalty. It is a reasonable conjecture that products with low levels of loyalty and hard core, call for higher advertising budgets than is the case for products with higher loyalties.

## Predictions from Markov Chains

### (a) The steady state

The mathematics of a stationary chain yields a very simple method of making predictions of the absolute probabilities using the initial probability vector and the transition matrix $P$. The absolute probabilities are given by

$$\alpha_1 = \alpha_0 P,$$
$$\alpha_2 = \alpha_1 P = \alpha_0 P^2,$$

and in general $\quad \alpha_{t+1} = \alpha_t P = \alpha_0 P^{t+1}.$

In the application of the model to brand switching, the absolute probabilities are brand shares derived from the consumer panel. As the power $n$ of $P$ becomes large, the rows of the matrix $P^n$ approach a constant vector called *the steady state*. In practice, even over short periods of time, this method of making predictions indicates the direction of change but overstates the magnitude of such change.

Thus far, the discussion has been restricted to stationary chains. Stationarity implies that the transition probabilities are constant over time. However, the most interesting marketing situations are those in which the transition probabilities are changing. The steady state is an important device for evaluating the meaning of a particular sequence of transition probabilities that the market is experiencing. For a particular set of transition probabilities, the steady state provides an estimate of the probable outcome of the forces at work.

It is within this context that the steady-state predictions of brand shares can be useful for evaluating advertising and promotion activity. Since the steady-state shares are predictions in the future, it is possible to make relative comparisons between advertising campaigns at a number of points in time. This is particularly valuable in advertising experiments, which should be conducted for extended periods of time, but which frequently break down because of other factors.

## (b) Average absorbing time before trying the brand

A highly useful prediction device has been the 'average absorbing time'. Conceptually, this involves designating a specific brand in question as an absorbing state and computing the number of time periods on the average required for it to capture the entire market. Starting with the transition probability matrix $P$, the row and column of the brand in question are ruled out, leaving a residual matrix designated as $Q$. The average absorbing time is given by *the fundamental matrix*, as defined by Kemeny and Snell [13], namely the inverse of $(I-Q)$. Figure 13 shows this fundamental matrix for three different brand situations. The total column is a measure of the average absorbing time on the assumption that consumers first try all brands in the market.

It is of some interest to compare the total column in Fig. 13 for each of the three marketing situations designated as Examples 1, 2, and 3. For the first example, the total time is approximately 70 purchase periods. For the second example, the total time is 42 and for the last, about 11 purchase periods. These relations have immediate value in planning new promotions, advertising, and new product introductions. They also demonstrate that some brands require a longer period of maturation before they can be

127

properly appraised and begin to return profits to the company. The magnitudes of these absorbing times are not without meaning. There is evidence that the average absorbing time is an approximation of actual market behavior. These average absorbing times are useful guides of the average number of purchase periods required for consumers to have tried the absorbing brand.

Of equal interest is the internal composition of these fundamental matrices. The average absorbing times are determined by the transition probabilities. However they are considerably easier to interpret and are important in evaluating the market structure. In Example 1, the absorption time is much less for Brand A than

*Example 1*

|   | Total | Brands | | | | | |
|   |       | A | B | C | D | E | F |
|---|-------|---|---|---|---|---|---|
| A | 68.2 | 3.3 | 2.3 | 7.7 | 10.7 | 22.0 | 22.2 |
| B | 70.6 | 2.2 | 3.9 | 8.0 | 12.1 | 22.1 | 22.3 |
| C | 70.7 | 2.2 | 2.4 | 9.2 | 11.1 | 22.8 | 23.0 |
| D | 72.2 | 2.2 | 2.4 | 8.1 | 13.1 | 23.2 | 23.2 |
| E | 71.5 | 2.2 | 2.4 | 8.0 | 11.1 | 24.8 | 23.0 |
| F | 70.3 | 2.2 | 2.4 | 8.0 | 11.0 | 22.9 | 23.8 |

*Example 2*

|   | Total | G | H | I | J | K | L |
|---|-------|---|---|---|---|---|---|
| G | 42.4 | 2.6 | 4.8 | 1.1 | 6.5 | 13.6 | 13.8 |
| H | 41.7 | 1.3 | 5.9 | 1.0 | 6.5 | 13.4 | 13.6 |
| I | 42.1 | 1.4 | 4.7 | 2.8 | 6.3 | 13.4 | 13.5 |
| J | 42.6 | 1.3 | 4.7 | 1.0 | 8.4 | 13.6 | 13.6 |
| K | 42.8 | 1.3 | 4.8 | 1.0 | 6.5 | 15.5 | 13.7 |
| L | 41.8 | 1.3 | 4.8 | 1.0 | 6.5 | 13.7 | 14.5 |

*Example 3*

|   | Total | M | N | O | P | Q | R |
|---|-------|---|---|---|---|---|---|
| M | 11.3 | 1.6 | 0.4 | 1.3 | 0.4 | 3.7 | 3.9 |
| N | 11.3 | 0.4 | 1.8 | 1.3 | 0.3 | 3.7 | 3.8 |
| O | 11.1 | 0.4 | 0.4 | 2.5 | 0.3 | 3.7 | 3.8 |
| P | 12.5 | 0.5 | 0.4 | 1.4 | 2.1 | 4.0 | 4.1 |
| Q | 11.8 | 0.3 | 0.4 | 1.3 | 0.3 | 5.7 | 3.8 |
| R | 10.9 | 0.4 | 0.4 | 1.3 | 0.3 | 3.8 | 4.7 |

Figure 13

any other brand. This is a clue that marketing efforts at least in the beginning should be directed to this brand, since consumers of this brand are relatively easier to reach. In Example 2 there are at least two brands A and C that have very low absorption times. This suggests both that there is a relation between these two brands, and that some single marketing strategy may be directed to consumers of both brands.

By contrast, in Example 3, the absorbing brand completely dominates the market. Over a relatively short period of time, most consumers will have switched to this absorbing brand. Most of the absorption times in the fundamental matrix for Example 3 are less than one purchase period, and very few brands require 3 or 4 purchase periods.

## (c) New product introduction

One of the most important problems in test marketing is to determine at a reasonably early date what the share position of the product is likely to be. In the short run, brand shares can be quite unreliable. Working with standard-brand share data, one must wait a considerable length of time to obtain this information. We have found, Lipstein [17], a number of concepts derived from chain analysis to be exceedingly valuable in evaluating new products in test markets. Shown in Fig. 14 are the basic measures that have been used in evaluating a new product introduction. The curve of Fig. 14 (B) shows the brand-share data derived from store audits. Hard-core buyers are arbitrarily taken as those consumers who make at least three quarters of their purchases in a single brand over a specified period of time. Figure 14 (A) represents the changes in the hard-core portion. Finally, Fig. 14 (C) contains repeat rates derived from the main diagonal of the first order matrix for the new brand. The standard for evaluating the repeat rates is the 'modified trace' before introduction derived from the first order matrix. This 'modified trace' is the average of the diagonal entires of $P$. The dashed curve of Fig. 14 (C) represents new triers of the product.

Finally Fig. 14 (D) presents a series of measures called 'stability indexes'. For the new brand, these indexes are the column sums divided by the row sums based upon numbers of people in the brand-movement matrix, as in Fig. 6. A value of one indicates equality of entrance and exit. A stability index of more than one means greater entrance into the brand than exit from it.

The *stability index for brand i* is the ratio in the brand movement matrix of the *i*th column sum to the *i*th row sum.

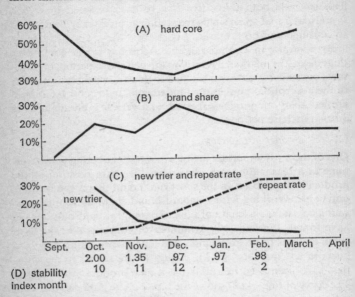

Figure 14 Behavior of a new product.

The stability index has given us an interesting view of how a new product first disturbs the market and then becomes a part of the market. An effectively introduced new product disrupts old loyalties in the market and the proportion of hard-core buyers. After a specified amount of time, which will vary by product category, the market tends to return to a modified equilibrium as measured by the position of hard-core buyers. At that point the new product has become part of the market.

Let us examine how the new product develops. At its introduction, the brand share starts rising at a very sharp rate. This is brought about by the high rate of first-time triers. The level of loyalty for the new brand is materially lower than that of other brands in the market. In the ensuing period the number of first-time triers begins to diminish. However, the brand position is reinforced by the increasing level of loyalty. The decline in the number of people classified as hard core is an over-all measure of the upset of the market.

As the new brand evolves, its loyalty level rate begins to approach an asymptotic value, which is influenced by the average loyalty for all brands. First-time triers diminish to a small trickle. The hard core of buyers begins to return to their original level. We have found that when the loyalty rate for the new brand is close to the modified trace of all brands and the hard core is almost back to its original position that it is reasonable to assume that this is the most likely share that this brand is going to achieve.

It should be noted that during this period, the stability index reflects the growth or development of the brand. Immediately after introduction it has a value of 2. As the new triers fall off it drops to 1.3. In the third period it is approximately 1. The brand at this point is in balance. However, there is a risk of too early evaluation since the brand has not yet matured in terms of levels of loyalty. It is only after the brand has achieved the average loyalty for the category that we can be sure of its maturity.

These four measures (1) brand shares, (2) new triers, (3) repeat-buying rates, and (4) hard-core buyers provide a rather dramatic and dynamic description of how a new brand evolves in test markets.

## Summary

Our purpose in this article is the development of mathematical techniques for the analysis and prediction of marketing phenomena. The kinds of mathematics that prove fruitful are finite stationary Markov chains and directed graphs. These were exploited to develop new measures for both the magnitude and structure of brand switching.

In the empirical sections of the paper, a variety of structural relations of brands are explored and their strategy implications suggested. Mathematical relations derived from transition matrices are provided with marketing interpretations and comments are made on the usefulness of some measures for predictive purposes. Lastly, a few key concepts of chains are used in a non-stationary sense to provide a framework for evaluating new product introductions.

## References

1. ANDERSON, T. W. (1954) 'Probability models for analyzing time changes in attitudes', in P. F. Lazarsfeld's (Ed.), *Mathematical thinking in the social sciences*, pp. 17–66, Free Press, Glencoe, Ill.
2. BERGE, C. (1958) *Théorie des graphes et ses applications*, Dunod, Paris.
3. BLUMEN, I., KOGAN, M., and McCARTHY, P. J. (1955) *The industrial mobility of labor as a probability process*, Cornell Studies in Industrial and Labor Relations, **6**.
4. BUSH, R. R., and MOSTELLER, F. (1955) *Stochastic models for learning*. Wiley.
5. DOOB, J. L. (1952) *Stochastic processes*. Wiley.
6. ESTES, W. K. (1950) 'Towards a statistical theory of learning', *Psych. Rev.*, **57**, 94–107.
7. FELLER, W. (1957) *An introduction to probability theory and its applications*, **1** (2nd edn.). Wiley.
8. HARARY, F. (1959) 'A criterion for unanimity in French's theory of social power', in D. Cartwright's (Ed.), *Studies in social power*, pp. 168–82 Inst. Social Research, Ann Arbor, Mich.
9. HARARY, F. (1959) 'Graph theoretic methods in the management sciences', *Management Sci.*, **4**, 387–403.
10. HARARY, F. and NORMAN, R. Z. (1953) *Graph theory as a mathematical model in social science*, Inst. Social Research, Ann Arbor, Mich.
11. HARARY, F., NORMAN, R. Z., and CARTWRIGHT, D. (1962 *Introduction to digraph theory for social scientists*. Inst. Social Research, Ann Arbor, Mich.
12. KAC, M. (1959) *Statistical independence in probability, analysis, and number theory*. Math. Assoc. of America, Carus Math. Monograph No. 12.
13. KEMENY, J. G. and SNELL, J. L. (1960) *Finite Markov chains*. Van Nostrand.
14. KÖNIG, D. *Theorie der endlichen und unendlichen graphen*. Leipzig, 1936; reprinted Chelsea, New York, 1950.
15. KUEHN, A. A. (1958) 'An analysis of the dynamics of consumer behavior and its implications for marketing management', Doctoral dissertation, Carnegie Institute of Technology.
16. LIPSTEIN, B. (1959) 'The dynamics of brand loyalty and brand switching', *Proc., Fifth Annual Conference, Advertising Research Foundation*, 101–8, New York.

17. LIPSTEIN, B. (1961) 'Tests for Test Marketing', *Harvard Business Rev.*, **39**, 74–7.

18. MARSHALL, A. W. and GOLDHAMER, H. (1955) 'An application of Markov processes to the study of the epidemiology of mental disease', *J. Am. Stat. Assoc.* **50**, 99–129; RICHARD B. MAFFEI (1960) 'Brand preferences and simple Markov processes', *Opns. Res.* **8**, 210–18.

19. SHANNON, C. E. (1948) 'A mathematical theory of communication', *Bell System Technical J.*, **27**, 379–423 and 623–56.

20. SHEPHARD, R. (1957) 'A stochastic model for stimulus generalization', *Psychometrika*, **22**, 325–45.

# 5 R. M. Cyert, H. J. Davidson, and G. L. Thompson

## Estimation of the Allowance for Doubtful Accounts by Markov Chains

R. M. Cyert, H. J. Davidson, and G. L. Thompson (1962), 'Estimation of the allowance for doubtful accounts by Markov chains', *Management Science*, **8**, 287–303.

In retail establishments and in other businesses that commonly use the reserve method of accounting for bad debts, the estimation at fiscal year-end of the allowance for doubtful accounts[1] has a direct, and often significant, effect on income. The allowance, which represents the estimated amount of receivable balances which will ultimately prove uncollectible, is estimated. The difference between the estimated allowance and the allowance on the books is taken into income via a charge or credit to bad debt expense. Where a significant portion of a firm's assets are tied up in accounts receivable, the accurate estimation of the allowance for doubtful accounts assumes a special importance.

In most retail establishments, the method of determining the allowance for doubtful accounts has historically been a two-step process. First, the accounts have been classified into age categories which reflect the stage of account delinquency, e.g. current accounts, accounts one month past due, accounts two months past due, and so forth. If the enterprise has a large number of accounts, the aging has been customarily performed on a sample basis and the frequency distribution of dollars, grouped according to age category, estimated from the sample for the total universe of accounts.

The second step in the process of estimating the allowance for doubtful accounts involves the application of 'loss expectancy' rates to the dollars in each age group of the frequency distribution obtained by the sampling process. The loss expectancy rates are

1. The reader may be more familiar with the 'allowance for doubtful accounts' as the 'reserve for bad debts'. The former terminology is preferred by the accounting profession.

judgment estimates of the proportion of dollars in each age category liable to become uncollectible. In a sense, these loss expectancy rates are 'policy parameters' for they are not only based on past experience but are also functions of such things as the firm's expectations of economic conditions, the firm's conservatism in financial policy, and other similar factors.

Investigation of more accurate and efficient methods of estimating the allowance for doubtful accounts was begun in the early 1950s by R. M. Cyert and R. M. Trueblood.[2] At this time, studies were confined primarily to investigation of more efficient methods of performing the first step in the estimation procedure: determining the age distribution of accounts. In particular, the applicability of statistical sampling techniques was evaluated. A number of retail establishments now use scientific sampling methods to perform the first step in the estimation of the allowance for doubtful accounts.

As a continuation of research, the second phase of the allowance estimation problem was a logical area for investigation. While it did not seem likely that all of the judgment factors involved in the setting of loss expectancy rates could be eliminated, it did appear feasible to develop a scientific approach to determining these rates. Accordingly, research into this problem was initiated. This paper discusses a method which has been developed. In addition, some of the managerial implications of the method are discussed.

## Model Development

Before describing the methods which have been developed for estimating loss expectancy rates, it will be helpful to define the allowance for doubtful accounts. *The allowance for doubtful accounts at any point in time is the dollar amount (estimated) of accounts receivable at that point in time which will, in the future, prove to be uncollectible.* For example, on 31 December 1960, the XYZ Department Store might have $4,000,000 of accounts receivable. If each of these 4,000,000 dollars were followed, subsequently, one would find that a fraction of the dollars would

2. R. M. Cyert and R. M. Trueblood (1957) 'Statistical sampling techniques in the aging of accounts receivable in a department store', *Management Sci.*, 3, No. 2, 185–95.

eventually be repaid; a small number of dollars, say 40,000 would never be repaid. In this situation, a perfect estimate of the reserve for doubtful accounts as of 31 December 1960, would be $40,000.

From this description of the allowance for doubtful accounts, it may be noted that a loss process is involved. Our approach to developing a method of estimating loss expectancy rates and the allowance has been through development of a model describing this loss process.

Consider a balance of accounts receivable at time $i$. The dollars of this balance can be classified then, or at any subsequent time, into each of $n$ age categories.[3] For a balance of receivables at time $i$, let:

$B_0$ = dollars of receivables which are 0 periods or payments past due (current).

$B_1$ = dollars of receivables which are 1 period or payment past due.

$\vdots$

$B_j$ = dollars of receivables which are $j$ periods or payments past due.

$\vdots$

$B_{n-1}$ = dollars of receivables which are $n - 1$ periods or payments past due.

$B_n$ = dollars of receivables which are *n or more* periods or payments past due.

These classifications correspond to the customary classifications used in aging. $B_0$ is the dollar amount in the current age category; $B_1$, the dollar amount in the one month past due category; and so forth. $B_n$ corresponds to the aging classification commonly called the 'bad debt' category. A delinquent account may be repaid eventually, however, it is customary accounting procedure to lump all accounts more than some fixed number of periods or payments past due into a bad debt category.

Consider now a balance of receivables as of time $i$, at the next

3. The number of age categories will vary in practice. The last category will depend upon the rules for 'writing off' accounts. The data in Exhibit 1 and 2 are taken from a store which classifies the accounts as bad debt when the dollars pass out of age category 6.

later time period $i + 1$. At time $i + 1$, the balance at time $i$ can be classified in two ways, according to the age category from which it came and according to the age category where it now is. In general, we will let $B_{jk}$ equal the balance in category $k$ at time $i + 1$ which came from category $j$ at time $i$.

Using this two way classification, we must make one modification to account, at time $i + 1$, for all the receivables at time $i$. Another 'age' category must be added to those categories previously described. This category, which we will denote by the subscript $\bar{0}$ corresponds to a 'paid' classification. Dollars in any age category at time $i$ may move to category $\bar{0}$ as well as to categories 0 to $n$ at time $i + 1$.

Using this sytem of classification, a balance of receivables at time $i$ can, in general, be described by an $n + 2$ square matrix, $B$. The individual entries, $B_{jk}$, equal the amount of the balance in category $j$ at time $i$ which moves to category $k$ at time $i + 1$.

$$B = \begin{bmatrix} B_{\bar{0}\bar{0}} \ldots B_{\bar{0}k} \ldots B_{\bar{0}n} \\ B_{j\bar{0}} \ldots B_{jk} \ldots B_{jn} \\ B_{n\bar{0}} \ldots B_{nk} \ldots B_{nn} \end{bmatrix}.$$

From this $n + 2$ matrix of balances, $B$, it is possible to develop an $n + 2$ matrix of transition probabilities, $P$. The transition probability entries in this matrix, $P$, measure the likelihood that dollars in a particular category will move to another category during the applicable period of time. An implicit assumption is that this transition probability is measured over the same period of time that is used for the classification of accounts receivable.

In general, the transition probability, $P_{jk}$, will be defined as the probability of a dollar in classification $j$ at time $i$ transiting to classification $k$ at time $i + 1$. In terms of the balance matrix entries, $B_{jk}$, the transition probabilities, $P_{jk}$, are defined:

$$P_{jk} = \frac{B_{jk}}{\sum_{\bar{0}}^{n} B_{js}} \qquad (k = \bar{0}, 0, 1, \ldots, n)$$

As applied to the movement of receivable balances, several special characteristics of the matrix of transition probabilities may be noted. First, any dollar amount entering the $\bar{0}$ (paid) category cannot transit to another category, but must remain in the paid category. It follows that: $P_{\bar{0}\bar{0}} = 1.00$, $P_{\bar{0}0} = 0$, $P_{\bar{0}1} = 0$, ..., $P_{\bar{0}k} = 0$, ..., $P_{\bar{0}n} = 0$. A second special characteristic involves the bad debt classification. It is assumed in our model that any amount reaching the bad debt classification remains in this classification.[4] Thus:

$$P_{n\bar{0}} = 0, \ P_{n0} = 0, \ P_{n1} = 0, \ldots, P_{nn} = 1.00$$

Note that many of the probabilities in the $P$ matrix are zero or small. The number of zero entries that occur will depend upon the aging method employed. There are two general approaches that are used in aging. In one – the total balance method – all dollars in the account balance are put in the age category corresponding to the oldest dollar. Thus a current purchase charge by a customer with a five-months past due balance would be classified in the five-months age category. The 'partial balance' method, which is the second approach, allocates the dollar balance of an account among the age categories on the basis of the age of each of the dollars. Under either method an amount in age classification $j$ at time $i$ cannot move beyond age classification $j + 1$ at time $i + 1$. Thus all entries in the diagonals above the one beginning with $P_{12}$ will be zero.

The calculation of transition probabilities and the resulting matrix of transition probabilities as prepared from a random sample of approximately 1,000 department store accounts is illustrated in Exhibit 1 and Exhibit 2.

To complete the description of the model, two assumptions that are made must be noted. First it is assumed that the matrix of transition probabilities is constant over time and independent of the initial age distribution of account balances. The empirical validity of this assumption is discussed in more detail in a later section. Second, it is assumed that all accounts are the same size when the 'total balance' method of aging is used. This assumption is necessary because it is not the individual dollars which

4. In practice, some accounts are repaid after reaching the bad debt category. This does not materially affect the realistic nature of the model. First, the bad debt category may be selected so that the prospect of subsequent recovery is small. Second, the model treatment corresponds to common accounting treatment, i.e. accounts are 'written off' on reaching a specified age category and recoveries are treated as separate transactions.

move but rather all of the dollars in the account. Thus a skewed distribution of account balances could distort the limiting probabilities. Empirically this assumption is troublesome. However, the difficulty can be handled by stratifying balances on the basis of size and making the estimate of the limiting probabilities on this basis. Still another, and perhaps simpler, way of avoiding this assumption would be to follow the transitions of accounts rather than account balances. The assumption does not need to be made when the 'partial balance' method of aging is used.

## The Model as a Markov Chain Process

The model as previously described can be recognized as a Markov chain process with $n + 2$ states and transition matrix given by $P$. Moreover, since there are two absorbing states (the collection state 0 and the bad debt state, $n$) and since, from every non-absorbing state it is possible to reach one of these two absorbing states, we see that the process is a Markov chain with two absorbing states.[5] We shall make use of certain known results from Markov chain theory, and also derive some additional results. These will be interpreted in terms of the accounts receivable problem.

There are three questions that can be answered by the use of Markov chain theory:

1. Suppose that at a given time, $i$, there are certain amounts in each of the various age classifications. We know that if the process is permitted to continue indefinitely all of these dollars will end up in either the paid state, $\bar{0}$, or the bad debts state, $n$. What fraction of the total dollars involved will end up in each of these states?

2. Suppose a retail establishment receives $c$ new dollars (charge sales) in its accounts each period. These $c$ dollars enter distributed in the various age categories. If $c$ new dollars are received in this manner each period, what will be the steady state distribution of receivables by age category?

3. Suppose a retail establishment receives $c_i$ new dollars (charge sales) in its accounts each period. The amount of new dollars, $c_i$,

5. J. G. Kemeny and L. J. Snell (1959) *Finite Markov Chains*, 35. Van Nostrand.

## Exhibit 1
## Dollar Movement and Transition Probabilities

| Age movement | | Oct.–Nov. 1959 | | Nov.–Dec. 1959 | | Combined | |
|---|---|---|---|---|---|---|---|
| From | To | Dollars | Probability | Dollars | Probability | Dollars | Probability |
| 0 | 0̄ | $9,608 | 0.194 | $11,623 | 0.228 | $21,232 | 0.211 |
| 0 | 0 | 33,769 | 0.682 | 33,112 | 0.648 | 66,881 | 0.665 |
| 0 | 1 | 6,173 | 0.124 | 6,358 | 0.124 | 12,530 | 0.124 |
| Total | | $49,550 | 1.000 | $51,093 | 1.000 | $100,643 | 1.000 |
| 1 | 0̄ | $2,107 | 0.141 | $2,002 | 0.125 | $4,108 | 0.133 |
| 1 | 0 | 2,827 | 0.189 | 2,965 | 0.186 | 5,792 | 0.187 |
| 1 | 1 | 6,576 | 0.440 | 7,070 | 0.443 | 13,646 | 0.442 |
| 1 | 2 | 3,434 | 0.230 | 3,923 | 0.246 | 7,356 | 0.238 |
| 1 | 3 | | | | | | |
| 1 | 4 | | | | | | |
| Total | | $14,944 | 1.000 | $15,960 | 1.000 | $30,902 | 1.000 |
| 2 | 0̄ | $1,583 | 0.117 | $1,701 | 0.138 | $3,284 | 0.127 |
| 2 | 0 | 1,121 | 0.083 | 958 | 0.078 | 2,079 | 0.081 |
| 2 | 1 | 2,054 | 0.152 | 3,116 | 0.254 | 5,170 | 0.200 |
| 2 | 2 | 5,315 | 0.394 | 4,026 | 0.328 | 9,341 | 0.362 |
| 2 | 3 | 3,422 | 0.254 | 2,492 | 0.202 | 5,913 | 0.230 |
| Total | | $13,495 | 1.000 | $12,293 | 1.000 | $25,787 | 1.000 |
| 3 | 0̄ | $788 | 0.101 | $732 | 0.094 | $1,520 | 0.098 |
| 3 | 0 | 82 | 0.011 | 123 | 0.016 | 210 | 0.014 |
| 3 | 1 | 210 | 0.027 | 493 | 0.064 | 704 | 0.045 |
| 3 | 2 | 1,731 | 0.222 | 867 | 0.112 | 2,598 | 0.167 |
| 3 | 3 | 1,879 | 0.241 | 2,617 | 0.334 | 4,497 | 0.288 |
| 3 | 4 | 3,109 | 0.398 | 2,928 | 0.380 | 6,037 | 0.388 |
| Total | | $7,799 | 1.000 | $7,760 | 1.000 | $15,566 | 1.000 |
| 4 | 0̄ | $590 | 0.189 | $416 | 0.101 | $1,005 | 0.138 |
| 4 | 0 | 2 | 0.001 | 169 | 0.041 | 170 | 0.024 |
| 4 | 1 | — | — | — | — | — | — |
| 4 | 2 | 376 | 0.120 | 297 | 0.072 | 674 | 0.093 |
| 4 | 3 | 600 | 0.192 | 800 | 0.195 | 1,400 | 0.194 |
| 4 | 4 | 1,068 | 0.342 | 1,905 | 0.464 | 2,972 | 0.411 |
| 4 | 5 | 488 | 0.156 | 517 | 0.126 | 1,005 | 0.140 |
| 4 | 6 | | | | | | |
| Total | | $3,124 | 1.000 | $4,103 | 1.000 | $7,226 | 1.000 |

Exhibit 1 *(continued)*

| Age movement | | Oct.–Nov. 1959 | | Nov.–Dec. 1959 | | Combined | |
|---|---|---|---|---|---|---|---|
| From | To | Dollars | Probability | Dollars | Probability | Dollars | Probability |
| 5 | 5 | 1,739 | 0.538 | 1,601 | 0.413 | 3,340 | 0.470 |
| 5 | 6 | 158 | 0.049 | 1,148 | 0.296 | 1,306 | 0.184 |
| Total | | $3,234 | 1.000 | $3,879 | 1.000 | $7,114 | 1.000 |
| 5 | 0̄ | $355 | 0.110 | $268 | 0.069 | $623 | 0.087 |
| 5 | 0 | 55 | 0.017 | | | 55 | 0.008 |
| 5 | 1 | 43 | 0.013 | 88 | 0.023 | 131 | 0.018 |
| 5 | 2 | | | 91 | 0.023 | 91 | 0.013 |
| 5 | 3 | 624 | 0.193 | 91 | 0.023 | 715 | 0.100 |
| 5 | 4 | 261 | 0.081 | 592 | 0.153 | 853 | 0.120 |

Exhibit 2

Matrix of Transition Probabilities (P)

| To/ From | Paid (0̄) | Current (0) | Months past due | | | | | |
| | | | 1 (1) | 2 (2) | 3 (3) | 4 (4) | 5 (5) | 6: Bad debt (6) |
|---|---|---|---|---|---|---|---|---|
| (0̄) | 1.00 | 0 | 0 | 0 | 0 | 0 | 0 | 0 |
| (0) | 0.21 | 0.67 | 0.12 | 0 | 0 | 0 | 0 | 0 |
| (1) | 0.13 | 0.19 | 0.44 | 0.24 | 0 | 0 | 0 | 0 |
| (2) | 0.13 | 0.08 | 0.20 | 0.36 | 0.23 | 0 | 0 | 0 |
| (3) | 0.10 | 0.01 | 0.04 | 0.17 | 0.29 | 0.39 | 0 | 0 |
| (4) | 0.14 | 0.02 | 0 | 0.09 | 0.20 | 0.41 | 0.14 | 0 |
| (5) | 0.09 | 0.01 | 0.02 | 0.01 | 0.10 | 0.12 | 0.47 | 0.18 |
| (6) | 0 | 0 | 0 | 0 | 0 | 0 | 0 | 1.00 |

and the distribution of the dollars among the age categories varies cyclically. The amounts, $c_i$, may also be affected by a growth trend. If $c_i$ new dollars are received in this manner each period, what will be the distribution of receivables by age category at the end of any period?

## Results and Interpretation

In the following discussion, we shall adopt the notation of Kemeny and Snell.[6] The transition matrix, $P$, is square with $n + 2$ rows and columns. Reorder the states so that the first state is the absorbing (paid) state, $\bar{0}$, the second state is the absorbing (bad debt) state, $n$; and the remaining transient states are the age categories $0, 1, \ldots, n - 1$. The matrix, $P$, can be partitioned:

$$P = \left[ \begin{array}{c|c} I & O \\ \hline R & Q \end{array} \right]$$

$I$ is the $2 \times 2$ identity matrix; $O$ is a $2 \times n$ zero matrix; $R$ is a $n \times 2$ matrix; and $Q$ is an $n \times n$ matrix. The matrix:

$$N = (1 - Q)^{-1} = I + Q + Q^2 + Q^3 + \ldots + Q^k + \ldots$$

exists and is called the *fundamental matrix* of the absorbing Markov chain.

The entries of the $n \times 2$ matrix, $NR$ give the probabilities of absorption in each of the absorbing states, $\bar{0}$ and $n$.[7] The entries in the first column give the probabilities of dollars in each of the age categories being paid; the second column gives the probabilities of becoming bad debts. These entries in the second column correspond to the loss expectancy rates now developed on a judgment basis by most retail establishments.

As noted above, Markov chain theory provides an estimate of loss expectancy rates; however, its results are more general. A direct estimate of the allowance for doubtful accounts and the variance of this estimate can also be obtained. First, we must define some matrix operations. If $A$ is any matrix, let $A_{sq}$ be the matrix obtained by squaring each entry in $A$; let $A_{rt}$ be the matrix obtained by taking the square root of each entry in $A$.

Suppose that, at time $i$, the $n$-component vector:

$$B_i = (B_{i0}, B_{i1}, \ldots, B_{i,n-1})$$

gives the dollars in each age category. Let $b$ be the sum of all these amounts, the total value of accounts receivable. The vector

6. J. G. Kemeny and L. J. Snell (1959) *Finite Markov Chains*, 35. Van Nostrand. See especially Ch. 3.

7. Ibid. pp. 52–3.

$\pi = (1/b)B$ is a probability vector with non-negative components whose sum is one. The components of the vector represent the fraction of total accounts receivable in each age category. If we assume that the movement of small blocks of the dollars in each of these age categories is independent, then we can regard the vector, $\pi$, as being the initial vector for the Markov chain.

The following theorem can be proved. (Note: In an Appendix we work out numerical examples of the formulas to be derived. The reader may wish to read the appendix in parallel with the text.)

*Theorem 1.* The entries of the 2-component vector, $BNR$, give the expected payments and bad debts resulting from the accounts receivable vector, $B$. The components of

$$A = b[\pi NR - (\pi NR)_{sq}] \qquad (1)$$

give the variances of payments and bad debts. The components of $A_{rt}$ give the standard deviations of these same amounts.

*Proof.* As previously noted, the components of the first column of the matrix, $NR$, give the probabilities of a dollar moving from each of the transient states to the absorbing (paid) state. The components of the vector, $\pi = (1/b)B$ give the initial probabilities of a dollar moving to each of the transient states each time the process is started. Hence, the probability of a dollar ending in the paid state is given by the first component of the vector, $\pi NR$. If the process is started $b$ times, the mean number of dollars ending in the paid state is the first component of $b\pi NR = BNR$. The first component of the vector, $\pi NR$, is the mean value of a function, $f$, that takes a value of one when a dollar ends in the paid state and otherwise takes on value zero. The variance of this function is given by the first component of

$$V(f) = M(f^2) - [M(f)]^2$$

Since $f^2 = f$, then $M(f^2) = M(f)$, and hence the variance of $f$ is given by the first component of $\pi NR - (\pi NR)_{sq}$. If the process is started $b$ times, the variance of the total amount in the paid state is given by the first component of (1). The analysis for the bad debt state is similar.

143

The reader may note the similarity of the mean and variance of the above function with the corresponding formulas for a binomial distribution. Theorem 1 thus gives the answer to the first question posed.[8] Note also that the variances of the two components of $BNR$ are equal.

At this point we turn to the second question, the predition of the steady state age distribution of receivable balances. Suppose that $c$ dollars of new receivables are received each period and that these dollars are distributed among the different categories as indicated by the components of the vector:

$$C = (C_0, C_1, \ldots, C_{n-1})$$

Define the vector, $\eta = (1/c)C$. The vector, $\eta$ is a probability vector and can be regarded as the initial vector for the Markov chain. Suppose, the Markov process is started $c$ times each period with the initial vector, $\eta$. What is the steady state distribution of receivable balances and what are the variances of these balances? We may also inquire as to the amount each period of expected payments and bad debts, and their respective variances.

8. Mr Yuji Ijiri has kindly pointed out to us that the present value of the accounts receivables can be computed in a similar manner as follows. If $b$ is the interest rate let $\beta = 1/(1 + b)$ be the discount factor. Then, if $B$ is the accounts receivables vector and $R_1$ is the first column of the matrix $R$, we can expect collections of $BR_1$ during the present time period; $BQR_1$ from the next time period when it will be worth only $\beta BQR_1$; etc.; and in the $(k + 1)$st time period we expect $BQ^kR_1$ when it will be worth $\beta^k BQ^kR_1$; etc. Adding these discounted values together we get as the present value of the accounts receivables,

$$BR_1 + \beta BQR_1 + \ldots + \beta^k BQR_1 + \ldots$$
$$= B[I + \beta Q + \ldots + \beta^k Q^k + \ldots]R_1$$
$$= BN_\beta R_1,$$

where we have set $N_\beta = I + \beta Q + \ldots + \beta^k Q^k + \ldots$

Most department stores follow the practice of charging interest on certain kinds of accounts. Exactly the same kind of reasoning can be used to compute the present value of these accounts with the interest charge added. Thus, if $b$ is the interest charged the customer and we set $\beta = 1 + b$, then the formula just given will compute the present value of these accounts. Of course, if we both discount and charge interest on future payments, then there will be either a net discount factor or a net interest factor and again the same formula, namely, $BN_\beta R_1$, will give the present value, where $\beta$ is the net discount or interest factor.

*Theorem 2.* If the Markov chain process is started $c$ times each period with the initial vector, $\eta$, the components of the vector, $CN$, give the steady state receivable balances in each age category. The number $CN\xi$ (where $\xi$ is an $n$-component column vector with all entries one) gives the steady state value for the total accounts receivable balance. The two component vector, $CNR$, gives steady state values for payments and bad debts each time period.

*Proof.* If the process described has run for many periods, the amount in the various states will consist of $\eta$ from new receivables, $\eta Q$ from new receivables of the previous month, $\eta Q^2$ from new receivables of two months past, and so forth. The sum of all these is:

$$\eta + \eta Q + \eta Q^2 + \eta Q^3 + \ldots = \eta(1 + Q + Q^2 + Q^3 + \ldots)$$
$$= \eta N$$

If this process is started $c$ times each period, accounts receivables balances in each of the states are given by the vector $c\eta N = CN$.

If $\xi$ is a column vector with unitary components, $CN\xi$ is the sum of the components of the vector, $CN$, and represents the total balance of accounts receivable.

If the process has run for many periods, there will be a $\eta R$ dollars absorbed from the new receivables of the first period, $\eta Q R$ absorbed from the new receivables of last month, $\eta Q^2 R$ from the new receivables of two months past, and so forth. The sum of these is

$$\eta R + \eta Q R + \eta Q^2 R + \ldots = \eta(1 + Q + Q^2 + \ldots)R$$
$$= \eta N R$$

If the process is started $c$ times, steady state payments and bad debts each period are given by $c\eta N R = CNR$. This completes the proof of the theorem.

Combining Theorems 1 and 2 we get the following corollary.

*Corollary.* Let $t = CN\xi$ and $\pi = (1/t)CN$; then $CN^2R$ and $t[\pi NR - (\pi NR)_{sq}]$ are the predicted mean and variance of collections and bed debts.

Note that this prediction is made by using the new charges to estimate the accounts receivable.[9]

9. Combining Theorem 2 with the results of [8] we find $CNN_\beta R_1$ to be the estimated value of the steady state accounts receivables.

Let us call a *repetitive Markov chain* the process in which we start off a Markov chain a number of times each period, and follow all of these until absorption. Then Theorem 2 shows that the mean number of dollars in each transient state is the same as the expected number of times a nonrepetitive Markov chain will be in each transient state. However, as we will see in Theorem 3 the variances of two quantities will not be the same.

*Theorem 3.* The variances for the quantities in Theorem 2 are given by the formulas

$$V = c[\eta N - \sum_{k=0}^{\infty} (\eta Q^k)_{sq}] \tag{2}$$

$$v = c[\eta N \xi - \sum_{k=0}^{\infty} (\eta Q^k \xi)_{sq}] \tag{3}$$

$$W = c[\eta NR - \sum_{k=0}^{\infty} (\eta Q^k R)_{sq}] \tag{4}$$

where Eq. (2) gives the variances of the components of $CN$, Eq. (3) gives the variances of the components of $CN\xi$, and Eq. (4) gives the variances of the components of $CNR$. The standard deviations are, of course, given by the square roots of these quantities, $V_{rt}$, $v_{rt}$, and $W_{rt}$, respectively.

*Proof.* The proofs of these assertions involve the rearrangement of absolutely convergent series and are all very similar. We give the details of Eq. (2) only. If $\eta$ is the starting vector of new charges made in the current month, and $c$ new dollars are charged, then the variance vector of amounts of new charges in each age category is given by $c[\eta - \eta_{sq}]$, by reasoning similar to the proof of Eq. (1). Similarly, the variance vector of charges carried over from last month is given by $c[\eta Q - (\eta Q)_{sq}]$, and those carried from the month before are given by $c[\eta Q^2 - (\eta Q^2)_{sq}]$, etc. Adding up these quantities we get

$$
\begin{aligned}
V &= c[\eta - \eta_{sq} + \eta Q - (\eta Q)_{sq} + \eta Q^2 - (\eta Q^2)_{sq} + \ldots] \\
&= c\{(\eta + \eta Q + \eta Q^2 + \ldots) - [\eta_{sq} + (\eta Q)_{sq} + (\eta Q^2)_{sq} + \ldots]\} \\
&= c\{\eta N - [\eta_{sq} + (\eta Q)_{sq} + (\eta Q^2)_{sq} + \ldots]\},
\end{aligned}
$$

which is Eq. (2).

Note that the variances of the two components of $CNR$ are equal.

Formulas (2–4) involve unsummed series. Lower bound estimates for them can be made by taking a few terms of each series. It is also possible to find upper bound formulas for these quantities that may be useful for computation. These are given in the next theorem.

*Theorem 4.* Let $N^* = (I - Q_{sq})^{-1}$; then the variances given in Theorem 3 may be estimated by the following upper bounds,

$$V \leqslant c[\eta N - \eta_{sq} N^*] \tag{5}$$

$$v \leqslant V\xi \leqslant c[\eta N - \eta_{sq} N^*]\xi \tag{6}$$

$$W \leqslant c[\eta NR - \eta_{sq} N^* R_{sq}]. \tag{7}$$

*Proof.* Let $A$, $B$, and $C$ be nonnegative matrices with $C$ a square matrix and such that the product $ACB$ is defined. Then

$$(AC^k B)_{sq} \geqslant A_{sq}(C^k)_{sq} B_{sq} \geqslant A_{sq}(C_{sq})^k B_{sq}. \tag{8}$$

These inequalities are established by noting that a given expression is obtained from the one on its immediate left by ignoring certain nonnegative crossproduct terms. To prove Eq. (5) we note that, using Eq. (8)

$$\begin{aligned}
-[\eta_{sq} + (\eta Q)_{sq} + (\eta Q^2)_{sq} + \ldots] & \\
\leqslant & - \eta_{sq}[I + Q_{sq} + (Q^2)_{sq} + \ldots] \\
\leqslant & - \eta_{sq}[I + Q_{sq} + (Q_{sq})^2 + \ldots] \\
= & - \eta_{sq} N^*.
\end{aligned}$$

The proofs of Eqs. (6) and (7) are similar.

## Cyclical Monthly Inputs

The results of Theorems 2, 3, and 4 were based on the assumption that the monthly input of dollars, $c$, was constant. In most retail establishments, however, the monthly input – charge sales – follows a cyclical pattern with peaks at Christmas, Easter, and the opening of schools in autumn. In addition, yearly sales of a company may expand or contract due to growth, inflation, and so forth. Here, we consider the effect on the model of introducing these considerations.

To be specific, let $C_i$ be the vector of new charges at a given month $i$; let $c_i$ be the total amount of new charges; let $\eta_i = (1/c_i)C_i$ be the $i$th probability starting vector; we assume that

$$\eta_{i-T} = \eta_i \tag{9}$$

$$C_{i-T} = \alpha C_i, \tag{10}$$

where $\alpha$ is the reciprocal of the growth factor. [E.g. if the business expands at the rate of 2 per cent a year then $\alpha = 1/(1 + .02) = 1/1.02$.] The length of the cycle period is $T$, where in the department store case $T = 12$, typically. Note that Eqs. (9) and (10) imply $c_{i-T} = \alpha c_i$. Let us answer question 2 again under these assumptions.

Recall that a repetitive Markov chain was an ordinary Markov chain that was started off the same number of times each period, always with the same initial vector. By a *cyclic repetitive Markov chain* we shall mean a repetitive Markov chain in which the number of times the process is started and the initial vectors used vary in a cyclic pattern. Thus Eqs. (9) and (10) define a cyclic repetitive Markov chain in which the pattern repeats every $T$ periods. We shall generalize, the results for repetitive Markov chains to those for cyclic repetitive Markov chains.

*Theorem 5.* Let $N_\alpha = (I - \alpha Q^T)^{-1}$; then the entries of

$$A_i = [\sum_{k=0}^{T-1} C_{i-k}Q^k]N_\alpha \tag{11}$$

$$a_i = [\sum_{k=0}^{T-1} C_{i-k}Q^k]N_\alpha \xi \tag{12}$$

$$D_i = [\sum_{k=0}^{T-1} C_{i-k}Q^k]N_\alpha R \tag{13}$$

give for month $i$ the expected amounts in the various age categories [formula (11)], the expected total accounts receivable [Eq. (12)], and the expected collections and bad debt [Eq. (13)].

*Proof.* Let $C_i, C_{i-1}, \ldots, C_{i-T+1}$ be the actual new charges in the $i$th month and in the preceding $T - 1$ months. By means of Eq. (10) we can deduce, knowing the expansion rate, all charges for earlier months as well. From the $i$th month we can expect $C_i$ to be the charges to the various age categories; from the $(i-1)$st month we can expect $C_{i-1}Q$; from $C_{i-2}$ we can expect $C_{i-2}Q^2$, etc.; from $C_{i-T+1}$ we can expect $C_{i-T+1}Q^{T-1}$; from $C_{i-T} = \alpha C_i$ we expect $\alpha C_i Q^T$, etc. Adding together these vectors, we obtain

$$
\begin{aligned}
A_i &= C_i + C_{i-1}Q + C_{i-2}Q^2 + \ldots + C_{i-T+1}Q^{T-1} \\
&\quad + \alpha C_i Q^T + \alpha C_{i-1}Q^{T+1} + \ldots + \alpha C_{i-T+1}Q^{2T-1} \\
&\quad + \alpha^2 C_j Q^{2T} + \alpha^2 C_{j-1}Q^{2T+1} + \ldots + \alpha^2 C_{i-T+1}Q^{3T-1} + \ldots \\
&= C_i(I + \alpha Q^T + \alpha^2 Q^{2T} + \ldots) + C_{i-1}Q(I + \alpha Q^T \\
&\quad + \alpha^2 Q^{2T} + \ldots) + \ldots + C_{i-T+1}Q^{T+1}(I + \alpha Q^T \\
&\quad + \alpha^2 Q^{2T} + \ldots) \\
&= [C_i + C_{i-1}Q + C_{i-2}Q^2 + \ldots + C_{i-T+1}Q^{T-1}]N_\alpha,
\end{aligned}
$$

which is Eq. (11). Formulas (12) and (13) are established similarly.

Note that these estimates for the $i$th month depend on the new charges in the $i$th and preceding $T - 1$ months. It is not surprising that this should give a more accurate prediction than the one given by Theorem 2. Also note that if $Q^n$ goes to zero rapidly it may be possible to use only the new charges in the last few months to obtain a reasonably accurate estimate.

*Corollary.* Combining Theorems 1 and 5 we find $A_i NR$ and $a_i[\tau_i NR - (\tau_i NR)_{sq}]$, where $a_i = A_i\xi$ and $\tau_i = (1/a_i)A_i$, as the mean and variance estimates of the collections and bad debts[10] that will result from the accounts receivables existing at time $i$.

*Theorem 6.* Let $N_\alpha{}^* = (I - \alpha Q^T{}_{sq})^{-1}$; then the entries of

$$V[A_i] = A_i - \sum_{k=0}^{T-1} c_{i-k}\left[\sum_{h=0}^{\infty} \alpha^h(\eta_{i-k}Q^{Th+k})_{sq}\right] \tag{14}$$

$$\leqslant A_i - \left[\sum_{k=0}^{T-1} c_{i-k}(\eta_{i-k})_{sq}(Q_{sq})^k\right]N_\alpha{}^*$$

$$V[a_i] = a_i - \sum_{k=0}^{T-1} c_{i-k}\left[\sum_{h=0}^{\infty} \alpha^h(\eta_{i-k}Q^{Th+k}\xi)_{sq}\right] \tag{15}$$

10. Continuing the results of [8] and [9] we find $A_i N_\beta R_1$ as the estimated present value of the accounts receivables at time $i$.

$$\leq a_i - [\sum_{k=0}^{T-1} c_{i-k}(\eta_{i-k})_{sq}(Q_{sq})^k]N_\alpha{}^*\xi$$

$$V[D_i] = D_i - \sum_{k=0}^{T-1} c_{i-k}[\sum_{h=0}^{\infty} \alpha^h(\eta_{i-k}Q^{Th+k}R)_{sq}] \qquad (16)$$

$$\leq D_i - [\sum_{k=0}^{T-1} c_{i-k}(\eta_{i-k})_{sq}(Q_{sq})^k]N_\alpha{}^*R_{sq}$$

give the variance and variance estimates for the corresponding quantities in Theorem 5.

We shall not give proofs for these formulas since no new ideas beyond those used in the proofs of Theorems 3 and 4 are involved. Note that formulas (14–16) generalize formulas (2–4) and (5–7).

The amount of work needed to use the formulas for cyclic repetitive Markov chains is more than that for repetitive chains, largely due to the fact that more data is being utilized. How much more accurate the new formulas are than the old we do not know at present. However, we plan to make tests on real data in the near future.

## Summary

### Direct results

In the preceding sections, we have developed a model describing the behavior of accounts receivable balances. Given a matrix of transition probabilities, $P$, and given a vector of new sales (either constant or variable by period), the following results may be obtained:

1. Estimated loss expectancy rates by age category.
2. The estimated allowance for doubtful accounts.
3. The steady state age distribution of accounts receivable.
4. Variances for the estimates in (2) and (3) above.
5. Generalization of the above results to the cyclic case.

All of these results are useful in managing and in accounting for accounts receivable.

## The constant P matrix assumption

The results enumerated above are subject to the assumption, stated earlier, that the matrix of transition probabilities is constant over time. We do not, of course, expect this assumption to be perfectly true. There may well be cyclical changes in transition probabilities just as there are cyclical changes in sales of most retail assumptions. The validity of the constant transition probability assumption will depend on the magnitude of these changes. Empirical investigation of the actual changes in transition probabilities and their effect on model results is currently under way.

The primary problems associated with changing transition probabilities would seem to be one of estimation. If these probabilities change, however, it seems likely that they change as a function of changes in business activity. It may be possible to predict the changes in transition probabilities, if any, by correlation with indices of local economic conditions.

## Indirect results

As noted earlier, research leading to development of the model described was initiated with the aim of estimating loss expectancy rates. Gratifyingly, the formal results obtained go beyond this initially limited aim. More importantly perhaps, the informal results of the approach developed are believed to be of value. These informal results stem from the fact that the transition probability-Markov Chain description of accounts receivable behavior provides a valuable insight into better methods of managing accounts receivable.

Accounts receivable management in most retail establishments is a major problem. Typically, accounts receivable are the most important single asset in the balance sheet of many retail firms. The overall control of this asset by means of credit policy continually poses questions. Should credit terms be tightened and a more active collection policy be pursued? Should credit restrictions be relaxed in order to stimulate sales?

To aid in arriving at a decision on these matters, a variety of statistics are used by retail establishments to reflect current economic conditions and the overall status of accounts receivable.

151

Many stores rely heavily upon collection data in various forms: ratios to sales, accounts receivable balances, previous months' collections, and so forth. Some stores rely on the comparison of annual aging results, and, in many instances, supplement annual aging data with agings on a monthly basis. Bad debt write-offs and any subsequent recoveries are followed closely. Periodic service charge income, which is related to accounts receivable outstanding, is also used as an overall measure of credit conditions.

All of these measures have some value as indices of the current behavior of accounts receivable. None, however, seem to provide the comprehensive picture of accounts receivable behavior that is provided by the matrix of transition probabilities and allied model results. This indirect use of model results – the use of transition probabilities for management information for accounts receivable control – promises to be as fruitful as the use of results directly obtainable from the model.

The techniques of this paper are obviously applicable to many other kinds of problems. Such problems can be characterized as 'inventory' problems in which we consider items produced and stored in inventory. Eventually the items leave the inventory either by being 'sold' or by 'spoiling'. Any class of items that is perishable or otherwise subject to obsolescence can be so studied. Examples of such goods are: metal coins, automobiles, produce, photographic film, employees, style goods (dresses, etc.), canned goods, etc. The reader will doubtless think of other possibilities.

## Appendix

To illustrate the computation of the formulas derived in the paper we shall work out several variants of a simple problem. Suppose $n = 2$, i.e. accounts 2 periods old are declared bad debts. Suppose the transition matrix is

$$P = \begin{array}{c} \\ \bar{0} \\ 2 \\ 0 \\ 1 \end{array} \begin{array}{c} \bar{0} \quad\; 2 \quad\; 0 \quad\; 1 \end{array} \left( \begin{array}{cccc} 1 & 0 & 0 & 0 \\ 0 & 1 & 0 & 0 \\ .3 & 0 & .5 & .2 \\ .5 & .1 & .3 & .1 \end{array} \right)$$

where we have already arranged the states so that the absorbing states appear first. From the matrix we see that

$$R = \begin{pmatrix} .3 & 0 \\ .5 & .1 \end{pmatrix} \quad \text{and} \quad Q = \begin{pmatrix} .5 & .2 \\ .3 & .1 \end{pmatrix}$$

From $Q$ we can obtain

$$N = (I - Q)^{-1} = \begin{pmatrix} .5 & -.2 \\ -.3 & .9 \end{pmatrix}^{-1} = \begin{pmatrix} 2.31 & .51 \\ .77 & 1.28 \end{pmatrix}$$

$$NR = \begin{pmatrix} .95 & .05 \\ .87 & .13 \end{pmatrix}$$

(A) To illustrate Theorem 1 we assume $B = (70, 30)$ to be the accounts receivable vector; then

$$BNR = (70,30) \begin{pmatrix} .95 & .05 \\ .87 & .13 \end{pmatrix} = (92.6, 74.)$$

The variances of each component are equal to

$$100 \, [.926 - (.926)^2] = 6.2,$$

which makes the standard deviation equal to 2.5. Hence of the $100 accounts receivables we expect to collect 92.6 and to lose 7.4 to bad debts. If, for safety, we wanted to reserve one standard deviation more than the expected bad debt we would set aside $7.4 + 2.5 = 9.9$ as the reserves for bad debts.

(B) To illustrate present value calculations, suppose that the period in question is a six-month interval, and that we discount accounts 3 per cent per period. Then $BN_\beta R_1$ can be calculated as follows:

$$B = 1/1.03 = .97$$

$$N_\beta = (I - \beta Q)^{-1} = \begin{pmatrix} .515 & -.194 \\ -.281 & .903 \end{pmatrix}^{-1} = \begin{pmatrix} 2.19 & .47 \\ .68 & 1.25 \end{pmatrix}$$

so that

$$BN_\beta R_1 = (70, 30) \begin{pmatrix} 2.19 & .47 \\ .68 & 1.25 \end{pmatrix} \begin{pmatrix} .3 \\ .5 \end{pmatrix} = 87.3$$

and we see that the expected collections of 93.2 have present value of 87.3.

Suppose the retail establishment charges a 9 per cent service charge per half year on its accounts, and discounts them at 3 per cent per half year, leaving a net interest charge of 6 per cent per half year. Then $\beta = 1.06$ and

$$N_\beta = (I - \beta Q)^{-1} = \begin{pmatrix} .470 & -.212 \\ -.318 & .894 \end{pmatrix}^{-1} = \begin{pmatrix} 2.53 & .60 \\ .90 & 1.34 \end{pmatrix}$$

so that

$$BN_\beta R_1 = (70, 30) \begin{pmatrix} .253 & .60 \\ .90 & 1.34 \end{pmatrix} \begin{pmatrix} .3 \\ .5 \end{pmatrix} = 102.4$$

is the present discounted value of the accounts receivable.

(C) To illustrate Theorem 2 and its corollary suppose $C = (40, 10)$ is the steady state vector of new charges; then

$$CN = (40, 10) \begin{pmatrix} 2.31 & .51 \\ .77 & 1.28 \end{pmatrix} = (100.1, 33.2)$$

gives the steady state amounts in each of the receivables age categories. Also

$$CNR = (100.1, 33.2) \begin{pmatrix} .3 & 0 \\ .5 & .1 \end{pmatrix} = (46.7, 3.3)$$

are the steady state average collections and bad debts per period.

To estimate the eventual collections and bad debts from a given period's accounts receivables (which total 133.3) we compute

$$CN^2R = (CN)(NR) = (100.1, 33.2) \begin{pmatrix} .95 & .05 \\ .87 & .13 \end{pmatrix} = (124.0, 9.4)$$

The variances of each of these quantities are 9.32, which gives standard deviations of 3.05. We leave present value calculations to the reader.

(D) To illustrate Theorems 3 and 4 we compute

$$N^* = (I - Q_{sq})^{-1} = \begin{pmatrix} .75 & -.04 \\ -.09 & .99 \end{pmatrix}^{-1} = \begin{pmatrix} 1.36 & .055 \\ .124 & 1.03 \end{pmatrix}$$

$$\eta = (.8, .2)$$

$$\eta N = (.8, .2) \begin{pmatrix} 2.31 & .51 \\ .77 & 1.28 \end{pmatrix} = (2.00, .664)$$

$$\eta NR = (2.00, .664) \begin{pmatrix} .3 & 0 \\ .5 & .1 \end{pmatrix} = (.932, .07)$$

$$\eta_{sq} N^* = (.64, .04) \begin{pmatrix} 1.36 & .055 \\ .124 & 1.03 \end{pmatrix} = (.875, .076)$$

$$\eta_{sq} N^* R_{sq} = (.875, .076) \begin{pmatrix} .09 & 0 \\ .25 & .01 \end{pmatrix} = (.098, .001)$$

so that $\quad V \leqslant 50[(2.00, .664) - (.88, .076)] = (55.6, 29.3)$

$\qquad v \leqslant 84.9$

$\qquad W \leqslant 50[(.932, .07) - (.098, .001)] = (41.7, 3.5).$

By computing a few terms of the exact formulas for these variances it was found that the above variance estimates were about 5 per cent larger than the true value.

(E) To illustrate the cyclical case, assume that $T = 2$ and $\alpha = 1/1.02$ (i.e. the growth rate is 2 per cent per year). Then

$$\alpha Q^2 = \begin{pmatrix} .316 & .122 \\ .184 & .071 \end{pmatrix}$$

$$N_\alpha = (I - \alpha Q^2)^{-1} = \begin{pmatrix} .684 & -.122 \\ -.184 & .929 \end{pmatrix}^{-1} = \begin{pmatrix} 1.51 & .199 \\ .30 & 1.11 \end{pmatrix}$$

Suppose $C_0 = (35, 15)$ and $C_1 = (40, 10)$. Then

$$C_0 + C_1 Q = (35, 15) + (40, 10) \begin{pmatrix} .5 & .2 \\ .3 & .1 \end{pmatrix}$$

$$= (58, 24)$$

and

$$A_i = (58, 24) \begin{pmatrix} 1.51 & .199 \\ .30 & 1.11 \end{pmatrix} = (94.8, 38.2)$$

$$a_i = 133$$

$$D_i = (94.8, 38.2) \begin{pmatrix} .3 & 0 \\ .5 & .1 \end{pmatrix} = (47.5, 3.82)$$

We omit variance and present value calculations for this example.

# Part Three Financial Decision-Making

Investment decisions have always been considered to be of central importance to a firm's survival. However, the criteria by which these decisions are judged have varied over the years. It is instructive to examine the conditions under which the currently recommended ones – discounted present value and internal rate of return – lead to different conclusions. The paper by Teichroew–Robichek–Montalbano provides an excellent analysis of the effects of using these decision criteria. In so doing they also present a useful survey of previous work in this area.

Problems of capital budgeting are no less important than those classified as investment decisions. Indeed, the principal analytic framework is common to both. However, when capital budgets are concerned with interrelated and interdependent projects computational problems come rapidly to the fore. Weingartner surveys the available mathematical techniques and discusses the computational problems as they arise. The techniques employed are linear, integer, and dynamic programming. Any reader who requires additional information on these techniques is requested to read the papers in Part Five which explain these procedures in some detail.

# 6 D. Teichroew, A. A. Robichek, and M. Montalbano

## An Analysis of Criteria for Investment and Financing Decisions Under Certainty

D. Teichroew, A. A. Robichek, and M. Montalbano (1965) 'An analysis of criteria for investment and financing decisions under certainty', *Management Science*, **12**, 151–79.

## 1 Introduction

### 1 The decision problem

A firm may be considered as an entity, represented by the center rectangle in Fig. 1, which acquires capital from a source of funds (phase 1), invests it (phase 2), receives returns from the investment (phase 3) and then returns funds to the source of funds (phase 4). In the typical business firm these phases are all occurring simultaneously: the firm is continuously evaluating possible sources of funds and possible opportunities to invest funds.

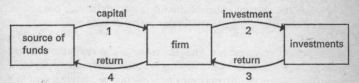

Figure 1 A firm's cycle of acquisition and investment of capital.

In the usual terminology used in the financial community, each possibility for investment of funds is called a project. Usually firms treat the acquisition of capital (financing) completely separately from the investment of capital and do not ordinarily refer to possibilities for financing as projects. However, as will be shown later, there can exist possibilities which can be characterized neither as straight financing nor straight investment, since they combine features of both. These will be called mixed projects. All opportunities for investment, for financing, or for a combination of both will be termed projects in this paper.

159

The firm may therefore be thought of as having available a number of opportunities, or 'projects'. In the most general form there may be a number of projects in existence at a point in time as well as a number of 'new' ones which could be started. The decisions that must be made include whether or not to accept any or all of the new projects, whether to make changes in the present projects, etc. There is a large body of literature [1–7] dealing with these problems and with rules and criteria for making the decisions. Some of the results and statements in the literature appear to be inconsistent [1]. This is in large part due to the lack of precise statement of the problem; in particular, the firm's objective must be clearly stated and the assumptions must be specified. The assumptions can be conveniently grouped into three major categories: available alternatives, the constraints on feasible decisions, and the degree of certainty.

*Objective.* One frequently finds in the literature a statement that such-and-such a method for arriving at a decision is not consistent with another method, or that one decision-making procedure is better than another. In many cases the criteria by which one procedure is judged better than another are not explicitly stated. Most frequently it is implicitly assumed that the objective is to maximize the present value of the firm or to maximize the future value of the firm at some particular point in time.[1]

*Assumptions: Alternatives.* The statement of the available alternatives must include the descriptions of the individual opportunities. One of the most important aspects of the statement of the problem is how the set of alternatives changes over time. This is particularly important when the projects do not cover exactly the same length of time. In the literature this problem is frequently referred to as the 'reinvestment' problem. *Constraints.* Most analyses implicitly assume a limit in either the amount of money available or the amount of money that can be invested. *Degree of Certainty.* One must explicitly state whether the interest rates, the cash flows, and the alternatives available at future times are assumed to be known with certainty, assumed to be probabilistic,

1. Other objectives such as maximizing stockholder value, etc., have also been suggested. However, an examination of such objectives is not relevant or essential to this paper.

assumed to be uncertain, or assumed to be known from external factors.

## 2 Decision procedures

Since the decision problem under general conditions is extremely complicated, much of the literature is concerned with simplifying the problem by assigning to each project a single number which indicates a 'preference'. The numbers that have been used may be divided into two major categories:

(a) *Those not involving discounting over time*. These include such measures as the payback period, accounting rate of return, etc. Frequently these techniques work only for particular types of projects. Sometimes they include such factors as qualitative judgments.

(b) *Those involving discounting over time*. The two most generally used are the *discounted present value* (DPV) and the *internal rate of return* (IRR). These methods are widely discussed in the literature and several difficulties in their use have been investigated. Some of the difficulties center around the fact that the internal rate of return for a particular project may not be unique and therefore both acceptance and rejection of a project may seemingly be justified for the given project, and around the fact that the decision reached for some projects on the basis of present value analysis seems contrary to intuition.

## 3 Objective and assumptions

In this paper the decision to accept or reject projects will be investigated under the following conditions:

(a) The objective is to select projects so as to maximize the discounted present value of the firm, where the rate of discount is $\rho$.

(b) The firm has available a finite set of projects. The cash flows associated with all projects are finite and known with certainty. Actual transfers of money occur only at the ends of periods; each project is completely identified by a sequence of net cash flows,

$$a_0, a_1, \ldots a_n$$

where $a_j$ is negative if outflows from the firm (to the project) exceed inflows to the firm (from the project) in the $j^{th}$ period

161

of the project's life and positive if inflows exceed outflows. $a_0$ is the net cash flow at the beginning of the project, i.e. now; $a_1$ at the end of the first period, etc.; $a_n$ is the last net cash flow. Since under the conditions assumed here a project need not be considered until the point at which the net cash flow is not zero, one can without loss of generality assume $a_0 \neq 0$. Similarly, $a_n$ is the last nonzero cash flow and therefore $a_n \neq 0$.

(c) Unlimited funds are available to the firm at a known rate $\rho$ which is constant for all periods. Unlimited funds can be employed outside the firm to yield the same rate $\rho$. The acceptance or rejection of any of the projects has no effect on $\rho$. Usually $\rho$ is termed the firm's cost of capital.

(d) There may exist some investment type projects which yield a rate of return greater than $\rho$ and others which yield less. There may exist some financing type projects, which provide funds at a cost of less than $\rho$ and some at rates greater than $\rho$. There may also exist mixed projects.

(e) The acceptance or rejection of any project does not affect the firm's ability to accept or reject any other project.

The effect of these assumptions (b–e) is to make the decision to accept or reject any project completely independent of the decision on any other project. There is no need to 'choose' between projects; each project stands completely on its own.

The effect of assumption (c) is to reduce the decision problem under study to a problem of one parameter $\rho$. For any given problem the cash flows and $\rho$ are assumed to be known. In this paper we will be concerned with how the decision, for a given project or class of projects, depends on the parameter $\rho$.

*Outline.* The objective of this paper is to study the decision-making procedure for accepting or rejecting projects under the assumptions made above. We will be concerned with properties of the two usual decision rules based on DPV and IRR for the class of all projects which can be completely described by a finite sequence of cash flows of which the first and the last are not zero.

We are concerned with *two* properties of the decision-making procedure. These are defined in detail in Section II. The first property is *applicability*. A decision rule is said to be *applicable* if it is possible to apply it unambiguously to all projects of the type being considered. The second property is *consistency* relative to the parameter $\rho$. This property is a formal statement of the intuitive notion that if an investment opportunity is desirable for some value of $\rho$ say .10 then it should be desirable for all values of $\rho$ less than .10. The paper is concerned with the characterization of classes of projects for which the two usual decision rules possess both of these properties.

In Section II, the rules are applied, and the properties shown to hold, for the class of projects in which $a_0$ has a sign different from all the remaining $a_j$'s. This class is defined as the class of *simple* projects. Both rules lead to identical decisions for this class of projects. Most of the practical problems and the literature until relatively recently dealt with this class.

In Section III the rules are applied to three nonsimple projects, i.e. projects which do not belong to the class of simple projects. The two rules are shown to be applicable and consistent and to lead to identical decisions for *two* of the projects. Neither rule has both properties for the *third* project. Project balances are defined as the net, compounded, amount the firm has invested in, or acquired from, the project at the end of each period. Computation of these balances shows that the third example is a mixed project, which is a project that for some periods is an investment and for others is a source of funds to the firm. It is then shown that the class of all projects may be divided into two classes: pure projects and mixed projects. Mixed projects are all projects that are not pure projects. It is then shown that the two rules are both applicable and consistent and lead to the same decision for all pure projects.

The class of mixed projects is examined in Section IV. A future value (and a present value) function is defined for all projects as a function of an investment rate $(r)$, which is applied for periods when the project balance is negative, and a financing rate $(k)$, which is applied for periods when the project balance is positive. A number of properties of these functions of two variables are described. In particular the function is shown to be a strictly increasing function of $k$ and a strictly decreasing function of $r$. In Section V it is shown that the contour line obtained by setting the future value function equal to zero defines $r$ as a strictly increasing function of $k$, $k$ as a strictly increasing function of $r$.

The function $r(k)$ is greater than, equal to, or less than $k$ if and only if $DPV$ as a function of $i$, where $i = r = k$, is positive, zero, or negative respectively.

The usual rules for accepting or rejecting projects are generalized to the class of mixed projects. They are based on the function of $r(k)$. A complete procedure for acceptance or rejection of any project (under the assumptions made above) is developed in Section VI and summarized in Fig. 7 and Tables 4 and 5.

## II The Internal Rate of Return (IRR) and Discounted Present Value (DPV)

The *present value* of a project at interest rate $i$[2] is denoted by $P(i)$, and is defined to be

$$P(i) = a_0 + a_1/(1 + i) + \ldots + a_n/(1 + i)^n \qquad (1)$$

The *future value* of a project at interest rate $i$, $S(i)$, is given by

$$S(i) = a_0(1 + i)^n + a_1(1 + i)^{n-1} + \ldots + a_n \qquad (2)$$

The relationship between the present and future value function is given by

$$S(i) = P(i)[(1 + i)^n]$$

The reason for introducing the future value is that it leads naturally to the concept of the *project balance*. The project balance at the end of period $j$, at interest rate $i$, is the amount the firm has invested in the project, or has required from the project, at the end of period $j$ if the outstanding balance at the end of each period $0, 1, 2, \ldots j - 1$ is compounded at interest rate $i$ during the following period. The balance of a project at the end of the first period, $S_1$, is the initial cash flow $a_0$, compounded at rate $i$, plus the cash flow at the end of the first period, or

$$S_1 = a_0(1 + i) + a_1$$

Similarly

$$S_2 = (1 + i)S_1 + a_2 = a_0(1 + i)^2 + a_1(1 + i) + a_2$$

2. The range for $i$ is $0 \leqslant i < \infty$.

and in general the balance of a project at the end of period $j$, at interest rate $i$, is

$$S_j(i) = (1 + i)[S_{j-1}(i)] + a_j$$
$$= a_0(1 + i)^j + a_1(1 + i)^{j-1} + \ldots + a_j \quad j = 1, 2, \ldots n$$

and $S_n(i)$ is the final balance of the project.

For reasons which will become clear in the next section, it is convenient to classify projects into three groups on the basis of the sign of the $S_j$s.

(a) *A pure investment project*, at rate $i$, is a project for which $S_j(i) \leq 0$ for $j = 0, 1, 2, \ldots, n - 1$. A pure investment project is one in which the firm has money invested in the project during every period.

Table 1
Usual Acceptance Rules Using $IRR$ and $DPV$

| Rule based on | Type of project Investment | Financing |
| --- | --- | --- |
| IRR | $IRR \geqq \rho$ | $IRR \geqq \rho$ |
| DPV | $P(\rho) \geqq 0$ | $P(\rho) \geqq 0$ |

(b) *A pure financing project*, at rate $i$, is a project for which $S_j(i) \geqq 0$ for $j = 0, 1, \ldots, n - 1$. A pure financing project is one in which the firm owes money to the project during every period.

(c) *A mixed project*, at rate $i$, is one which is neither a pure investment nor a pure financing project. A mixed project is one in which the firm has money invested in the project during some periods and the firm owes the project money during other periods.

The *internal rate of return* ($IRR$)[3] is usually defined as any rate which makes the present value of the positive cash flows equal to the present value of the negative cash flows. This definition is equivalent to defining $IRR$ as the rate (or rates) for which

3. $IRR$ is defined here for any project, investment, financing or mixed. In a financing project, $IRR$ is really the rate of financing rather than the rate of return.

$P(i)$ is zero. (Clearly IRR can be obtained also by setting $S(i) = 0$.) Since

$$P(0) = \sum_{j=0}^{n} a_j \quad \text{and} \quad \lim_{i \to \infty} P(i) \equiv P(\infty) = a_0 \quad (3)$$

there will be at least one positive IRR whenever the sum of all the $a_j$s has a different sign from that of $a_0$; however, there may be more than one positive IRR. If the signs of $a_0$ and the sum of all the $a_j$s are the same there may be no positive IRR, there may be only one, or there may be many.

The *discounted present value* (DPV) of a project is the value of $P(i)$ in Eq. (1), for a specified interest rate $\rho$:

$$\mathbf{DPV} = P(\rho) = a_0 + a_1/(1 + \rho) + \ldots + a_n/(1 + \rho)^n \quad (4)$$

Table 1 summarizes the usual rules for accepting projects using the IRR and DPV. A project is accepted if it satisfies the stated condition and rejected if it does not. $\rho$ is used as the minimum acceptable rate for IRR and as the discount rate for DPV. The reason for these rules is that the present value of a firm (sum of all the present values of all its projects) will be greater if these rules are used than if any other rule is used (under the assumptions made in Section I). The objective stated in Section I is to maximize present value of the firm. Since the projects are independent, the present value will be increased by accepting a project with $P(\rho) > 0$ and decreased by accepting a project with $P(\rho) < 0$. A strict application of the objective would result in applying these rules without the equality sign. However, here we follow standard practice by accepting a project if equality holds.

Suppose two projects have net cash flows as follows:

|  | Project | |
| --- | --- | --- |
| Cash flows | A | B |
| $a_0$ | −1,000 | +1,000 |
| $a_1$ | +700 | −400 |
| $a_2$ | +200 | −400 |
| $a_3$ | +480 | −407 |

The two projects A and B are examples of simple projects. A *simple project* is defined as one where the sign of $a_0$ is different

166

from the sign of $a_j$ for $j \geqq 1$. For simple projects, the first and second derivatives of the function $P(i)$ for $i > 0$ have the following signs:

|            | *First derivative* | *Second derivative* |
|------------|--------------------|---------------------|
| If $a_0 < 0$ | Negative           | Positive            |
| If $a_0 > 0$ | Positive           | Negative            |

Therefore, from the sign of the first derivative it follows that the function $P(i)$ is decreasing over the entire range (as $i$ increases) if $a_0 < 0$ and is increasing if $a_0 > 0$. From the sign of the second derivative it follows that $P(i)$ is convex if $a_0$ is negative and concave if $a_0$ is positive. Furthermore, from Eq. (3) it follows that the function $P(i)$ is asymptotic to $a_0$ for large $i$ in both instances. *Consequently a unique solution for* $P(i) = 0$ *will exist for simple projects if the sign of the sum of all coefficients,* $\sum_{j=0}^{n} a_j$, *is different from the sign of* $a_0$.

Fig. 2 shows the function $P(i)$ for the two projects A and B. For both projects there is only one positive rate $i$ at which $P(i) = 0$, i.e. the IRR is unique for both projects. For project A, $IRR_A = 20$ per cent; for project B, $IRR_B = 10$ per cent.

The discounted present value (DPV) will depend on $\rho$. For project A, $DPV_A$ is positive for all $\rho < 20$ per cent, negative for $\rho > 20$ per cent, and zero for $\rho = 20$ per cent $= IRR_A$. For project B, $DPV_B$ is positive for all $\rho > 10$ per cent, negative for $\rho < 10$ per cent, and zero for $\rho = 10$ per cent $= IRR_B$.

Under both rules given in Table 1, project A would be accepted as an investment project if $\rho \leqq .20$ and project B would be accepted as a financing project if $\rho \geqq .10$.

We shall be concerned with two properties of the acceptance rules given in Table 1. In particular,

(a) A rule will be said to be *applicable* to a class of projects if it gives a unique decision for all projects in that class, and

(b) A rule will be said to be *consistent* if it leads to decisions which are consistent with the intuitive interpretation of interest. Specifically, consistency of a rule requires that if an investment project is acceptable for some $\rho_0$ then it is acceptable for all

167

$\rho < \rho_0$ and if it is not acceptable for some $\rho_0$ then it is not acceptable for all $\rho > \rho_0$. If a financing project is acceptable for some $\rho_0$ then it is acceptable for all $\rho > \rho_0$ and if it is not acceptable for some $\rho_0$ then it is not acceptable for all $\rho < \rho_0$.

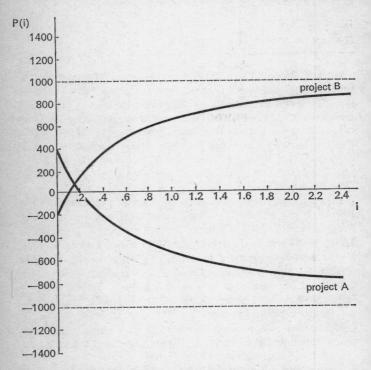

Figure 2 Present value of projects A and B as functions of the interest rate.

From the properties of simple projects developed above, it follows that the rules based on the IRR and DPV are applicable and consistent for all simple projects. This is illustrated by projects A and B. However, these rules are not both applicable and consistent for *all* nonsimple projects. This will be shown in the next section.

## III IRR and DPV for Non-Simple Projects

The cash flows for three nonsimple projects, C, D, and E are given in Table 2. The present value functions for the three projects are shown in Fig. 3.

Table 2

Description of Projects C, D, and E

| | Project | | |
|---|---|---|---|
| Cash flows | C | D | E |
| $a_0$ | −1,000 | +1,000 | −1,600 |
| $a_1$ | +1,100 | −500 | +10,000 |
| $a_2$ | −180 | +660 | −10,000 |
| $a_3$ | +840 | −1,800 | |
| $P(0) = \sum a_j$ | +760 | −640 | −1,600 |
| $P(\infty) = a_0$ | −1,000 | +1,000 | −1,600 |
| IRR | 40% | 20% | 25%, 400% |

The present value function for project C is

$$P(i) = -1,000 + 1,100v - 180v^2 + 840v^3 \text{ where } v = 1/(1 + i)$$

The equation $P(i) = 0$ has one positive solution: $i = 40$ per cent. The present value function for project D is

$$P(i) = 1,000 - 500v + 660v^2 - 1,800v^3$$

and $P(i) = 0$ has one positive solution: $i = 20$ per cent.

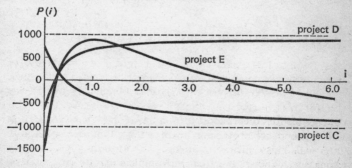

Figure 3 Present value function for projects C, D, and E.

*Projects C and D illustrate the fact that multiple sign changes in the sequence of cash flows do not necessarily lead to more than one positive solution to the equation $P(i) = 0$.* From an examination of Fig. 3 it is clear that the acceptance rules based on the DPV and on IRR are both applicable and consistent for nonsimple projects C and D. However, the rules are neither applicable nor consistent for project E, which is the 'pump' project originally discussed by Lorie and Savage (1955). The present value of project E, at interest $i$, is

$$P(i) = -1,600 + 10,000/(1 + i) - 10,000/(1 + i)^2 \quad (5)$$

Since the internal rate of return (IRR) was defined as the rate (or rates) for which $P(i)$ is zero, in this example

$$P(i) = 0$$
if $\quad -10,000(1/1 + i)^2 + 10,000(1/1 + i) - 1,600 = 0 \quad (6)$

i.e. if

$$1/(1 + i) = \{-10,000 \pm [(10,000)^2 - 64,000,000]^{1/2}\}/-20,000$$
$$= .80 \text{ or } .20$$

Hence, $P(i) = 0$ if $i = .25$ or $4$; that is, if the interest rate is 25 per cent or 400 per cent.

The internal rate of return can also be computed from the future value, $S(i)$, of the project at the end of its life. For project E

$$S(i) = -1,600(1 + i)^2 + 10,000(1 + i) - 10,000$$

and $\quad S(i) = 0$

if $\quad -1,600(1 + i)^2 + 10,000(1 + i) - 10,000 = 0 \quad (7)$

$1 + i = 5$ or $1.25$ and $i = 4$ or $.25$ as before. The internal rate (or rates) of return computed from $S(i)$ must be identical with those obtained from $P(i)$ because Eq. (7) can be obtained by multiplying Eq. (6) by $(1 + i)^2$.

The rule for accepting the project based on IRR given in Table 1 is not applicable whenever there is more than one solution to $P(i) = 0$. This difficulty in attempting to use the IRR for decisions is well known. It is frequently implied that the rule based on the DPV method is applicable and consistent even in cases where there are multiple solutions to $P(i) = 0$. For example, Lorie and Savage (1955), in their discussion of the 'pump' project, state:

. . .The rate-of-return criterion for judging the acceptability of investment proposals, as it has been presented in published works, is then ambiguous or anomalous. This is in contrast to the clarity and uniform accuracy of the decisions indicated by the principle proposed earlier, which relates to the present value of an investment at the cost of capital rather than to a comparison between the cost of capital and the rate of return.

The present value of project E as a function of rate $i$, shown in Fig. 3, reaches a maximum of \$900 for $i = 100$ per cent and then decreases. Examination of Fig. 3 shows that except for $i = 100$ per cent, the project has identical present values for numerous pairs of rates; e.g. DPV = 0 for $i = 25$ per cent and 400 per cent. Under the DPV rule the project would be acceptable (i.e. $P(i) \geqq 0$) if the rate is greater than or equal to 25 per cent but less than or equal to 400 per cent. The present value is negative for rates less than 25 per cent or greater than 400 per cent; e.g. $P(.10) = \$-760$. Consequently this project would be rejected by firms with $\rho < .25$ or $>4.00$ and would be accepted by a firm in which $.25 \leqq \rho \leqq 4.00$. Clearly there is something strange in the implication that a firm with $\rho = .20$ would not accept this project, but would accept the project if it could only increase its $\rho$ (cost of capital) to over 25 per cent; moreover, it would attach a greater and greater value (present value) to the project as it increased its cost of capital up to 100 per cent. We must therefore conclude that while the rule based on the DPV is applicable and consistent for all simple projects, it is not consistent for all nonsimple projects. This particular project has been discussed by several writers; one solution was offered by Solomon (1956):

The correct solution for the investment worth of the project is simple and straightforward. But it requires an explicit answer to a relevant question: 'What is it worth to the investor to receive \$10,000 one year earlier than he would have otherwise received it?' This is actually all that the installation of the larger pump achieves. If the investor expects to be able to put the \$10,000 to work at a yield of $x\%$ per annum, then getting the money a year earlier is worth \$100$x$. If $x$ is 23%, for example, getting \$10,000 a year earlier is worth \$2,300. In other words, if he spent \$1,600 on the larger pump now (at time $t_0$), he would end up at time $t_2$ having \$2,300 more than he otherwise would have had. This can be stated as an equivalent 'rate of return', which in this case would be about 20% (\$1,600 at 20% per annum would amount to \$2,304 at the end of two years). Using this approach, a unique and meaningful rate of return can always be found for any set of cash inflows and outflows.

Although the above statement provides an interpretation of the pump project problem, it needs to be extended to provide the methodology for the general problem with any sequence of cash flows.

In the pump project the present value $P(i)$ given by (5) is not a monotonic function because the project is an investment only during the first period. During the second period the firm has 'borrowed' a net amount of money from the project equal to

$$-1,600(1 + i) + 10,000$$

where $i$ is the interest rate on money invested in the project. This money is repaid at interest $i$ at the end of the second period by the \$10,000.

*The crucial assumption in this formulation of the present value is that the same interest rate applies whether the balance of the project is negative, i.e. an investment, or positive, i.e. a source of funds.* A more general formulation distinguishes between these two rates. During the first year the firm has \$1,600 invested in the project.

$$S_0 = -1,600$$

Part of the money that is returned at the end of the first year is a repayment with interest, say at rate $r$.

$$S_1 = -1,600(1 + r) + 10,000$$

As long as the rate $r$ is less than 525 per cent, the difference between the \$10,000 received at the end of the first year and \$1,600(1 + r) is in effect being provided *by* the project *to* the firm. The \$10,000 required at the end of year two represents a repayment of this amount at say, interest rate $k$:

$$S_2 = (1 + k)S_1 - 10,000$$
$$(1 + k)[-1,600(1 + r) + 10,000] - 10,000$$

The function $S_2$, which is a function of two variables $k$ and $r$, reduces to the future value function defined earlier if $k = r = i$. In particular, the values of $k$ and $r$ which make $S_2 = 0$ are the solution of

$$10,000 = [10,000 - 1,600(1 + r)](1 + k)$$
$$= 10,000(1 + k) - 1,600(1 + r)(1 + k)$$
$$0 = -1,600(1 + r)(1 + k) + 10,000(1 + k) - 10,000$$

If $r = k = i$ then

$$0 = -1,600(1 + i)^2 + 10,000(1 + i) - 10,000$$

which is identical to Eq. (7).

If $r$ is less than 525 per cent, the project balances for project E have opposite signs since

$$S_0 < 0 \quad \text{and} \quad S_1 > 0;$$

project E therefore is a *mixed* project as defined in Section II.

This formulation of the future value function shows that the reason the present value function in Eq. (5) is not monotonic is that the project is an investment in the first period and a source of funds in the second, i.e. a mixed project. If the rate earned by an investment and the rate charged when funds are acquired are forced to be equal then the resulting present value function in general need not be monotonic.

Whether a particular project is a mixed project or a pure project depends on the interest rate. In fact for a sufficiently high interest rate any mixed project becomes a pure project – a pure investment if $a_0$ is negative and a pure financing if $a_0$ is positive. The reason for this is that if $a_0$ is positive it will be possible to find an interest rate so large that the terms

$$a_0(1 + i); \quad (1 + i)S_1, \quad (1 + i)S_2, \ldots, (1 + i)S_{n-2}$$

are large enough to make $S_1, S_2, S_3, \ldots S_{n-1}$ all nonnegative. Similarly, if $a_0$ is negative there will exist a rate that will make

$$S_1, S_2, S_3, \ldots S_{n-1} \text{ all nonpositive.}$$

We define $i_{min}$ to be the minimum rate at which a project becomes a pure project.

173

For example, project E is a mixed project for low interest rates: if $i = 25$ per cent

$$S_0 = -1,600$$
$$S_1 = -1,600(1 + .25) + 10,000 = +8,000$$
$$S_2 = 8,000(1.25) - 10,000 = 0$$

here $S_0 < 0$; $S_1 > 0$. If $i = 400$ per cent

$$S_0 = -1,600$$
$$S_1 = -1,600(5) + 10,000 = +2,000$$
$$S_2 = 2,000(5) - 10,000 = 0$$

here $S_0 < 0$; $S_1 > 0$. However, at $i = 525$ per cent, the project becomes a pure project

$$S_0 = -1,600$$
$$S_1 = -1,600(6.25) + 10,000 = 0$$
$$S_2 = 0 - 10,000 = -10,000$$

here $S_0 \leqq 0$; $S_1 \leqq 0$.

This project will be a mixed project if $i < 525$ per cent, because $S_0$ is negative and $S_1$ is positive; the project will be a pure investment if $i > 525$ per cent because $S_0$ is still negative and $S_1$ is nonpositive. For project E, $i_{min} = 525$ per cent.

If a project is a pure project at some interest rate $i_0$ it will also be a pure project for all $i > i_0$, because all the $S_j$s are of the same sign for $i = i_0$ and any increase in $i$ merely makes them more so. Furthermore $P(i)$ will be a strictly increasing function of $i$ if $a_0$ is positive and a strictly decreasing function of $i$ if $a_0$ is negative for all $i > i_0$. A mathematical proof is given in Teichroew, Robichek, and Montalbano (1965); however, the result is intuitively obvious. A pure project has all the $S_j$s either $\geqq 0$ or $\leqq 0$ for $j = 0$, $1, \ldots n - 1$. If the $S_j$s are all nonnegative for example, then $S_j(i_1) > S_j(i_2)$ if $i_1 > i_2$, because the compounding factor is larger.

For all $i > i_{min}$ $P(i)$ will be monotonic; hence there can be no more than one solution to $P(i) = 0$ for $i > i_{min}$ and there will be exactly one solution if the sign of $P(i_{min})$ is different from the sign of $a_0$. From this follows a basic result: if $i_{min} \leqq 0$ (a project is a pure project at $i = 0$) then $P(i) = 0$ will have a single unique positive solution if and only if the sign of $a_0$ is different from the sign of *the sum of all the $a_j$s.* (The converse, however, is not true. A project may have $i_{min} > 0$ and still have a unique positive solution.)

Projects C and D are nonsimple projects with unique positive internal rates of return. Table 3 gives the $S_j$s for $i = 0$ and

Table 3

Analysis of Project C, D, and E

|  | Project C | D | E | |
|---|---|---|---|---|
| $a_0$ | −1,000 | +1,000 | −1,600 | |
| $a_1$ | +1,100 | −500 | +10,000 | |
| $a_2$ | −180 | +660 | −10,000 | |
| $a_3$ | +840 | −1,800 | | |
| $\sum_{j=0}^{3} a_j$ | +760 | −640 | −1,600 | |
| $i_{min}$ | 10% | −50% | 525% | |
| IRR | 40% | 20% | 25% | 400% |
| $S_0(0)$ | −1,000 | +1,000 | −1,600 | |
| $S_1(0)$ | 100 | +500 | +8,400 | |
| $S_2(0)$ | −80 | +1,160 | −1,600 | |
| $S_0$ (IRR) | −1,000 | +1,000 | −1,600 | −1,600 |
| $S_1$ (IRR) | −300 | +700 | 8,000 | 2,000 |
| $S_2$ (IRR) | −600 | +1,500 | 0 | 0 |

$i = \text{IRR}$. D is a project with $i_{min} \leqq 0$ (actually $i_{min} = -.5$) and is a pure project for all positive $i$; hence it has a unique positive IRR by the result given above. C is a project with $i_{min} = .10$ and a unique IRR $= .40$. *Project C illustrates that the condition $i_{min} < 0$ is sufficient but not necessary for a unique solution of $P(i) = 0$.* A project can have a unique positive solution to $P(i) = 0$ even when $i_{min} > 0$. Project E becomes a pure project at $i = 525$ per cent but has no solution for IRR $\geqq 525$ per cent.

The three examples considered in this section have shown that the classification of projects into simple and nonsimple is not the same as the classification into projects for which the rules are applicable and consistent and those for which they are not, because there are some nonsimple projects for which the rules based on the IRR and DPV are applicable and consistent and others for which they are not. The next classification to be examined is that of pure and mixed projects. To fully understand the present

175

value function in mixed projects it is necessary to generalize the concept, illustrated here for project E, of the future value function to a function of two variables. This is done in the next section.

## IV The Future and Present Value Functions as a Function of Two Interest Rates

The formulation described here is based on two different rates of interest.[4] The *project financing rate* (PFR), denoted by $k$, is defined as the rate which the project 'receives' when the balance of the project is positive, i.e. the project is a net financing source. The *project investment rate* (PIR) denoted by $r$ is defined as the rate which the project 'earns' when the balance of the project is negative, i.e. the project is a net investment.[5]

The first step in this formulation is to define the future value of a project, denoted by $F(k, r)$. Let $F_j(k, r)$ be the balance of the project at the end of the $j^{th}$ period if the project receives $k$ when the balance is positive and yields $r$ when the balance is negative. Then

$$
\begin{aligned}
F_0(k, r) &= a_0 \\
F_1(k, r) &= (1 + k)a_0 + a_1 \quad \text{if} \quad F_0 \geqq 0 \\
&= (1 + r)a_0 + a_1 \quad \text{if} \quad F_0 < 0 \\
F_2(k, r) &= (1 + k)F_1 + a_2 \quad \text{if} \quad F_1 \geqq 0 \\
&= (1 + r)F_1 + a_2 \quad \text{if} \quad F_1 < 0
\end{aligned}
$$

and, in general

$$
\begin{aligned}
F_j(k, r) &= (1 + k)F_{j-1} + a_j \quad \text{if} \quad F_{j-1} \geqq 0 \\
&= (1 + r)F_{j-1} + a_j \quad \text{if} \quad F_{j-1} < 0 \\
&\qquad j = 1, 2, \ldots n
\end{aligned}
\tag{8}
$$

and
$$
\begin{aligned}
F_n(k, r) &= (1 + k)F_{n-1} + a_n \quad \text{if} \quad F_{n-1} \geqq 0 \\
&= (1 + r)F_{n-1} + a_n \quad \text{if} \quad F_{n-1} < 0
\end{aligned}
$$

4. In this paper, the two rates will be assumed as constant from period to period. The computional procedure and the approach are unchanged if the given rates vary from period to period, as long as all but one of the rates are known.

5. The range of the rates is $0 \leqslant k < \infty$ and $0 \leqslant r < \infty$.

where $F(k, r) \equiv F_n(k, r)$. An example of these computations for project E is given in Section III; $F_j$ as defined by Eq. (8) corresponds to the $S_j$ defined there.

This definition of future value and the function $F(k, r)$ have a number of interesting properties which are examined mathematically in Teichroew, Robichek, and Montalbano (1965). Only a brief summary of the results needed for a discussion of the uses of $F(k, r)$ is given here.

(a) if the project is a pure investment project $F(k, r)$ will be independent of $k$. To show this it is merely necessary to substitute successively for $F_{n-1}, F_{n-2}, \ldots F_0$ in $F_n$ in order to obtain the expression for $F_n$ in terms of the $a_j$'s. If the project is always an investment all the $F_j(k, r)$ for $j = 1, 2, \ldots n - 1$ as defined by Eq. (8) will be negative; if they were not negative, the project would not always be an investment. Then

$$
\begin{aligned}
F_n &= (1 + r)F_{n-1} + a_n \\
&= [(1 + r)F_{n-2} + a_{n-1}](1 + r) + a_n \\
&= (1 + r)^2 F_{n-2} + a_{n-1}(1 + r) + a_n \\
&= \{(1 + r)[F_{n-3} + a_{n-2}](1 + r) + a_{n-1}\}(1 + r) + a_n \\
&= (1 + r)^3 F_{n-3} + a_{n-2}(1 + r)^2 + a_{n-1}(1 + r) + a_n \\
&\quad \cdots \cdots \cdots \\
&= a_0(1 + r)^n + a_1(1 + r)^{n-1} + \ldots + a_n
\end{aligned}
$$

$F_n$ in this case is the polynomial equivalent to (b). The solution of $F_n(k, r) \equiv F(r) = 0$ gives the internal rate of return as ordinarily defined. Similarly, if a project is a pure financing project $F(k, r)$ will be independent of $r$.

(b) In general $F(k, r)$ is a polynomial in $k$ and $r$. By successive substitution similar to that used above for the special case it can be seen that the form is

$$
\begin{aligned}
F(k, r) = a_0(1 + r)^{\alpha_0}(1 + k)^{\beta_0} \\
+ a_1(1 + r)^{\alpha_1}(1 + k)^{\beta_1} + \ldots + a_n
\end{aligned}
\tag{9}
$$

where
$$
\alpha_j + \beta_j = n - j
$$

and $\alpha_j$ represents the number of periods after the $j^{\text{th}}$ period, for which the project earns interest at the rate $r$; $\beta_j$ is the number of periods for which the project received interest at the rate $k$.

(c) It is also possible to use a discounting procedure instead of compounding to the future. The discounting method is presented here because it gives a simple, though not entirely self-evident, financial interpretation.

The general form of $F(k, r)$ from Eq. (9) may be written as

$$F(k, r) = a_0 A_0 + a_1 A_1 + a_2 A_2 + \ldots + a_{n-1} A_{n-1} + a_n A_n \tag{10}$$

where $A_j = (1 + r)^{\alpha j}(1 + k)^{\beta j}$. Dividing Eq. (10) by $A_0$ gives
$$P(k, r) = F(k, r)/A_0$$
$$= a_0 + a_1 A_1/A_0 + a_2 A_2/A_0 + \ldots + a_{n-1}(A_{n-1})/A_0 + A_n a_n/A_0$$

$P(k, r)$ can be interpreted as a present value because $a_0$ is not discounted at all, $a_1$ is discounted for one period, $a_2$ is discounted for two periods, $\ldots$, $a_n$ is discounted for $n$ periods. The important point is the rates at which the cash flows are discounted. From the definition of the algorithm Eq. (8) it is immediately clear that $a_1$ is discounted at rate $k$ if $F_0 > 0$ and at rate $r$ if $F_0 < 0$; i.e.

$$A_1/A_0 = 1/(1 + k) \quad \text{if} \quad F_0 > 0$$
$$= 1/(1 + r) \quad \text{if} \quad F_0 < 0$$

The cash flows in the remainder of the project $a_2, a_3, \ldots a_n$ do not affect the discounting of $a_1$. Similarly

$$A_2/A_0 = 1/(1 + k)^2 \qquad \text{if} \quad F_0 \geqq 0 \quad \text{and} \quad F_1 \geqq 0$$
$$= 1/(1 + k)(1 + r) \qquad \text{if} \quad F_0 \geqq 0 \quad \text{and} \quad F_1 < 0$$
$$\textit{or if} \quad F_0 < 0 \quad \text{and} \quad F_1 \geqq 0$$
$$= 1/(1 + r)^2 \qquad \text{if} \quad F_0 < 0 \quad \text{and} \quad F_1 < 0$$

and again the later cash flows $a_3, \ldots a_n$ do not affect the discounting of $a_2$.

A procedure for computing $P(k, r)$ directly may therefore be stated as follows:

Let
$$D_0 = 1$$

and
$$P_0(k, r) = a_0$$

Then for $j = 1, 2, \ldots n$

$$D_j = (D_{j-1})/(1 + k) \quad \text{if} \quad P_{j-1} \geqq 0$$
$$\quad = D_{j-1}/(1 + r) \quad \text{if} \quad P_{j-1} < 0$$
$$P_j = P_{j-1} + a_j D_j$$

This procedure may be described verbally as follows: Suppose that at the end of the $j^{\text{th}}$ period the project has been an investment for $\gamma_j$ periods and a lender of money to the firm for $j - \gamma_j$ periods (at rates $r$ and $k$ respectively). The net cash flows received at the end of period $j$ will be discounted $\gamma_j$ times at rate $r$ and $j - \gamma_j$ times at rate $k$. In other words, *the order of the periods in which the project is an investment or source of funds is irrelevant to the discounting*. The only factor that matters is for how many of the previous periods the project has been an investment and for how many it has been a source of funds.

(d) The form of the function $F(k, r)$ can best be described in conjunction with a diagram such as Fig. 4 showing the contour lines.

If $F(0, 0)$ is a function of $k$ only, or $r$ only, the project is a pure project for all nonnegative interest rates and the future value function is a function of one variable only.

If $F(0, 0)$ is a function of the two variables, then there exists a value of $k$ or $r$ such that for greater values of this variable $F(k, r)$ is a function of only one variable. In Section III project E became a pure project at $r = 5.25$. Another case is illustrated in Fig. 4.

The contour line

$$F(k, r) = C$$

depends on both $k$ and $r$ for $r < .10$. For $r \geqq .10$ the contour lines are straight lines. The reason for this was discussed in Section III in connection with project E. A more specific statement is the following:

If $a_0 > 0$, there exists a $k_{\min}$ such that $F(k, r)$, for $k > k_{\min}$ is independent of $r$.

The region $0 < k < k_{\min}$, $r \geqq 0$ is termed the *mixed* region.

The region $k_{\min} \leqq k$, $r \geqq 0$ is termed the *pure financing* region.

If $a_0 < 0$, there exists an $r_{\min}$ such that $F(k, r)$, for $r > r_{\min}$, is independent of $k$.

The region $k \geqq 0$, $0 < r < r_{\min}$ is termed the *mixed* region.

The region $k \geqq 0$, $r_{\min} \leqq r$ is termed the *pure investment* region.

Financial Decision-Making

(e) $F(k, r)$ is a continuous function of $k$ and $r$ for all non-negative $k$ and $r$. This can be proved by induction using the definition in Eq. (8).

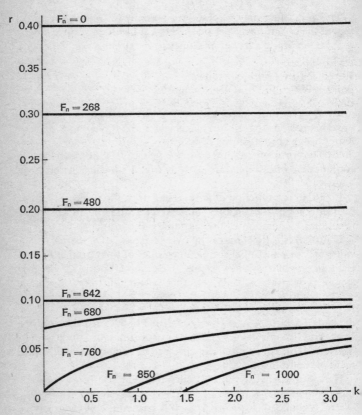

Figure 4 Contour lines for project C.

(f) The partial derivatives $\partial F/\partial k$, $\partial F/\partial r$, exist at all points in the mixed region except for the points at which one or more project balances are zero. The partial derivative $\partial F/\partial k$ is greater than zero and the partial derivative $\partial F/\partial r$ is less than zero at all points except where one or more project balances are zero. This can also be proved by induction from the definition in Eq. (8).

(g) The contour lines of

$$F(k, r) = c$$

are continuous and monotonic. As an example the contour lines shown in Fig. 4 represent selected values for $F(k, r)$ as functions of $k$ and $r$, for project C in Table 2. In general the contour lines are asymptotic to the line $r = r_{min}$ if $a_0 < 0$ and $k = k_{min}$ if $a_0 > 0$. In the region where the contour lines are not straight lines, the contour lines may be convex, concave, or both in their region of definition. An example is shown in Fig. 6.

## V The Project Investment Rate (PIR) and the Project Financing Rate (PFR)

The internal rate of return $IRR$ is defined as the solution of the equation

$$P(i) = 0$$

From the last two results in the previous section it follows that setting the future value of a project equal to zero $F(k, r) = 0$ defines implicitly a set of functions

$$k = k(r) \quad \text{or} \quad r = r(k)$$

$k(r)$ is a strictly increasing function of $r$ and $r(k)$ is a strictly increasing function of $k$. The *project financing rate*, PFR, is the value of $k$, given $r$, for which

$$F(k, r) = 0 \tag{11}$$

and similarly the *project investment rate*, PIR, is the value of $r$, given $k$, which satisfies the same equation (11).

For the pump project, E

$F_0 = 1,600$

$F_1 = 1,600(1 + r) + 10,000$    Since $F_1 > 0$ if $r < 525$ per cent

$F_2 = [-1,600(1 + r) + 10,000](1 + k) - 10,000$

$F_3 = 0$

if         $[-1,600(1 + r) + 10,000](1 + k) = 10,000$

or if        $r = 5.25 - 6.25 \, 1/(1 + k)$

Some selected values satisfying this equation are given in the following table. The function $r(k)$ is shown in Fig. 5.

| $k$ | $r$ |
|---|---|
| (%) | (%) |
| 0 | −100 |
| 25 | 25 |
| 100 | 212.5 |
| 150 | 275 |
| 200 | 317 |
| 300 | 369 |
| 400 | 400 |
| 500 | 421 |

Not unexpectedly, $r$, the PIR, increases as $k$, the PFR, increases. This results from the fact that the higher the rate imputed by the firm to the project when the project is a source of funds (PFR), the higher will be the project's PIR.

In the pump example, $r(k)$ is a concave increasing function. While $r(k)$ will always be increasing it need not be convex or concave for all values of $k$. In general it may have many inflection points. As an example, consider project $F$ with cash flows, IRR, and $i_{min}$ as follows:

| $a_0$ | $a_1$ | $a_2$ | $a_3$ | IRR | $i_{min}$ |
|---|---|---|---|---|---|
| +1,000 | −4,550 | +6,675 | −3,150 | .05 | 3.55 |
|  |  |  |  | .50 |  |
|  |  |  |  | 1.00 |  |

And project G with cash flows

| $a_0$ | $a_1$ | $a_2$ | $a_3$ | IRR | $i_{min}$ |
|---|---|---|---|---|---|
| +1,000 | −4,550 | +6,675 | −6,500 | 2.10 | 3.55 |

For project F, $P(i) = 0$ has three solutions, IRR = .05, .50, and 1.00. The function $r(k)$ defined implicitly by $F(k, r) = 0$ is shown in Fig. 6. The function $r(k)$ is asymptotic to the straight line $k = 355$ per cent, which is the rate $k$ at which all the project balances for $j < n$ become independent of $r$. *The contour line $r = r(k)$ crosses the line $r = k$ at $k = .05, .50, and 1.00, i.e. at every root of the equation where the solution to $P(i) = 0$ is used to define an internal rate of return.*[6] This is not a coincidence.

6. The curvature in the contour lines is exaggerated for illustrative purposes.

The function $F(k, r)$ in general is given by Eq. (9). Along the line $k = r = i$ the function reduces to

$$F(i, i) = a_0(1 + i)^n + a_1(1 + i)^{n+1} + \ldots + a_n$$

which is identically equal to $S(i)$ defined by Eq. (2).

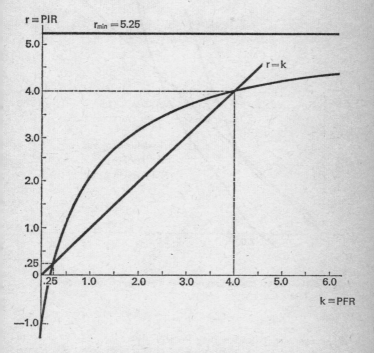

Figure 5 The project investment rate P I R is a function of the project financing rate P F R for the pump project (project E).

The contour line[6] $F_n(k, r) = 0$ for project G is also shown in Fig. 6. This contour line crosses the line $k = r$ only once; this shows that $P(i) = 0$ has a unique root and hence both rules DPV and IRR are applicable and consistent for this mixed project.

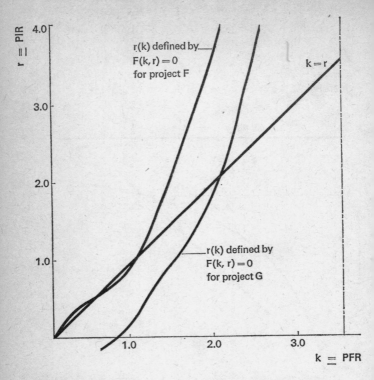

Figure 6 The project investment rate $r$ as a function of the project financing rate $k$ for project F and project G.

## VI Acceptance Rules for Any Project

With the extension of the concept of present and future values in terms of two rates any project may be analyzed in terms of either discounted present value and rates of return or a combination of both. The steps in the following procedure are illustrated in Fig. 7. The decision rules are shown in Tables 4 and 5.

The first step is to compute the project balances with $k = r = 0$, i.e. $F(0, 0)$, for $j = 0, 1, \ldots n$, to determine whether the project is a pure project for all nonnegative interest rates.

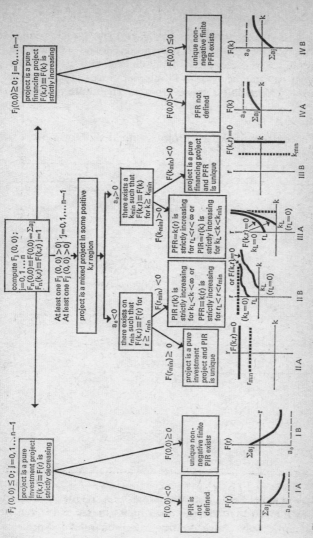

Figure 7 Summary flow chart for analysis of any project with given cash flows: $a_0, a_1, \ldots a_n$.

If the $F_j(0, 0)$ project balances for $j = 0, 1, \ldots n - 1$ are all of the same sign the project is a pure project for all nonnegative interest rates. The present value function is monotonic and there will exist a unique positive internal rate of return if $F_n(0, 0) = \sum_{j=0}^{n} a_j$ differs in sign from $a_0$. The future value func-

Table 4

Acceptance Rules for Mixed Projects with $a_0 < 0$ for Various Values of $\rho$

| | | $\rho < r_{\min}$ | $\rho \geqq r_{\min}$ |
|---|---|---|---|
| $F(r_{\min}) \geqq 0$ | | $r(k) \geqq \rho$ for all $k > 0$ | accept if: $P(\rho) \geqq 0$ or |
| Fig. 7d11 A | | always accept | $: \text{IRR} \geqq \rho$ two rules lead to identical results |
| | Example. Project C $a_0 = -1{,}000$, $a_1 = 1{,}100$ $a_2 = -180$, $a_3 = 760$ $r_{\min} = .10$, $F(r_{\min}) = 654$ $\text{IRR} = .40$ | accept if $\rho \leqq .10$ | accept if $.10 < \rho \leqq .40$ reject if $.40 < \rho$ |
| $F(r_{\min}) < 0$ | | accept if $r(\rho) \geqq \rho$ or $k(\rho) \leqq \rho$ | $r(k) < \rho$ for all $k > 0$ |
| Fig. 7-II B | | This rule is equivalent to: accept if $P(\rho) \geqq 0$ | always reject |
| | Example. Pump Project. $a_0 = -1{,}600$, $a_1 = 10{,}000$ $a_2 = -10{,}000$ $r_{\min} = 5.25$, $F(r_{\min}) = -10{,}000$ $\text{IRR} = .25, 4.00$ | reject if $0 < \rho < .25$ accept if $.25 \leqq \rho \leqq 4.00$ reject if $4.00 < \rho < 5.25$ | reject if $5.25 \leqq \rho$ |

tions for pure projects are shown in Fig. 7, IA, IB for $a_0 < 0$ and IVA, IVB for $a_0 > 0$. The two cases are illustrated by Projects A and B respectively above. The two decision rules for projects which are pure projects for all nonnegative interest rates were discussed in Section III and shown to be applicable and consistent.

If at least one $F_j(0, 0)$ project balance is positive and at least one is negative there is a positive $(k, r)$ region where the project is a mixed project. There also will exist a minimum $k$, $k_{min}$, if $a_0 > 0$ or a minimum $r$, $r_{min}$, if $a_0 < 0$ for which the function becomes of zero degree in $r$ or $k$, respectively. The four possible

Table 5

Acceptance Rules for Mixed Projects with $a_0 > 0$ for Various Values of $\rho$

|  |  | $\rho < k_{min}$ | $\rho \geqq k_{min}$ |
|---|---|---|---|
| $F(k_{min}) > 0$ | | accept if $k(\rho) \leqslant \rho$ or $r(\rho) \geqq \rho$ | $k(r) \leqq \rho$ for all $r > 0$ |
| Fig. 7-III A | | This rule is equivalent to: accept if $P(\rho) \geqq 0$ | always accept |
| | Example $a_0 = 1,600,$ $a_1 = -10,000$ $a_2 = 10,000$ | IRR = .25, 4.00 accept if $0 < \rho \leqq .25$ reject if $.25 < \rho < 4.00$ accept if $4.00 \leqq \rho < 5.25$ | accept if $\rho \leqslant 5.25$ |
| | $k_{min} = 5.25,$ $F(k_{min}) = 10,000$ IRR = .25, 4.00 | | |
| $F(k_{min}) \geqq 0$ Fig. 7-III B | | $k(r) > \rho$ for all $r > \rho$ always reject | accept if: $P(\rho) \geqq 0$ or : IRR $\leqq \rho$ two rules lead to identical results |
| | Example $a_0 = 1,000,$ $a_1 = -1,100$ $a_2 = 180, a_3 = -760$ $k_{min} = .10,$ $F(k_{min}) = -654$ IRR = .40 | reject if $\rho < .10$ | accept if $.10 < \rho \leqq .40$ reject if $.40 < \rho$ |

forms of the future value function are shown in Fig. 7, II A and B, and III A and B respectively.

The decision rule in these cases depends on the relative values of $\rho$, $r_{min}$ or $k_{min}$, and on whether $F(r_{min})$ or $F(k_{min})$ is positive or negative.

The rules for the four cases are given and illustrated in Table 4 for $a_0 < 0$. Project E is used as the example for the case where $F(r_{min}) < 0$ and project C as the example for the case $F(r_{min}) > 0$.

Consider first the case where $a_0 < 0$; $F(r_{min}) > 0$ which is illustrated in Fig. 7-IIA.

(a) $\rho < r_{min}$

Since $F(r, k)$ is a function of $r$ only the equation $F(r) = 0$ gives IRR $> r_{min}$. Here $r(k)$, for all nonnegative $k$, is less than $\rho$ for all $k$ and hence the rate of return from the project is always greater than $\rho$. Therefore a project in this category is always accepted.

(b) $\rho > r_{min}$

In this case $F(k, r)$ is a function of $r$ only and a decreasing function of $r$. Since $F(r_{min}) > 0$ and since $a_0 < 0$ there will be a unique IRR $> r_{min}$. There will therefore be a range of values of $\rho$ for which the project will be accepted and another range for which it will be rejected. Either decision rule may be used; both lead to the same decision.

Next consider the case where $a_0 < 0$; $F(r_{min}) < 0$ which is illustrated in Fig. 7-IIB.

(c) $\rho < r_{min}$

$\rho$ falls in a range where $F(k, r)$ is a function of two variables and the function $r(k)$ or $k(r)$ may be computed. The analysis for this case is illustrated in Fig. 8 using the $r(k)$ function for project E. Suppose $.25 < \rho < 4.00$ and suppose the project is considered an investment. If the cost of capital is say, $\rho_1$, the corresponding return on the project is $r_1 = r(\rho_1)$. If $r_1 > \rho_1$ the project is accepted because acceptance increases the present value of the firm. If $r_1$ were less than $\rho_1$ the project would not be accepted because present value would be decreased. (Funds are being borrowed at rate $\rho$ and invested to return less than rate $\rho$.) If the project is considered a source of funds when the cost of capital is say $\rho_2$, then the project provides funds at rate $k_2 = k(\rho_2)$. The project would be accepted only if $k_2 < \rho_2$. Since $k(r)$ and $r(k)$ are inverse functions, the two ways of looking at the project lead to identical decisions, namely:

a project is accepted for a given $\rho$ only if $r(\rho) \geqq \rho$

or if $k(\rho) \leqq \rho$

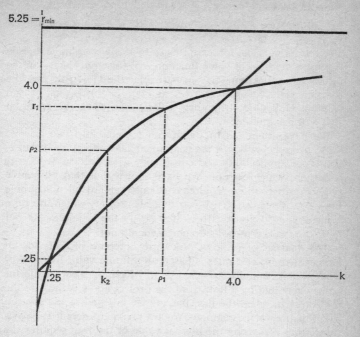

Figure 8 Justification for decision rule for $a_0 < 0$, $F(r_{min}) < 0$, $\rho < r_{min}$.

This rule is also identical with the one based on DPV with $k = r = i$ since

$$\text{DPV}(\rho) > 0 \quad \text{if} \quad r(\rho) > \rho$$
$$< 0 \quad \text{if} \quad r(\rho) < \rho$$
$$= 0 \quad \text{if} \quad r(\rho) = \rho$$

This is illustrated for project E by Figs. 3 and 8.

(d) $\rho > r_{min}$

Then $r(k)$ is always less than $\rho$ for all $k$ and hence by the rule in (c) the project is always rejected.

The analysis for the case $a_0 > 0$ is analogous and is given in Table 5. The projects in the examples are the same as in Table 4 except that the signs of the coefficients have been reversed.

## VII Summary and Remarks

The traditional rules for accepting or rejecting projects have been based on the present value function $P(i)$ [or equivalently on the future value function $S(i)$]. In particular the IRR rule uses the solution to the equation $P(i) = 0$ and the DPV rule uses the sign of $P(\rho)$. Difficulties with these rules occur when the equation $P(i) = 0$ has multiple roots.

We have attempted to classify all projects into two classes: those projects for which the traditional rules satisfy the requirements for applicability and consistency as defined in Section II and those which do not. We have shown first that all simple projects satisfy these requirements but that not all non-simple ones do. We have next shown that all projects which are pure projects for all nonnegative rates satisfy the requirements but that some mixed projects do and some do not.

The analysis of projects which are not pure projects for all nonnegative interest rates is based on a future value function of two variables $k$ and $r$. $k$ is the rate at which a project is paid for money acquired by a firm from the project and $r$ is the rate the project earns when the firm has money invested in the project. This function can be computed for any project. A detailed analysis shows that increasing the present value of the firm requires the use of rules which may be stated as

$$\text{accept project if } r(\rho) > \rho \quad \text{or} \quad \rho > k(\rho)$$

where $r(k)$ and $k(r)$ are the functions implicitly defined by $F(k, r) = 0$.

Since $\rho$ is assumed given, mixed projects may be considered either as financing projects $k(\rho)$ or as investment projects $r(\rho)$. In either case the decision is the same. This rule is exactly equivalent to the DPV rule if the traditional present value function $P(i)$ is used. ($S(i)$ is identically equal to $F(i, i)$.)

The formulation in terms of $k$ and $r$ has therefore not resulted in a new rule. What it has done is to provide the reason for the occurrence of multiple roots in the present value function: if a project is sometimes an investment and sometimes a source of funds, then the rate that the project can return on invested funds depends on the rate it receives when it is a source of funds. The more the project is paid when it provides funds to the firm, the more it earns when the firm invests in it. There may be many rates at which the future value function is zero; each of these rates is an IRR, i.e. a solution to $P(i) = 0$. It is possible to state *necessary* conditions for multiple roots: in particular the project must be a mixed project at $k = r = 0$. However, this is not a sufficient condition; there are mixed projects which have a unique positive IRR.

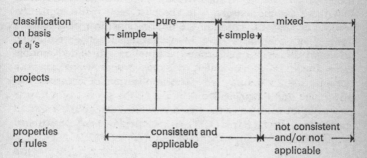

Figure 9 Classification of projects on the basis of the $a_j$'s and on properties of decision rules. Pure and mixed projects are defined for $r = k = 0$.

The results of the analysis are shown graphically in Fig. 9. The rectangle represents the class of all projects with finite, known, cash flows. The class of projects for which the traditional rules are applicable and consistent contains: (a) some members of the class of projects which are mixed projects at $k = r = 0$, and (b) all members of the class of pure projects at $k = r = 0$. These two categories contain all members of the class of simple projects.

It may be noted that the definition of consistency in particular is based on the assumptions made above. If the assumptions were relaxed to incorporate any factors which would involve ranking of projects, then a definition of consistency would require monotonicity of the present value function. This is more restrictive than merely the existence of one root and hence would cause some projects which satisfied our initial definitions of applicability and consistency to move from the class of those that satisfy into the class of those that do not.

All the analysis in this paper has been restricted to non-negative rates, $k$ and $r$. However, the results can be extended immediately to $-1 < k < 0$, $-1 < r < 0$. The necessary mathematical results are included in Teichroew, Robichek, and Montalbano (1965).

The assumptions made in Section I.3 may at first glance appear excessively restrictive. While this may be, it must be remembered that these assumptions have in the past been made implicitly without explicit realization of the implications. In recent years a number of techniques have been developed for determining optimum decisions under complex situations. Included among these are linear programming, dynamic programming, general optimization techniques, etc. The application of these to the investment and financing problem will be the subject of a future paper but the solution to the general problem will not be a simple function of the IRR or DPV, as has already been shown for certain cases by Weingartner (1963).

## References

1. BERNHARD, R. H. 'Discount methods for expenditure evaluation – a clarification of their assumptions', *Journ. Industrial Eng.*, January–February 1962.
2. BIERMAN, H., and SMITH, S. (1960) *The capital budgeting decision.* Macmillan.
3. HIRSCHLEIFER, J. (1958) 'On the theory of optimal investment decision', *Journ. Pol. Econ.*
4. LORIE, J., and SAVAGE, L. J. 'Three problems in capital rationing', *Journ. Business*, October 1955.
5. RENSHAW, E. 'A note on the arithmetic of capital budgeting decisions', *Journ. Business*, July 1957.
6. ROBERTS, H. V. 'Current problems in the economics of capital budgeting', *Journ. Business*, January 1957.
7. SOLOMON, E. 'The arithmetic of capital budgeting decisions', *Journ. Business*, April 1956.
8. SOPER, C. S. (1959) 'The marginal efficiency of capital – a further note', *Econ Journ*, 1959, 174–7.
9. TEICHROEW, D., ROBICHEK, A. A., and MONTALBANO, M. (1965) 'Mathematical analysis of rate of return under certainty', *Management Sci.* 2, No. 3, 395–403.

10. WEINGARTNER, H. M. (1963) *Mathematical programming and the analysis of capital budgeting problems.* Prentice Hall.

11. DUIGUID, A. M. and LASKI, J. G. (1964) 'The final attractiveness of a project: A method of assessing it', *Operational Res. Quart.*, **15**, No. 4, 317–28.

12. LEFKOVITS, H. C., KANNER, H., and HARBOTTLE, R. B. (1959) 'On multiple rates of return', *Proc. Fifth World Petroleum Congress*, Section IX – Paper 8, 67–74.

7. Reprinted in Solomon, E., ed. (1959) *The management of corporate capital.* Univ. Chicago Press.

# 7 H. M. Weingartner

## Capital Budgeting of Interrelated Projects: Survey and Synthesis

H. M. Weingartner (1966) 'Capital budgeting of interrelated projects: survey and synthesis, *Management Science*, **12**, 485–516.

## 1 Introduction

The literature on capital budgeting generally confines itself at best to a few of the relevant aspects of the investment decision problem, omitting certain others which are nonetheless essential ingredients of the problem which managers of firms must solve. Most, though by no means all, discussions of formal decision models assume certainty. Further, they make either of two extreme assumptions: that a meaningful investment demand schedule already exists, as in the manner of Fisher's transformation function,[1] or that all investment alternatives are independent in the sense that the acceptance of any set of them does not affect the feasibility or profitability of accepting any different set. With some notable exceptions [32, 29, 11, 46, and 45] the literature also disregards the case of capital rationing, usually on the ground that rationing ought not to exist when firms behave rationally (in the narrow economic sense). A more cogent basis for reticence, although seldom expressed, is that the appropriate criterion for the choice of investments under rationing has not been agreed upon. Nevertheless, project selections are being made all the time, even without all the theoretical niceties having been resolved, although the need for such work is recognized.

The present paper is designed to survey the techniques available to the practitioner who must decide on an investment program consisting of a potentially large number of interrelated projects, possibly also subject to constraints on capital or other resources,

---

1. See [21]. Fisher called it the 'Opportunity Line'. This is not the same as Keynes' Marginal Efficiency of Capital Schedule [30] or Dean's investment demand schedule in [17]. See Alchian [2].

and who is willing to utilize the framework of certainty for making part of his analysis or who can adapt his problem to fit within the capabilities of relatively simple methods for dealing with random events. The basic outlook behind such a presentation would include the following points. First, short-run limitations on the availability of resources are a common experience. These may not be in the form of capital shortages, but rather on critical manpower or other inputs[2] which have to be accepted by the decision-maker. Second, although the theory of investment under uncertainty is not yet in an advanced state of development,[3] some progress has been made in providing aids to the decision-maker. Mathematical models are being developed by means of which the consequences of a series of complex assumptions can be followed to their conclusions, and optimization of specified objectives may be achieved [37]. Directly related is the availability of efficient computational methods, usually employing computers, which enhances or even makes possible the application of formal methods. This combination of analysis and automatic calculation can then be utilized to obtain a 'generalized sensitivity analysis' for the essential parameters of the problems. Thus a variety of intricate and sophisticated considerations can be brought to bear on capital budgeting decisions in such a way that the talents and energies of management may be devoted to those aspects of the problem which may benefit most from informed and experienced judgment, e.g. the data inputs.

## II The Lorie–Savage Problem

### A. *Integer programming*

A now familiar problem, first discussed by J. H. Lorie and L. J. Savage in 1955 [32] may serve as the point of departure for our discussion. Given the net present value of a set of independent investment alternatives, and given the required outlays for the projects in each of two time periods, find the subset of projects which maximizes the total net present value of the accepted ones

2. Cf. [46, Secs. 7.2 and 7.5].
3. Witness the problem of intertemporal comparisons and aggregation of utilities, which is reflected in part in the determination of the appropriate rate for discounting.

while simultaneously satisfying a constraint on the outlays in each of the two periods. The problem may be generalized to an arbitrary number of time periods and stated formally as an integer programming problem, using the following notation. Let $b_j$ be the net present value of project $j$, when discounting is done by the appropriate rate of interest;[4] let $c_{tj}$ be the outlay required for the $j^{\text{th}}$ project in the $t^{\text{th}}$ period; let $C_t$ be the maximum permissible expenditure in period $t$. We define $x_j$ to be the fraction of project $j$ accepted, and require that $x_j$ be either zero or one. The model may then be written as,

$$\text{Maximize} \quad \sum_{j=1}^{n} b_j x_j \tag{1a}$$

$$\text{Subject to} \quad \sum_{j=1}^{n} c_{tj} x_j \leq C_t, \qquad t = 1, \ldots, T \tag{1b}$$

$$0 \leq x_j \leq 1, \qquad j = 1, \ldots, n \tag{1c}$$

$$x_j \text{ integral.} \tag{1d}$$

Given these data then the solution of this problem depends only upon finding a good integer programming code. Furthermore, if the $c_{tj}$ are nonnegative the problem is bounded, and a finite optimum exists.[5] However, integer programming algorithms still perform unpredictably[6] and so it may be useful to mention alternative methods which will also be relevant for our later discussion. Before doing so it should be pointed out that the budgets expressed in constraints (1b) may refer to resources which are limited in supply in the short run, in addition or alternative to constraints on capital expenditures. An example might be drawn from a retail store chain when it is planning a sharp increase in the number of stores. A limit on its expansion could come about from the availability of managers for the new stores, a number that cannot be increased simply by bidding managers away from competitors and immediately putting them in charge of new stores. A period of time is required for the new personnel

4. This is usually referred to as the cost of capital. See also Baumol and Quandt [5].

5. Cf. [46, Chap. 4].

6. Cf. [36]; also the author's experience with an All-Integer code, IPM3, was that a problem of this type with three constraints (II.1b) and 10 projects failed to converge within 5000 iterations. However, developments in this area are coming steadily; see [8, 4, 25, and 47]. See also [22 and 23] in relation to the problems under consideration here.

to learn the ways of the organization and thereby make possible effective communication and execution of management policies. Such an interpretation of budgets probably carries more realism than the model of capital rationing implied by the original Lorie–Savage formulation.[7]

A related point requires some amplification here. The example above suggests models in which the constraints also express generation or release of resources through the adoption of new projects. Thus a store might also produce future managers by training assistant managers for that duty. Basically the only change required in the formal model (1) would be to allow the coefficients $c_{tj}$ to be negative as well as nonnegative. However, such changes require some more fundamental reinterpretations of the explicitly dynamic character of the process being modeled, and this falls outside the sphere of interest here. In addition, these problems have been treated at length.[8]

## B. The linear programming solution

The Lorie–Savage problem may also be regarded as a simple linear programming problem by dropping the requirement (1d) that the $x_j$ be integers. Then, of course, some of the $x_j*$, the values of $x_j$ in the optimal solution, may turn out to be proper fractions. Fortunately it is possible to prove that there is an upper limit on the number of fractional projects given by $T$, the number of periods for which budget constraints exist.[9] The difficulties in the use and interpretation of the linear programming solutions may be summarized by citing the following points. First, the projects may not, in fact, be completely fixed in scale, and the budgets, designed primarily for control purposes, do permit a degree of flexibility. On the other hand, some projects are essentially discrete, as in location problems, and also the budgeted inputs may be rigidly limited. In addition, the maximum number of fractional projects increases when inter-relationships between projects must also be taken into account. Our concern in this paper is exclusively with the problem involving discrete projects, and hence we shall put aside the linear programming solution.

7. Cf. [46 pp. 126–7].
8. Cf. [46, Ch. 8 and 9].
9. Proofs of this and related propositions are given in [46, Sec. 3.8].

Before going on to alternative approaches, however, it should be pointed out that Lorie and Savage proposed a trial and error method for finding the integer solution. Their method, based on 'generalized Lagrange multipliers' [19], is closely related to that discussed in the next section in relation to the dynamic programming solution. It fails to achieve the integer solution in many cases, due to the nonexistence of the desired quantities. These difficulties have been analyzed at length in the context of the duals to integer programming problems;[10] however, see also below.

## C. Dynamic programming

The problem as formulated in Eq. (1) may be recognized as a special case of the knapsack or flyaway kit problem[11] when the number of 'budget' constraints is small. It arises, for example, when a camper must choose the number of each of $n$ items he wishes to carry in his knapsack when the utility to him of each is given, and total volume and weight limitations are imposed by the size of the knapsack.[12] It may also be interpreted as the number of spare parts to be taken along by a submarine for which similar limitations on weight and volume exist, but for which the benefit of the spare-parts kit involves the probability that a part is needed and the cost of being without it. Leaving stochastic aspects for a later section of this paper, we may write down the dynamic programming formulation of this general problem and briefly discuss some shortcuts for the Lorie–Savage problem.

As in the dynamic programming solution to the knapsack problem, the time sequence is replaced by the sequence of projects being considered, and the ordering of the projects is arbitrary.[13] The method consists of determining the list of projects which would be accepted if the 'budgets' in the $T$ periods were $C'_1, C'_2, \ldots, C'_T$, and selection were restricted to the first $i$ projects. This is done for $i = 1, \ldots, n$, and within each 'stage' $i$, for all feasible vectors, $C' = (C'_1, C'_2, \ldots, C'_T)$, where feasibility

10. Cf. [46, Ch. 2, Secs. 3.5, 4.2 and 5.8].

11. Cf. [15, 7 pp. 42–47].

12. This differs from the problem stated in (1) in that constraints (1c) are omitted, or replaced by larger right-side terms.

13. Some preliminary screening and rearranging can help to cut computation time. See, e.g. Glover [23].

means that $0 \leq C'_t \leq C_t$, $t = 1, \ldots, T$. We define $f_i(C'_1, C'_2, \ldots, C'_T)$ as the total value associated with an optimal choice among the first $i$ projects when funds employed are as defined. The basic recurrence relationship then may be stated as

$$f_i(C'_1, C'_2, \ldots, C'_T) \tag{2a}$$
$$= \max_{x_i = 0,1}[b_i x_i + f_{i-1}(C'_1 - c_{1i} x_i, \ldots, C'_T - c_{Ti} x_i)]$$
$$i = 1, \ldots, n$$

for
$$C'_t - c_{ti} \geq 0, \qquad t = 1, \ldots, T \tag{2b}$$

and
$$f_0(C') = 0 \tag{2c}$$

where $f_i(C')$ is the total value of the optimally selected projects with projects $i + 1$, $i + 2$, $\ldots$, $n$ still to be considered and the unallocated funds are given by $C'$.

Two departures from the usual dynamic programming version of the knapsack problem may be noted.[14] First, the number of 'budget' constraints is an arbitrary number $T$, which may be significantly greater than two. Also, the $x_j$ are either zero or one here, whereas in the knapsack problem they may be any integers usually up to some upper limit on each item. Dantzig regards even two budgets for the knapsack problem to be one too many,[15] and Bellman [6] suggests that a second constraint be handled by use of a Lagrangian multiplier by maximizing

$$\sum_{i=1}^{n} b_i x_i - \lambda \sum_{i=1}^{n} c_{2i} x_i \tag{3}$$

subject to the single constraint

$$\sum_{i=1}^{n} c_{1i} x_i \leq C_1. \tag{4}$$

A value of $\lambda$ is assumed and the one-dimensional recurrence relation

$$f_i(C'_1) = \max_{x_i = 0,1} [(b_i - \lambda c_{2i}) x_i + f_{i-1}(C'_1 - c_{1i} x_i)] \tag{5}$$

14. An additional requirement in the dynamic programming solution to the knapsack problem is that all coefficients must be nonnegative – e.g. no negative payoff or negative resource use (resource increase). This condition may be too restrictive for certain applications, for which a more general integer programming formulation is necessary. To handle interrelations between projects we shall relax this requirement partially, in Sec. IIIB, below.

15. 'It [the dynamic programming approach to the knapsack problem] is recommended where there are only a few items and only one kind of limitation' [15, p. 275].

is solved as before. Bellman comments, 'The value of $\lambda$ is varied until the second [original] constraint is satisfied. In practice, only a few tries are required to obtain the solution in this manner'.[16] As was pointed out in the previous section, issues of the existence of the Lagrange multipliers are involved here. It was shown[17] that it is possible to prove that Lagrange multipliers do not exist for some examples of the Lorie–Savage problem, model (1). It is apparent that the same technical difficulties are involved here. The work of Everett [19], partially anticipated by Lorie and Savage [32] and Bellman [6] applies this technique to arbitrary real valued functions. Everett shows, but does not emphasize, that the problem actually solved may not (and often is not) the problem originally stated.[18] Further questions have also been raised in an exchange between Charnes and Cooper and Everett [10a, 19a].

We may best illustrate the above remarks by means of an example which appeared in this journal. Joel Cord [14] utilized dynamic programming for investment project selection in exactly the way Bellman suggested, although his constraints were on total outlay and on average variance of return. We shall return to the substance of Cord's article below. For the moment we focus entirely on the computational aspects, use of the Lagrangian multiplier parametrically to reduce the problem to a one-constraint recursive optimization, as in Eq. (5).

Cord illustrates the model with a numerical example.[19] The solution he arrives at is not, however, the optimum, a possibility he allows for[20] though he attributes it to the coarseness of the increment in the parameter $\lambda$ he employed. In this he is incorrect. The optimum cannot be located by means of the Lagrangian multiplier technique, although the value of the solution he obtained is close to that of the true optimum.[21] These conclusions

16. Cf. [6, p. 274].

17. Cf. [46, Sec. 4. 2 and p. 101].

18. The problem under consideration here, however, is the strict integer problem, i.e. that in which it is assumed that a solution for the *given* constraints is sought.

19. Cf. [14, pp. 340–1].

20. [14, p. 339].

21. The true optimum, given his definition of the problem, consists of projects 8, 9, and 23, with payoff of $90,930 vs. Cord's projects 3, 8, 11, 20

were obtained by use of a program which takes advantage of the zero-one limitation on the variables, and which can handle a reasonable number of constraints without Lagrangian multipliers providing the number of projects is not excessive.[22] The computer flow chart for the program is presented in Appendix A.

Finally, a question to be resolved is the interpretation of the Lagrangian solution as opposed to the strict integer solution when these differ. It is possible to interpret the Lagrangian multiplier as the trade-off between the constrained quantity and the payoff. Thus is it possible to 'cost' the projects to determine

---

with payoff of $88,460. The correct optimum was contained in Dyckman's 'Communication' [18]. (It is not at all clear how Cord obtained his numerical solution even with the use of the Lagrangian multiplier in his second constraint. Attempts at reproducing his numerical results show that with the multiplier set at 1,400 the solution consists of projects 3, 8, 9, 23 with average variance of .0084745, as Cord reports [14, p. 341]. When the multiplier is increased to 1,410 the solution changes and consists of projects 1, 5, 8, 13, 20 with average variance of .0020345. This is the first solution which satisfies the variance constraint and thus would be the one which Cord was looking for, but did not find. With the multiplier set at 1,410 the value of the *Lagrangian function* being maximized is $81,381.355 for {1, 5, 8, 13, 20} vs. $81,380.955 for {3, 8, 11, 20}. While small, the difference is sufficient to insure that Cord's solution will never be generated by the dynamic programming computations since it is dominated: its payoff is less (and increasingly so with larger multipliers) and its required outlay is greater by $1. It is true, though not germane, that the payoff from projects 3, 8, 11, 20 is greater than that from projects 1, 5, 8, 13, 20.)

Cord's formal statement of the problem can also be criticized, because he calculated his average variance on the basis of funds available rather than funds expended. When this correction is made, the solution 8, 9, 23 is seen to violate the variance constraint. However, the optimum then is again not Cord's solution but projects 5, 8, 12, 13, and 20, with payoff of $88,650. It is interesting to note that use of Lagrangian multipliers for both constraints in the manner suggested by Lorie and Savage also does not yield either of these additional solutions. See also Eastman [18a].

22. The program was written to be entirely within core of a 32K memory machine, and the limitation on the number of constraints depends also on other dimensions. A sample problem with six constraints has been run. (Added in proof: subsequent to the writing of this report, further work has led to the development of programs for the solution of the 'complement' problem and other devices have been employed which speed up the computations in certain numerical problems. These will be described in a forthcoming report.)

whether the payoff is sufficient in the face of consumption of resources (or other constrained quantities) whose opportunity cost may be high. The linear programming model (1a–c) yields a positive[23] residual for each project accepted in the optimal solution while the rejected ones have a nonpositive residual.[24] These conclusions do not necessarily apply to the strict integer optimum, whether obtained by dynamic programming or by other means. Specifically, they do not apply when the true integer optimum cannot be obtained by means of Lagrangian multipliers, either in the dynamic programming formulation or with a systematic search for these quantities as implied by Lorie and Savage. This raises the important question of the meaning of the resource constraint. If it is merely an intermediate administrative device to control the budgetary process[25] then it would be unreasonable to disregard the pricing information contained in the Lagrangian multipliers and to accept projects which happen to allow use of the last small amount of the budget.[26] On the other hand, some resources are only available in small amounts, and full utilization of them is at the heart of the problem. In the latter case it would probably be best to search beyond the optimum obtained through use of the Lagrangian multiplier technique, or perhaps to eschew it entirely.

## III Interdependent Projects without Budget Constraints

Difficulties with the usual 'text-book' methods of capital expenditure evaluation, e.g., internal rate of return or present value, arise when the independence assumption between projects does not hold. How strong this assumption is may be seen when one considers that alternative to almost every project is the possibility of its postponement for one or more periods, with concomitant changes in outlays and payoffs. These, of course, form a mutually-exclusive set of alternatives since it would be deemed uneconomical, if not impossible, to carry out more than one of

23. More precisely, nonnegative.

24. The residuals are defined as $b_i - \lambda_1^* c_{1i} - \lambda_2^* c_{2i}$, where $\lambda_t^*$ is the optimal dual to the $t$th constraint. See [46, Sec. 3.4] for a detailed analysis.

25. See [46, Chap. 6].

26. This would imply that expenditures can be forecast with extreme accuracy, among other requirements.

them.[27] Mutual exclusion is by no means the only alternative to independence, even though this is the only other possibility which is usually raised in the literature. Contingent or dependent projects can arise, for instance, when 'acceptance of one proposal is dependent on acceptance of one or more other proposals'.[28] One simple example would be the purchase of an extra-long boom for a crane which would be of little value unless the crane itself were also purchased; the latter however, may be justified on its own. When contingent projects are combined with their independent 'prerequisites' we may call the combination a 'compound project'. Thus a compound project may be characterized by the algebraic sum of the payoffs and costs of the component projects plus, perhaps, an 'interaction' term. Although contingent projects generally can be represented by sets of mutually-exclusive compound projects, in practice this is likely to prove an undesirable way of handling them, for the resulting number of compound projects may be very large. In the present section of this paper we shall take up the treatment of interdependent projects in the context of the models discussed in the previous section. We shall also take up an alternative formulation which allows a wider variety of interrelationships, omitting, for the present, consideration of budget constraints.[29]

## A. Linear and integer programming

The methods of handling interrelationships of the types mentioned in the paragraph above were discussed at length elsewhere, and hence a brief summary here will suffice.[30]

Consider a set $J$ of mutually-exclusive projects from which at most one is to be selected. This constraint may be expressed by

$$\sum_{j \in J} x_j \leqq 1. \tag{6}$$

27. See, for example, Marglin's analysis of the 'Myopia Rule' in [34].
28. Cf. [46, p. 11].
29. In this paper we omit consideration of interdependence between existing projects and new ones. Models which deal with such problems will be of the type referred to at the end of Sec. IIA, although the tools developed here will still be applicable.
30. See [46, pp. 10–11, 32–43], and the analysis of the duals to these constraints, [46, pp. 147–52].

With the implied nonnegativity constraint on the $x_j$, this has the effect of limiting the sum of projects accepted from the set $J$ to a single one. When an integer programming algorithm is utilized to solve the problem one is assured that at most one of the $x_j$ equals unity, $j \in J$, while the remaining ones from the set are zero. Solution by linear programming leads to the possibility that several projects from the set $J$ will be fractionally accepted. The total number of such projects will still be limited although a situation with fractional $x_j{}^*$ for more than one project in the set $J$ can arise.[31] Note that the unity upper bound constraint on the $x_j$ individually, $j \in J$, are now superfluous.

Contingent projects may be handled in a similarly simple manner. If project $r$ may be undertaken only if project $s$ is accepted, but project $s$ is an independent alternative, then we may express the relationship by

$$x_r \leqq x_s \tag{7a}$$

and

$$x_s \leqq 1. \tag{7b}$$

Thus, if $x_s{}^* = 1$, i.e. it is accepted in the optimal solution, then $x_r \leqq 1$ is the effective constraint. Otherwise, $x_r \leqq 0$, together with the nonnegativity requirement, forces $x_r{}^* = 0$. If projects $u$ and $v$ are mutually-exclusive alternatives, and project $r$ is dependent on acceptance of either project $u$ or project $v$, this interrelationship may be expressed by

$$x_u + x_v \leqq 1 \tag{8a}$$

$$x_r \leqq x_u + x_v \tag{8b}$$

Hence, if one of the pair $u$ and $v$ is accepted, then constraint Eq. (8b) becomes $x_r \leqq 1$. If neither $u$ nor $v$ is accepted, then Eq. (8b) becomes $x_r \leqq 0$, implying, once again, that $x_r{}^* = 0$. Similarly, if projects $r$ and $s$ are mutually-exclusive and dependent on the acceptance of either project $u$ or $v$, two mutually-exclusive alternatives, the interdependence may be represented by the two constraints

$$x_u + x_v \leqq 1 \tag{9a}$$

$$x_r + x_s \leqq x_u + x_v. \tag{9b}$$

31. See [46, p. 37]. For an interpretation of this result, see also [46, p. 32].

Contingent chains can easily be built up, as when acceptance of project $r$ is dependent on acceptance of project $s$, which in turn is dependent on acceptance of project $u$:

$$x_u \leqq 1 \tag{10a}$$

$$x_s \leqq x_u \tag{10b}$$

$$x_r \leqq x_s, \tag{10c}$$

etc.

## B. Dynamic programming

A glance at inequality Eq. (6) which states the restriction on mutually-exclusive projects reveals that its algebraic form is exactly that of the budget constraints, restrictions Eq. (1b), i.e. the coefficients are all nonnegative. This was the only requirement necessary for applying the knapsack problem formulation, and hence solution by dynamic programming hinges only on the computational problem derived from having additional constraints. Since at most a few of the projects will be mutually-exclusive at one time, although there may be many such sets, the number of nonzero coefficients will be small. This has the effect of speeding up the calculations and keeping the 'in-lists' – the lists of accepted projects – relatively small.

In principle, contingent projects can be handled as sets of mutually-exclusive compound alternatives, as was pointed out above. The difficulty with the dependency relation Eq. (7a) may be seen by putting both unknowns on the same side of the inequality, as in

$$x_r - x_s \leqq 0. \tag{11}$$

The zero right side presents no difficulty. However, the negative coefficient of $x_s$ does. The nonnegativity condition on the co-efficients of the knapsack problem derives from the requirement that the payoff function be monotonically non-decreasing in the $x_i$. With this condition imposed it is not possible that the space of solution vectors $(x_1, \ldots, x_n)$ becomes enlarged at one stage subsequent to the elimination of some solutions. A way for handling negative coefficients such as arise in connection with dependent projects is to preorder the projects such that the in-dependent members of a set (with the negative coefficients) always

205

precede the dependent ones.[32] This implies that the solution space is expanded at the start and the above difficulty is avoided. Unfortunately it is possible to construct examples in which no such preordering is possible. It seems likely, however, that these are atypical and afford no substantial obstacle to the application of dynamic programming for interrelated projects.[33]

## C. Quadratic integer programming and the generalization of second-order effects

Although contrary to the teaching of the principle of 'Occam's Razor', it is possible to represent the above interdependencies by means of quadratic constraints superimposed on the 0-1 integer requirement for the $x_j$. For two mutually-exclusive projects, $r$ and $s$, the relevant restriction, in addition to nonnegativity on the unknowns, would be

$$x_r . x_s = 0 \tag{12}$$

which makes either $x_r^* = 1$ or $x_s^* = 1$, but not both $x_r^* = 1$ and $x_s^* = 1$. For the dependence of project $r$ on project $s$, we require

$$x_r(1 - x_s) = 0. \tag{13}$$

Thus, if $x_s^* = 1$, $x_r^*$ may be either zero or one and the restriction will be satisfied. However, if $x_s^* = 0$ then $x_r^* = 0$ necessarily.

A generalization to include all pair-wise second-order effects, i.e. involving interaction terms between pairs (but not larger sets) of projects has been offered by S. Reiter [40]. A triangular payoff matrix

$$B = \begin{pmatrix} b_{11} & b_{12} & b_{13} \ldots b_{1n} \\ 0 & b_{22} & b_{23} \ldots b_{2n} \\ 0 & 0 & b_{33} \ldots b_{3n} \\ & & \cdots \quad \cdots \\ 0 & 0 & 0 \ldots b_{nn} \end{pmatrix} \tag{14}$$

---

32. A program for the knapsack problem must be modified to allow violation of a 'feasibility condition', e.g. Eq. (2b) during part of the computations.

33. A problem was solved in which constraints Eqs. (9) and (10) (III.4) and (III.5) were applied.

is defined for the set of $n$ investment alternatives such that the payoff (e.g. net present value) from the acceptance of project $r$ alone is $b_{rr}$, and the additional payoff from acceptance of both projects $r$ and $s$ is $b_{rs}$, apart from the payoff from acceptance of project $r$, $b_{rr}$, and project $s$, $b_{ss}$. An optimal partitioning of the set of project indices, $i = 1, \ldots, m$ into two mutually exclusive and exhaustive subsets, $\{i_1, \ldots, i_r\}$ and its complement is sought such that the total payoff from the first subset, the 'in-list', is maximum. Given any such partitioning the payoff $\Gamma_\alpha$ associated with an in-list $\alpha$ may be thought of being obtained by crossing out all rows and columns of $B$ which are not on the in-list and adding up the $b_{ij}$ that remain. In Reiter's context such a payoff matrix represents an optimization problem only if some $b_{ij}$ are negative, for otherwise the optimal in-list, $\alpha^*$, would be the entire list of projects. However, in some of our extensions, below, this need not be the case. It is also clear that the elements below the diagonal are not needed to represent any of the interaction effects which can be handled in an $n \times n$ array.

A few examples paralleling our earlier discussion will bring out some of the features of this development. If projects $r$ and $s$ are mutually-exclusive, all that is necessary to prevent their simultaneous adoption is to make $b_{rs}$ a highly negative penalty.[34] Of course, all that is required here is the value $b_{rs}$ which makes the total $b_{rr} + b_{ss} + b_{rs}$ represent the net value of adopting both alternatives, a quantity which will certainly be smaller than either $b_{rr}$ or $b_{ss}$, the value of either alternative alone. Hence, $b_{rs}$ will be negative. Using the penalty of $-M$ we may represent a set of mutually-exclusive projects, for purposes of illustration assumed to be the first $k$ projects, by

$$B = \begin{pmatrix} b_{11} & -M & -M \ldots -M \\ 0 & b_{22} & -M \ldots -M \\ 0 & 0 & b_{33} & \ldots -M \\ & & \cdots & \cdots \\ 0 & 0 & 0 & \ldots b_{kk} \end{pmatrix} \quad (15)$$

A dependence of project $r$ on project $s$ is handled by letting $b_{rr}$ be the cost, a negative quantity, while $b_{rs}$ represents the benefit

34. This is analogous to the penalty for keeping artificial vectors out of the optimal basis of a linear programming solution. See, e.g. [10, p. 176].

from having $r$ in addition to $s$. $b_{ss}$ would be the net payoff from accepting project $s$ alone. We may finally illustrate this formulation with the situation expressed by Eq. (9a and b), in which projects $u$ and $v$ are mutually-exclusive, as are projects $r$ and $s$, and in addition to which acceptance of project $r$ or $s$ is dependent on acceptance of project $u$ or $v$.

$$B = \begin{pmatrix} -b_r & -M & b_{ru} & b_{rv} \\ 0 & -b_s & b_{su} & b_{sv} \\ 0 & 0 & b_{uu} & -M \\ 0 & 0 & 0 & b_{vv} \end{pmatrix} \quad (16)$$

Here the quantities $-b_r$ and $-b_s$ represent the cost of projects $r$ and $s$, respectively; $b_{uu}$ and $b_{vv}$ represent the net benefit from doing project $u$ or $v$ alone; and $b_{ru}, b_{su}, b_{rv}, b_{sv}$ represent the additional benefits from selecting both projects $r$ and $u$, $s$ and $u$, $r$ and $v$, and $s$ and $v$, respectively. Once again the quantity $-M$ is a large penalty intended to dominate its row and column by a substantial amount.

Before presenting an outline of Reiter's method for finding the optimal partitioning of the project indices, we may show that his problem is actually an integer quadratic programming problem:

$$\text{Maximize} \quad XBZ^t = \sum_{i=1}^{n} \sum_{j=1}^{n} b_{ij} x_i x_j \quad (17)$$

where $X = (x_1, x_2, \ldots, x_n)$, $X^t$ is its transpose, and $x_i = 0$ or $1$. Thus the pay-off $b_{ij}$ is realized only if both $x_i^* = 1$ and $x_j^* = 1$. Otherwise the product $b_{ij} x_i^* x_j^* = 0$. Similarly, since the $x_i$ are restricted to zero and unity it is unnecessary to distinguish between $x_i$ and $x_i^2$. We shall return to other problems in which this formulation is of utility later on.

Reiter's method for maximizing Eq. (17) is not algorithmic in the usual sense. It locates a local maximum (guaranteed to exist by the finiteness of the number of projects) by a gradient method that traverses 'connected in-lists'. By starting at random in-lists it generates a variety of local optima which can be arranged in ascending order. Whether the global optimum is reached depends on whether an initial in-list is selected which leads to the global optimum as its local optimum. Often it is possible to estimate probabilistically the chances that the global optimum will be reached. Optimal stopping rules (based on the value of improvement vs. the computational cost of obtaining it) and optimal fixed sample-size plans have also been developed.[35]

The method may be described as follows. Given an arbitrary in-list $\alpha$, compute the corresponding payoff $\Gamma_\alpha$. A connected in-list $\alpha'$ is one which differs from $\alpha$ either by including one project not contained in $\alpha$, or by excluding one project which is included in $\alpha$. The quantity $\Gamma_{\alpha'}$ is computed for each $\alpha'$ connected to $\alpha$, and so is the gradient $G_{\alpha'} = \Gamma_{\alpha'} - \Gamma_\alpha$. The $\alpha'$ corresponding to the largest $G_{\alpha'}$ is selected as the starting point for the next iteration and these are continued until no $\alpha'$ can be found for which $G_{\alpha'} > 0$. Once this point has been reached the in-list with a local maximum has been found. [In the event of ties between $G_{\alpha'}$ along the way, a simple rule such as choosing that $\alpha'$ with the smallest first index (where a difference exists) can be used to break the tie.]

Having found a local optimum one seeks to choose a new starting in-list which has not already been evaluated, so as to find another local optimum. The connected in-lists constitute branches on a tree which has many starting points that lead to the top (the local maximum). The 'broader' the tree having the global optimum as its local maximum, the more likely it is that the global optimum will be found. The method guarantees only that the global maximum will be found with 'probability one'. Unfortunately, it will not be recognized as such short of evaluating every possible in-list along the way. However, by careful use of prior information [42] and aspiration levels to indicate when the procedure should be stopped, one can arrive at 'good' programs rapidly.[36] A numerical example with its tree-structure is presented in Appendix B.

One final note regarding this approach to the selection of interdependent projects is required here. Although Reiter restricts himself to a consideration of second-order interactions exclusively, there is nothing in the method which requires this. A generalization to $k^{th}$ order effects requires computations involving an $n^k$ array, for which specifying the numerical values of the parameters will be more difficult than obtaining a good solution.

35. Cf. [41 and 42].
36. In any case, one would partition the matrix $B$ into independent submatrices, if such exist, and use the method on the submatrices separately.

Increasing the dimensionality of the array does not change anything essential in the structure of the problem – the connectedness or finiteness of the iterative process for finding a local optimum – and hence only the computational problems are affected, though perhaps drastically.

## IV Interdependent Projects with Budget Constraints

The methods outlined in the previous section, in addition to handling the interrelationships between projects, permit inclusion of budget constraints with varying degrees of difficulty. For linear and integer linear programming formulations the interrelationships are essentially like budgets, and this holds approximately for the dynamic programming formulation, as was discussed in Section III. The formulation as an integer quadratic programming problem also allows the introduction of linear restrictions such as the budget constraints, although progress toward an algorithm for such problems has not been rapid to date [31].

The only point which bears a brief discussion in this section is the introduction of side-conditions of the budget type into the Reiter format. To accomplish this end with a single restriction one may utilize a Lagrangian multiplier [37] as did Bellman in the knapsack problem. That is, the terms $c_j$ from the constraint

$$\sum_{j=1}^{n} c_j x_j \leqq C \qquad (18)$$

are introduced into the matrix $B$ of Eq. (14) with the Lagrangian $\lambda$:

$$B = \begin{pmatrix} b_{11} - \lambda c_1 & b_{12} & b_{13} \ldots & b_{1n} \\ 0 & b_{22} - \lambda c_2 & b_{23} \ldots & b_{2n} \\ & \cdots & \cdots & \\ 0 & 0 & 0 \ldots b_{nn} - \lambda c_n \end{pmatrix} \qquad (19)$$

and the optimization procedure is repeated with varying values of $\lambda$ until restriction Eq. (18) is met. This procedure is not without pitfalls. Suppose $\alpha^0(\lambda)$ is the in-list accepted as the best obtainable for the given aspiration level (stopping rule) and the given value of $\lambda$. Suppose, further, that $\alpha^*(\lambda)$ is the optimal in-list for this value of $\lambda$. The difference between $\Gamma_{\alpha 0}(\lambda)$ and $\Gamma_{\alpha *}(\lambda)$ may arise (a)

37. With the attendant qualifications indicated in Sec. IIC above.

because larger $b_{ij}$ are available, or (b) smaller $c_j$ are available, or (c) both.[38] Only in case (a) are the constrained quantities $c_j$ not involved. In both other instances, the most likely case being (c), this difference implies that the global optimum (for the given value of $\lambda$) will show a greater amount of slack or smaller surplus in constraint Eq. (18) than does $\alpha^0(\lambda)$. A reasonable procedure for changing $\lambda$ in the direction indicated by the presence of slack or violation of the restriction would be to begin the computations with the previous in-list $\alpha^0$. The grid for such changes in $\lambda$ should reflect the bias in the estimation of the optimal value of the Lagrangian multiplier.[39] It should be borne in mind, nevertheless, that feasible solutions, which satisfy the constraint Eq. (18), will always be found (assuming that the constraint is consistent with the interrelationships) even though it is not guaranteed to be a global optimum.

One final observation which will be followed by a detailed discussion of a particular application below concludes this section. Given the discrete optimization technique of Reiter the cost structure may also express the whole range of second-order interactions, generalizing to the following payoff matrix:

$$B = \begin{pmatrix} b_{11} - \lambda c_{11} & b_{12} - \lambda c_{12} & b_{13} - \lambda c_{13} \ldots & b_{1n} - \lambda c_{1n} \\ 0 & b_{22} - \lambda c_{22} & b_{23} - \lambda c_{23} \ldots & b_{2n} - \lambda c_{2n} \\ 0 & 0 & b_{33} - \lambda c_{33} \ldots & b_{3n} - \lambda c_{3n} \\ & & \cdots & \cdots \\ 0 & 0 & 0 & \ldots b_{nn} - \lambda c_{nn} \end{pmatrix}$$

$$(20)$$

Should the payoff matrix be partitionable into submatrices, as e.g. in

$$B = \left( \begin{array}{cc|cc} b_{11} - \lambda c_{11} & b_{12} - \lambda c_{12} & 0 & 0 \ldots 0 \\ 0 & b_{22} - \lambda c_{22} & 0 & 0 \ldots 0 \\ \hline 0 & 0 & b_{33} - \lambda c_{33} \ldots \\ & & \cdots & \cdots \end{array} \right) \quad (21)$$

38. The $c_j$ are nonnegative quantities, and are multiplied by the positive constant $\lambda$ and then subtracted from the $b_{jj}$.

39. More complete ways of handling this problem are being investigated.

the problem may be restated as

$$\text{Maximize} \qquad Z(\lambda) = \sum_{k=1}^{s} (XBX^t)_k \qquad (22)$$

where each $(XBX^t)_k$ is a similar subproblem. The value of $\lambda$ remains the same for all subproblems at any state since the budget constraint applies to all simultaneously.

## V Probabilistic Considerations

Introduction of probability distributions into the models considered earlier cannot automatically be regarded as dealing with the problems of uncertainty. In the selection of projects whose outcomes are stochastic, it is not, in general, clear what the random variables are or how they are distributed, although some attempts at the organization of data have recently been proposed.[40] More important, it is not yet clear how such outcomes should be evaluated.[41] We shall waive these matters in order to pursue our original aim of clarifying and expanding on simple methods of analyzing the consequences from given assumptions, hopefully useful considering the current state of the art.

### A. Independent investment projects

Even investment alternatives which are independent in the physical sense but which have probabilistic payoffs introduce a hierarchy of difficulties in the selection of an optimal set. The foremost of these is the choice of criterion function for optimization.[42] Confining ourselves, as before, to economic benefits, we first look at expected value maximization. Under this criterion, and assuming that the decision-maker is satisfied that he has defined meaningful random variables and that he knows the shapes and parameters of their distributions, we distinguish between situations where the payoffs are independently distributed and where they are not. For the present we consider the quantities subject to budget constraints to be certain.[43]

40. See, for example, [26] and [27].

41. This problem remains conspicuously unsolved in [26]. However, see also [28].

42. We are not concerned with a general discussion of utility here.

43. This assumption is relaxed via chance-constrained programming, in [12] and [38]. Further work following up on some of the ideas presented in this paper is being carried on by the author.

With independently distributed outcomes the problem has not been altered in any essential way.[44] The form of the original Lorie–Savage problem still applies, expected payoffs being substituted for certain ones. Integer programming or dynamic programming may be used to solve the problem, as before, or linear programming may be applied if its limitations are not important here. It should be obvious that most of the problems of uncertainty have been assumed away, although a model of this type of uncertainty has been used [3]. If the outcomes of investments are jointly distributed nothing new is introduced under expected value maximization.

The same is not the case if the conditional distribution of outcomes of a particular project, given that another is undertaken, is different from the unconditional distribution. Such is the case, for example, if the probability distribution for a manufacturing facility is affected by the decision to build a warehouse nearby. Such second-order effects[45] may be handled by quadratic integer programming, as in Section IIIC, and solved by Reiter's method or our extension provided that no more than a single constraint is imposed. The off-diagonal elements of the payoff matrix $B$ would then express the expected value of the joint adoption of two projects while the diagonal elements are expected payoffs from acceptance of the projects by themselves. The costs would be subtracted from the diagonal elements, as in matrix Eq. (19).

## B. Nonlinear utility functions

When the stochastic nature of the outcomes is given prominence in the problem, consideration must also be given to the form of the function whose optimization is being sought. Questions of risk aversion or risk preference lead to inclusion of quantities other than expected payoffs into the criterion or utility function. The meanings of the terms 'risk aversion' and 'risk preference' have been sharpened considerably in a recent paper by Pratt [39],

44. In attempting to solve an explicitly dynamic problem, in which decisions are made periodically, one would also have to take into account that the decision taken at one time may affect the statistical distributions which are pertinent for later decisions.

45. i.e. again involving only interaction terms between projects, two at one time.

a few of whose conclusions will be referred to below. This subject, which is intertwined with the concept of uncertainty, raises such additional issues as whose utility should be optimized, as well as the effect of expectations concerning the availability of future prospects on the current decision. The latter difficulty has already been relegated to another time by omitting consideration here of sequential decision procedures. The former we leave to others, assuming that a determination can be made by the decision-maker.

As Markowitz has pointed out [35, 20] the step to the simplest nonlinear utility function can be taken directly or indirectly. First one may assume that the utility function is quadratic. Unfortunately, the quadratic is not risk-averse in Pratt's sense.[46] However, if all outcomes are normally distributed only the mean and variance of the total payoff enter into the utility function.[47]

We assume first that the outcomes are jointly normally distributed, but that the distributions are not contingent on the decisions themselves as in the preceding section. The resulting problem has a form exactly analogous to the Markowitz Portfolio Selection problem with the following exceptions. First, the projects are discrete, unlike the portfolio problem in which for a given security there are constant returns to scale. As a result, the problem is not to determine the proportion of the portfolio to be allocated to each eligible security, but to determine the list of projects to be accepted. Formally, this problem may be written as

Maximize
$$\mu - \lambda\sigma^2 \equiv \sum_{i=1}^{n} \mu_i x_i - \lambda \sum_{i=1}^{n} \sum_{j=1}^{n} x_i \sigma_{ij} x_j \qquad (23)$$

subject to $\qquad x_i = 0, 1, \qquad i = 1, \ldots, n$

46. One consequence of the quadratic utility function is that the 'risk premium' – that additional amount which makes a fair gamble acceptable to a risk-averse gambler – *increases* with his initial wealth.

47. To obtain a quadratic utility function requires a further simplification. In a series expansion of an arbitrary utility function, if all terms of degree higher than the second are discarded, the resulting approximation can be made to take the form of Eq. (23) by a suitable linear transformation. The utility function under discussion here (based on the von-Neumann–Morgenstern postulates (33, Sec. 2.5]) is, in any case, unique only up to a linear transformation.

for a preassigned value of $\lambda$, where $\mu$ is the expected value of the payoff of the accepted projects and $\sigma^2$ is the variance of the total payoff. $\lambda$ may be accorded the interpretation of a measure of risk aversion – the rate of trade-off between reduction in expected value for reduction in variance. Here $\mu$ is the sum of the expected payoffs $\mu_i$ from the individual projects which are accepted. The $\sigma_{ij}$ are the covariances between the outcomes of projects $i$ and $j$, $i \neq j$, and $\sigma_{ii} = \sigma_i^2$ are the variances. Since we have restricted the values of $x_i$ to zero or one, $x_i = x_i^2$, and functional Eq. (23) has a form similar to one treated before by Reiter's Discrete Optimization Method:

$$B = \begin{pmatrix} \mu_1 - \lambda\sigma_1^2 & -2\lambda\sigma_{12} & -2\lambda\sigma_{13} & \dots & -2\lambda\sigma_{1n} \\ 0 & \mu_2 - \lambda\sigma_2^2 & -2\lambda\sigma_{23} & \dots & -2\lambda\sigma_{2n} \\ 0 & 0 & \mu_3 - \lambda\sigma_3^2 & \dots & -2\lambda\sigma_{3n} \\ & & \dots & \dots & \\ 0 & 0 & 0 & \dots & \mu_n - \lambda\sigma_n^2 \end{pmatrix} \quad (24)$$

We may contrast this formulation with the one recently suggested by J. Cord which was referred to earlier.[48] Cord considers the problem of 'optimally selecting capital investments with uncertain returns, under conditions of limited funds and a constraint on the maximum average variance allowed in the final investment package'.[49] Although Cord's figure of merit is 'interest rate of return' of a project which is multiplied by the required outlay for the project,[50] nothing essential is changed by substituting the expected present value for this quantity. Similarly, the variance of the present value may be used in place of the variance he uses.[51]

48. See p. 200, above.

49. [14, p. 335].

50. In his discussion, Cord indicated that by 'interest rate of return' he means internal rate of return – that rate which equates the discounted value of inflows to the (assumed by Cord, sole) outflow. For this he was properly criticized by T. R. Dyckman [18] because of the effect of project lives on total benefit. Actually, Cord's use of this quantity is not consistent with application of the internal rate of return, which he multiplies by the outlay to obtain the figure of merit used in the objective function. His model can be made consistent, however, simply by interpreting 'interest rate of return' as the uniform perpetual rate of return.

51. Cord's variance constraint is based on the variance of total funds available rather than on funds allocated to investments; i.e. in our notation, the project variances per dollar outlay are weighted by $c_i/C$ rather than by

Cord solves this problem by dynamic programming utilizing the Lagrangian multiplier technique to obtain a solution which satisfies the constraint on variance. Using the notation of the preceding paragraph and of Section IIC, above, we may restate his recurrence relation as

$$f_i(C') = \max \{[\mu_i x_i - \lambda \sigma_i^2 x_i + f_{i-1}(C' - c_i x_i)] \mid \\ 0 \leqq x_i \leqq 1, 0 \leqq C' \leqq C\} \quad (25)$$

where $C'$ is the unallocated budget and $f_i$ the total value of the selected projects when $C'$ remains to be allocated and $n - i$ projects still to be considered.

Cord explicitly assumes independence in the statistical sense between the project payoffs. Hence his total variance is the sum of the variances of the accepted projects, avoiding the quadratic terms and covariances. Although it simplifies the computations, this assumption, which he has difficulty in justifying, is not strictly necessary for application of dynamic programming. Having consciously patterned his approach after Markowitz he might also have considered Sharpe's Diagonal Model [43] which is designed to simplify the computations for obtaining optimal portfolios by allowing only a restricted covariance between the eligible securities.

Specifically, Sharpe assumes that the returns on securities are related only through a relationship with some common factor, e.g. an index of general activity. If the random variable, the return on the $i^{th}$ security, is denoted by $p_i$, and the level of the index is $I$, he expresses this return by

$$p_i = \mu_i + \beta_i I + w_i \quad (26)$$

where $\mu_i$ and $\beta_i$ are parameters, and $w_i$ is a random variable with mean of zero and variance of $\sigma_i^2$. Further, the level of $I$ is given by

---

$c_i/\sum c_i x_i$*. The former weighting will understate the variance unless it is assumed that unallocated funds are actually maintained as cash with zero variance and return. On the other hand, the more reasonable second weighting makes the problem computationally more difficult since the weighting depends on the projects accepted. Dyckman [18, p. 349] suggests improving the solution by investing funds unallocated to projects in bonds at a nominal return and zero variance. This again assumes that the cash is on hand, having been procured at the cost of capital which is presumably much higher than the 'nominal rate'.

the sum of a systematic component, $\mu_I$, and a random part, $w_I$, with mean of zero and variance of $\sigma_I^2$,

$$I = \mu_I + w_I, \tag{27}$$

with $w_i$ and $\sigma_i^2$ independent of $I$. Putting these relations together, with the assumption that Cov $(w_i, w_j) = 0$ he obtains

$$\begin{aligned}
\text{Exp } (p_i) &= \mu_i + \beta_i(\mu_I) \\
\text{Var } (p_i) &= \sigma_i^2 + \beta_i^2 \sigma_I^2 \\
\text{Cov } (p_i, p_j) &= \beta_i \beta_j \sigma_I^2
\end{aligned} \tag{28}$$

In the portfolio problem the unknowns are the proportions of the total amount invested which are allocated to various securities. By contrast, our variables are integer-valued; $x_i = 0$ or $1$. Hence we may maximize total expected investment program payoff $\mu$ subject to an expenditure ceiling of $C$ and a variance limit of $\sigma^2$, or alternatively, maximize payoff less $\lambda \sigma^2$ subject to the budget constraint, where

$$\mu = \sum_{i=n}^{n} (\mu_i + \beta_i \mu_I) x_i \tag{29}$$

$$\sigma^2 = \sigma_I^2 \left( \sum_{i=1}^{n} \beta_i x_i \right)^2 + \sum_{i=1}^{n} \sigma_i^2 x_i. \tag{30}$$

The recurrence relation may then be written as

$$f_i(C') = \max \left\{ \mu_i x_i - \lambda x_i [\sigma_i^2 + \sigma_I^2 (\beta_i^2 + 2\beta_i \sum_{j=1}^{i-1} \beta_j x_j)] \right.$$
$$\left. + f_{i-1}(C' - c_i x_i) \mid 0 \leqq x_i \leqq 1, 0 \leqq C' \leqq C \right\} \tag{31}$$

where the term enclosed in braces results from the factoring

$$\begin{aligned}
\sigma^2 &= \sigma_I^2 \left( \sum_{j=1}^{i} \beta_j x_j \right)^2 + \sum_{j=1}^{i} \sigma_j^2 x_j \\
&= \sigma_I^2 \left( \sum_{j=1}^{i-1} \beta_j x_j \right)^2 + \sum_{j=1}^{i-1} \sigma_j^2 x_j + \sigma_I^2 x_i \left( \beta_i^2 + 2\beta_i \sum_{j=1}^{i-1} \beta_j x_j \right) \\
&\qquad\qquad + \sigma_i^2 x_i. \tag{32}
\end{aligned}$$

Contrary to Cord's viewpoint, the generalized or parametric Lagrangian multiplier formulation[52] above has the advantage here of tracing out a variety of efficient investment programs in the Markowitz sense[53] instead of requiring the decision maker to specify his tolerance for variance abstractly.

52. In the sense of Everett [19].
53. I. e. one with minimum variance for given mean, or maximum mean for given variance.

Utilization of an index to capture the major effect of covariation seems more appropriate in our context than in portfolio selection. For a single product-line firm, the payoffs from capital expenditures are apt to be related to each other mostly through a variable such as total sales. An extension of Sharpe's work to a number of uncorrelated indexes by K. J. Cohen [1] doubtlessly may be applied within this framework also [13].

## C. Interdependent investments with probabilistic returns

Taking cognizance of covariance between investment payoffs may be thought of as the simplest form of interdependence, and strict independence in our original sense does not apply. However, it is still necessary to consider such explicit interrelationships as mutual-exclusion and dependence in order to see what these concepts imply given that outcomes are random variables.

Continuing, then, with jointly normally distributed payoffs from all investments (thus narrowing our concern to mean, variance and covariance), we observe first that the choice among mutually-exclusive investments in the absence of budget or other constraints cannot be made without reference to the whole set of alternatives. That is, if the projects within set $J$ are mutually-exclusive, so that acceptance of more than one of them can be ruled out in advance, the quantities $\mu_j$ and $\sigma_j$, $j \epsilon J$, are insufficient for selection of the preferred one (if any). The covariances between the mutually-exclusive project and the independent ones enter into the choice, which may be formulated once more as a quadratic integer program solved by use of Reiter's method:

$$B = \begin{pmatrix} \mu_1 - \lambda\sigma_1{}^2 & -M & -2\lambda\sigma_{13} & \dots & -2\lambda\sigma_{1n} \\ 0 & \mu_2 - \lambda\sigma_2{}^2 & -2\lambda\sigma_{23} & \dots & -2\lambda\sigma_{2n} \\ 0 & 0 & \mu_3 - \lambda\sigma_3{}^2 & \dots & -2\lambda\sigma_{3n} \\ & & \dots & & \dots \\ 0 & 0 & 0 & \dots & \mu_n - \lambda\sigma_n{}^2 \end{pmatrix} \quad (33)$$

In Eq. (33), projects 1 and 2 are considered mutually-exclusive, introducing the penalty $-M$ into the second column of the first row to prevent their joint acceptance. The matrix otherwise resembles Eq. (24). [54]

54. There is obviously no need for $\sigma_{12}$ since the $-M$ will rule out $x_1{}^* = 1$, $x_2{}^* = 1$ from the optimal solution.

218

Great care must be exercised in utilizing this approach for the generalized second order effect matrix, as in Eq. (14). A difficulty arises around the meaning of the covariance terms, $\sigma_{ij}$, when the off-diagonal elements include expected values. Consider, for example, a machine tool for which accessories are available which increase the range of products which the machine can produce, and at the same time, increase its reliability. We can consider the tool itself project $r$, its accessories project $s$, and thus denote the random payoff from the machine tool alone by $b_{rr}$ with expectation $\mu_{rr}$ and variance $\sigma_{rr}$; the cost of the accessories by $b_{ss} = \mu_{ss}$, with $\sigma_{ss} = 0$; and the increase in payoff due to the accessories by $b_{rs}$ with expectation of $\mu_{rs}$. However, we shall need $\sigma_{rs}$ to denote more than the variance of $b_{rs}$. If we define $\pi_{rs} = b_{rr} + b_{rs} + b_{ss}$, i.e. $\pi_{rs}$ is the payoff from the compound project [55] and $V_{rs}$ is its variance, then [56]

$$V_{rs} = \sigma_{rr} + \sigma_{ss} + \sigma_{rs} = \sigma_{rr} + \sigma_{rs} \qquad (34)$$

or $\qquad \sigma_{rs} = V_{rs} - \sigma_{rr} - \sigma_{ss} = V_{rs} - \sigma_{rr}.$

With these definitions it is possible to treat complex interrelationships by use of Reiter's method, although the data preparation requires, in effect, computing the parameters of all possible (or likely) compound projects, which could then be handled via matrix Eq. (33) just as well. Using this earlier method also has the advantage of preserving the meaning of the covariance term between independent projects which would be clouded when covariances between a dependent project and unrelated independent projects are needed.

A final note regarding the quantities subject to budget constraints is needed before this section may be concluded. We have assumed that these are known with certainty. Should they also be regarded as stochastic the character of the problem would change in a significant way. One alternative would be to make compliance with the constraint less rigid, e.g. by stating only a probability less than unity with which the condition must hold. This places the problem into the realm of chance constrained programming [9]. Another would be to proceed sequentially in the allocation

55. $b_{ss} < 0$.
56. Presumably $\sigma_{rs} < 0$, in this example.

process, to make certain that expenditures stay within the preset ceilings.[57] The latter problem, which may be formulated as a dynamic programming problem, does take us outside the framework set for this paper and will be taken up elsewhere.

## VI R & D Project Selection

### A. Expected value maximization

The final section of this paper is devoted to consideration of an additional class of project interrelationships which can arise in the context of constructing a research and development program. In order to concentrate on those aspects we consider a drastically simplified problem in which the payoff from one successful development of a product or process is known with certainty (again denoted by $b_i$), in which the development cost, $c_i$, is similarly known with certainty, and in which the probability of success is believed to be $p_i$ for a single project $i$.

If projects are mutually independent in all respects, acceptance is contingent only on the condition

$$p_i b_i - c_i > 0. \qquad (35)$$

Where simultaneously resource limitations are also imposed, the problem has the format of the original Lorie–Savage problem, and the methods offered for this still apply. The project payoff is now given by the left side of Eq. (35). This much is of little interest. Consider, however, two projects, $r$ and $s$, which are mutually-exclusive in the following sense. They may represent alternative products to serve the same function, or products, e.g. chemicals or drugs, synthesized by two different methods. Then it may be that if research on both projects is undertaken and success is achieved on both, only the better project will actually be taken past the development stage. Thus, if $b_r > b_s$, $p_r$ is the probability of success on project $r$ independent of undertaking project $s$, and $p_s$ similarly for project $s$, and $p_{rs}$ is the probability of success on both projects $r$ and $s$, then the payoff from undertaking re-

57. I.e. to insure this with probability one as in linear programming under uncertainty as formulated by G. B. Dantzig [16].

search on both is given by the applicable box in the following payoff matrix:

|              | Success on $r$           | Failure on $r$      |
| ------------ | ------------------------ | ------------------- |
| Success on $s$ | $b_r - c_r - c_s$        | $b_s - c_r - c_s$   |
| Failure on $s$ | $b_r - c_r - c_s$        | $-c_r - c_s$        |

The expected payoff then is

$$\pi_{rs} = p_r(b_r - c_r - c_s) + (p_s - p_{rs})(b_s - c_r - c_s)$$
$$+ (1 - p_r - p_s + p_{rs})(-c_r - c_s)$$
$$= p_r b_r + (p_s - p_{rs})b_s - (c_r + c_s) \quad (36)$$

and in the absence of budgets the decision to undertake both is based on a comparison of $\pi_{rs}$ with the expected payoff on the better of the two projects alone, where 'better' means a higher expected value of the undertaking. Thus, if

$$p_r b_r - c_r > p_s b_s - c_s \quad (37)$$

then

$$\pi_{rs} > p_r b_r - c_s$$

implies

$$(p_s - p_{rs})b_s - c_s > 0 \quad (38)$$

or

$$p_s - p_{rs} > c_s / b_s$$

and research on both should be undertaken. If the inequality Eq. (37) were reversed, i.e. if research on project $s$ were more attractive than research on project $r$ given that only a single one were to be undertaken, even though $b_r > b_s$ (the value of success on $r$ is greater than success on $s$) as is assumed in Eq. (36), then the comparable criterion would require

$$p_r b_r - c_r > p_{rs} b_s. \quad (39)$$

This argument may easily be generalized to an arbitrary number of alternatives. Where consideration of such mutually-exclusive alternatives is to be made alongside independent ones (to be discussed below) the matrix formulation of Reiter again suggests itself:

$$B = \begin{pmatrix} p_r b_r - c_r & -p_{rs} b_s & \dots \\ 0 & p_s b_s - c_s & \dots \\ 0 & 0 & \dots \end{pmatrix} \qquad (40)$$

Should both projects $r$ and $s$ be selected the payoff using Eq. (40) is the same as in Eq. (36). In the matrix formulation it is possible to add an additional term, $c_{rs}$ (which may be positive or negative), to express an adjustment to the total development costs resulting from the joint development program. This formulation also lends itself to the simultaneous consideration of three or more projects which are mutually-exclusive in this special sense. However, for every additional project we require an additional dimension in the array, the need for which arises from a term involving $p_{ijk\dots s}$, the joint probability of success on all such projects. [58]

Additional interrelationships can arise when the probability of success on one project is affected by the undertaking of research on a non-competing project as when, for example, the research embodies similar approaches or instrumentation. These effects may be reciprocal, though not necessarily symmetric. A project $r$ may involve a process jointly with $s$, so that if both developments are undertaken the probability of success on each is enhanced. However, it may be that the joint process is only a small part of the problem involved in project $s$ although it comprises the major component of project $r$. Hence, if we denote by $p_{rs}$ the probability of success on project $r$ given that project $s$ is also undertaken [59] it may be that $p_{rs} \neq p_{sr}$. Hence we require a non-symmetric matrix $P$:

$$P = \begin{pmatrix} p_{11} & p_{12} & p_{13} \dots p_{1n} \\ p_{21} & p_{22} & p_{23} \dots p_{2n} \\ & \dots & \dots \\ p_{n1} & p_{n2} & p_{n3} \dots p_{nn} \end{pmatrix} \qquad (41)$$

58. Arrays of higher dimension than two can be avoided by constructing mutually exclusive compound projects into which all the interactions have already been absorbed. This may, however, not be the preferable way of proceeding.

59. This is a change in definition from that used above.

where $p_{ii}$ represents the probability of success on project $i$ taken by itself. This may be combined with a diagonal payoff matrix $B$ and the triangular cost matrix $C$, viz.,

$$B = \begin{pmatrix} b_1 & 0 & 0 \ldots 0 \\ 0 & b_2 & 0 \ldots 0 \\ 0 & 0 & b_3 \ldots 0 \\ & & \cdots \\ 0 & 0 & 0 \ldots b_n \end{pmatrix}$$

(42)

$$C = \begin{pmatrix} c_1 & c_{12} & c_{13} \ldots c_{1n} \\ 0 & c_2 & c_{23} \ldots c_{2n} \\ 0 & 0 & c_3 \ldots c_{3n} \\ & & \cdots \\ 0 & 0 & 0 \ldots c_n \end{pmatrix}$$

in the quadratic integer programming problem [60]

Maximize $\qquad X[BP - C]X^t$ (43)

where $X$ is a vector of $x_i$ as before. The quantity in brackets is a matrix which may be solved using Reiter's method. In addition, a budget constraint may be placed on the expenditures $c_{ij}$ by utilizing a Lagrangian multiplier, as in Section IV, which may be represented by

Maximize $\qquad X[BP - (1 - \lambda)C]X^t$ (44)

for various values of $\lambda$. We may substitute $\lambda'$ for the term $(1 - \lambda)$ and solve

Maximize $\qquad X[BP - \lambda'C]X^t$ (45)

where

$$BP - \lambda'C = \begin{pmatrix} p_{11}b_1 - \lambda'c_1 & p_{12}b_1 - \lambda'c_{12} & p_{13}b_1 - \lambda'c_{13} \ldots \\ p_{12}b_2 & p_{22}b_2 - \lambda'c_2 & p_{23}b_2 - \lambda'c_{23} \ldots \\ p_{31}b_3 & p_{32}b_3 & p_{33}b_3 - \lambda'c_3 \ldots \\ & & \cdots \end{pmatrix}$$

(46)

Finally, the methods for handling mutually-exclusive projects and mutually independent projects may be combined. Some of the

60. The matrix $C$ is still triangular since terms $c_i$, enter only once.

columns of Eq. (46) would then be as given in matrix Eq. (40), with $p_{rs}$ as defined there, and with terms below the diagonal as defined for Eq. (46).

## B. Nonlinear criterion functions

Nonlinear utility or criterion functions give rise to a host of considerations not present when simple expected value of outcomes maximization serves as the criterion. A brief discussion of some of the issues in the context of R & D project selection will conclude this presentation. As before, we continue to regard the objective of the decision maker to select the set of projects which maximizes expected utility, but the utility function is not linear in the outcomes. For simplicity we shall illustrate our remarks by reference to a quadratic utility function,

$$U(y) = y - \alpha y^2 \qquad (47)$$

recognizing that this criterion is increasingly risk averse in Pratt's sense [39]. For present purposes, however, it is adequate. ($\alpha$ here is a preassigned, hence known and fixed, coefficient of risk aversion.)

The first observation to be made is that the assumption of a static decision procedure, i.e. one which fails to take into account other decisions which have been made in the past and will be made in the future, is no longer tenable. Utility is defined for the entire 'portfolio' of projects, including both the project being considered and those already accepted and in process of being carried out. Consider, under perfect certainty, an existing portfolio of value $y$ and two potential projects, worth $z_1$ and $z_2$. From Eq. (47) we may express the utility of a sum of two outcomes, $y + z$, by

$$U(y + z) = U(y) + U(z) - 2\alpha yz \qquad (48)$$

so that, given $y$, the requirement for acceptance of $z$ is an increase in total utility. Since $y$ is not subject to reduction (unlike the securities portfolio of Markowitz) the condition for acceptability reduces to

$$U(z) > 2\alpha yz \qquad (49)$$

With two potential independent projects with payoffs of $z_1$ and $z_2$, the outcome of a decision procedure based on criterion Eq. (49) alone could depend on the order in which the projects were considered. If project one were taken up first, acceptance of both would require

$$U(z_1) > 2\alpha z_1 y \tag{50a}$$
$$U(z_2) > 2\alpha z_2(y + z_1) = 2\alpha z_2 y + 2\alpha z_1 z_2 \tag{50b}$$

if the first had been accepted. Alternatively, taking up the decision about the second project first requires

$$U(z_2) > 2\alpha z_2 y \tag{51a}$$
$$U(z_1) = 2\alpha z_1(y + z_2) = 2\alpha z_1 y + 2\alpha z_1 z_2 \tag{51b}$$

if the second project had been accepted. Suppose that both projects would be acceptable if they were the only ones being considered, i.e.

$$U(z_1) > 2\alpha z_1 y \tag{52a}$$
$$U(z_2) > 2\alpha z_2 y \tag{52b}$$

but that while
$$U(z_1) > 2\alpha z_1(y + z_2) \tag{53}$$

also
$$U(z_2) < 2\alpha z_2(y + z_1). \tag{54}$$

Given such values of $z_1$, $z_2$, and $y$, the second project would be accepted only if it were taken up first, while this restriction would not apply to the first project.

It is clearly undesirable for a decision procedure to depend on the order in which projects are taken up. Yet, this would be the effect with naive application of a nonlinear utility function.[61] While it is true that both projects $r$ and $s$ would be accepted given the condition of accepting both or neither,[62] maximization of utility would lead to acceptance of project $r$ alone. This may be seen by regarding Eq. (53) as an equation, and rewriting Eq. (52b) as

$$U(z_2) = 2\alpha z_2 y + \epsilon, \qquad \epsilon < 2\alpha z_1 z_2. \tag{55}$$

61. Although these illustrations make use of a quadratic utility function, the conclusion applies to a large variety of nonlinear criterion functions, in particular also to ones which are decreasingly risk averse.

62. $U(y + z_1 + z_2) > U(y)$.

**Financial Decision-Making**

From these one may derive

$$U(y + z_1) \equiv U(y) + U(z_1) - 2\alpha y z_1 = U(y) + 2\alpha z_1 z_2 \quad (56a)$$

$$U(y + z_2) \equiv U(y) + U(z_2) - 2\alpha y z_2 = U(y) + \epsilon$$
$$< U(y) + 2\alpha z_1 z_2 \quad (56b)$$

$$U(y + z_1 + z_2) \equiv U(y) + U(z_1) + U(z_2)$$
$$-2\alpha(y z_1 + y z_2 + z_1 z_2) = U(y) + \epsilon < U(y) + 2\alpha z_1 z_2 \quad (56c)$$

leading to the stated conclusion.

An additional complication when the outcomes are random variables (as they are in the present context) is that $y$ itself, the value of the previously accepted portfolio, is also random. This requires that the joint distribution of the outcomes of present and potential projects must enter the calculations.

In the strictly static case in which selection is to be made so as to maximize the utility of the projects being chosen without regard to past selections, we first derive the criterion for the Markowitz-type of R & D project portfolio consisting only of projects which are not interrelated in the physical sense. Statistical independence however, is not assumed. We begin with two independent projects and generalize from there. Given two projects, $r$ and $s$, with development costs (negative revenues) of $(-c_r)$ and $(-c_s)$, with net present values after successful development of $b_r$ and $b_s$, and with probabilities of $p_{rs}$ of joint success, $(p_r - p_{rs})$ and $(p_s - p_{rs})$ of success on $r$ alone and $s$ alone, respectively, expected utility from acceptance of both projects, $U_{rs}$, is given by

$$U_{rs} = p_{rs}U(b_r - c_r + b_s - c_s) + (p_r - p_{rs})U(b_r - c_r - c_s)$$
$$+ (p_s - p_{rs})U(b_s - c_s - c_r) + (1 - p_r - p_s + p_{rs})U(-c_r - c_s) \quad (57)$$

which simplifies to

$$U_{rs} = U_r + U_s - 2\alpha E_{rs} \quad (58)$$

where
$$U_j = p_j U(b_j - c_j) + (1 - p_j)U(-c_j) \quad (59)$$

and
$$E_{ij} = p_{ij}b_i b_j - p_i b_i c_j - p_j b_j c_i + c_i c_j. \quad [63] \quad (60)$$

Expression Eq. (58) may be generalized to any number of independent projects, so that maximization of expected utility from

63. Note that the term $E_{ij}$ is simply the product of expected outcomes, $(p_i b_i - c_i)(p_j b_j - c_j)$ with the term $p_i p_j b_i b_j$ replaced by $p_{ij}b_i b_j$.

acceptance of a set of projects may be written in terms parallel to model Eq. (23), viz.,

Maximize

$$\sum_{i=1}^{n} U_i x_i - 2\alpha \sum_{i=1}^{n} \sum_{j=i+1}^{n} x_i E_{ij} x_j \tag{61}$$

subject to $\qquad x_i = 0, 1, \qquad i = 1, \ldots, n$

which is once more in a form suitable for solution by Reiter's method, with payoff matrix

$$B = \begin{pmatrix} U_1 & -2\alpha E_{12} & -2\alpha E_{13} \ldots & -2\alpha E_{1n} \\ 0 & U_2 & -2\alpha E_{23} \ldots & -2\alpha E_{2n} \\ 0 & 0 & U_3 & \ldots -2\alpha E_{3n} \\ \ldots\ldots\ldots\ldots\ldots\ldots\ldots\ldots\ldots \\ 0 & 0 & 0 & \ldots \; U_n \end{pmatrix} \tag{62}$$

A budget constraint may be appended here by use of a Lagrangian multiplier.

Unfortunately, the relatively simple structure of Eq. (62) is lost in the face of any number of the project interrelationships already discussed. We single out one of these, the situation in which if parallel research is undertaken and success is achieved on both lines of attack only the project with higher expected payoff[64] is actually carried out. For two such projects, $r$ and $s$, the expression for expected utility corresponding to Eq. (57) is

$$U_{rs} = p_r U(b_r - c_r - c_s) + (p_s - p_{rs})U(b_s - c_s - c_r)$$
$$+ (1 - p_r - p_s + p_{rs})U(-c_r - c_s) \tag{63}$$

which reduces to

$$U_{rs} = U_r + U_s - 2\alpha E_{rs} - p_{rs}[U(b_s) - 2\alpha b_s(b_r - c_r - c_s)]. \tag{64}$$

Adding an independent project, $v$, however, requires introduction of terms involving $p_{rsv}$, the probability of joint success on projects $r$, $s$, and $v$ into $U_{rsv}$, hence losing the important property of separability, which has been the chief characteristic of our models of capital budgeting of interrelated projects.

64. This quantity strictly should be expected utility. However, we can make our point without opening a Pandora's Box of problems of evaluating the utility of future events today, especially without complete knowledge of future outcomes which will obtain then.

## Appendix A: Flow chart of the dynamic programming code for capital budgeting[65]

The program flow-charted was written in MADTRAN[66] with the exception of the strategy vectors and their manipulation. Since these consist of strings of zeros and ones, memory space and time were conserved by programming these in binary arithmetic. The program as written allows for a maximum of 2,000 strategies at each stage and is able to handle ten separate constraints.[67] Cord's problem[68] involving 25 projects was solved in 63 seconds on an IBM 7094. For a rough estimate, this compares with 12 minutes reported by Cord in his application of the Lagrangian multiplier technique, but using an IBM 7070. As pointed out in the text, Cord did not obtain the optimum, and additional time would have been required to reduce the search interval. The program was also tried out on a number of interdependencies, the total number of constraints actually utilized in any one problem was six. Three additional constraints in Cord's problem increased the time utilized to 90 seconds.

The program does its house-keeping on multiple constraints by lexicographically ordering the vectors of payoffs and allocated budgets, weeding out intermediate solutions which are dominated. The definitions used in the flow chart are as follows:

$NN$ = No. of projects in problem

$N(I)$ = No. of strategies at stage $I$

$b_i$ = payoff on project $i$

$LM$ = No. of constraints in problem

$M$ = Maximum number of strategies permitted

$C_j$ = amount of resource of type $j$ available

65. The program was written by Stanley Sachar and David Ness, making use of the time-shared computer of Project MAC, an MIT research program sponsored by the Advanced Research Projects Agency, Department of Defense under the Office of Naval Research.

66. MADTRAN is a language almost identical with FORTRAN which, however, while compiling more rapidly, is generally slower in execution.

67. The maximum number of strategies is variable and must be smaller when ten constraints are employed. As written the computations are entirely in core.

68. Cf. [14, p. 340].

$c_{ij}$ = amount of resource of type $j$ used by project $i$

$b = (b_1, b_2, \ldots b_{NN})$ $c_j = (c_{1j}, c_{2j}, \ldots, c_{NN,j})$

$C = (0, C_1, C_2, \ldots, C_{LM})$

$P(I) = (b_i, -c_{i1}, -c_{i2}, \ldots, -c_{i,LM})$

$R(I) = (b_i, C_1 - c_{i1}, C_2 - c_{i2}, \ldots, C_{LM} - c_{i,LM})$

$X(I) = (0, 0, \ldots, 0, 1, 0, \ldots, 0)$ with 1 in the $i^{th}$ position

$X(J) = j^{th}$ strategy, i.e. a vector of 0's and 1's with 1 in the $i^{th}$ position if $x_i = 1$.

$\Gamma(J)$, $T(J) = (C^t - (-b, c_1, c_2 \ldots, c_{LM})^t [X(J)]^t)^t$, a vector of payoffs and unused resources of the $j^{th}$ strategy. $T(J)$ is a temporary list, $\Gamma(J)$ is the revised list.

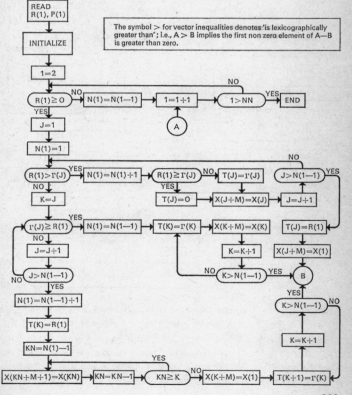

The symbol $>$ for vector inequalities denotes 'is lexicographically greater than'; i.e., $A > B$ implies the first non zero element of $A-B$ is greater than zero.

229

## Appendix B: Example Using Reiter's Discrete Optimizing Method

We seek the optimal list of projects for the following payoff matrix

$$B = \begin{pmatrix} 3 & 0 & 2 & -1 \\ 0 & 2 & 1 & 0 \\ 0 & 0 & -1 & -3 \\ 0 & 0 & 0 & 4 \end{pmatrix} \qquad (A.1)$$

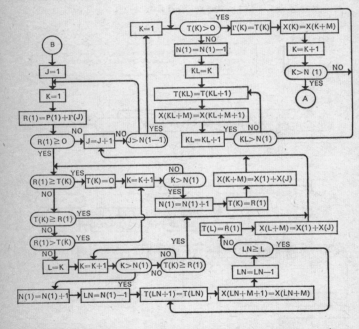

Let the (randomly or otherwise selected) starting in-list $\alpha = \{1, 3, 4\}$; i.e. we begin with a list consisting of projects 1, 3, and 4. Crossing out row 2 and column 2, we add the payoff elements not crossed out: $3 + 2 + (-1) + (-1) + (-3) + 4 = 4$. Therefore the payoff corresponding to this in-list $\alpha$ is $\Gamma_\alpha = 4$. In the table we give the payoffs and gradients $G_{\alpha'} = \Gamma_{\alpha'} - \Gamma_\alpha$ for all in-lists $\alpha'$ 'connected' to $\alpha$ – lists which differ in only a single project index.

| $\alpha'$ | $\Gamma_{\alpha'}$ | $G_{\alpha'}$ |
|---|---|---|
| 1, 3 | 4 | 0 |
| 1, 4 | 6 | 2 |
| 3, 4 | 0 | −4 |
| → 1, 2, 3, 4 | 7 | 3 |

The largest improvement resulting from dropping one project or adding one to the in-list $\alpha = \{1, 3, 4\}$ is 3, which is associated with $\alpha' = \{1, 2, 3, 4\}$. This forms the next starting in-list, which is once again evaluated in the table.

| $\alpha'$ | $\Gamma_{\alpha'}$ | $G_{\alpha'}$ |
|---|---|---|
| 1, 2, 3 | 7 | 0 |
| → 1, 2, 4 | 8 | 1 |
| 1, 3, 4 | 4 | −3 |

Here the largest improvement is associated with the move to $\alpha' = \{1, 2, 4\}$, yielding a total payoff of 8. It may be seen to be a local maximum from the next table, which takes this in-list as the starting point. Only negative values for $G_{\alpha'}$ result.

| $\alpha'$ | $\Gamma_{\alpha'}$ | $G_{\alpha'}$ |
|---|---|---|
| 1, 2 | 5 | −3 |
| 1, 4 | 6 | −2 |
| 1, 2, 3, 4 | 7 | −1 |

The local optimal list $\alpha = \{1, 2, 4\}$ turns out to be the global optimum. The tree-structure of this example is

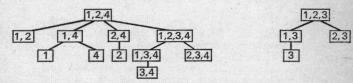

The other local optimum consists of projects 1, 2, 3 with a pay-off of 7. Since the 15 possible lists are divided into two groups of 11 on the tree of the global optimum list (at left) and 4 on the tree

of the local non-global optimum list (at right), the prior odds that a random starting in-list leads to the global optimum here are $\frac{11}{15} = .73$. For further discussion see [42].

## References

1. ADLER, M. 'The Cohen extension to the Sharpe diagonal model for Portfolio selection', unpublished paper, Carnegie Inst. Tech., 15 May 1963, revised and corrected by K. J. Cohen.

2. ALCHIAN, A. A. (1955) 'The rate of interest, Fisher's rate of return over cost, and Keynes' internal rate of return', *Am. Econ. Rev.* 938–42; also in Solomon, [44].

3. ASHER, D. T. (1962) 'A linear programming model for the allocation of R and D efforts', *IRE Trans. on Eng. Management*, 154–7.

4. BALINSKI, M. L. (1964) *On finding integer solutions to linear programs.* Princeton: Mathematica.

5. BAUMOL, W. J., and QUANDT, R. E. (1965) 'Mathematical programming and the discount rate under capital rationing', *Econ. J.* 317–29.

6. BELLMAN, R. (1957) 'Comment on Dantzig's paper on discrete variable extremum problems, *Operations Res.*, 723–4.

7. BELLMAN, R., and DREYFUS, S. (1962) *Applied dynamic programming.* Princeton Univ. Press.

8. ISRAEL, A. BEN, and CHARNES, A. (1962) 'On some problems of diophantine programming', *Cahiers du Centre de l'Recherche Operationelle*, 215–80.

9. CHARNES, A., and COOPER, W. W. (1959) 'Chance-constrained programming', *Management Sci.*, 73–9.

10. CHARNES, A., and COOPER, W. W. (1961) *Management models and Industrial applications of linear programming.* Wiley.

10a. CHARNES, A., and COOPER, W. W. (1965) 'A note on the "fail-safe" properties of the "generalized Langrange multiplier method" ', *Operations Res.*, 673–7.

11. CHARNES, A., COOPER, W. W., and MILLER, M. H. (1959) 'Application of linear programming to financial budgeting and the costing of funds', *J. Business*, 20–46: also in Solomon, [44].

12. CHARNES, A. and THORE, S. (1964) 'Planning for liquidity in savings and loan associations', ONR Research Memorandum No. 95. Evanston: Northwestern Univ. Tech. Inst.

13. COHEN, K. J., and FITCH, B. P. (1965) 'The average investment performance index', Working paper No. 3, workshop on capital market equilibrating processes. Pittsburgh: Carnegie Inst. Tech., Graduate School of Industrial Administration.

14. CORD, J. (1964) 'A method for allocating funds to investment projects when returns are subject to uncertainty', *Management Sci.* 335–41.

15. DANTZIG, G. B. (1957) 'Discrete variable extremum problems', *Operations Res.* 266–77.

16. DANTZIG, G. B. (1965) 'Linear programming under uncertainty', *Management Sci.*, 197–206.

17. DEAN, JOEL (1951) *Capital budgeting*. Columbia Univ.

18. DYCKMAN, T. R. (1964) 'Allocating funds to investment projects when returns are subject to uncertainty – a comment', *Management Sci.* 348–50.

18a. EASTMAN, W. L. (1965) 'Allocating funds to investment projects when returns are subject to uncertainty: a further comment', *Management Sci.*

19. EVERETT, H., III (1963) 'Generalized Lagrange multiplier method for solving problems of optimum allocation of resources', *Operations Res.*, 399–417.

19a. EVERETT, H. (1965) 'Comments on the preceding note', *Operations Res.* 677–8.

20. FARRAR, D. E. (1962) *The investment decision under uncertainty*. Prentice-Hall, Englewood Cliffs.

21. FISHER, IRVING (1930) *The theory of interest*. Macmillan, New York.

22. GILMORE, P. C. and GOMORY, R. E. (1963) 'A linear programming approach to the cutting stock problem – part II', *Operations Res.*, 863–88.

23. GLOVER, F. (1965) 'The knapsack problem: some relations for an improved algorithm', Management Sci. Res. Rep. No. 38. Pittsburgh: Carnegie Inst. Tech., Graduate School of Industrial Administration.

24. GRAVES, R. and WOLFE, R. (eds.) (1963) *Recent advances in mathematical programming*. McGraw-Hill, New York.

25. HALDI, J. and ISAACSON, L. (1964) 'A linear integer programming Code', paper presented at the 1964 Annual Meeting of the Econometric Society, Chicago.

26. HERTZ, D. B. (1964) 'Risk analysis in capital investment', *Harvard Business Rev.*, 95–106.

27. HILLIER, F. (1963) 'Derivation of probabilistic information for the evaluation of risky investments', *Management Sci.* 443–57.

28. HIRSHLEIFER, J. (1964) 'Efficient allocation of capital in an uncertain world', *Am. Econ. Rev.*, 77–85.

29. HIRSHLEIFER, J. (1958) 'On the theory of optimal investment', *J. Pol. Econ.*, 329–52; also in Solomon, [44].

30. KEYNES, J. M. (1936) *The general theory of employment, money and interest*. London.

31. KUNZI, H. P. and OETTLI, W. (1936) 'Integer quadratic programming', in Graves and Wolfe, [24].

32. LORIE, J. H. and SAVAGE, L. J. (1955) 'Three problems in rationing capital', *J. Business*, 229–39; also in Solomon, [44].

33. LUCE, D. and RAIFFA, H. (1958) *Games and decisions*. Wiley, New York.

34. MARGLIN, S. (1963) *Approaches to dynamic investment planning.* North Holland Publishing Co., Amsterdam.

35. MARKOWITZ, H. M. (1959) *Portfolio selection.* Wiley, New York.

36. MARTIN, G. T. 'An accelerated euclidean algorithm for integer linear programming', in [24], pp. 311–18.

37. NÄSLUND, B. (1965) 'A model of capital budgeting under risk', Department of Forestry Products, Royal College of Forestry (Sweden), (Mimeo).

38. NÄSLUND, B. (1964) 'Decisions under risk: economic applications of chance constrained programming', ONR Res. Memorandum No. 114, Management Sci. Res. Group. Carnegie Inst. Tech., Graduate School of Industrial Administration, Pittsburgh.

39. PRATT, J. W. (1964) 'Risk aversion in the small and in the large'. *Econometrica,* 122–36.

40. REITER, S. (1963) 'Choosing an investment program among interdependent projects', *Rev. Econ. Studies,* 32–6.

41. REITER, S. and SHERMAN, G. (1962) 'Allocating indivisible resources affording external economies or diseconomies', *Int. Econ. Rev.,* 108–35.

42. REITER, S. and SHERMAN, G. 'Discrete optimizing', Inst. for Quantitative Res. in Economics and Management, Paper 37, Krannert Graduate School of Industrial Administration, Purdue University.

43. SHARPE, WILLIAM F. (1963) 'A simplified model of portfolio selection', *Management Sci.,* 277–93.

44. SOLOMON, E. (ed.) (1959) *The management of corporate capital.* The Free Press, Glencoe.

45. WEINGARTNER, H. MARTIN (1963) 'The excess present value index – a theoretical basis and critique', *J. Accounting Res.,* 213–24.

46. WEINGARTNER, H. MARTIN (1963) *Mathematical programming and the analysis of capital budgeting problems.* Prentice-Hall, Englewood Cliffs.

47. YOUNG, R. D. (1964) 'A primal (all integer) integer programming algorithm: antecedents, description, proof of finiteness, exemplification', Working Paper No. 52. Stanford Univ. Grad. School of Business.

# Part Four Production and Inventory Systems

Important applications of quantitative methods have also taken place in the areas of production scheduling, sales forecasting, inventory management, and the scheduling and control of large project. The Dzielinski–Baker–Manne paper is an example of the use of linear programming and simulation in the economic planning of lot sizes, work force, and inventories.

The authors employ certain sales forecasting techniques, which are not described in detail. For additional information it is suggested that the reader pursue the references to the exponential and statistical forecasting techniques cited in this paper.

The critical path scheduling method was developed to assist in the planning, scheduling, and control of large projects. The MacCrimmon–Ryavec paper describes how PERT works. In addition they analyse the assumptions upon which this technique is based, and note the conditions under which it is most suitably applied.

# 8 B. P. Dzielinski, C. T. Baker, and A. S. Manne

## Simulation Tests of Lot Size Programming

B. P. Dzielinski, C. T. Baker, and A. S. Manne (1963) 'Simulation tests of lot size programming', *Management Science*, 9, 229–58.

## Introduction

We consider the following production planning problem. Given a forecast of the demand for each product over a finite horizon of discrete planning periods, determine, for all component parts, the optimum number of parts to make on each manufacturing order, and the planning period in which to place each order so that the total variable cost of operations is minimized. The planning procedure should take the following costs into account: setup costs, inventory costs, shortage or stockout costs, regular and overtime labor costs, and hiring and firing costs.

In the case of some metal parts fabricating industries, such production planning problems may become intractable because of the large number of different parts involved. Each part competes in different ways for the available production equipment and work force; also each has future orders that are of a dynamic uncertain nature. Usually each part can satisfy requirements from one of several alternative production sequences, and here is where the difficulty arises: matching the sequences for individual items so as to remain within the over-all limitations on equipment and work force availability.

The purpose of this paper is to show how to adapt to this dynamic, uncertain environment through a deterministic programming method proposed by A. S. Manne [1]. The study involved a simulation test of a scaled-down metal fabrication plant, utilizing a linear programming model as the tool for planning production for the component parts over a multi-period planning horizon. Because of the dynamic, uncertain environment only the initial step of each programming solution was assumed to be implemented. At the end of each period newer information on orders, etc., was obtained, the simulation program reformulated the planning task so that newer solutions were computed and implemented as before; and, the planned activity was updated period-by-period, using new information as it became available.

The linear programming model consists of making lot size decisions simultaneously for each part, where each part could be produced from one of several production schedules. For realistically large numbers of parts, this resulted in a computing bottleneck as of 1960. Therefore, for this study, a small number of parts were defined from a sample of data collected in an actual manufacturing process. These data were used throughout the simulation tests.

As a bench-mark for the method considered here, a standard Economic Order Quantity model was also simulated. The standard *EOQ* formula assumes that no significant interactions exist between the choice of optimal lot size for the many items produced in a plant. This model was preferred for comparison purposes for the following reasons: (1) comparison with actual past operations would be difficult and expensive to obtain; (2) the *EOQ* system could inexpensively simulate the individual items so that in effect it provided a check on the parts aggregation developed for the linear programming model; and (3) it is a familiar technique in industrial engineering practice.


The Factory Model

For our purposes, we regard this study as being comprised of a planning model for a scaled-down fabrication shop that was observed in actual operation. This plant supplied manufactured parts to an inventory. In turn this inventory satisfied the demands of an assembly shop, that is it served as the buffer between the two shops.

The scaling-down amounted to planning production for a sample of products; the demands for component parts were determined directly from the demands for the products. Independent demands were not part of these component part demands. The machine facilities were combined into a lesser number $K$ of facility types, and finally the adjustments on the plant capacities were made to conform with this scaling procedure.

Therefore we can discuss the simulation model in terms of a sketch (Fig. 1).

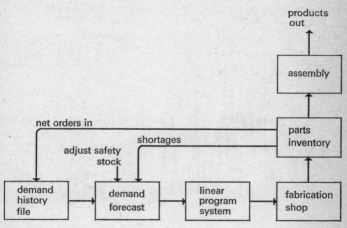

Figure 1

The net orders for each product were received and accumulated in the order history file. At the end of each period these data were extrapolated to produce a forecast of net orders for each product for each of several future time periods. The inventory required for each period was then augmented by a safety stock allowance, in recognition of the dynamic uncertain nature of the problem. Furthermore, if the forecasts revealed either an increasing or a decreasing trend, adjustments were made either to increase or to decrease the safety stock allowance accordingly through the several future periods of the forecast. If for example, the forecast for one product in some month was for nine net orders and the policy was to hold a one-month safety stock allowance, then the inventory requirement consisted of 18 net orders altogether. In addition to the safety stock allowance, the inventory requirements were augmented by the amount of any backlogs carried over from the preceding period.

239

The forecast was made by extrapolating the past data on the net orders received, using the following method described by Brown [2, 3].

$\hat{S}(t + \tau)$, the forecast of the net orders received at a time $\tau$ units in the future, is given by

$$\hat{S}(t + \tau) = \bar{S}(t) + \bar{b}(t)[1/\alpha + \tau - 1], \qquad 0 < \alpha < 1, \quad (1)$$

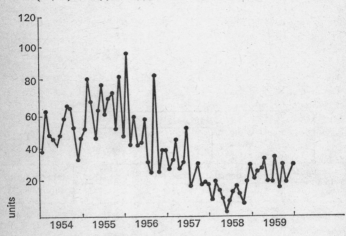

Figure 2 Net orders received by months for six years.

where $\bar{S}(t)$ and $\bar{b}(t)$ are the estimates at time $t$ of the average of the net orders received and the trend in these orders, respectively. $\bar{S}(t)$ and $\bar{b}(t)$ are obtained from the following relations

$$\bar{S}(t) = \alpha S(t) + (1 - \alpha)\bar{S}(t - 1), \quad \text{and} \quad (2)$$

$$\bar{b}(t) = \alpha[S(t) - \bar{S}(t - 1)] + (1 - \alpha)\bar{b}(t - 1), \quad (3)$$

where $S(t)$ is the number of net orders actually received in period $t$.

Several values of $\alpha$ were tested with net order data taken from an operating firm for 1954 and 1955. The analysis showed that a value of $\alpha = 0.1$ provided the minimum forecasting error, when forecasting one month into the future. In order to avoid the benefit of hindsight, no direct use was made of the 1954–5 data in the subsequent experiments.

240

More explicitly, the adjusted net requirements for the $i^{\text{th}}$ part at time $t + \tau$ could be expressed directly from the product forecasts as follows:

$$r_{i1} = (1 + \lambda)\hat{S}_i(t + 1) - y_i(t + 1) \qquad \tau = 1$$
$$r_{i\tau} = \hat{S}_i(t + \tau) \qquad\qquad\qquad \tau = 2, 3, \ldots T \quad (4)$$

where $r_{i\tau}$ were the net requirements; $\hat{S}_i(t + \tau)$ was the basic forecast; $\lambda$ was the safety stock factor; and $y_i(t + 1)$ was the initial inventory (or backlog, if negative) for period $t + 1$.

## The Linear Programming System

The formulation of this production planning problem in linear programming terms is similar to that given by Manne in [1]. However, certain variations and approximations were made in order to gain computing feasibility with the linear programming codes in existence as of 1960. These differences are described later.

One important aspect of the formulation in [1] is its ability to take setup costs into account. By their very nature, these costs appear to preclude the use of linear programming. However, setup costs may be taken into account through the use of activities related to alternative possible *production sequences*. A *production sequence* for one part over a planning horizon of $T$ periods is a sequence of $T$ non-negative integers that specify the quantities of that part that are to be produced in each of the $T$ periods. (A zero quantity may be specified in some of these periods.) The specified requirements for the part during $T$ periods can be satisfied by a number of different setup sequences, i.e. lot-splitting plans. However, because of certain 'dominance' considerations, not all of the possible sequences need be considered. [1, 4] The function of the linear programming computations is to select the optimal combination of production sequences for all of the parts in the system over the entire planning period.

The $r_{i\tau}$ coefficients defined in the preceding section constituted the inputs to the lot size programming computations. From their values the setup sequences were generated according to the rules in Appendix A.3.

The output of the linear programming computations is a set of

241

production orders for the parts to be fabricated in order to satisfy the inventory and sales requirements. This computation indicates whether or not the required number of pieces for a part should be made in one batch, two batches, or more. It also determines the batch size $s$ and the period in which they should be made. These decisions are made so that the total *discounted* cost of future operations is minimized. The minimand was composed of all cost elements previously mentioned, with just one exception – the shortage costs. These costs were not recognized explicitly within the linear programming model. However, the dollar value of these shortages was recorded separately, once each period, as the simulation progressed.

The simulation was conducted as though the linear programming solution for the immediate planning period was actually released to the fabrication shop as a set of orders for production during that period. The remainder of the solution that pertained to the subsequent periods was ignored, and a new linear programming computation using the revised sales information was performed between each period's operation. It was assumed that all orders released for production at the start of a period were completed by the end of that period and sent immediately to the parts inventory and were available at the end of that period to satisfy the demand for them. Thus the problem of detailed scheduling or optimum sequencing of the jobs through the various facilities was not considered in this experiment. Finally, backlogs were regarded as occurring only when an insufficient number of parts were on hand to completely satisfy all the current demands and prior backlogs.

The unknowns, coefficients, and constants for the linear programming formulation were defined as follows.

(a) Unknowns

$\theta_{ij}$      fraction of the total requirement for the $i^{th}$ part produced with the $j^{th}$ alternative setup sequence.

$$(i = 1, 2, \ldots, I), \qquad (j = 1, 2, \ldots, J).$$

$W^1_{kr}$      number of workers assigned to first-shift operations on facility $k$ during period $(t + \tau)$; *no overtime*

$$(k = 1, 2, \ldots, K), \qquad (\tau = 1, 2, \ldots, T).$$

$W^2_{kr}$     number of workers assigned to first-shift *overtime* operations on facility $k$ during period $(t + \tau)$; each of these workers works a fixed number of straight time and overtime hours during the period.

$W^3_{kr}$     number of workers assigned to second-shift operations on facility $k$ during period $(t + \tau)$; *no overtime*.

$W^4_{kr}$     number of workers assigned to second-shift *overtime* operations on facility $k$ during period $(t + \tau)$; each of these workers works a fixed number of straight time and overtime hours during the period.

$D^+W_{kr}$     increase in the total number of workers employed at facility $k$ from period $(t + \tau - 1)$ to period $(t + \tau)$.

$D^-W_{kr}$     decrease in the total number of workers employed at facility $k$ from period $(t + \tau - 1)$ to period $(t + \tau)$.

**(b) Parameters recalculated each period**

$L_{ijkr}$     labor input required during period $(t + \tau)$ to carry out the $j^{\text{th}}$ alternative setup sequence on the $k^{\text{th}}$ facility for part $i$.

$$L_{ijkr} = \begin{Bmatrix} 0 \\ a_{ik} + b_{ik}x_{ijr} \end{Bmatrix} \text{ when } x_{ijr} \begin{Bmatrix} =0 \\ >0 \end{Bmatrix}$$

where $a_{ik}$ and $b_{ik}$ refer, respectively, to the standard labor setup time and the standard unit running time for the $i^{\text{th}}$ part on the $k^{\text{th}}$ facility. The numbers $x_{ijr}$ refer to the amount of part $i$ required by sequence $j$ during period $\tau$. These numbers define the alternative production sequences. They are generated from the requirement forecasts $r_{i\tau}$ according to the rules given in Appendix A.3.

**(c) Constants**

$W_k$     maximum number of workers that can be assigned to facility $k$ during a single shift.

$H^1$     total number of first-shift hours per period, excluding overtime.

$H^2$     total number of first-shift hours per period, including a fixed amount of overtime.

243

$H^3$      total number of second-shift hours per period, excluding overtime.

$H^4$      total number of second-shift hours per period, including a fixed amount of overtime.

$R^1{}_{k\tau}$      first-shift wage for facility $k$, no overtime; discounted over $\tau$ periods.

$R^2{}_{k\tau}$      first-shift wage for facility $k$, with overtime; discounted over $\tau$ periods.

$R^3{}_{k\tau}$      second-shift wage for facility $k$, no overtime; discounted over $\tau$ periods.

$R^4{}_{k\tau}$      second-shift wage for facility $k$, with overtime; discounted over $\tau$ periods.

$\Gamma_{0\tau}$      cost of laying off one worker; discounted over $\tau$ periods.

$\Gamma_{h\tau}$      cost of hiring one worker; discounted over $\tau$ periods.

$c_{i\tau}$      unit material cost of part $i$; discounted over $\tau$ periods.

The linear programming problem was stated as follows:

$$\text{Min} \sum_{i,k,r} \left\{ \sum_{r=1}^{4} [R^r{}_{kr} W^r{}_{kr} + \Gamma_{0r} D^- W_{kr} + \Gamma_{hr} D^+ W_{kr}] + \sum_j \theta_{ij} c_r x_{ijr} \right\}$$

subject to:

$$\sum_j \theta_{ij} = 1 \qquad i = 1 \ldots I \quad \text{(A)}$$

$$\sum_{i,j} L_{ijk\tau} \theta_{ij} \leqq \sum_{r=1}^{4} H^\tau W^\tau{}_{\tau k} \qquad \begin{aligned} k &= 1 \ldots K \\ \tau &= 1 \ldots T \end{aligned} \quad \text{(B)}$$

$$\sum_{r=1}^{4} W^\tau{}_{k\tau} = \sum_{r=1}^{4} W^\tau{}_{k,\tau-1} + D^+ W_{k\tau} - D^- W_{k\tau} \qquad \begin{aligned} k &= 1 \ldots K \\ \tau &= 1 \ldots T \end{aligned} \quad \text{(C)}$$

$$\begin{aligned} W^1{}_{k\tau} + W^2{}_{k\tau} &\leqq W_k \\ W^3{}_{k\tau} + W^4{}_{k\tau} &\leqq W_k \end{aligned} \qquad \begin{aligned} k &= 1 \ldots K \\ \tau &= 1 \ldots T \end{aligned} \quad \text{(D)}$$

and $\qquad \theta_{ij}, \ W^\tau{}_k, \ D^+ W_{k\tau}, \ D^- W_{k\tau}, \quad \text{all} \geqq 0.$

There are $I$ equations in group A. These restrictions specify that the total planned requirements for each part must be satisfied by a convex combination of the admissible production sequences. Values for the unknowns $\theta_{ij}$ usually turn out to be either 0 or 1. Manne [1] proves that there will be no more than a small number of instances – here, $KT$ items – for which the $\theta_{ij}$ may take on proper fractional values. The fractional $\theta_{ij}$ were given the following physical interpretation in this simulation experiment, assuming a solution with just two such proper fractions $\theta_{i1}$ and $\theta_{i2}$:

| period, $\tau$ | 1 | 2 | 3 | |
|---|---|---|---|---|
| requirements, $i_\tau$ | 10 | 8 | 9 | |
| production sequence 1 | 18 | 0 | 9 | $\theta_{i1} = 0.40$ |
| production sequence 2 | 10 | 17 | 0 | $\theta_{i2} = 0.60$ |
| .40 production sequence 1 | 7.2 | 0 | 3.6 | |
| .60 production sequence 2 | 6 | 10.2 | 0 | |
| total (rounded) | 13 | 10 | 4 | |

The resulting sequence, (13, 10, 4), although a physically feasible one, could not have been generated by the rules given in Appendix A.3. In fact, this sequence violates a 'dominance theorem' which states that the only sequences that need to be considered within a lot size programming model are as follows: those in which the delivery requirements are fully satisfied out of production from the *nearest* preceding period in which setup costs for that item are incurred [1, 4].

There are $KT$ inequations in group B. These inequations ensure that the total capacity of machine group $k$ during period $\tau$ will be sufficient to produce the assigned work load.

There are $KT$ equations in group C. These are simply the balance equations that relate the size of the work force from one period to the next. Note that the initial work force availability is predetermined prior to each lot size programming calculation.

There are 2 $KT$ inequations in group D. These inequations limit the number of workers that can be assigned to machine group $k$ in period $\tau$ for both the first and second shifts.

The linear programming model was formulated for carrying inventories for anticipated usage beyond the stated planning horizon. However, this feature was not tested in these experiments. The effects of inventory holding costs were not considered explicitly in the minimand of the programming formulation but they entered through the discounting of labor and puchased raw material costs.

*Approximations in the linear programming system*

There are a total of $I + 4KT$ constraining equations in the linear programming formulation. The sample of data on four final products gathered from the metal fabricating plant was composed of 950 fabricated component parts. There were 13 groups of machine tools in the plant's fabrication shop. Thus, with $I = 950$ and $K = 13$ there were far more constraining equations than could be accommodated within any currently available linear programming code. It was apparent that further reductions and approximations would be required in order to reduce the number of restraining equations to a manageable level.

The first step was to restrict the planning horizon to three periods. Then the thirteen machine groups were combined into two larger groups. A correlation analysis of the manufacturing data for the 950 fabricated component parts revealed a high positive correlation in the use of machine groups, and this provided the basis for defining just two major machine groups. These changes gave a value of $4KT = 24$, to which the $I$ equations for the component parts had to be added.

In order to make these simulation tests, it was desirable to simulate many months of sales history. Since one- and two-month planning periods were used, this required making dozens of linear programming computations within a reasonable amount of computing time. From these considerations, it appeared that a system with 60–70 restraining equations should be employed. We obtained such a system by defining a set of 35 aggregate parts which were used in place of the original 950 fabricated component parts. This put $I = 35$ which, with $4KT = 24$, gave a 59 equation system. One further consideration added somewhat to the size of the linear programming matrix. Although the model was set up in terms of a two-shift maximum operation, a 'third shift' with higher costs and with unlimited machining capacity was also defined. This 'third shift' provided a safety valve to by-pass the total infeasibility that could have arisen from large up-swings in the requirements during certain peak demand periods. In order to provide a bookkeeping record of this factor, 12 more restraint equations were occasionally added to the model.

Since the defined aggregate parts consisted of two or more

component parts, there arose a problem with regard to the component parts that were used in more than one distinct product. Unless this physical aspect of the problem was recognized, difficulties would arise in deriving the demand for the aggregate parts from the demands for the products. Also, other difficulties could arise in relating the quantities of the aggregate part to the quantities of the individual parts in the inventories.

In order to avoid the difficulties of common usage of component parts, a set of pseudo-products were defined as follows: Consider the four basic products A, B, C, D, and every possible combination of them – AB, AC, AD, BC, BD, CD, ABC, BCD, ACD, ABCD. These defined every possible way that an individual part could be used in common among four products. Each such possibility was called a pseudo-product. We then computed the number of labor hours needed for each pseudo-product in order to produce one unit of each parent product. It was found that only two of the eleven possible pseudo-products were of any significant magnitude. Therefore, the system was regarded as being comprised of six products; four actual and two pseudo. The individual parts for the four final products were separated into these size categories, and within each category, a number of aggregate parts were defined.

In defining the aggregate parts, three attributes of the component parts were taken into consideration: setup time, unit running time, and the unit raw material cost. These attributes appeared important because of their role in the linear programming computations. An aggregate part was defined as a collection of component parts entering into the identical final product and having similar values for their machining times and material costs.

The number of aggregate parts categories assigned to each product was determined by the relative production volume of the product, based upon a ten-month sample of the actual sales data. Thus, more categories were assigned to products having relatively high volumes of production. The number of categories was assigned as follows:

| product A | 11 | product D | 5 |
|-----------|----|-----------|---|
| product B | 6 | pseudo I | 4 |
| product C | 6 | pseudo II | 3 |

For each aggregate part, the standard setup time for each machine group was the sum of the setup times in that machine group for all of the individual parts. Similarly, the standard unit running times per machine group and the unit raw material costs were the sums of the unit running times and unit costs for all of the individual parts in the aggregate part. The two latter sums reflected any multiple use of a part on a product. In other words, the simulation proceeded as though the production rates, and inventory levels were identical for each individual part belonging to a given aggregate.

## The *EOQ* System

The use of the typical *EOQ* formula as a tool to control production and inventories is well documented [5, 6]. The formula balances setup costs against inventory carrying costs in order to determine the economic order quantity. The balance point between the two costs is then determined by classical calculus methods, assuming a constant rate of future demand. This procedure usually ignores any effects of the lot size decision upon the plant's labor costs, overtime premium, shift pay differentials, and hiring and firing costs. (See Appendix A.2.)

As in the *LP* system, the *EOQ* system may be described with the aid of the sketch opposite. The net orders received accumulate in the historical file. Once each period these data are used to prepare a forecast of sales for each product for one period in the future. (This was the same forecasting method as was used in the linear programming tests.) The forecast of each product was in turn a forecast for each component part of that product. The forecasts for period $t + 1$ were then used as the constant rates of demand, $r_i$, for the component parts in the *EOQ* calculations.

At the beginning of each period if the inventory level for the $i^{th}$ part was forecast to be less than the safety stock allowance at the end of period $t$, an $EOQ_i$ was computed for the $i^{th}$ part. This $EOQ_i$ was augmented to produce the final order size, $q_i$ for the $i^{th}$ part

$$q_i = EOQ_i + \lambda r_i - y_i(t + 1)$$

where $\lambda$ is the safety stock control parameter ($0 \leq \lambda$), $r_i$ is interpreted as a constant future demand rate, and $y_i(t + 1)$ is the inventory on hand (or the backlog) for the $i^{th}$ part. The fabrication shop was then instructed to produce a batch of size $q_i$ for the $i^{th}$ part in period $t + 1$. At the end of each period, all of the parts needed to fill the current orders on hand plus any backlog orders from the previous period were subtracted from the current

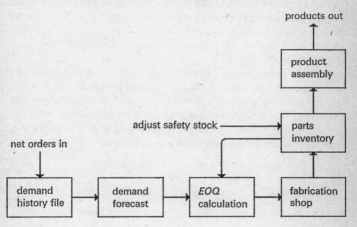

Figure 3

production and the previous inventory, and a new inventory (or backlog) level was calculated. The inventory levels of all the component parts were then tested to see if the current safety stock level had been reached. If so, the part was listed for production in the following period.

In these *EOQ* tests, we assumed that the size of the work force was re-adjusted each period according to the production requirements. Overtime costs, extra shift payments, and hiring and layoff costs were incurred – in descending order of preference – as required by the production load and the machine capacities.

Measures of Performance

Since the *EOQ* system was used as a basis for appraising the linear programming system, the same measures of performance were recorded in the simulation tests for both systems. The several

249

summary measures recorded for this purpose were the total undiscounted operating costs, which included inventory holding costs, and all labor costs (straight, overtime, and shift premium, and changeover costs). No dollar cost was imputed to shortages. However, the total dollar volume of the individual part shortages was recorded. In addition, the dollar amount of the inventory on hand at the end of each period was recorded, along with the size of the work force at each facility.

### Discussion of the results

Four tests were conducted with the linear programming ($LP$) and $EOQ$ systems. The $LP$ problem, as formulated in this paper, was solved each time by the SCROL system available on the IBM 704. The $EOQ$ system was also simulated on the 704.

A general $LP$ problem matrix is shown in Fig. 11, page 268. The parameters in the four tests are as follows:

$T$ = maximum number of planning periods = 3
$\lambda$ = safety stock factor = 0 or 1
$m$ = production months in each planning period = 1 or 2.

| Test one: | Test two: |
|---|---|
| $T = 3$ | $T = 3$ |
| $\lambda = 0$ | $\lambda = 1$ |
| $m = 1$ | $m = 1$ |

| Test three: | Test four: |
|---|---|
| $T = 3$ | $T = 3$ |
| $\lambda = 0$ | $\lambda = 1$ |
| $m = 2$ | $m = 2$ |

The simulation tests were conducted over the late 1956 and complete 1957 demand history of the firm. The total demand pattern for this period on the four final products is shown in Fig. 4. Each test was started with identical initial inventories and initial work-force levels related to the average demand from previous periods. The cost data recorded for comparison here include the effect of these initial conditions.

Fig. 5 summarizes the difference between the two systems for three and six production months in the planning horizon and for two safety stock levels. Two measures of performance are plotted here: the dollar volume of backlogs and the undiscounted operating costs. These data indicate a substantial advantage for the *LP* over the *EOQ* system, a two-to-one difference in total cost at comparable backlog volumes.

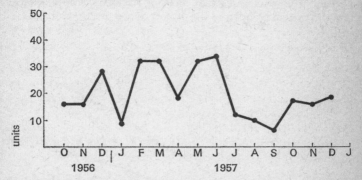

Figure 4 Net orders received by months – four products total.

As might be expected, increasing the safety stock increases the operating costs, but decreases the backlog dollar volume and increasing the number of production months in each planning period has a favorable effect on total operating costs for the *LP* system.

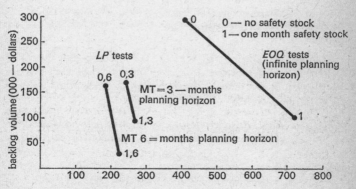

Figure 5 Relationship between backlogs and dollar volume of labor and inventory costs.

## Production and Inventory Systems

Figs. 6, 7, and 8 show the detailed comparison of undiscounted operating costs, inventory levels, and undiscounted labor costs between the two systems. The undiscounted operating costs are plotted as an accumulated time series over the simulated test period. Fig. 7 indicates that most of the savings obtained by the *LP* system come from the inventory cost component.

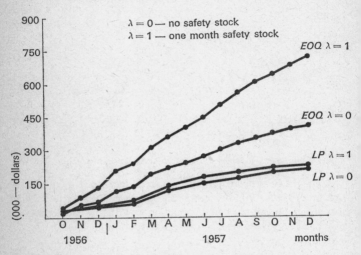

Figure 6 Accumulated total operating costs (labor and inventory) for *E O Q* and *L P* systems with two production months per planning period.

It must be remembered that the *LP* system, like the *EOQ* system, is making lot size decisions, but that these decisions are performed in a different context. For instance, the ordinary *EOQ* formula states:

$$EOQ = \sqrt{\left[\frac{2(\text{usage rate})(\text{hours per setup})(\text{wage rate})}{\rho(\text{hours/unit})(\text{wage rate}) + \rho(\text{material cost/unit})}\right]}$$

$$= \sqrt{\left[\frac{2(\text{usage rate})(\text{hours/setup})}{\rho(\text{hours/unit}) + \rho \dfrac{(\text{material cost/unit})}{\text{wage rate}}}\right]}$$

where $\rho$ represents the cost per unit of capital for one period.

252

Note how the *EOQ* decision rule is based upon the assumption of a constant wage rate from period to period. On the other hand, when the *LP* system makes its decision, the implicit labor cost varies with the relative scarcity, and this in turn affects the choice of lot sizes for the parts. For instance, during the upswing in the

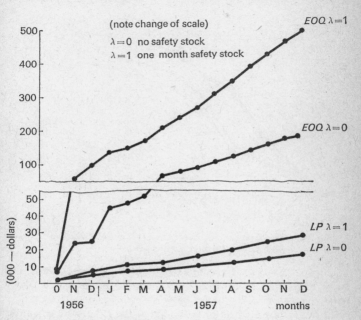

Figure 7 Accumulated inventory holding costs for *E O Q* and *L P* systems with two production months per period.

business cycle, implicit labor costs are higher, and hence the batch-size will be increased in order to save on labor costs. During the down-swing of the business cycle the implicit labor costs are lower, and hence shorter batches are produced. The *LP* system then tends to produce on a hand-to-mouth basis. Thus due to the consideration of hiring and firing costs within the linear programming model, large lots are produced during the upswings and small ones during downswings. These lot size adjustments

253

tend to reduce fluctuations in the plant's own work force, but accentuate the fluctuations in demand for materials produced by the plant's suppliers. What is best for the individual plant is not inevitably the best policy from the viewpoint of the economy taken as a whole.

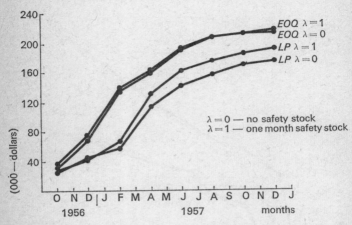

Figure 8 Accumulated labor costs for the *E O Q* and *L P* systems by months – with two production months per period.

Figure 8 shows the accumulated total labor costs, that is, the sum of straight time labor, overtime and shift premium labor, and changeover costs. In the *EOQ* system the safety stock policy had little effect upon these costs, but in the *LP* system when the one-month safety stock factor was introduced, the labor costs were increased about 8 per cent.

This figure indicates a labor cost advantage for the *LP* system of from 12 to 18 per cent over the *EOQ* system, depending upon whether costs are compared to the higher or lower accumulated cost line.

Note also from Fig. 8 that the labor costs for the *LP* system did not accumulate as rapidly in time as they did for the *EOQ* system. If the present values of these operating systems were computed by applying a present worth factor to these costs, a still more favorable comparison with the *LP* system would be evident.

254

In Fig. 9, the accumulated dollar volume of parts shortages is plotted over the same test period. In this measure, the effect of the safety stock factor is obvious – regardless of the system making lot size decisions. However, in the *LP* system the movement from a zero safety stock to a safety stock equal to one month's

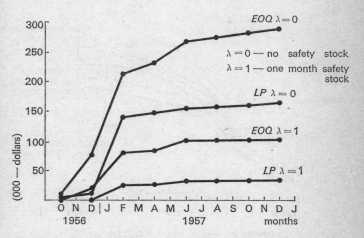

Figure 9 Accumulated dollar volume of parts backlogs for the *E O Q* and *L P* systems by months with two production months per planning period.

expected demand caused a reduction in accumulated shortages by factor of 5 to 1. Employing the same change in the *EOQ* system, the accumulated shortages were reduced by a factor 2.8 to 1. (This result was unexpected and may be the result of sampling only a short time series of backlogs.)

In summary, when the *LP* system was employed to make lot size decisions for six production months within the three-period planning horizon and when it is compared to a similar *EOQ* system without any safety stocks, the *LP* system is favoured by a factor of 11 to 1 with respect to inventory holding costs; accumulated labor costs are approximately 12 per cent lower; and accumulated dollar volume of parts shortages are lower by a factor of 1.7 to 1. When the safety stock factor is set equivalent to a month's expected demand, the inventory holding costs are lower by a factor of 17 to 1; accumulated labor costs are lower by 21 per cent; and the accumulated dollar volume of parts shortages are lower by a factor of 3 to 1 for the *LP* system over the fifteen-month simulation test period.

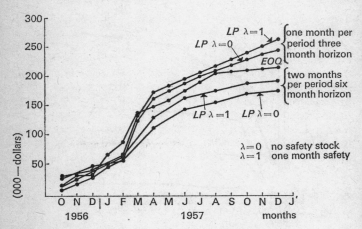

Figure 10 Accumulated labor costs for the *E O Q* and *L P* systems by months – with one and two production months per planning period for the *L P* systems.

A companion set of tests was performed when a single production month was assigned to a planning period. That is reviews and decisions were made each month and production was planned over only three months in the future. These tests still indicate a favorable performance for the *LP* system when inventory holding costs and dollar volume of parts shortages are compared, but not so when accumulated labor costs are compared. Figure 10 shows cumulative labor costs for the *LP* system when three and six production months are considered in the planning horizon, and compares these with a single *EOQ* system measure of accumulated labor costs.

This figure indicates that restricting the length of the planning horizon from six to three months increased the accumulated labor costs of the *LP* system from 36 to 38 per cent. Even crediting the savings in inventory holding costs resulting from the restricted time horizon, the difference in accumulated net labor cost amounts to approximately 30 per cent.

## A Comment

These results emerge from a single set of simulation experiments. Although extreme care was taken to eliminate all possible sources of numerical errors, there is no guarantee that the same favorable experience will be repeated in other tests. The authors feel that the basic theoretical framework of lot size programming appears sound – even in a dynamic, uncertain environment. At the practical level, there are many difficulties with the parts aggregation scheme designed to overcome the computing restrictions operative as of 1960. In attempting to gain computing feasibility through aggregation, there is always a possibility of major distortions.

## Appendix A: Outline of the Two Simulation Models

### A.1 General assumptions

The two alternative lot size planning models are described in some detail: the *Single-Item Economic Order Quantity* (*EOQ*) and the *Multi-Item Linear Programming of Lot Sizes* (*LP*) Models.

Briefly, the overall framework of the system under study is that of a manufacturing plant fabricating metal items in lot sizes on production facilities, and the items therefore compete with each other for service by these facilities.

The completed items are received into an inventory. The demands on the inventory represent the result of assembly schedules for final end products demanded by some customer of the firm. The control of inventory and production in the plant is performed by a lot-size and reorder level determination on each item.

Other assumptions for the system are:

(1) Maximum straight time work force levels are specified for each facility group.

(2) Maximum overtime hours are specified for each facility group.

(3) Overtime and second shift wage costs are specified multiples of straight time labor rates.

(4) Labor hiring and firing cost factors are also specified.

(5) A lot size or production run of an item started in a production period is completed within that period.

*The demand for each item is estimated by means of exponential smoothing of past actual demands for the item.*

Neither of the two control techniques to be described take explicit account of uncertainty in forecasting future demands. The chief object of computer simulation is to determine whether – in the presence of substantial forecasting errors – there remains any significant difference in the overall effectiveness of these two control techniques.

Two measures of performance will be used to evaluate the alternative control techniques. One measure will consist of the *total variable costs*. This total will consist of the following components:

(C1) *Straight-time and premium labor costs.* This cost is associated with the labor hours expended as straight and over-time labor at each facility group; it is obtained by knowing the labor force size, labor rates, and the capacity of each facility group.

(C2) *Labor change-over costs.* This is a cost associated with increases or decreases in work-force levels at any facility group, and it is proportional to the number of units of labor varied in the period.

(C3) *Carrying costs.* This is a cost that is proportional to the amount of inventory on hand at the beginning of each period. The value of inventory on hand is measured as the value of material purchased to manufacture these on-hand units. (In the *EOQ* formula, the inventory cost component consists of *both* labor and material costs.)

(C4) *Ordering costs.* This is a fixed cost incurred each time an order is placed. This is primarily an office clerical cost associated with preparing the order for factory production.

The second measure of performance associated with operating the production process is the value of any parts shortages *not* available to satisfy demand schedules. These shortages will be satisfied in the coming periods, i.e. no demands are lost. No numerical value as to the cost of incurring these backlogs will be specified.

## A.2 Single-item economic order quantity determination

The use of the Economic Order Quantity (*EOQ*) as a tool to control production and inventories is widely documented [5, 6]. This method assumes that there are no significant interactions between the choice of production run length for each of the many items produced for stock within a typical batch-type manufacturing plant. With this zero interaction assumption, the average monthly cost of producing and stocking each item will then consist of two major components. The first cost components are those that increase as lot size increases, and the second cost components are those that decrease.

$$\begin{matrix} \text{interest on average} \\ \text{invested capital} \end{matrix} + \begin{matrix} \text{average monthly cost of} \\ \text{each production run} \end{matrix}$$

$$\rho\left[\frac{ap + (bp + c)x}{2}\right] + \frac{r}{x}[ap + (bp + c)x] \qquad (A1)$$

where:

$x =$ Number of units in each production run.
$\rho =$ One-period interest rate on money.
$a =$ Total setup hours (plant labor plus clerical).
$b =$ Hours to produce one unit of the item.
$c =$ Material cost of one unit of the item.
$r =$ One-period expected demand rate per item.
$p =$ Hourly wage rate of factory workers.

The problem is to choose $x$ in order to minimize the sum of these costs. To find the minimum of Eq. (A1) with respect to $x$, we equate the derivative to zero, and obtain the conventional square root formula for $x^*$, the Economic Order Quantity (*EOQ*):

$$EOQ = x^* = \sqrt{\left[\frac{2ar}{\rho b + \rho(c/p)}\right]} \qquad (A2)$$

Note that the zero-interaction assumption for the cost expression (1) and for the derived square root formula (A2) is fully justified under steady state conditions. With demand rates constant over time and with the aggregate work force adjusted to equilibrium requirements, it is quite reasonable, in calculating the cost data in the formula, to assume that $p$ represents the straight-time labor costs.

## The simulation program

A computer simulation program is developed to study ordering decisions; that is, determining lot sizes and reorder levels in order to satisfy the expected demands on the items. Lot size and reorder levels denoted as $q$ and $z$ respectively, will be calculated for each production period by means of a set of equations. The procedure for calculating the values is as follows: The first task is to set the initial condition, after which simulation proceeds from the set of equations. The initial conditions needing specification are:

1. $y_i(0)$, assumed initial inventory for the initial period of the $i$th item.

2. $r_i(0)$, assumed demand rate for the initial period of the $i$th item.

3. $z_i(0)$, an assumed reorder level in the initial period of the $i$th item.

4. $$\left(\sqrt{\left[\frac{2a_i}{b_i + (c_i/p)}\right]}\right),$$

a constant term for the $i$th item required for the EOQ calculation.

5. Initial total number of workers available for assignments on facility $k$.

6. $\alpha$, a specified value for the parameter in the demand smoothing equation, where $0 < \alpha < 1$.

At the beginning of a specified period $t$, the primary task is to determine how much positive production on any item $i$ needs to be ordered. It will be determined in the following manner:

$$q_i = \begin{cases} 0 & \text{if } y_i(t) > z_{it} \\ x_i^* + (z_{it} - y_i(t)) & \text{if } y_i(t) \leq z_{it} \end{cases}$$

$$t = (1, 2, \ldots, T) \tag{A3}$$

where
$$x_i^* = \left(\sqrt{\left[\frac{2a_i}{(b_i + c_i/p)}\right]}\right)\left(\sqrt{\frac{r_{it}}{\rho}}\right) \tag{A2a}$$

and
$$z_{it} = (\lambda)(r_{it}) \qquad (\lambda \geq 0) \tag{A4}$$

Eq. (A2a) calculates the $(EOQ)$; Eq. (A4) determines the re-order level $z$ which is a function of the current expected demand rate $r$ and $\lambda$ is treated as a parameter which may be varied to represent the different levels of stock protection. The inventory level $(y_i)$ of the $i^{\text{th}}$ item may take on positive or negative values. Negative values of $(y_i)$ will represent backlogs of demand for the item in any period. The actual order quantity issued to the factory for production of the $i^{\text{th}}$ item is $q_i$.

This means that $q_i$ or the lot size for an item is composed of the $(EOQ)$ plus any deficiency between the inventory on hand and the current reorder level. The addition of the stated quantities to the $(EOQ)$ brings the inventories for the coming period up to a level to (1) satisfy expected demands for the coming period and (2) to replenish the safety stock to a specified level.

At the end of the period $t$ the actual demand for each item is computed from the demands of end products recorded for the period by

$$d_i = \sum_{l=1}^{L} g_{il} \times S_l \qquad l = (1, 2, \ldots, L) \qquad (A5)$$

where:

$g_{il}$, is the number of units of item $i$ per unit of end product $l$

$S_l$, is the actual demand of end product $l$ in period $t$.

The subtraction of actual demands from available stocks results in a new inventory balance for the subsequent production period. We previously mentioned that inventories may take on positive or negative values; positive inventories incur a carrying cost, and negative inventories are listed as a backlog for them.

Inventories (or backlogs) at the start of the $(t + 1)^{\text{th}}$ period will be calculated as follows:

$$y_i(t + 1) = y_i(t) + q_i - d_i. \qquad (A6)$$

Having completed this record-keeping for the $t^{\text{th}}$ period, it becomes possible to compute certain other quantities that are required for planning production in the $(t + 1)^{\text{th}}$ period. For instance, $r_i(t + 1)$, the new expected demand rate, needs to be calculated, as described in the main body of this report.

Once $r_i(t + 1)$ is calculated and $y_i(t + 1)$ is known, it then becomes possible to determine if the reorder level has been reached for any of the $i$ items. This process is repeated for each of the periods included in the simulation experiment.

*Calculating total variable costs for period t*

After all the $q_i$'s are known, it becomes possible to compute the labor requirements for each item $i$ and for each facility group $k$.

$$L_{ikt} = \begin{Bmatrix} 0 \\ a_{ik} + b_{ik} \cdot q_i(t) \end{Bmatrix}$$

$$\text{if } q_i(t) = 0 \quad (i = 1, \ldots, I; k = 1, \ldots, K) \quad \text{(A7)}$$
$$\text{if } q_i(t) > 0$$

Next we compute the amount of straight-time plus overtime manhours and changes in work-force levels from the preceding period.

The amount of straight-time plus overtime man-hours provided on both shifts during each time period must be sufficient to cover the labor requirements generated by the calculation of the production quantities (20 weekdays and four Saturdays in an average month; 1.6 hours per day on the first shift and 1.52 hours on the second shift):

$$[m][32 \; W^1{}_{kt} + 38.4 \; W^2{}_{kt} + 30.4 \; W^3{}_{kt} + 36.5 \; W^4{}_{kt}] \geqq \sum_{i}^{I} L_{ikt}$$
$$\text{(A8)}$$

where $m$ refers to the number of months included within planning period $t$.

Also, $$W^1{}_{kt} + W^2{}_{kt} \leqq W_k \qquad \text{(all } k, t)$$
$$W^3{}_{kt} + W^4{}_{kt} \leqq W_k$$

That is, the number of workers assigned to the first shift on both straight and overtime cannot exceed a maximum number denoted as $W_k$ for each facility group $k$. The same holds true for the second shift. In the event the $\sum_i^I L_{ikt}$ is greater than $W_k(38.4 + 36.5)$, a safety valve is provided for in the form of a third shift. That is, all excess workers required are supposedly assigned to a third shift at a double time penalty cost.

Once the manhour requirements are known, the rule for determining the values of $W^1{}_k$, $W^2{}_k$, $W^3{}_k$, and $W^4{}_k$ within the *EOQ* model is as follows:

1. Assign all work to first shift if it can be so done by straight time only or by straight and overtime work.

2. If the requirements are greater than the first shift capacity at full overtime, then assign a full straight-time shift (only on the first shift), and put the remaining hours on a straight-time second shift.

3. If the requirements are greater than the assignments of hours as in (2), the excess is assigned to overtime on the first shift. Any excess beyond that point is assigned to the second shift overtime.

4. If both shifts have labor hours assigned to them at a full straight and overtime basis and there still remains some required manpower, this excess is assigned to the 'third shift'.

Finally, the changes in the work force levels on each of the facilities needs to be computed. This is accomplished by the equations that link the size of the work force of period $t$ to the preceding period:

$$W^1{}_{kt} + W^2{}_{kt} + W^3{}_{kt} + W^4{}_{kt}$$
$$- (W^1{}_{k, t-1} + W^2{}_{k, t-1} + W^3{}_{k, t-1} + W^4{}_{k, t-1})$$
$$= D W_{kt}{}^+ - D^- W_{kt} \quad \text{(A9)}$$

## A.3 Multi-item linear programming of lot sizes[1]

The linear programming model described below is explicitly designed to handle the transient phenomena associated with non-equilibrium initial conditions, i.e. unbalanced inventory and work-force levels. If it is plausible to suppose that negligible change-over costs are involved in any transition from initial to equilibrium conditions, and if labor premium costs are negligible, there would be little point in investigating the lot size model described below.

1. These notes should be supplemented by referring to: Manne, A. S (1958) 'Programming of economic lot sizes', *Management Sci.*, 4, 115–35. Levitan, R. E. (1959) 'A note on Professor Manne's "dominance" theorem', *Management Sci.*, 5, 332–4.

*Calculation of alternative labor input sequences*

Here, a maximum of $T$ periods will be stipulated for the transition from initial to equilibrium conditions. Let each possible sequence of setup combinations during the transition phase be denoted by the subscript $j$ ($j = 1, 2, \ldots J; J = 2^T$).

Each such sequence consists of a vector, $\Delta_j$, whose components $\delta_{j\tau}$ take on the value of zero or one:

$$\Delta_j = \begin{pmatrix} \delta_{j1} \\ \vdots \\ \delta_{j\tau} \\ \vdots \\ \delta_{jT} \end{pmatrix}$$

Requirements for item $i$ in period $\tau$ are denoted by $r_{i\tau}$. The terminal inventory of item $i$ is to be sufficient to last for $n$ periods beyond $T (n \geqq 0)$.[2] Then for each value of $i$, $j$, and $n$, we are to construct the time-phased production vector, $Z_{ijn}$:

$$Z_{ijn} = \begin{pmatrix} x_{ijn,1} \\ \vdots \\ x_{ijn,\tau} \\ \vdots \\ x_{ijn,T} \end{pmatrix}$$

The output levels $x_{ijn\tau}$ are determined according to (A10) or (A11a and b) on the opposite page. These conditions are equivalent to the rule that each period's demand requirement first be satisfied out of any remaining initial inventory and then out of production during the most recent period in which setup costs have been incurred. The following rules generate a 'dominant' set of vectors:

If $\delta_{j\tau} = 0$, $x_{ijn\tau} = 0$ \hfill (A10)

*DEF.* of $f(j, \tau) : f(j, \tau) = \begin{Bmatrix} 0 \\ 1 \end{Bmatrix}$ according as $\sum_{p=1}^{\tau-1} \delta_{jp} \begin{Bmatrix} \geqq 1 \\ = 0 \end{Bmatrix}$

*DEF.* of $y_i : y_i = y_i(1) = $ initial inventory of item $i$

*DEF.* of $g(j, \tau) : g(j, \tau) = \max \left\{ p : \tau \leqq p \leqq T; \text{ and } \sum_{s=\tau}^{p} \delta_{js} = 1 \right\}$

2. In the simulation experiments, no allowance was made for carry-over beyond $T$, i.e. $n$ was set at zero.

If $\delta_{j\tau} = 1$ and $g(j, \tau) < T$,

$$x_{ijn\tau} = \sum_{p=\tau}^{g(j,\tau)} r_{ip} - f(j, \tau)\left[y_i - \sum_{p=1}^{\tau-1} r_{ip}\right] \quad \text{(A11a)}$$

If $\delta_{j\tau} = 1$ and $g(j, \tau) = T$,

$$x_{ijn\tau} = \left[\sum_{p=\tau}^{T} r_{ip} + nr_{i\tau}\right] - f(j, \tau)\left[y_i - \sum_{p=1}^{\tau-1} r_{ip}\right] \quad \text{(A11b)}$$

A production vector, $X_{ijn}$, is ruled out as 'infeasible' if, for the value of $\tau$ such that $f(j, \tau) = \delta_{j\tau} = 1$, then either (A12a) or (A12b) holds: [3]

$$x_{ijn\tau} < 0 \quad \text{(A12a)}$$

$$y_i < \sum_{p=1}^{\tau-1} r_{ip} \quad \text{(A12b)}$$

Finally, from among those production vectors that are feasible, we generate the labor input coefficients, $L_{ijkn\tau}$, for each of the parts $i$ and the facility groups, $k$, $(i = 1, \ldots, I; k = 1, \ldots, K)$

$$L_{ijkn\tau} = \begin{Bmatrix} 0 \\ a_{ik} + b_{ik} \cdot x_{ijn\tau} \end{Bmatrix} \quad \text{(A13)}$$

according as: $\quad x_{ijn\tau} \begin{matrix} = \\ > \end{matrix} \begin{Bmatrix} 0 \\ 0 \end{Bmatrix}$

and where $a_{ik}$ and $b_{ik}$ refer, respectively, to the labor setup and run time for the item $i$ on facility $k$.

The *maximum* number of positive coefficients $L_{ijkn\tau}$ to be generated for each simplex problem equals:

| $\begin{pmatrix}\text{number} \\ \text{of} \\ \text{items}\end{pmatrix}$ | $\begin{pmatrix}\text{number of} \\ \text{possible} \\ \text{sequences}\end{pmatrix}$ | $\begin{pmatrix}\text{number} \\ \text{of} \\ \text{facilities}\end{pmatrix}$ | $\begin{pmatrix}\text{number of} \\ \text{carry-over} \\ \text{possibilities}\end{pmatrix}$ | $\begin{pmatrix}\text{average number of} \\ \text{time periods with} \\ \text{positive production}\end{pmatrix}$ |
|---|---|---|---|---|
| $(=)$ $(I)$ | $(J = 2^T)$ | $(K)$ | $(N)$ | $(T/2)$ |
| $\approx$ $(35)$ | $(2^3)$ | $(2)$ | $(1)$ | $(3/2) = 840$ |

3. To reduce problems of machine interference, it might be desirable at this point also to rule out any production vectors implying run lengths which would tie up individual facilities for excessive periods of time, e.g. two weeks to four weeks.

*Equations of the linear programming model*

The first group of equations specify that the requirement for each item be satisfied by means of some convex combination of the stipulated sequence for that item:

$$\sum_{j,n} \theta_{ijn} = 1 \qquad \text{(all } i) \qquad \text{(A)}$$

The next group says that the amount of straight-time plus overtime man-hours provided on both shifts during each time period must be at least sufficient to cover the labor requirements generated by the production sequences employed (20 weekdays and four Saturdays in an average month; 1.6 hours per day on first shift and 1.52 hours on second shift):

$$[m][32\ W^1_{k\tau} + 38.4\ W^2_{k\tau} + 30.4\ W^3_{k\tau} + 36.5\ W^4_{k\tau}]$$
$$\geqq \sum_{i,j,n} L_{ijkn\tau}\theta_{ijkn\tau} \qquad \text{(all } k, \tau) \quad \text{(B)}$$

Next come the equations that link the size of the work-force of each period to the preceding one:[4]

$$W^1_{k\tau} + W^2_{k\tau} + W^3_{k\tau} + W^4_{k\tau} = W^1_{k,\tau-1} + W^2_{k,\tau-1} + W^3_{k,\tau-1}$$
$$+ W^4_{k,\tau-1} + D^+W_{k\tau} - D^-W_{k\tau} \qquad \text{(all } k; \tau = 1, \ldots, T)$$
$$\text{(C)}$$

And finally come the equations specifying that during each shift the number of workers assigned to each facility group must not exceed the capacity of that group:

$$W^1_{k\tau} + W^2_{k\tau} \leqq W_k \qquad \text{(all } k, \tau) \quad \text{(D)}$$
$$W^3_{k\tau} + W^4_{k\tau} \leqq W_k$$

The total number of equations in each simplex problem would be as follows:

| | | |
|---|---|---|
| Number of equations in (A) = $I$ | = | 35 |
| Number of equations in (B) = $KT$ | = | 6 |
| Number of equations in (C) = $KT$ | = | 6 |
| Number of equations in (D) = $2KT$ | = | 12 |
| = $\overline{I + 4KT}$ | | $\overline{59}$ |

4. If the model were to prescribe that the work force be at equilibrium levels at the end of period $T$, this restriction would require $K$ extra equations.

## Calculation of the payoff coefficients

The total variable costs to be minimized by means of the linear programming model consists of the *present value* of each of the following components:

(P1) straight-time and premium labor costs
(P2) labor change-over costs
(P3) carrying costs
(P4) ordering costs
(P5) carry-over credits for the terminal inventory at time $T$.

In order to calculate the present-worth factor for period $\tau$, it will be convenient to assume that all costs incurred during period $\tau$ are due for payment at the end of that period. Then, denoting by $\rho$ the one-period interest rate on money, the present worth factor for $\tau$ periods would be $e^{-\rho\tau}$.

The calculation of the first two cost components, (P1) and (P2), is straightforward, and will not be described in detail here. These costs are all proportional to the work-force variables: $W_{k\tau}$ and $DW_{k\tau}$. The remaining three components are associated with the unknowns $\theta_{ijn}$, and for each value of $i$, $j$, and $n$, must be summed together in order to form the payoff coefficient, $P_{ijn}$.

Material costs are directly proportional to the quantity produced in each time period, $x_{ijn\tau}$. Let $c_i$ denote the unit cost of material required for item $i$. Then, for a given value of $i$, $j$, and $n$:

$$(P3) = \sum_{\tau=1}^{T} [e^{-\rho\tau}][x_{ijn\tau}][c_i]$$

The clerical cost component is determined by the number and the timing of individual orders released. Let $w_i$ denote the clerical cost associated with each run of item $i$, and recall from p. 264 the definition of the zero-one variables $\delta_{j\tau}$. Then, for a given value of $i$ and $j$:

$$(P4) = \sum_{\tau=1}^{T} [e^{-\rho\tau}][\delta_{j\tau}][w_i]$$

Finally, a carry-over credit is to be assigned to any inventory carried forward from period $T$ into the equilibrium phase. If this inventory is estimated to be sufficient to last $n$ months beyond $T$,

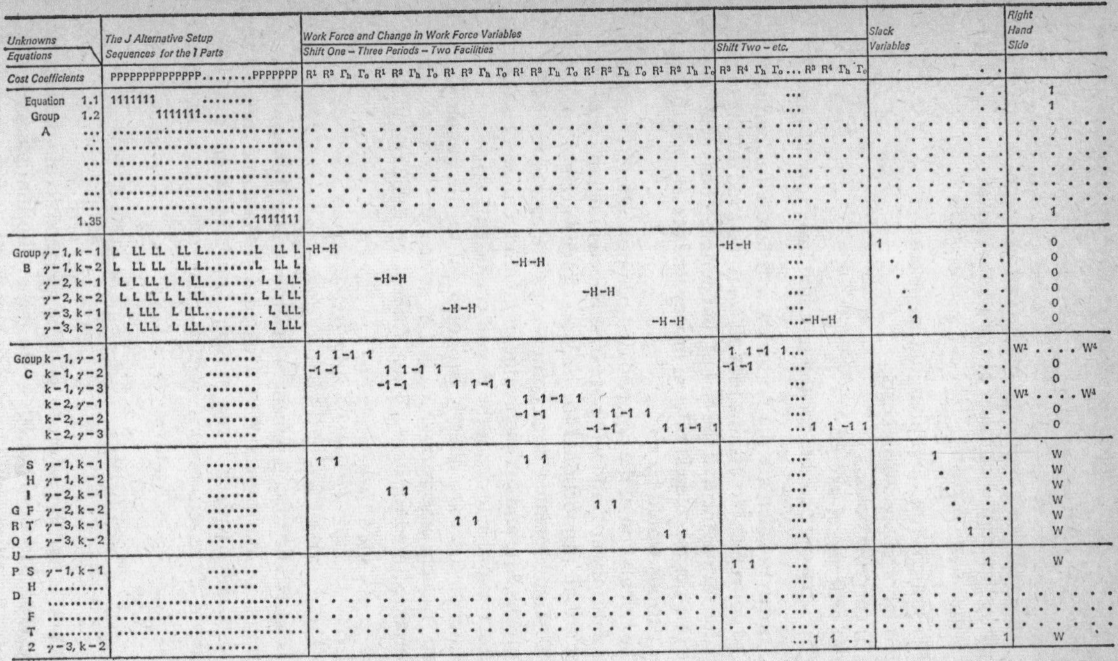


Figure 11 General problem matrix of *L P* model.

the carry-over credit for the item is based upon the difference in present value obtained by deferment of the onset of the steady-state cost level, as follows:

$P(5)$ = Credit for $n$ periods worth of terminal inventory

$$= \{1 - e^{-\rho n}\} \left\{ \begin{array}{l} \text{present value of all future labor and} \\ \text{material costs incurred during equilibrium} \\ \text{phase; see Eqs. A1, A2} \end{array} \right\}$$

$$= e^{-\rho T}\{1 - e^{-\rho n}\}\{(r_{i1}/x_i^*)[a_i p + (b_i p + c_i)x_i^*](1/\rho)\}$$

*Concluding remarks*

(1) The number of periods worth of carry-over, $n$, may be specified arbitrarily for all setup sequences other than the one in which $\delta_1 = \ldots \delta_\tau = \ldots = \delta_T = 0$. In this one exceptional case,

$$n = y_i/r_i - \sum_{\tau=1}^{T} r_{i\tau} = \frac{y_i - \sum_{\tau=1}^{T} r_{i\tau}}{r_{i1}}$$

(2) Three convenient values for $n$ are: 0, $x^*/2r$, $x^*/r$.

(3) The order quantities, $x^*$, given by Eq. (A2) in Appendix A.2, are needed not only for the *EOQ* simulation itself, but also for the calculation of the carry-over credits and of the $W_{k,T+1}$ within the linear programming model.

(4) Each 'feasible' sequence vector for the unknowns $\theta_{ijn}$ will contain $KT$ labor input coefficients, $L_{ijknr}$; a payoff row coefficient, $P_{ijn}$, consisting of material costs, clerical costs, and carry-over credits; and also a coefficient of $+1$ in the appropriate requirement row of equation group (A).

## Appendix B: Glossary of Terms

*The following is a list of mathematical symbols used in this paper. Any symbols defined below and used without indices in special cases are omitted from this list.*

$I$                 = the number of items manufactured by the plant and controlled by the two simulation models ($i = 1, 2, \ldots, I$).

| $J$ | = the number of possible production sequences by which each item can be produced ($j = 1, 2, \ldots, J$). |
|---|---|
| $n$ | = number of month's worth of inventory beyond the planning horizon ($n = 1, 2, \ldots, N$). (This subscript appears only in Appendix A.3., this aspect of the model was not tested in the simulation experiments). |
| $T$ | = number of planning periods in the planning horizon ($\tau = 1, 2, \ldots, T$). |
| $K$ | = number of different facility groups in the plant ($k = 1, 2, \ldots, K$). |
| $m$ | = number of production months included in each planning period $m = 1, 2, \ldots$ |
| $\hat{S}(t + \tau)$ | = the forecast of net orders received at a time $\tau$ units in the future. |
| $\bar{S}(t)$ | = the estimate of the average of the net orders received as of time interval $t$. |
| $\bar{b}(t)$ | = the trend estimate of the net orders received as of time interval $t$. |
| $\alpha$ | = smoothing parameter in forecasting equations. |
| $r_{i1}$ | = the adjusted net requirements for the $i$th part for period $\tau$, when $\tau = 1$ |
| $r_{i\tau}$ | = the net requirements for the $i$th part for period $\tau$ when $\tau = 2, 3, \ldots, T$. |
| $\lambda$ | = arbitrary safety stock level parameter. |
| $\theta_{ij}$ | = fraction of the total requirements for the $i$th part produced with the $j$th alternative setup sequence ($i = 1, 2, \ldots, I$); ($j = 1, 2, \ldots, J$). |
| $W^1{}_{k\tau}$ | = number of workers assigned to first operations on facility $k$ during period ($t + \tau$); *no overtime*; ($k = 1, 2, \ldots, K$); ($\tau = 1, 2, \ldots, T$). |
| $W^2{}_{k\tau}$ | = number of workers assigned to first shift *overtime* operations on facility $k$ during ($t + \tau$); each of these workers works a fixed number of straight time and overtime hours during the period. |
| $W^3{}_{k\tau}$ | = number of workers assigned to record-shift operations on facility $k$ during period ($t + \tau$); *no overtime*. |

$W^4{}_{k\tau}$ = number of workers assigned to record-shift *overtime* operations on facility $k$ during period $(t + \tau)$; each of these workers works a fixed number of straight time and a fixed number of straight time and overtime hours during the period.

$D^+ W_{k\tau}$ = increase in the total number of workers employed at facility $k$ from period $(t + \tau - 1)$ to period $(t + \tau)$.

$D^- W_{k\tau}$ = decrease in the total number of workers employed at facility $k$ from period $(t + \tau - 1)$ to period $(t + \tau)$.

$L_{ijk\tau}$ = labor input required during period $(t + \tau)$ to carry out the $j$th alternative setup sequence on the $k$th facility for part $i$.

$x_{ij\tau}$ = the amount of part $i$ produced by the sequence $j$ during the period $(t + \tau)$; these numbers define the alternative production sequences.

$W_k$ = maximum number of workers that can be assigned to facility $k$.

$H^1$ = total number of first-shift hours per period, excluding overtime.

$H^2$ = total number of first-shift hours per period, including a fixed amount of overtime.

$H^3$ = total number of second-shift hours per period, excluding overtime.

$H^4$ = total number of second-shift hours per period, including a fixed amount of overtime.

$b_{ik}$ = hours required to manufacture one unit of the $i$th item independent of setup time on facility $k$.

$z_{i\tau}$ = the reorder level of the $i$th item in period $t$.

$R^1{}_{k\tau}$ = first-shift wage for facility $k$, no overtime; discounted over $\tau$ periods.

$R^2{}_{k\tau}$ = first-shift wage for facility $k$, with overtime; discounted over $\tau$ periods.

$R^3{}_{k\tau}$ = second-shift wage for facility $k$, no overtime; discounted over $\tau$ periods.

$R^4{}_{k\tau}$ = second-shift wage for facility $k$, with overtime; discounted over $\tau$ periods.

271

| | |
|---|---|
| $\Gamma_{0\tau}$ | = cost of laying off one worker; discounted over $\tau$ periods. |
| $\Gamma_{h\tau}$ | = cost of hiring one worker; discounted over $\tau$ periods. |
| $c_{i\tau}$ | = unit material cost of part $i$; discounted over $\tau$ periods. |
| $q_i$ | = augmented final order size on the $i^{th}$ item as calculated in the Economic Order Quantity simulation program. |
| $x_i^* = EOQ_i$ | = economic order quantity calculated for the $i^{th}$ item by the standard formula balancing setup costs versus inventory carrying costs. |
| $y_i(\tau)$ | = inventory on hand for the $i^{th}$ item at the beginning of the $\tau^{th}$ period, if $y_i(\tau)$. $<0$; it is interpreted as a shortage. |
| $\rho$ | = one period interest rate on money. |
| $a_{ik}$ | = the number of hours required to setup and place a lot size order for manufacture (plant labor plus clerical) for the $i^{th}$ item on facility $k$. |
| $\delta_{j\tau}$ | = Kronecker delta, takes on the value of 0 or 1 in the $j^{th}$ possible production sequence at $\tau$. |
| $\Delta_j$ | = a column vector whose component $\delta_{j\tau}$ take on values of zero or one. |
| $Z_{ij}$ | = a time phased production vector whose $x_{ij\tau}$ components are the amount of production of part $i$ produced by the sequence $j$. |
| $e^{-\rho\tau}$ | = the present worth factor for $\tau$ periods applied to compute the *present value* of the several cost components explicitly expressed in the *LP* minimand. |
| $w_i$ | = the clerical cost associated with each run of item $i$. |

## References

1. MANNE, A. S. (1958) 'Programming of economic lot sizes', *Management Sci.*, 4, no. 2, 115–35.
2. BROWN, R. G. (1959) *Statistical forecasting for inventory control.* McGraw-Hill, New York.
3. BROWN, R. G. 'Exponential smoothing for predicting demand', *ORSA*, 16 November 1956, San Francisco, Calif.

4. LEVITAN, R. E. (1959) 'A note on Professor Manne's "dominance" theorem', *Management Sci.*, **5**, No. 3, 332–4.

5. MAGEE, J. F. (1957) *Production planning and inventory control.* McGraw-Hill, New York.

6. WHITIN, T. (1953) *The theory of inventory control.* Princeton Univ. Press.

7. BEACH, F. E. (1957) *Economic models.* Wiley.

8. BAUMOL, W. J. (1951) *Economic dynamics.* Macmillan.

9. *SCROL* A Comprehensive Operating System for Linear Programming on the I B M 704. C-E-I-R, Inc., 1200 Jefferson Davis Highway, Arlington 2, Virginia.

10. VAZSONYI, A. (1958) *Scientific programming in business and industry.* Wiley.

# 9 K. R. MacCrimmon and C. A. Ryavec

An Analytical Study of the PERT Assumptions

K. R. MacCrimmon and C. A. Ryavec (1964) 'An analytic study of the PERT assumptions', *Operations Research*, **12**, 16–37.

During the past several years, new techniques based on network models have been developed to aid management in planning and controlling large-scale projects. One such technique, which is discussed in this paper, is PERT (Program Evaluation and Review Technique). The PERT technique has received widespread interest and is currently being used for many types of projects.

## Network Models

### Network structures

In general, the type of project for which PERT is often used comprises numerous activities – sometimes thousands – many of which may be interrelated in complex, and often subtle, ways. One of the significant features of PERT and other similar techniques is that the activities as well as the interrelations are depicted in their entirety by a network of directed arcs (arcs with arrows, which denote the sequence of the activities they represent). The nodes, called events, represent instants in time when certain activities have been completed and others can then be started. All inwardly-directed activities at a node must be completed before any outwardly-directed activity of that node can be started. A path is defined as an unbroken chain of activities from the origin node (the beginning of the project) to some other node. An event is said to have occurred when all activities on all paths directed into the node representing that event have been completed.

## Time element in networks

Each activity takes time to perform. Thus, it will have some duration associated with it. The time at which an event occurs is the maximum of the durations of the inwardly-directed paths to that event, since all of the activities directed into the event must have been completed. The project duration is, then, the maximum of the elapsed times along all paths from the origin to the terminal node (the event marking the completion of the project). The path with the longest duration is called the 'critical path', and the activities on it, 'critical activities'. Any delay in a critical activity will obviously cause a corresponding delay in the entire project.

The duration associated with an activity can be a single number (the deterministic case), or, as in PERT, it can be a random variable with some distribution (the stochastic case). The times used for each activity duration are based on time estimates made by the managers or engineers most directly concerned with the performance of the activity.

## The PERT Procedure

The study reported herein will deal with those aspects of the PERT procedure which come after the establishment of the network itself. The following analysis assumes that a unique network representation has been established. However, whether or not a unique network representation can be established *a priori* is open to question. Nearly all the assumptions made in the PERT mathematical model will be analyzed in this paper. It has been found insightful to consider the assumptions on two separate levels – the level of the individual activities and the level of the whole network.

## I Activities

### Uncertainty in activity duration

### Uncertainty in research and development activities

The activities in complex research and development programs are usually unique to a particular program and are seldom of a

275

routine or repetitive nature. Those people most directly involved in the performance of these activities, however, usually have some experience in doing similar jobs. Thus, on the basis of their experience, it is felt that they can estimate how long some new activity will take to complete. On the other hand, the activities often require creative ability – something which is hard to measure in individuals. By the nature of these activities, then, any estimate of their length must be an uncertain one.

*A stochastic model to reflect uncertainty*

In order to reflect this uncertainty, a stochastic model may be used; that is, one in which some measure of the possible variation in activity duration is given. This may take the form of a distribution showing the various probabilities that an activity will be completed in its various possible completion times. Alternatively, it may just be some number that represents the standard deviation, range, or some other concept of variation. This latter method would not make any assumption about a distribution form.

*PERT activity duration – the beta distribution and its parameters*

PERT handles uncertainty by assuming that the probable duration of an activity is beta-distributed. The probability density function of the beta distribution is $f(t) = K \cdot (t - a)^{\alpha} \cdot (b - t)^{\beta}$. A few examples are plotted in Fig. 1.

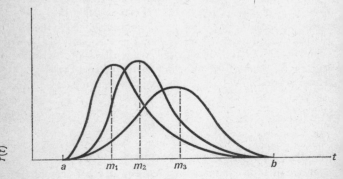

Figure 1 Examples of beta distributions.

In order to determine a unique beta distribution, the endpoints $a$ and $b$, and the exponents $\alpha$ and $\beta$ must be specified. PERT uses two time estimates (the optimistic time and the pessimistic time) to specify $a$ and $b$. The optimistic time is that time earlier than a time in which the activity could not be completed, and the pessimistic time is the longest time the activity could ever take to complete (barring 'acts of God'). A third time estimate $m$, the most likely time, is also obtained. The value of $m$ is the mode of the distribution, and this value, in conjunction with the PERT assumption that the standard deviation of the distribution is $\frac{1}{6}$ of its range, serves to determine the two parameters $\alpha$ and $\beta$.

## PERT activity duration – mean and standard deviation

It is often convenient to consider only the mean and the standard deviation of a distribution, rather than the entire distribution. Sometimes these two values determine a unique distribution, as in the case of a normal. With other distributions, such as the beta, the mean and standard deviation alone do not determine a unique distribution. Even though PERT deals with a beta distribution, it is convenient to characterize the activity duration in terms of a mean and standard deviation. As noted above, the standard deviation is assumed to be $\frac{1}{6}(b - a)$. In general, the determination of the mean involves the solution of a cubic equation. Various values of the mean were calculated from the roots of cubic equations, and in order to simplify the future calculations of activity means, a linear approximation, $\frac{1}{6}(a + 4m + b)$, to these values was made. These expressions for the mean and standard deviation are used to represent the activity duration in all future PERT calculations.[1]

1. Although these two expressions were derived from a beta distribution, the PERT literature is inconsistent about whether the activity durations are now normally or beta-distributed. This inconsistency appears in the original PERT report [6]. Appendix A of that report centers its discussion on a normal distribution (p. A2: 'Each activity has a *time*. The time is stochastic and normally distributed . . .'), whereas Appendix B discusses the beta distribution (p. B6: 'As a model of the distribution of an activity time, we introduce the beta distribution . . .').

## Actual activity distributions

Although the PERT model makes specific assumptions about the form of the activity distributions, the true distributions are unknown. However, once an activity has been specified precisely, the distribution of that activity's duration has, thereby, been determined (although the distribution may be, and probably is, unknown). To the extent of the authors' knowledge, no empirical study has been made to determine the form of activity distributions. Indeed, there would be many problems connected with such a study, not the least of which would be the nonrepetitive nature of the activities. The choice of a particular distribution, such as the beta, while seeming rather arbitrary, does have certain features that an actual activity distribution could be expected to possess.

## Expected properties of the actual activity distribution

Three properties that might be postulated for an actual activity distribution are unimodality, continuity, and two nonnegative abscissa intercepts. If the probability that an action will be completed in some small interval around some intermediate value of the activity duration is greater than the probability in a similar interval around some other point, then unimodality is a reasonable assumption. Even if an unknown distribution is discrete, a continuous distribution generally serves as a good approximation. The assumption that the distribution touches the abscissa at two nonnegative points reflects the property that an activity cannot be completed in a negative time.

## Possible Activity-based Errors

Three possible sources of error (caused by the PERT assumptions) in the PERT calculations of activity means and standard deviations will be considered:

1. The true distribution of an activity (and its mean and standard deviation) is probably not known. Given that the distribution is continuous, unimodal, and that it touches the abscissa at two nonnegative points, how much of an error would be introduced into the over-all PERT calculations of an activity mean

and standard deviation by the assumption that the activity duration is beta-distributed?

2. If it is assumed that an activity distribution is a beta, and that the expression for this function is known exactly, what errors are introduced into the PERT calculations by the assumption $\sigma_e = \frac{1}{6}(b - a)$ and the estimate $t_e = \frac{1}{6}(a + 4m + b)$, if $a$, $m$ and $b$ are known exactly?

3. Finally, if it is assumed that an activity is beta-distributed, with mean and standard deviation given by $\frac{1}{6}(a + 4m + b)$ and $\frac{1}{6}(b - a)$, respectively, what error can be introduced into the PERT calculations if the estimates of $a$, $m$ and $b$ are inexact?

*Possible error introduced by the assumption of a beta distribution*

If the actual activity distribution possesses the aforementioned three properties (i.e. unimodality, continuity, and two nonnegative abscissa intercepts), then the beta approximation to this distribution is at least correct with regard to its general shape. Different distributions, which possess these properties, however, could well have very different means and standard deviations; and hence – at least theoretically – an imprecise knowledge of the actual activity distribution could contribute significantly to any over-all error between the PERT-calculated mean and standard deviation of an activity and its actual mean and standard deviation.

Consider, for example, three distributions shown in Fig. 2. Each of these distributions possesses the three properties discussed previously; and if the use of a beta distribution, $D_1$, proceeded from intuitive grounds – from the belief that the actual activity distribution should satisfy the aforementioned three properties – then it can be assumed that $D_2$ and $D_3$ can also be possible activity distributions. With this assumption, the extent and direction of any possible errors resulting from the use of a beta distribution can be determined. The three distributions have the range $[0, 1]^2$ and have their modes at $m$. We further assume $0 \leqq m \leqq \frac{1}{2}$.

$D_1$ represents a beta distribution with a mean of $\frac{1}{6}(4m + 1)$ and

2. Zero and one were chosen as endpoints of the range for computational ease. The results, expressed as a per cent or proportion of the range, can be extended to an arbitrary range $[a,b]$.

a standard deviation equal to $\frac{1}{6}$ of the range (the standard PERT assumptions). $D_2$ represents a quasi-uniform distribution on the interval $[m, 1]$. Therefore, its mean and standard deviation will be very close to $\frac{1}{2}(m + 1)$ and $\sqrt{\frac{1}{12}(1 - m)}$, respectively. $D_3$ is a quasi-delta function with its mean very close to its mode, and its

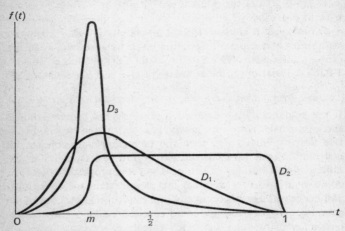

Figure 2 Examples of possibility activity distributions.

standard deviation very close to zero. Although $D_2$ and $D_3$ are extreme examples of possible activity distributions – and hence rather unlikely – they serve to put bounds on possible errors in the calculation of an activity mean and standard deviation caused by the use of an incorrect activity distribution.

Under these conditions, the worst absolute error[3] in the mean is

$$\max\left[\left|\tfrac{1}{6}(4m + 1) - \tfrac{1}{2}(m + 1)\right|, \left|\tfrac{1}{6}(4m + 1) - m\right|\right] = \tfrac{1}{3}\left(1 - 2\tfrac{m}{2}\right).$$

The worst absolute error in the standard deviation is

$$\max\left[\left|\sqrt{\left\{\tfrac{1}{12}(1 - m)\right\}} - \tfrac{1}{6}\right|, \left|0 - \tfrac{1}{6}\right|\right] = \tfrac{1}{6}.$$

It may be noted that the possible error in the mean is a function of the mode. If the mode is near the endpoint of the distribution,

3. For simplicity, errors in formulas are given as a proportion, rather than a percentage, of the range.

the error could be as much as 33 per cent. Even if the mode is more centralized, the maximum possible error would not drop below 25 per cent. The worst absolute error in the standard deviation, about 17 per cent, does not depend upon the mode.

The above expressions give the worst *absolute* error, but errors can be both positive and negative; and, thus, it could be expected that some degree of cancellation would occur when the individual activities were combined in series in a network. The extent, and the net result of such cancellation, are dependent on three factors: (1) the number of activities in series, (2) the ranges of the activity durations, and (3) the skewness of the activity distributions. If, in a network, there are a large number of activities in series, their ranges are about equal, and the extent and direction of their skewness is arbitrary, then a relatively high degree of cancellation can be expected.

It is often noted in practice, however, that the skewness of the activities tends to be biased to the right (i.e. the mean is to the right of the mode), and that the range of activity durations can differ by an order of magnitude. Moreover, many networks have a large number of activities in parallel, thus offering no chance for error cancellation. For these reasons there may be little cancellation.

## Possible error caused by the standard deviation assumption and the approximation of the mean

The possible errors resulting from the assumption $\sigma_e = \frac{1}{6}(b - a)$ and the approximation $t_e = \frac{1}{6}(a + 4m + b)$ will be analyzed by comparing them with the *actual* values for the mean and standard deviation, assuming a beta distribution (on [0, 1]). The expressions for the actual mode, mean, and standard deviation are:

Mode: $m = \alpha/(\alpha + \beta)$,

Mean: $\mu = (\alpha + 1)/(\alpha + \beta + 2)$,

Standard Deviation:
$$\sigma = \sqrt{[(\alpha + 1)(\beta + 1)/(\alpha + \beta + 2)^2(\alpha + \beta + 3)]}.$$

The mean and the standard deviation may be rewritten as functions of $\alpha$ and $m$, and these appear as the second terms in the error expressions below. The worst absolute error in the mean is

$$|\frac{1}{6}(4m + 1) - m(\alpha + 1)/(\alpha + 2m)|.$$

281

The worst absolute error in the standard deviation is

$$|\tfrac{1}{6} - \sqrt{[m^2(\alpha + 1)(\alpha - \alpha m + m)/((\alpha + 2m)^2(\alpha + 3m]}|.$$

The worst absolute error in the mean can be 33 per cent, and in the standard deviation 17 per cent. This occurs for extreme values of $\alpha$ and $m$. If we assume $1 \leqq \alpha \leqq 6$ and $|\tfrac{1}{2} - m| \leqq \tfrac{1}{6}$, then the errors in the mean and standard deviation reduce to 4 per cent and 7 per cent, respectively.

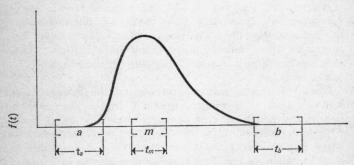

Figure 3 Beta distribution with assumed errors in a, m, and b.

*Possible error in the three time estimates*

Even if the random variable representing the duration of an activity is assumed to be beta-distributed, it is highly unlikely that any procedure could be devised to determine the exact parameters of the distribution, since, ultimately, any such procedure must rely on human estimates. Thus it is desirable to determine the contribution to the error in the PERT-calculated mean and the PERT-assumed standard deviation resulting from the PERT-estimating procedure itself.

In order to determine the magnitude and direction of possible errors in the estimates, it is assumed that the values $a$, $m$, and $b$ are the actual values of the lower bound, mode, and upper bound, respectively, of a beta distribution. The estimates of these values are $t_a$, $t_m$, and $t_b$ and it will be assumed that they could be incorrect to the following extent: $0.8a \leqq t_a \leqq 1.1a$; $0.9m \leqq t_m \leqq 1.1m$; $0.9b \leqq t_b \leqq 1.2b$. This is depicted in Fig. 3.

The sensitivity of the PERT expressions $t_e = \frac{1}{6}(a + 4m + b)$ and $\sigma_e = \frac{1}{6}(b - a)$ to incorrect estimates of $a$, $m$, and $b$ can be seen below. We again assume that $a \leqq m \leqq \frac{1}{2}(a + b)$. The worst absolute error in the mean is

$$\frac{1}{b-a} \max \left[ \left| \frac{(0.8a + 3.6m + 0.9b) - (a + 4m + b)}{6} \right|, \right.$$

$$\left. \left| \frac{(1.1a + 4.4m + 1.2b) - (a + 4m + b)}{6} \right| \right]$$

$$= \frac{1}{60} \left[ \frac{a + 4m + 2b}{b - a} \right].$$

The worst absolute error in the standard deviation is

$$\frac{1}{b-a} \max \left[ \left| \frac{(0.9b - 1.1a) - (b - a)}{6} \right|, \right.$$

$$\left. \left| \frac{(1.2b - 0.8a) - (b - a)}{6} \right| \right] = \frac{1}{30} \left[ \frac{b + a}{b - a} \right].$$

Note that the value of the mode again affects the error in the mean, but not the standard deviation.


## Summary of the Activity Section

As has been shown, the three factors discussed previously can each cause absolute errors in the PERT-calculated mean and the PERT-assumed standard deviation on the order of 30 per cent and 15 per cent of the range, respectively. The possible error caused by one of these factors – the human estimates of $a$, $m$, and $b$ – was based on the assumption that these estimates would be incorrect to only a certain extent, i.e. ±10 or 20 per cent of the range. These figures are thought to be conservative (unless the individuals are working to schedule), and the degree to which the estimates of $a$, $m$, and $b$ are imprecise will vary with each activity and the particular individuals involved. Thus, the errors resulting from imprecise time estimates will likely be larger than the results obtained in this paper.

On the other hand, the errors in the mean and standard deviation can be either positive or negative, so some degree of cancellation can be expected to occur when all the activities are combined in a network.[4] Furthermore, since many of the cases considered – although theoretically possible – are rather extreme, the errors may be considerably reduced from the 30 and 15 per cent stated above.

## Addendum

It is interesting to note that the error analysis would have yielded approximately the same results if the PERT model had employed a triangular distribution instead of a beta. In addition, with a triangular distribution there would be no error in the expressions of the mean and standard deviation, since the mean and the standard deviation of a triangular distribution are given *exactly* by $t_e = \frac{1}{3}(a + m + b)$ and $\sigma_e = \sqrt{\{\frac{1}{18}[(b - a)^2 + (m - a)(m - b)]\}}$. These values would be used rather than the approximations used now.

Another possible factor in favor of the triangular distribution is that the possible range of its standard deviation, $(b - a)/\sqrt{(18)}$ to $(b - a)/\sqrt{24}$, is more centralized than the PERT-assumed standard deviation, $\frac{1}{6}(b - a)$, is in the total range of possible standard deviation, 0 to $(b - a)/\sqrt{12}$ (assuming, again, the three properties discussed previously).

When the mode and the range of a triangular distribution are specified (for example, by three time estimates – $a$, $m$, and $b$), the entire distribution is then determined. This, as we have noted previously, is not the case for the class of beta distributions. The class of beta distributions, then, is basically more flexible in being able to handle more activity data. However, the PERT procedure does not take advantage of this extra flexibility, since it is assumed that $\sigma_e = \frac{1}{6}(b - a)$.

Therefore, since there is no *a priori* justification for either function as an activity distribution, and since the actual standard deviations are unknown, the fact that the mean and the standard deviation can be given exactly for a triangular distribution make it an equally meaningful, and more manageable, distribution. It would be equally meaningful if its mean and standard deviation

---

4. A Monte Carlo analysis of the effects of the three types of activity errors on actual networks might give some idea of the extent of possible cancellation, since the individual activity errors themselves could be calculated by the methods presented here.

were used in a similar way to the approximate expressions used now; it would be more manageable if it was necessary to use the whole distribution, say in an analysis or a Monte Carlo study.

## II The Network

### Network considerations

Up to this point, this study has been on the level of the individual activities within a PERT network. Now attention will be directed to the network as a whole. After the mean and standard deviation of each activity have been computed, they can be used to determine some measure of the criticalness of all activities taken together and to aid in the estimation of the completion time distribution of the whole project.

As it has been shown, the possible errors in the individual activities could, by themselves, cause errors in the calculation of a project mean and standard deviation, although the extent and direction of these errors might be difficult to determine. However, even if the PERT data (i.e. the mean, standard deviation, and distribution) obtained for each activity are correct, significant errors can still be introduced into the calculation of a network mean and standard deviation. As a result, probability statements concerning the various completion times of a project can also be incorrect.

### The Project Distribution – PERT and Actual

The PERT procedure for obtaining the project completion time distribution may be stated as follows. Assume that in a network there are $n$ different paths $P_1, P_2, \ldots, P_n$, which connect the origin node and the terminal node. Let $p_1, p_2 \ldots, p_n$ denote the $n$ random variables that represent, respectively, the durations of the $n$ paths $P_1, P_2, \ldots, P_n$. One of these random variables, say $p_1$, will have an expected value that is not less than the expected value of the other $n - 1$ variables, $p_2, p_3, \ldots, p_n$. Let the expected value and the standard deviation of $p_i$ be $E(p_i)$ and $\sigma_i$, respectively. Thus, $E(p_1)$ is the expected or mean duration of path $P_1$, and $\sigma_1$ is its standard deviation.

PERT now uses $E(p_1)$ and $\sigma_1$ as the project mean and standard deviation, and assumes that the project duration is normally distributed and given by $f_p(t) = K \exp(-[t - E(p_1)]^2/2\sigma_1^2)$. Path $P_1$ is called the critical path.[5] In actuality, the project distribution is given by $F(t) = \Pr(\max_i p_i \leq t)$. Clearly, the expected value of the random variable $u = \max_i p_i$ is not less than the expected value of any one of the $p_i$. Hence, the PERT-calculated mean is generally less than, and never greater than, the true project mean. In general, the PERT-calculated standard deviation is greater than the actual standard deviation. If the distributions are symmetric, and with compact support, the standard deviation of the random variable $u$ will be less than any of the $\sigma_i$. However, if the distributions are considerably skewed to the right (such as $e^{-t}$) the reverse may be true.

## Computational difficulties

In order to determine the error in the mean and standard deviation made by PERT in a particular network, it is necessary to calculate the actual project means and standard deviations from the data of each of the activities. The procedure used in this study to obtain the project mean and standard deviation relies exclusively on the calculation of an exact project distribution from the individual activity distribution by analytic methods.[6] Such a calculation is extremely difficult in all but a few simple networks, regardless of the distributions on the activities themselves.[7]

To get a feeling for the errors PERT makes by assuming that the project mean and standard deviation are given by $E(p_1)$ and $\sigma_1$, respectively, various simple networks are analyzed both analytically and according to the PERT procedure. In these calculations, it is assumed that the individual activity distributions are known exactly. This allows the determination of the errors made on the network level alone, without confounding them with possible errors made in the activities. Since calculations with beta and other continuous distributions are rather lengthy,

5. If there is more than one path with the largest expected value, PERT labels them all as critical paths, and uses the one with the largest standard deviation as $P_1$.

6. An alternative method, which could provide a close approximation, would be to use Monte Carlo techniques.

7. These difficulties are discussed in [4, App. G].

the distributions used in the network analyses are, in general, discrete. Some results, however, have been obtained for the beta, uniform, and normal distributions.

## Criticalness

To obtain a measure of the criticalness of each activity, PERT uses the critical path concept discussed above. Criticalness of an activity is a measure of the relative importance of the activity to the on-time completion of the over-all project. Some activities can obviously be delayed without delaying the project, while others cannot.

In PERT, only the means of the activity durations are used in determining the critical path. The stochastic element – the variance of the activity duration – is not incorporated. Thus, the model is reduced to a deterministic form. In a deterministic model (where no uncertainty in the activity durations is recognized) the longest path can be calculated by simple addition.

In a stochastic model, each path has a specific probability (in general, nonzero) of being the longest path at any particular time. However, if the network is large, the probability that any given path is the critical one may be very small. (An analogous situation would be one where a coin was tossed 1,000 times. The most probable number of heads is 500, but the probability of getting exactly 500 heads is very small.) Thus, the most probable critical path may occur only rarely, and an activity that has a high probability of being on a longest path may not be on this most probable critical path. The following example may clarify these points.

### Example of the critical path and the critical activity concept

Consider the network depicted in Fig. 4, with the customary time estimates of *a*, *m*, and *b* shown beside the corresponding activity. Using the PERT-calculated mean times (given in the circles below the activities), the PERT procedure would choose ABDF as the critical path because it has the maximum sum of means (13). If the activity time estimates are assigned equal weight, for computational simplicity, calculations will show that path ABF has the probability 0.30 of being the longest path, and this is a larger probability than any of the other three paths. The probability of each activity being on the longest path is: AB, 0.58; AC, 0.42; BF, 0.30; BD(F), 0.27; CF, 0.24; CE(F), 0.19. Note that although path ABF is the most probable longest path, it does not contain activity AC which is more critical than activity BF, which is on this most probable longest path. Similar results could be obtained by using distributions other than a uniform, such as a beta.

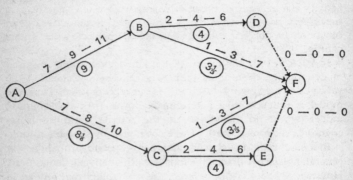

Figure 4 P E R T network showing activities with associated times.

This example suggests that a critical activity concept may be more valid in a stochastic model than a critical path concept, especially since the PERT-calculated critical path is not even necessarily the most probable longest path. The computation of some sort of index of criticalness, such as that indicated above, would supplement (or possibly replace) the slack determination, as done in the present PERT procedure.

Possible Network Configuration-based Errors – Some Examples

The possible errors in PERT networks depend on the particular network configurations; so generalizations can be made only to a very limited extent. The examples studied in this paper are of a very simple form because of the computational problems discussed earlier, and because larger networks are really no more 'typical' than small networks. They were chosen because they possessed some of the properties that may cause significant errors in regular PERT networks. The emphasis is on the factors causing the errors, the direction of the errors, and the magnitude of them. The subsection on network decomposition discusses the possible application of the results to much larger networks, such as those found in practice.

*Examples – simple series and parallel networks*

The first network configuration to be considered – a simple path – is one in which PERT makes no errors in calculating the project mean and standard deviation. This case, depicted in Fig. 5, will

Figure 5 Series path.

actually occur when there is one path through a network that is so much longer than any of the other paths that all other paths have no effect whatsoever on the determination of the project completion time distribution. The Central-Limit Theorem is applicable here, and the correct way to obtain the project mean and standard deviation is by adding the activity means and variances (squared standard deviations), along this (critical) path, the same procedure that PERT uses. Thus, whenever the network reduces to one very much longer[8] path, the only PERT errors that can occur will be on the level of the individual activities.

Consider next the case where there are two paths of approximately the same length through the network. This results in the parallel configuration shown in Fig. 6. One may wish to view a large number of intermediate nodes on each path (however, there cannot be any connection between any of the nodes of the two paths). The PERT procedure will take as the mean and standard deviation of the project, the sum of the means and the square root

8. The meaning of 'very much longer' will be discussed in the subsections on the effect of slack and on network decomposition.

of the sum of the variances along that path with the largest mean. However, if the other path has a mean very close to the first (for a limiting case assume they are equal), the activities on this second path (the one PERT ignores) will also be a major determinant of the project completion time distribution.

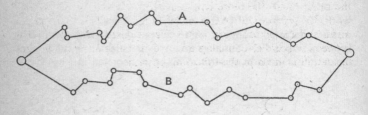

Figure 6 Two parallel paths.

As an example, if paths A and B are beta-distributed on the interval [0, 1] with parameters $\alpha = \beta = 1$, then each distribution has a mean at $\frac{1}{2}$. However, the mean of the maximum time distribution of the two distributions is not at 0.50, but rather 0.63. Similarly, if the distributions are assumed to be normally and identically distributed, with mean $\mu$ and standard deviation $\sigma$, the mean of the maximum time distribution is $\mu + \sigma/\sqrt{\pi}$.

If a third path is present that is approximately as long as the other two, and has no cross-connections with them, then there are three independent paths in parallel, and the error in the PERT-calculated mean increases. For example, in the beta distribution example above, the presence of a third path, with the same distribution as the other two, would raise the mean of the maximum time distribution to 0.69.

*Examples – parallel and cross-connected networks*

As indicated above, the more parallelism in a network, the larger will be the error in the PERT-calculated mean, other things being equal. However, there is a counter-balancing factor – correlation – which tends to offset the error resulting from parallelism. When activities are common to two or more paths, the paths are correlated. Thus, when one path has a very long duration, other paths that have activities in common with this first path are likely to have a long duration also.

The extent to which these two factors tend to compensate depends on the network configuration. Since parallelism tends to cause the actual mean to be larger than the PERT-calculated mean, the more parallelism will result in a larger discrepancy. On the other hand, the more common are the activities in the network, the greater will be the tendency for the PERT-calculated mean and the actual mean to be closer together. A comparison between a parallel configuration and a common activity configuration is given in the following example.

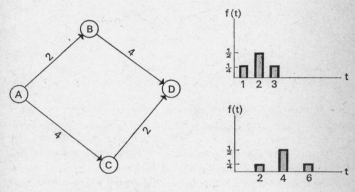

Figure 7 Four-event parallel network.

Consider the four-event example in Fig. 7. There are four activities, and the particular discrete distribution used on each activity can be identified by the corresponding mean on the network diagram. There are two paths, ABD and ACD, both having a mean length o} 6. The mean of the maximum time distribution is 6.89. Thus the error in the PERT-calculated mean is 12.9 per cent of the actual mean.

There are two possible ways a third path, with a mean length of 6, may be created by adding one more activity. In one case the path may be completely independent of the other two paths, thus resulting in a third parallel element, AD, as depicted in Fig. 8(a). Alternatively, an activity BC can be added with a mean time of 2, thus creating path ABCD, shown in Fig 8(b). In both cases there are three paths, all of mean length 6, and the network has four events and five activities.

The addition of the third path in parallel [Fig. 8(a)] leads to an increase in the deviation of the PERT-calculated mean (still 6) from the actual mean. The actual mean of the network in Fig. 8(a) is 7.336; thus the error has increased to 18.2 per cent.

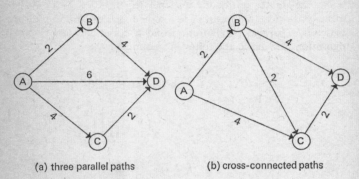

(a) three parallel paths      (b) cross-connected paths

Figure 8 Three-paths networks.

Figure 8(b), on the other hand, is a network configuration where there is a cross-connection between two parallel paths. Since there are three paths, one would expect a larger error than in a similar network with only two paths (such as Fig. 7), although not as large an error as in Fig. 8(a), where the three paths are in parallel. The correlation (resulting from the common activities) in the network of Fig. 8(b) does indeed have the effect discussed, and the mean of the maximum time distribution lies between these two bounds, being 7.074. The error as a per cent of the actual mean is 15.2 per cent.

*Examples – effect of slack in networks*

The examples given in the two previous sections are extreme cases since all the paths have the same expected duration – hence, they are all critical paths. If the durations of some paths are shorter than the duration of the longest path, their effect on the project mean and standard deviation would not be as great. However, if they have a mean duration very close to the mean duration of the critical path, they would not be critical but they would have an effect almost as significant as the examples of the previous sections. The following examples shown in Fig. 9 indicate the effect of slack in a path length.

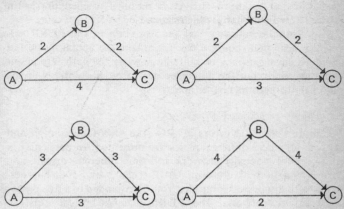

Figure 9 Networks with slack paths.

Table 1

Summary of Results from Figure 9

| Ratio of lengths:<br>path AC<br>path ABC | $\frac{1}{1}$ | $\frac{3}{4}$ | $\frac{1}{2}$ | $\frac{1}{4}$ |
|---|---|---|---|---|
| PERT-calculated mean | 4 | 4 | 6 | 8 |
| Analytically-calculated mean | 4.69 | 4.30 | 6.03 | 8.00 |
| Percent error (PERT from actual mean) | −17% | −8% | −0.5% | −0.00% |
| PERT-calculated standard deviation | 1 or 1.414 | 1.414 | 1.414 | 1.414 |
| Analytically-calculated standard deviation | 1.015 | 1.149 | 1.364 | 1.414 |
| Per cent error (PERT from actual std. dev.) | −1% or +39% | +23% | +4% | +0.00% |

The simple network has only two paths, ABC and AC. All activities are assumed to be normally distributed with standard deviation equal to 1, and the appropriate mean given on the diagram. It may be noted from the diagrams that various lengths were assumed for paths ABC and AC, ranging from both of them being of equal length, to path AC being only ¼ the length of path ABC. Table I summarizes the results.

This example indicates that the deviation of the PERT-calculated mean and standard deviation from the actual mean and standard deviation may be quite large when the paths are about equal in length, but the difference decreases substantially as the path lengths become farther apart.

*Examples – errors in small networks*

For more details on errors in networks see MacCrimmon and Ryavec [4] where more examples are presented. In particular, a four-event–five-activity network for four different distribution forms (beta, normal, uniform, and discrete) is analyzed. This network, with discrete distributions, is then expanded to a five-event–eight-activity network. The PERT-calculated mean was, of course, always smaller than the actual mean, and the error in the PERT-calculated mean increased monotonically, from 7 to 14 per cent, as the network was expanded. The PERT-calculated standard deviation was first larger than the actual standard deviation, then became smaller. The error in the PERT-calculated standard deviation thus changed sign (from $+7$ to $-9$ per cent).

*Examples – combinations of simple series and parallels*

An analysis of combinations of the most elementary series and parallel elements discussed earlier allow the results to be generalized to a certain extent.

Consider the network in Fig. 10, which is a simple connection of a series and parallel element.[9] As noted previously, no error will be made in combining activities along the series element.

9. Although this representation is not in strict accordance with PERT networking techniques, throughout this paper an arc may be considered as the resultant of numerous activities or subnetworks. The purpose of this type of representation is to highlight the symmetry of the particular network configuration.

However, the two paths comprising the parallel element lead to error in the PERT calculation. The error in the whole network is at some intermediate value between these two extremes. The location of this intermediate value in the possible interval of error depends on which element is the dominant one. If the series ele-

Figure 10 Simple series-parallel network.

ment is dominant, the parallel error would not have much effect, and the net error in the PERT-calculated mean for the whole network will be small. However, if the parallel combination is the dominant one, the error in the whole network may be nearly as large as it is in the parallel configuration alone.

Now suppose that two identical series-parallel combinations are joined together in series. The percentage error in the total will be the same as the percentage error in either individual one. This configuration is shown in Fig. 11(a). However, if in another

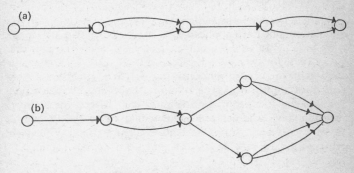

(a) arrangement of two identical series-parallel combinations
(b) arrangement of three identical series-parallel combinations

Figure 11 Series-parallel arrangements.

arrangement, three identical combinations are joined in a series-parallel arrangement, as shown in Fig. 11(b), the error in the total will be greater than the error in any of the three individual series-parallel elements.

By this sort of procedure one might be able to determine the approximate error in simple series and parallel combinations, if the error in the individual elements were known along with the various relative values of the corresponding means.

## Probability Statements

At this stage, it should be obvious that the PERT probability statements concerning the various possible project completion times may be considerably in error. Since these statements are based on a normal distribution having the PERT-calculated mean and standard deviation as parameters, and since it has been shown that these PERT calculations can be seriously in error, considerable doubt is cast on the validity of these statements. In addition, the normal approximation to the project distribution may be a poor one, since the parallelism in a network will tend to skew the distribution to the left.

## Decomposition of Networks

Although the networks analyzed in this paper are very small, the results obtained are applicable, to some extent, to much larger networks. Most of the examples here have dealt with networks whose activities were all critical (i.e. they all made some contribution to the project distribution). However, in large networks many activities are not of a critical nature. Dropping all of the non-critical activities from consideration may reduce the network substantially. Another procedure would be to try to identify simple series and parallel elements in a network and to collapse parts of the network on the basis of the network configuration alone.

Examining this latter procedure first, one may find that some networks, or at least parts of them, are composed of simple series and parallel elements with few cross connections. Two activities in series can be treated as one larger activity by adding the two durations. Two activities in parallel can be treated as one activity by taking the maximum of the two durations. By such reduction, a large network can possibly be broken down into a number of small networks for which approximate results are known. Then, since the effects of combining errors in simple series and parallel arrangements are roughly known, an estimate of the error in the whole network may be obtained.

Unfortunately, this technique does not generally reduce the PERT network very much because of the numerous cross connections. However, if use is made of the time estimates given for each activity, and not just the network configuration alone, many noncritical activities can be eliminated from consideration. One method would be to compare the sum of the minimum times (i.e. optimistic estimates) of all activities along every path to a given node with the sum of the maximum times (i.e. pessimistic estimates) of all activities along every path to the same node. If the sum of the minimum times along one path is greater than the sum of the maximum times along another path, then the latter path cannot (by the definition of these times) be a determinant of the time distribution at that node. The latter path can thus be disregarded in the computation of the distribution at that node. The activities that are unique to this latter path can be removed from the analysis of distributions at the given node and all nodes farther along.

## Summary of the Network Section

The examples of this section demonstrate the possible sources of error in the PERT calculation of the project mean and standard deviation. They should also provide an indication of the magnitude and direction of the possible error in some very basic network configurations. The errors in the PERT-calculated mean and standard deviation for the examples studied were around 10 to 30 per cent.

The PERT-calculated mean will always be biased optimistically, but the PERT-calculated standard deviation may be biased in either direction. Precise statements about the magnitude of the errors, however, cannot be made since errors in the project mean and standard deviation vary with different network configurations. If there is one path through a network that is significantly longer than any other path, then the PERT procedure for calculating the project mean and standard deviation will give approximately correct results. However, if there are a large number of paths having approximately the same length, and having few activities in common, errors will be introduced in the PERT-calculated project mean and standard deviation. The more parallel paths there are through the network, the larger will be the errors. If, however, the paths share a large number of common activities, the errors will tend to be lower. The extent to which these two factors compensate depends on the particular network configuration.

The errors in the PERT-calculated project mean and standard deviation will tend to be large if many noncritical paths each have a duration approximately equal to the duration of the critical path. However, the more slack there is in each of the noncritical paths, the smaller will be the error.

Because of the possible errors in the PERT-calculated project mean and standard deviation, there may be correspondingly large errors in the probability statements that are based on these parameters.

It is suggested that for a stochastic model (such as PERT) a critical activity concept is more valid than, and probably as useful as, a critical path concept. This is based on the fact that the PERT-calculated critical path does not necessarily contain the most critical activities.

Networks very often contain many activities that are not of a critical nature. Eliminating these activities from consideration may reduce the network considerably without affecting to any large extent the final results. In general, if the sum of the minimum times along one path is greater than the sum of the maximum times along a parallel path, then the latter path will not influence the calculation of the time distribution at the common end node.

### References

1. CLARK, C. E. (1961) 'The greatest of a finite set of random variables', *Opns. Res.*, 9, 145–62.
2. FULKERSON, D. R. (1962) 'Expected critical path lengths in PERT networks', Research Memorandum RM-3075-PR, The Rand Corporation, Santa Monica, Calif.
3. GRUBBS, F. E. (1962) 'Attempts to validate certain PERT statistics or "picking on PERT"', *Opns. Res.*, 10, 912–15.

4. MacCrimmon, K. R. and Ryavec, C. A. (1962) 'An analytical study of the PERT assumptions', Research Memorandum RM-3408-PR, The Rand Corporation, Santa Monica, Calif. (DDC Number: AD 293 423).

5. Murray, J. E. (1962) 'Consideration of PERT assumptions', Conductron Corporation, Ann Arbor, Mich.

6. 'PERT, Program Evaluation Research Task', Phase I Summary Report, Special Projects Office, Bureau of Ordnance, Department of the Navy, Washington, D.C., July 1958.

7. Lukaszewicz, J. 'On the estimation of errors introduced by the standard assumptions concerning the distribution of activity duration in PERT calculations', *Operations Research*, vol. 13, no. 2, March—April 1965, pp. 326–7.

# Part Five Mathematical Programming

Managerial economics consists, to a large extent, of applying analytic models and computational techniques to a variety of decision problems. Two frequently used techniques are those of linear and dynamic programming. In actual fact they are more than computational procedures. They are analytic models that contain their own solution procedures. As such they are important in their own right as mathematical models and as decision procedures that are used to generate optimal solutions to numerous specific problems.

The Charnes–Cooper paper describes linear programming and a number of its applications in great detail. The Appendix provides an excellent description of solution techniques. This paper can be read both by those who are and those who are not competent linear programmers.

Howard's article on dynamic programming is equally appropriate. It is another expository piece and leads the initiated and uninitiated alike through the sequential decision procedures of dynamic programming.

# 10 A. Charnes and W. W. Cooper

## Management Models and Industrial Applications of Linear Programming

A. Charnes and W. W. Cooper (1957) 'Management models and industrial applications of linear programming', *Management Science*, **4**, 38–91.

## 1 Introduction

An accelerating increase in linear programming applications to industrial problems has made it virtually impossible to keep abreast of them, not only because of their number (and diversity) but also because of the conditions under which many are carried out. Industrial (and governmental) secrecy is often present. Other conditions also bar access to ascertainment and assessment of the pattern of applications. Lack of a tradition for publication is one. Failure to ascertain the general significance of particular findings is another, as is discouragement arising from the fact that similar applications have previously been published by others. Immediate remedies are not available for these difficulties. Presumably conventions such as this will help, over a period of time, by encouraging informal contacts between interested persons.

A talk on 'industrial applications of linear programming' must be altered to suit these circumstances. In place of a survey or evaluation of industrial studies, two broad issues which are relevant to all such applications will be discussed. These are, (1) use of linear programming models as guides to data collection and (2) analysis (and prognosis) of fruitful areas of additional research, especially those which appear to have been opened by industrial applications.

The first topic may be summarized in the statement that model formation and data requirements are twin aspects of the same process. The two should be regarded flexibly and, at different study stages, adjusted to each others purposes, limitations, and possibilities. The second topic (potential areas of research) will be based on our own experiences buttressed by reference to reports which we have been able to obtain access to. The discussion, largely conjectural in character, will center on the possible isolation of basic model types (and methods of approximation thereto) which might serve as building blocks in synthesizing more complete models for a wide variety of management planning problems.

## 2 Planning, Operations, and Control

To clarify subsequent discussion, three areas of management activity may be distinguished: (1) planning, (2) operations, and (3) control.

The planning phase of management (perhaps this should be called 'pure planning') involves considering various proposals, assessment of alternatives – including procedures for insuring that all relevant alternatives are considered (explicitly or implicitly) – and tracing through and evaluating their consequences in order to map a course of action. The relative stress which is placed on the question of choice and the question of altering the range of choices will depend to some extent on the tier of management considered – e.g. top management or down the line – and other factors as well.

It will help to distinguish between planning and operations by regarding the latter as that stage of management in which resources are actually committed. Notice, in particular, that this distinction between plans and operations allows for some divergence between the two. The resource commitments which are planned may differ from those actually undertaken. It is probably even desirable to have such divergences especially when plans and operations are evolved by different persons or processes.

Analysis of these divergencies between plans and operations requires recourse to the subject of management control. In fact, the question of conformance between plans and operations forms the core of the problem of management control. It must be remembered, however, that plans and operations are both subject to change in order to secure conformance. Exact conformance is, moreover, usually regarded as undesirable. It indicates lack of independence between the two sources of activity on which the controls themselves depend. In these respects (and others as well) standard versions of control in physical systems require adaptation before they can be translated satisfactorily for managerial application.

It is not possible to enter here into the ubiquitous problems of management control. The procedures involved are subtle, complex, and various.[1] The topic is mentioned here primarily to lend perspective for subsequent discussion of planning studies. A good plan (e.g. a budget or a sales forecast) does not necessarily yield a good control. Usually some adjustments are necessary in passing from the planning to the control (or operating) stage. Indeed, the very procedures by which the participants are made a party to the plan are likely to require careful consideration when control is the objective.

Good planning data and good control data are not necessarily the same. It is possible that neither may prove suitable for operations. These distinctions should be borne in mind when forming (or testing) models in any of these three areas – planning, operations, and control. The fact that most business decisions and data wind back and forth between these areas underscores the importance of keeping these distinctions in mind. Plans (or at least pure plans) should be formed and tested with reference to planning data.[2] The fact that results do not square with operations is not decisive unless that is the area of analysis.

To date, linear programming applications have been, by and large, centered in planning. Applications to daily operations – e.g. blending models used by refineries – have been reported but sufficient details are not available for an assessment. There have been no applications reported in the control area.


## 3 Ceteris Paribus and Mutatis Mutandis Models

Linear programming models are *systems* models. Data requirements (and validity) should be judged accordingly. The requirements of system models (*vis-à-vis* data and objectives) are occasionally overlooked. It is therefore worthwhile to spend some time on this subject.

1. See, for instance, the discussion of 'activity accounting' as practiced in the Tennessee Valley Authority [48]. See also [52 Ch. 7].
2. For further elaboration see [42].

The point is simple but nonetheless important. It has received recent and explicit attention in the discussion of so-called 'figures of merit' in the literature of operations research.[3] The choice of such figures of merit is important but their assessment for systems purposes is not always obvious. Consider, for example, the case of a manufacturer who wishes to minimize the total cost of meeting his orders. It may be difficult or impossible to ascertain the cost of producing the output required. The firm need not abandon its objective of cost minimization, however, simply because the indicated merit figure is not available. Recent research in linear programming[4] has suggested that procedures may be available so that under fairly reasonable circumstances, surrogate variables may be used to substitute or 'stand for' the missing cost figures. Thus, labor hours may be used as a surrogate and the total cost minimized by following prescribed scheduling procedures. The problem of cost minimization may then be regarded as solved provided management does not wish to know (or cannot know) the magnitude of these costs. Moreover, these procedures may optimize other criteria as well. Fluctuations in production rates, choice of optimum planning intervals and other such criteria can be comprehended by these same rules [18].

How far (and when) one set of criteria – or figures of merit – may be used in place of another has not been fully assessed. This subject is, in principle, amenable to scientific research which will lead to a theory of surrogates. One byproduct of current applications of linear programming and related techniques is increased knowledge of relevant management objectives (and criteria). This material is, moreover, now being reported in a form suitable for supplying guidance to scientific research. An example may be drawn from recent literature dealing with problems of forecasting and prediction for managerial purposes. Holt, Simon, and Modigliani in their study of a paint factory [40] report that cost savings attributable to improvement in decision rules (of a mathematical programming variety) were found to be greater than those which

3. A figure of merit may be briefly defined as the score (or scores) assigned to the outcomes which are possible under various plans. E.g. two different kinds of naval formations may yield different probable submarine 'kills' or 'contacts'. The probable number of kills or contacts form the figures of merit for these possible plans. See [49].

4. The term is here used broadly.

could be attributed to elimination of forecasting errors. Modigliani and Hohn [61] have also shown that, under certain situations, only parts of an unknown product demand need to be accurately ascertained in order to schedule production optimally. Still other suggestions and findings are available.

It need not (and should not) be contended that either prediction problems or criterion-and-objective problems can be eliminated [47a, 47b]. Differing requirements in control, operations, and planning have already been suggested as well as the issue of systems applications. A flexible use of programming models may sometimes reduce the apparent importance of issues of data collection, prediction, and assessment. The use of surrogates has been mentioned and the development of more adequate means for dealing with numerous variables on a stochastic (conditional probability) basis offer further promise in this direction.[5] Indeed, one contribution that linear programming may make is to reduce and simplify the data requirements of management planning.

Table 1

Machine Loading Model

| minimize | Direct/ Dual | Maximize $x_1$ | $x_2$ | Stipulations (hrs.) | |
|---|---|---|---|---|---|
| | $w_1$ | 3 | 2 | $\leq 12$ | $= b_1$ |
| | $w_2$ | 5 | 0 | $\leq 10$ | $= b_2$ |
| | | IIV | IIV | | |
| | Criteria ($) | $c_1 = 1$ | $c_2 = \frac{1}{2}$ | Solution $3.50 | |

A good deal of this planning is currently conducted on the basis of what may be called *ceteris paribus* models. Such a model alters one variable while holding all others constant. It may be distinguished from *mutatis mutandis* models in which all variables are adjusted to each such alteration. A study of proposed price variations for one product in a mix, holding all other products at given levels, is a *ceteris paribus* specimen. To convert it to a

5. [79], [25], [4], [5], and [20].

*mutatis mutandis* study all variables must be adjusted to the indicated change. Linear programming tends in the *mutatis mutandis* direction.

The requirements of data accuracy are likely to differ in the two cases. Thus a high degree of absolute accuracy may be necessary in a *ceteris paribus* study and not in its *mutatis mutandis* counterpart. As a rough characterization of the latter case it may be said that it is better to have the data of relatively uniform quality (accurate or inaccurate) than to have part of the data highly exact and the remainder less so.

A simple machine loading model (Table 1) will help to clarify (and qualify) these remarks. From the unit processing times presented in the body of the table, the machine capacities in the right-hand column, and the criterion elements in the bottom row the following direct and dual linear programming problems may be formed:

*Direct*

Maximize: $\$1x_1 + \$\frac{1}{2}x_2$
Subject to:

$$
\begin{aligned}
3x_1 + 2x_2 &\leq 12 \\
5x_2 &\leq 10 \\
x_1, x_2 &\geq 0
\end{aligned}
$$

*Dual*

Minimize: $12w_1 + 10w_2$
Subject to:

$$
\begin{aligned}
3w_1 + 5w_2 &\geq 1 \\
2w_1 &\geq \tfrac{1}{2} \\
w_1, w_2 &\geq 0 \qquad (1)
\end{aligned}
$$

The solutions are as follows:

*Direct*

$x_1 = 2, \qquad x_2 = 3$
$\$1x_1 + \$\frac{1}{2}x_2 = \$3.50$

*Dual*

$w_1 = \$.25, \qquad w_2 = \$.05$
$12w_1 + 10w_2 = \$3.50 \qquad (2)$

Graphs of these problems are shown in Figs. 1 and 2. The shaded areas are regions of feasibility and the solid lines their boundaries. The broken lines are the functionals for the direct and dual problems which attain their maximum and minimum values at the coordinates $(2, 3)$ and $(.25, .05)$, respectively.

The dual variables, of course, provide evaluators for the stipulations in the direct problem. Thus, $w_1 = \$.25$ asserts that a one-hour increase in the value of $b_1 (= 12)$ hours of capacity on the first machine will increase profits by $\$.25$. This increase is obtainable, however, only if all of the variables are adjusted, *mutatis mutandis*, to the new situation in order to achieve an optimum. Similarly, the value $w_1 = \$.05$ asserts that a one-hour alteration in capacity for $b_2(= 10)$ will only add $\$.05$ to total profit for the new optimum which it admits. Hence, at anything like the same cost for securing a one-hour's alteration in capacity the first machine is to be preferred to the second when optimization is the objective.

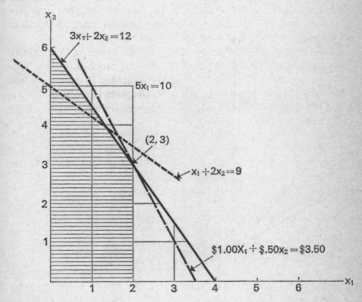

Figure 1 Graph of direct problem.

How far do these values hold? What if inaccuracies in the data are present? Or, to align the discussion more closely with the preceding sections of this paper, how accurate must the data be for this model?

Consider, first, the unit profits for the direct problem. Let $c_1$ and $c_2$ represent any unit profit imputed to $x_1$ and $x_2$ respectively. Any ratio

$$\frac{c_2}{c_1} = \frac{\frac{1}{2}}{1} = \frac{1}{2} \tag{3}$$

will yield exactly the same optimum programme ($x_1 = 2$, $x_2 = 3$) although total returns will, of course, alter with each choice of numerator and denominator. Moreover, the region over which this program will remain an optimum can be immediately ascertained by examining the possible rotations of the broken line in

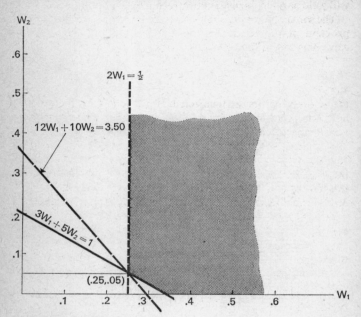

Figure 2 Graph of dual problem.

Fig. 1 which do not force it into the interior of the shaded region. Different ratios are associated with different slopes of this line. Thus

$$\frac{0}{5} \leqq \frac{c_2}{c_1} \leqq \frac{2}{3} \qquad (4)$$

prescribes the limits of tolerable error in unit profits – $66\frac{2}{3}$ per cent in this case – for this program.[6] At the lower limit a new

6. Only positive values of the $c$'s and $b$'s will be considered in order to avoid questions such as prices sufficient to cover average variable costs, etc.

optimum (2, 0) is obtained and at the upper limit another optimum (0, 6) is also available. These are, however, alternate optima. The fact that they are available in no way affects the fact that (2, 3) retains its optimum character. So long as an optimum is desired, therefore, any ratio $c_2/c_1$ within this $66\frac{2}{3}$ per cent margin of error will yield as good results as any other.

The same observations may be made with reference to the dual problem of Fig. 2. So long as the ratio of the two machine capacities are in the following limits

$$\frac{0}{2} \leq \frac{b_2}{b_1} = \frac{10}{12} \leq \frac{5}{3} \tag{5}$$

the dual evaluators are unaffected. It still remains true that each hour's increase in capacity on the first machine will return (as a variable profit) five times as much as the second.

For example, let the capacity of $b_2$ be doubled, or raised from 10 hours to 20, while the capacity of $b_1$ remains fixed. This raises the capacity ratio to the upper limit in Eq. (5) and thus rotates the functional to a position of coincidence with the line $3w_1 + 5w_2 = \$1.00$ in Fig. 2. An alternate optimum – at $(.33\frac{1}{3}, 0)$ – is therefore available.[7] This does not, however, affect the fact that $(.25, .05)$ remains an optimum.[8] The predicted program value $12w_1 + 20w_2 = \$4.00$ is obtained by using $x_1 = 4$, $x_2 = 0$ for the direct problem in place of the solution described in Eq. (2).[9]

This illustration can be extended in a variety of ways.[10] In the

7. See [9], [16], or [81] for a discussion of these alternate optima and means for locating them.

8. The fact that uniqueness in the direct problem may exist alongside nonuniqueness in its dual does create 'shadow-pricing problems' especially in the case of 'delegation models' – which will be discussed later in this paper.

9. Thus the vertical constraint, $5x_1 = 10$, in Fig. 1 is moved to the verge of redundancy. Any further movement in this direction will make this constraint entirely redundant. This is the meaning of the alternate optimum secured by the rotation in Fig. 2. At such points management has to make up its mind, so to speak, with respect to future courses of expansion.

10. E.g. both $b_1$ and $b_2$ may be simultaneously varied. Thus, if new levels $b_1 = b_2 = 15$ are inserted in Eq. (1) the new profit level will be $\$4.50$, an increment given by $\Delta b_1 w_1 + \Delta b_2 w_2 = 3 \times \$.25 + 5 \times \$.05 = \$1.00$. The dual method of C. E. Lemke [56] can be combined with the modified simplex method [21] in order (a) to establish the limits for such variations and (b)

more complex examples encountered in 'live' applications specific error analyses such as these may be obtained from information provided in the tableaus.[11] Used with imagination or ingenuity, this information makes it possible to simplify the tasks of model construction and data assessment.

## 4 Redundant Constraints and Extraneous Variables

A redundant constraint enters into an optimum program with positive slack. An extraneous variable enters at zero. The omission of such constraints and variables offers a path for simplifying the initial models. They may be added at a later stage either by entering the solutions directly or, if there is some question about their status, by using the data of the tableaus either for purposes of testing or solution. Each tableau provides a linearly independent set of vectors which form a basis. By means of slack or artificial vectors an additional constraint may be introduced at any stage without disturbing previous calculations. If the constraint be critical rather than redundant the required new row in the tableau is easily obtained from the information which is already available. Additional variables may also be introduced by adjoining new columns to the tableau. Comparison with optima obtained prior to such alterations also provides by-product information such as the 'opportunity cost' of additional restrictions.[12] Rather simple modifications of the tableau makes it possible to use the inverse of the basis (which appears under the slack vectors) to effect a number of such extensions in relatively easy fashion.[13]

No new constraint (in the same number of variables) can improve an optimum and no new variable (in the same number of constraints) can worsen it. By definition, neither redundant con-

---

to provide a systematic method for securing the new program values (starting from previously calculated tableaus) when these limits are violated. A code for such computations on an electronic computer has been developed by R. Graves of Standard Oil Co., Indiana.

11. See Appendix. See also [16].

12. Further discussion of these costs and the related concept of 'profit bottlenecks' is provided in [14]. See also [5].

13. *Vide* [21], [65], [29], or [30].

straints nor extraneous variables can affect the value of an optimum program. They may have secondary effects, however, when considering the possibility of program alteration – e.g. in studying data inadequacies.

In principle a new variable, extraneous or not, always increases the sensitivity of a program by providing an additional dimension for variation. A new extraneous variable need not, however, cut down the minimum angle of rotation (in any direction) which determines whether a new physical program is required in order to achieve optimality.

A redundant constraint cannot decrease this angle of rotation. Consider the constraint

$$x_1 + 2x_2 \leqq 9 \tag{6}$$

with the boundary indicated by the dotted line in Fig. 1. This may be interpreted, for example, as the limit allowed by a receiving facility for processing raw materials into the machines.

Clearly this constraint is redundant since the optimum program $x_1 = 2$, $x_2 = 3$ leaves one unit of slack in the receiving facility. Moreover, this constraint intersects one of the boundaries adjacent to the extreme point (corner point) optimum so that it can possibly become critical as a candidate for a 'second best' program. Inspection of the diagram shows that it does not affect the minimum angle through which the functional may sweep, as shown in Eq. (4), so that it cannot affect this error range. It does, however, affect the error range in the dual by adding a new (extraneous)[14] variable for possible managerial evaluation. When the boundary is pierced by breaking the upper limit in Eq. (4) this constraint also reduces the range of possible program response and hence the possible optimum profit level as well.

These examples are relatively simple and are intended only to illustrate some of the ways in which programming models may be used to study aspects of the subject (such as data requirements) which are important for industrial applications. The spreading use of linear programming has stimulated scientific research. Models, methods, and theorems are now available for handling a variety of problems. New applications will supply needed guidance

14. Via the so-called theorem of the alternative the corresponding dual variable has the value zero. Cf. [80].

for this research, especially as the really large and complex problems of management are brought into view and stated in a form which renders them suitable for scientific research.

Some of these needs are already apparent. Improved methods for obtaining approximate solutions will be required [12] as well as methods for obtaining 'advanced starts' which take full advantage of existing managerial 'know how', experience, and judgment. Bounding techniques,[15] dominance analyses, and other such devices will also prove valuable (if not indispensable) as well as the types of redundancy and sensitivity analyses which have here been illustrated in an elementary fashion. Finally, more knowledge is needed of the nature of essential (and important) non-linearities, if such there be, which are likely to occur in management-type problems.

Progress of a fundamental nature has been made in each of these areas and the stage is set for future developments. The simplex method of Dr Dantzig [50a] and subsequent developments have provided the path for one course of development which has now been extended to handling general kinds of non-linear functionals.[16] The dual theorem of Gale, Kuhn, and Tucker [50c] has many applications ranging from evaluation of stipulations to bounding, or otherwise controlling, solutions. (See Appendix.) Tucker's 'geometric lemma', 'existence theorem', and related topics – e.g. the theorem of the alternative – provide bases for exploitation in many directions [80]. Finally, the presence of so-called 'balance restrictions'[17] in problems of production, marketing, and finance suggest that methods akin to the so-called 'bounded variables technique' [22, 26] will be of value in handling special aspects of many kinds of industrial problems.

New theorems and suitable notations which compress and simplify the tasks of analysis will undoubtedly be required. This is, of course, only another way of saying that new mathematics is needed.[18] The field commonly thought of as applied mathematics

15. E.g. via the dual theorem.

16. See [12] for a summary.

17. A balance restriction prescribes an upper or lower limit, or both, on specified products or processes. Further discussion may be found in [19].

18. *Vide*, P. M. Morse [62]: 'Just as with any other field of science, we [in operations research] are finding that we need our own kind of mathematics.'

has provided tools which have greatly aided progress in classical laboratory science.[19] These tools have proved effective for dealing with problems of great subtlety. Management problems typically occur outside the laboratory. They may, in some respects, be less subtle than some of the traditional problems in mathematics but they are certainly complex in the sense that even though the relations involved often appear to be simple (when viewed separately) they are also likely to be numerous in kind and to involve a large number of interactions.[20] Progress in handling problems of this character is vital for science (as well as mathematics) in order to continue extending its scope.

## 5 Types of Management Planning Models

### (a) Model approximations

Early research in linear programming was occupied with (1) devising general methods of solution and (2) establishing relations with other scientific disciplines. Considerable success has been achieved and more may be expected.

It will now be suggested, however, that progress in still other directions is essential for extending the area of industrial applications. In particular, special methods need to be developed which will make it possible to handle the truly large-scale management problems which are now coming into view. Various paths may be taken and numerous suggestions have been offered. One more may be ventured here, even though it be of a conjectural nature. Recent industrial applications have suggested the possibility that it may, perhaps, be possible to develop relatively few basic model types which may be combined in various ways to comprehend a large variety of management problems. If this be true then research on special methods of solution and synthesis of particular models becomes more appealing from a scientific standpoint.

19. Work in statistics, especially in experimental design, represents a somewhat different genre. It may be viewed as a response to the inadequacies of the biological laboratories (including agronomy) and thus stands part way between the requirements of laboratory work and managerial applications. Survey sampling, decision theory (and hence game theory as well) represent still further stages of evolution in these methods.

20. An interesting and illuminating example is provided by the so-called of travelling salesman problem. See [28] and [31].

Numerous management models have now been developed often with specialized highly efficient methods of solution. The 'machine loading' model of Table 1 is a case in point. One variant is the so-called 'shop loading' model which assigns the same costs to each product irrespective of the technological process used [14]. Central to both types of models – machine- and shop-loading – is a fundamental similarity of structure which renders differences in detail a relatively unimportant matter.

By the structure of a model is meant the patterns of coefficient arrays as well as their relative numerical magnitudes. Often the models for apparently dissimilar problems produce strikingly similar structures. Thus, structural properties originally identified with models for blending aviation gasolines [17] have been found in sufficient number to make it appear worthwhile identifying a class of such blending models for fields such as producing animal feeds and fertilizer production, and in industry-wide studies[21] as well as at the individual firm level.

To be sure the more basic models may often be mixed with other types in a larger structure. They may also present a different appearance under different modes of formulation. The constraints of a warehousing model [8], for example, may be taken up in a different manner when restated in the form of functional equations [11, 16]. These variations simply serve to extend the research issue to include proper methods of identification, transformation, decomposition, and synthesis of the basic model types.

The preceding examples cover what may be called 'exact' model types. The possibility of finding only a few basic model types which provide building blocks for a truly wide variety of management planning problems is enhanced by admitting model approximations as well.[22]

The distinction between 'exact' and 'approximate' models may best be illustrated by examples. Consider Table 2. It furnishes a

21. *Vide* [58] for a 'process analysis' study of this type. Process analysis may be regarded as an extension of the original input–output models [57] by allowing substitute processes in addition to the fixed (square) arrangement of the original inter-industry studies. Rather striking elements of structure are thus allowed to come to the fore.

22. These developments may also bear on other areas of science – e.g. on the development of better models of the firm for economic analysis. See [24].

systematic way of synthesizing the constraints for one of the best known (and simplest) of all linear programming examples, the so-called transportation model.[23]

## Table 2
### Transportation Table

| Destinations/ Origins | $D_1$ | $D_2$ | $D_3$ | $D_4$ | $D_5$ | Amount available |
|---|---|---|---|---|---|---|
| $O_1$ | $x_{11}$ | $x_{12}$ | $x_{13}$ | $x_{14}$ | $x_{15}$ | 5 |
| $O_2$ | $x_{21}$ | $x_{22}$ | $x_{23}$ | $x_{24}$ | $x_{25}$ | 5 |
| $O_3$ | $x_{31}$ | $x_{32}$ | $x_{33}$ | $x_{34}$ | $x_{35}$ | 6 |
| Amount required | 2 | 2 | 4 | 4 | 4 | 16 |

A schematic array of these conditions is shown in Fig. 3. The coefficients of each relevant $x$ is plus one or zero. The unit coefficients appear in the striking echelon-diagonal array shown in the table.

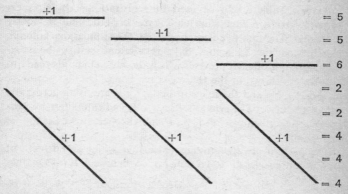

Figure 3 Transportation schema.

The structure of this problem has attracted a good deal of attention. At an early date, G. B. Dantzig [50b] devised an efficient computational technique. By reference to the dual of this problem he noted that row numbers, $R_i$, and column

23. Independently formulated by Hitchcock [39] and Koopmans [51].

numbers, $K_j$, could be assigned to each occupied cell in an array such as Table 2. Starting with one arbitrary row or column number the remaining values can be ascertained rapidly by reference to the unit costs, $c_{ij}$, associated with each cell for which a routing is scheduled. At each stage, a test of optimality is thereby provided by reference to the vacant cells and an optimum program finally obtained. (See Appendix.)

Further research has since yielded improvements in these methods.[24] The initial versions of the 'transportation' model have also been extended in a variety of directions:[25] problems in personnel assignment [67c], flows of current (or traffic) through a network [27], aircraft maintenance [70], determining engine-crew assignments for freight loads [23], minimization of machine set-up times [13], etc., have thus been comprehended in one class of linear programming models, or their game theoretic counterparts.[26]

These models are all 'exact' for at least extended versions of the transportation model. Consider now how even this more extended scope may be widened by reference to 'model approximations'. Table 3 will be used for illustration.[27] It is an expanded version of a machine loading model of the kind previously discussed. The first five rows under $P_0$, the stipulations column, lists the machine capacities. Sales restrictions, stating the maximum amount of each product which the market stands ready to absorb, are shown in the following ten rows. The ten products, $\pi_1, \pi_2, \ldots, \pi_{10}$ and the relevant unit profits are listed across the top of the table. The symbols $P_1, \ldots, P_5$ indicate alternate processes for producing $\pi_1$; $P_6, \ldots, P_9$ are alternate processes for $\pi_2$; and so on.

The pattern of echelon-diagonal arrays which stand forth in this table are suggestive of a transportation model. It fails in only

24. See [53], [32], and [70]. The 'flooding techniques' of A. W. Boldyreff [7] should also be mentioned in this connection.

25. See, e.g. [1e] and [65].

26. Further elaborations by the U.S. Department of the Air Force to, e.g. problems in contract bidding evaluations are described in [42] with additional references. See also [54a].

27. The authors are indebted to Mr F. G. Walker and D. Jennings of the Management Services Department, Touche, Niven, Bailey, and Smart with whom they were associated in the research underlying this example.

two respects: (a) the arrays of echelons and diagonals are not of equal length and (b) some of the non-zero coefficients are not unity. The first defect is easily remedied by inserting artificial processes with large penalty rates, $(-M)$, in the usual manner (in order to assure that these processes will not be used in an optimum program). The second defect may be adjusted (though not perfectly) by a variety of devices.

In this case, as often happens, there is a rough proportionality[28] in the machine times for (a) different machines which might be employed on the same product and (b) the same machine employed on different products. The following two rules, which are available for scaling any linear programming problem, may therefore be used to bring these elements 'close' to unity:

(i) *Row rule:* Multiply any row (including the element in the stipulations column) by a positive number.

(ii) *Column rule:* Multiply any column (including the criterion element) by a positive number.

The scaling factors used in this case are shown in the right-hand column and bottom row of Table 3. Thus, upon multiplying the first row by $1/.534$, the reciprocal of the machine time under $P_1$, the 6,864 available hours under $P_0$ are converted to 12,854 tons, the value under $P_1$ becomes unity, the value under $P_{14}$ becomes $.448/.534$, and so on. After each of the five rows are thus scaled by the row rule, attention is turned to the column rule. The values under $\pi_1$ require no further adjustment since they have already been converted to 'ones'. (See Table 4.) The median values remaining under each of $\pi_2$, $\pi_3$, . . ., $\pi_{10}$ after the row scalings, are then used to provide additional scalings for each product. For example, $.469/.501$ is selected as the 'median' under $\pi_2$. The reciprocal of this factor is then used to scale each column under $\pi_2$. The values $.480/.511$, $.415/.471$, $.469/.501$, $.245/.246$ which resulted from the previous row scalings used in these columns are then each multiplied, in turn, by $.501/.469$ to yield (to something less than slide-rule accuracy) 1, $.94$, 1, $1.06$, as shown in Table 4. The $c$'s appearing at the top of each of these columns must, similarly, be multiplied by this same scaling factor

28. When this proportionality is absent – e.g. in multi-stage processes – the standard rules of calculation need to be altered. See Appendix.

# Table 3
## Machine Loading—Maximum Sales Restrictions with Scaling Adjustment Factors

| | Stipulations $C_j$ | Inequality | $P_0$ | Structural vectors $\pi_1$ $P_1$ 80.76 | $P_2$ 70.77 | $P_3$ 76.15 | $P_4$ 65.30 | $P_5$ 79.11 | $\pi_2$ $P_6$ 119.49 | $P_7$ 89.09 | $P_8$ 75.30 | $\pi_3$ $P_9$ 116.30 | $P_{10}$ 91.49 | $P_{11}$ 102.11 | $P_{12}$ 64.14 | $P_{13}$ 54.13 | $P_{14}$ 62.98 | $P_{15}$ 64.14 | $P_{16}$ 86.25 | $P_{17}$ 45.57 | $P_{18}$ 29.03 | $P_{19}$ 39.87 | $P_{20}$ 42.05 | $P_{21}$ 38.23 | Row adjustment factors used |
|---|---|---|---|---|---|---|---|---|---|---|---|---|---|---|---|---|---|---|---|---|---|---|---|---|---|
| Machines | hrs 6,864 | ≧ | | .534 | | | | | .480 | | | | .473 | | | | .448 | | | .427 | | | | .440 | $1/.534$ |
| | 6,864 | ≧ | | | .511 | | | | | .415 | | | | .424 | | | | | .436 | | | | .496 | | $1/.511$ |
| | 6,864 | ≧ | | | | .471 | | | | | .469 | | | | .376 | | | | | | | | | | $1/.471$ |
| | 6,864 | ≧ | | | | | .501 | | | | | .245 | | | | .183 | | | | | .456 | | | | $1/.501$ |
| | 6,864 | ≧ | | | | | | .246 | | | | | | | | | | .236 | | | | .248 | | | $1/.246$ |
| Sales Restrictions | $10^6$ units 126,151 | ≧ | | 1 | 1 | 1 | 1 | 1 | | | | | | | | | | | | | | | | | None |
| | 11,714 | ≧ | | | | | | | 1 | 1 | 1 | | | | | | | | | | | | | | $.469/.501 = .94$ |
| | 11,463 | ≧ | | | | | | | | | | 1 | 1 | 1 | | | | | | | | | | | $.91$ |
| | 10,776 | ≦ | | | | | | | | | | | | | 1 | 1 | | | | | | | | | $.76$ |
| | 5,679 | ≦ | | | | | | | | | | | | | | | 1 | 1 | | | | | | | $.90$ |
| | 3,410 | ≦ | | | | | | | | | | | | | | | | | 1 | | | | | | $.436/.471 = .93$ |
| | 2,834 | ≦ | | | | | | | | | | | | | | | | | | 1 | | | | | $.86$ |
| | 1,109 | ≦ | | | | | | | | | | | | | | | | | | | 1 | | | | $.248/.246 = 1.01$ |
| | 948 | ≦ | | | | | | | | | | | | | | | | | | | | 1 | 1 | | $.496/.534 = .93$ |
| | 144 | ≦ | | | | | | | | | | | | | | | | | | | | | | 1 | $.440/.534 = .82$ |
| Column adjustment factors used | | | None | | | | | | $\dfrac{.501}{.469} = \dfrac{1}{.94}$ | | | $\dfrac{1}{.91}$ | | | $\dfrac{1}{.76}$ | | $\dfrac{1}{.90}$ | $1:$ | $\dfrac{.471}{.436} = \dfrac{1}{.86}$ | $\dfrac{1}{.86}$ | $1$ | $\dfrac{.246}{.248}$ | $1$ $\dfrac{.534}{.496}$ | $\dfrac{.534}{.440}$ | |

## Table 3-A
### Reconversion Table and Program $7,240,961

| Row numbers \ Column numbers (Machines \ Products) | π₁ | π₂ | π₃ | π₄ | π₅ | π₆ | π₇ | π₈ | π₉ | π₁₀ | π_φ | Machine capacities (hrs) |
|---|---|---|---|---|---|---|---|---|---|---|---|---|
| *(column numbers)* | 0 | $119 - \ldots\times102 - \ldots\times64 = 29.83$  ( $\times71 \risingdotseq 52.31$ ) | 0 | 0 | 0 | $86 - \ldots\times64 \risingdotseq 74.21$ | 0 | 0 | 0 | 0 | 0 | |
| $M_1$  $\frac{81}{534}\risingdotseq 151.68$ | 81  .534  (12854) | | | | 63  .448 | | | | | | | 6,864 |
| $M_2$  $\frac{71}{511}\risingdotseq 138.94$ | 71  .511  (2429) | 119  .480  (11714) | 91  .473 | | | | | | | | | 6,864 |
| $M_3$  $\frac{64}{376}\risingdotseq 170.21$ | 76  .471 | 89  .415 | 102  .424  (11463) | 64  .376  (1374) | | 86  .436  (3410) | | | | | | 6,864 |
| $M_4$  $\frac{65}{501}\risingdotseq 129.74$ | 65  .501  (13701) | 75  .469 | | 54  .183 | 64  .236 | | 46  .427 | | | | | 6,864 |
| $M_5$  $\frac{79}{246}\risingdotseq 321.14$ | 79  .246  (27902) | 116  .245 | | | | | 29  .456 | 40  .248 | 42  .496 | 38  .440 | | 6,864 |
| $M_\phi$ | 0  (69265) | 0 | 0 | 0  (9402) | 0  (5679) | 0 | 0  (2834) | 0  (1109) | 0  (948) | 0  (144) | 0  .404  (84847) | (tons) 174,228 |
| 0 | 0 | 0 | 0 | 0 | 0 | 0 | 0 | 0 | 0 | 0 | 0 | |
| Limits on product demand (tons) | 126,151 | 11,714 | 11,463 | 10,776 | 5,679 | 3,410 | 2,834 | 1,109 | 948 | 144 | 84847  (hrs) 34,320 | 174,228  208,548 |

# Table 3-B
## Optimum Program: $7,252,844

| Products \ Machines (Row numbers) | Column numbers → | π1 | π2 | π3 | π4 | π5 | π6 | π7 | π8 | π9 | π10 | πφ | Machine capacities (hrs) |
|---|---|---|---|---|---|---|---|---|---|---|---|---|---|
| | Column numbers | 0 | $119-\frac{489}{473}$ $[91-\frac{3.916}{3.916}$ $64]\doteq57.9$ | $102-\frac{65\sigma}{..}\times64$ $\doteq29.9$ | 0 | 0 | $86-\frac{5\sigma}{3\sigma}\times64$ $\doteq11.8$ | 0 | 0 | 0 | 0 | 0 | |
| $M_1$ | $\frac{81}{.334}\doteq152$ | 81 .534 (12854) | | | | 63 .448 | | 46 .427 | | | 38 .440 | 0 | 6,864 |
| $M_2$ | $\frac{105}{473}-\ldots\doteq129.3$ | 71 .511 | 119 .480 (11714) | 91 473 (2624)+ | | | | | | | | 0 | 6,864 |
| $M_3$ | $\frac{64}{.473}\doteq170.1$ | 76 .471 | 89 .415 | 102 .424 (8839)− | 64 .376 (4334)+ | | 86 .436 (3410) | | | | | 0 | 6,864 |
| $M_4$ | $\frac{65}{.501}\doteq129.5$ | 65 .501 (13701) | 75 .469 | | 54 .183 | 64 .236 | | 29 .456 | | | | 0 | 6,864 |
| $M_5$ | $\frac{79}{.246}\doteq320.1$ | 79 .246 27902 | 116 .245 | | | | | | 40 .248 | | | 0 | 6,864 |
| $M_φ$ | 0 | 0 (71694)+ | 0 | 0 | 0 (6442)− | 0 (5679) | 0 | 0 (2834) | 0 (1109) | 0 (948) | 0 (144) | 0 .401 (85378) | (tons) 174,228 |
| Limits on product demand (tons) | | 126,151 | 11,714 | 11,463 | 10,776 | 5,679 | 3,410 | 2,834 | 1,109 | 984 | 144 | (hrs) 34,320 | 208,548 |

# Table 4
## Scaled Machine Loading Problem

| Stipulations | | | | $\pi_1$ | | | | | $\pi_3$ | | | | $\pi_3$ | | $\pi_4$ | $\pi_4$ | $\pi_5$ | | $\pi_6$ | $\pi_7$ | | $\pi_8$ | $\pi_9$ | $\pi_{10}$ |
|---|---|---|---|---|---|---|---|---|---|---|---|---|---|---|---|---|---|---|---|---|---|---|---|---|
| | $C'_j$ | | | 80.76 | 70.77 | 76.15 | 65.30 | 79.11 | 127 | 95 | 80 | 123 | 101 | 112 | 84 | 71 | 70 | 71 | 93 | 53 | 34 | 40 | 45 | 46 |
| | Inequality | | $P_0$ | $P_1$ | $P_2$ | $P_3$ | $P_4$ | $P_5$ | $P_6$ | $P_7$ | $P_8$ | $P_9$ | $P_{10}$ | $P_{11}$ | $P_{12}$ | $P_{13}$ | $P_{14}$ | $P_{15}$ | $P_{16}$ | $P_{17}$ | $P_{18}$ | $P_{19}$ | $P_{20}$ | $P_{21}$ |
| Machines | | $\leqq$ | 12,854 | 1 | | | | | | | | | | | | | .93 | | | .93 | | | | |
| | | $\leqq$ | 13,432 | | 1 | | | | 1 | | | | | | | | | | | | | | | |
| | | $\leqq$ | 14,573 | | | 1 | | | | .94 | | | 1.02 | .99 | 1.05 | | | | 1 | | | | | |
| | | $\leqq$ | 13,701 | | | | 1 | | | | 1 | | | | | | | | | | 1.06 | | | |
| | | $\leqq$ | 27,902 | | | | | 1 | | | | 1.06 | | | | .97 | | 1.07 | | | | 1 | | |
| Sales restrictions | | $\leqq$ | 126,151 | | | | | 1 | 1 | 1 | 1 | 1 | | | | | | | | | | | | |
| | | $\leqq$ | 11,011 | | | | | 1 | 1 | 1 | | 1 | | | | | | | | | | | | |
| | | $\geqq$ | 10,431 | | | | | | | | | | 1 | 1 | | | | | | | | | | |
| | | $\leqq$ | 8,190 | | | | | | | | | | 1 | 1 | 1 | 1 | | | | | | | | |
| | | $\leqq$ | 5,111 | | | | | | | | | | | | 1 | 1 | 1 | 1 | | | | | | |
| | | $\leqq$ | 3,171 | | | | | | | | | | | | | | 1 | 1 | | | 1 | | | |
| | | $\leqq$ | 2,437 | | | | | | | | | | | | | | | | 1 | 1 | | | | |
| | | $\geqq$ | 1,120 | | | | | | | | | | | | | | | | | 1 | | | | |
| | | $\leqq$ | 882 | | | | | | | | | | | | | | | | | | | 1 | 1 | |
| | | $\geqq$ | 119 | | | | | | | | | | | | | | | | | | | | | 1 |

and the unity elements (opposite the relevant sales restrictions) as well. Scaling of these unity elements may, however, be omitted since these rows are rescaled at the next stage by the reciprocals of these medians, as shown in the right-hand column under the row adjustment factors for rows 6 through 15. It is necessary, therefore, only to remember to alter the sales stipulations by these reciprocals at the next stage.

Table 4-A

Schedule of Rates ($ Profit/ton) and Availabilities

| Origins \ Destinations | Products | | | | | | | | | | | Total (hundred tons) |
|---|---|---|---|---|---|---|---|---|---|---|---|---|
| | $\pi_1$ | $\pi_2$ | $\pi_3$ | $\pi_4$ | $\pi_5$ | $\pi_6$ | $\pi_7$ | $\pi_8$ | $\pi_9$ | $\pi_{10}$ | $\pi_\phi$ | |
| $M_1$ | 81 | $-M$ | $-M$ | $-M$ | 70 | $-M$ | 53 | $-M$ | 45 | 46 | 0 | 128 |
| $M_2$ | 71 | 127 | 101 | $-M$ | $-M$ | $-M$ | $-M$ | $-M$ | $-M$ | $-M$ | 0 | 134 |
| $M_3$ | 76 | 95 | 112 | 84 | $-M$ | 93 | $-M$ | $-M$ | $-M$ | $-M$ | 0 | 146 |
| $M_4$ | 65 | 80 | $-M$ | $-M$ | $-M$ | $-M$ | 34 | $-M$ | $-M$ | $-M$ | 0 | 137 |
| $M_5$ | 79 | 123 | $-M$ | 71 | 71 | $-M$ | $-M$ | 40 | $-M$ | $-M$ | 0 | 279 |
| $M_\phi$ | 0 | 0 | 0 | 0 | 0 | 0 | 0 | 0 | 0 | 0 | 0 | 1,686 |
| Total (hundred tons) | 1,261 | 110 | 104 | 82 | 51 | 32 | 24 | 11 | 9 | 1 | 825 | 2,510 |

The results of these scaling operations are shown in Table 4. The figures are deemed to be close enough to unity to warrant classification as an approximate transportation model and to justify recourse to the transportation routines in order to secure an approximate optimum. This can be done by inserting 'slack' and 'artificial' variables as required.[29] Within the accuracy of the data the solution thus secured is often sufficient. As explained in the Appendix such solutions may always be 'bounded' relative to the true optimum and, if desired, an exact solution obtained from a relatively advanced start. Present purposes are therefore served by identifying this scaled machine loading as an approximate

29. Cf. [16] for an explanation of these terms.

transportation model. By suitable extensions, multi-stage machine processes and balance restrictions (minimal as well as maximal) may also be handled.

Via this approximation concept the seemingly distinct models of machine (and shop) loading, transportation, and other prob-

## Table 4-B

An Initial Solution $7,202,000

| Row Nos. $R_i$ | Column Nos. $K_j$ | 0 | 54 | 28 | 0 | 0 | 9 | 0 | 0 | 0 | 0 | 0 | Total |
|---|---|---|---|---|---|---|---|---|---|---|---|---|---|
| | Destination / Origins | $\pi_1$ | $\pi_2$ | $\pi_3$ | $\pi_4$ | $\pi_5$ | $\pi_6$ | $\pi_7$ | $\pi_8$ | $\pi_9$ | $\pi_{10}$ | $\pi_\phi$ | |
| 81 | $M_1$ | 81 (128) | | | 70 | | 53 | | 45 | 46 | 0 | | 128 |
| 73 | $M_2$ | 71 | 127 (110) | 101 (24) | | | | | | | 0 | | 134 |
| 84 | $M_3$ | 76 | 95 | 112 (80) | 84 (34) | | 93 (32) | | | | 0 | | 146 |
| 65 | $M_4$ | 65 (137) | 80 | | | | | 34 | | | 0 | | 137 |
| 79 | $M_5$ | 79 (279) | 123 | | 71 | 71 | | | 40 | | 0 | | 279 |
| 0 | $M_\phi$ | 0 (717) | 0 | 0 | 0 (48) | 0 (51) | 0 | 0 (24) | 0 (11) | 0 (9) | 0 (1) | 0 (825) | 1,686 |
| Total | | 1,261 | 110 | 104 | 82 | 51 | 32 | 24 | 11 | 9 | 1 | 825 | 2,510 |

lems as well may be classified within the one rubric. Still other examples can be cited. It is better perhaps, to forego a more extended discussion of these cases in order to offer conjectures on other possible candidates for basic model types.

### (b) Hierarchical, hierarchoid, and delegation models

It is not possible at this time to compile either an exhaustive or decisive list of potential candidates. It is important, however, to ensure that consideration is given to a wide variety of industrial-type problems. Attention will therefore be turned to problems where extension or interpretation is required in order to bring them into focus as linear programming problems. Hierarchical

Table 4-C

An Optimum Program for the Transportation Model
$7,250,000

| Row Nos. $R_i$ | Column Nos. $K_j$ | 0 | 44 | 18 | -10 | 0 | -1 | 0 | 0 | 0 | 0 | 0 | Total |
|---|---|---|---|---|---|---|---|---|---|---|---|---|---|
| | Destination / Origins | $\pi_1$ | $\pi_2$ | $\pi_3$ | $\pi_4$ | $\pi_5$ | $\pi_6$ | $\pi_7$ | $\pi_8$ | $\pi_9$ | $\pi_{10}$ | $\pi_\phi$ | |
| 81 | M₁ | 81 (128) | | | | 70 | | 53 | | 45 | 46 | 0 | 128 |
| 83 | M₂ | 71 | 127 (62) | 101 (72) | | | | | | | | 0 | 134 |
| 94 | M₃ | 76 | 95 | 112 (32) | 84 (82) | | 93 (32) | | | | | 0 | 146 |
| 65 | M₄ | 65 (137) | 80 | | | | | 34 | | | | 0 | 137 |
| 79 | M₅ | 79 (231) | 123 (⊗) | | 71 | 71 | | | 40 | | | 0 | 279 |
| 0 | M₄ | 0 (765) | 0 | 0 | 0 √ | 0 (51) | 0 | 0 (24) | 0 (11) | 0 (9) | 0 (1) | 0 (825) | 1,686 |
| Total | | 1,261 | 110 | 104 | 82 | 51 | 32 | 24 | 11 | 9 | 1 | 825 | 2,510 |

models, hierarchoids, and delegation models will therefore be briefly discussed.

Dominances and redundancies are extreme examples of an hierarchical art arrangement. More generally, an hierarchy states the constraints in the following form

$$\sum_{j=1}^{n} a_{(i-k)j} x_j \leqq \sum_{j=1}^{n} a_{ij} x_j, \qquad i = 1, 2, \ldots, m, \qquad (7)$$

so that the problem is one of determining values $x_j \geqq 0$ which yield the desired ordering.[30] When these constraints are interpreted probabilistically – viz.,

$$P\left\{ \sum_{j=1}^{n} a_{(i-k)j}x_j \leqq \sum_{j=1}^{n} a_{ij}x_j \right\} \geqq \alpha_{ik}, \tag{8}$$

with $P$ for probability and $\alpha_{ik}$ a prescribed confidence coefficient, an hierarchoid arrangement is achieved.[31]

Little attention appears to have been devoted to models of this kind, despite their rather apparent appeal in terms of, say, usual forms of business organization. One such example [15] has been reported in the form of a linear programming application to the problem of determining executive compensation patterns in an industrial organization. This report focused on the relevance of the methods there used (a) for dealing with non-linear functionals[32] and (b) for treating statistical regressions which are subject to inequality constraints. The objective in this problem (meeting competition 'as closely as possible') as well as the criterion elements, can also be given an economic interpretation, which aligns it more closely with the usual form of linear programming objectives – cost minimization, profit maximization, etc. The model is, to be sure, probabilistic in nature. It is, nevertheless a cost minimizing model if the objective is interpreted by reference to standard versions of the economic theory of distribution. By meeting competition as closely as possible the firm seeks to minimize the total cost of holding (and attracting) a representative mix of the executives required to man the company's organization. For, by standard versions of distribution theory in economics, the potential productive contribution of any executive[33] (value in dollars) sets an upper limit to his worth to the

30. Usually prescribed constants – ceilings, floors, and intermediate values – are inserted at various points in the constraints.

31. See [20] for a discussion of probabilistic constraints and [71] for a somewhat different approach to organization hierarchoids.

32. See [12] for further extensions.

33. Some adjustment of standard versions of the economic theory of distribution is required, of course, in order to consider executive posts in a hierarchy since the usual versions of this theory do not allow for such 'factors' or the possible attraction of 'promotions' to other echelons in the hierarchy. The probabilistic context of the problem also requires further adjustment in this theory.

company. Offers by competition provide a lower limit. Hence the objective, of meeting competition as closely as possible, is also an attempt to reach the lowest cost level that the company's organization allows, on the assumption that this representative mix is worth at least as much as the competition offers.

To be sure, some reaches in the hierarchy will be compensated at lower values and others at higher values relative to competitive offers. The assumption is that these will cancel out in an overall sense and provide the necessary degree of attraction throughout the hierarchy – including 'representative' leakages and additional recruitment. When desired, weights can be inserted in the functional to allow for the relative importance assigned to various rankings which can, alternatively, be interpreted either as measures of the relative force of competition in each such bracket or else as an allowance for productive contributions in the various hierarchies.

The model used in this instance is, of course, too simple to bear the entire weight of potential linear programming applications to problems of organization planning, relative priority, or preference, etc.[34] Other parts of programming – e.g. constrained games[35] – will need to be adjoined for further penetration into these areas. At any rate, the main issue is not this particular instance. The question is whether hierarchical and hierarchoid models are, potentially, fundamental types. A plausible argument for their candidacy appears to be possible.

Delegation models appear to be another class of candidates. T. C. Koopmans' 'activity analysis models' [50d] are an example. In fact, little progress, at least as far as industrial applications are concerned, appears to have been made since Koopmans' original research. Perhaps this has resulted from the rather extreme

34. *Vide*, e.g. [71] for an analysis of communication nets in hierarchoid structures.

35. The initial use of 'ordinal' probabilities with imputed dollar valuations, and other relevant commercial interpretation of strategic components which seem to arise in rather natural fashion from these kinds of game formulations provide an attraction for possible applications. See [10], [73], and the references cited therein. Such constrained game models themselves contain rather striking structures, the constraints for each player being provided by new rows and those of his opponents appearing as new columns, thus providing a hollow of zeros between them.

example used by Koopmans, a completely delegated, almost egalitarian model of an organization. Perhaps the orientation toward the general problems of an economic system, in the classical tradition, or Koopmans' lack of detailed attention to expedient computation devices account for the fact that inadequate attention has been devoted to the possible value of further developments for industrial applications. This situation should be remedied by devoting attention to the adaptations, modifications, and extensions required to make these models suitable for industrial applications.

It is true that Koopmans' formulation needs to be interpreted if it is to be brought within the framework of the more usual forms of linear programming. It is not one, but a series of linear programming problems. (See Appendix.) The crux of Koopmans' formulation rests on the concept of efficiency prices. These prices, or their 'accounting' counterparts, are intended as internal guides for a decentralized organization – analogous to, say, the so-called internal profit-and-loss control systems employed by many large commercial organizations.[36] The objective is to supply price guides, including prices of fixed facilities, which can be used for bidding by the various departments both for services supplied within the firm itself and from outside sources.

In order to see what is involved the machine loading example of Sections 3 and 4 may be used even though a 'forced' interpretation is required in order to fit it into the activity analysis mold. Table 5 provides the necessary extension by incorporating Eq. (6) and two other conditions – e.g. raw materials supplied from inventory – in order to complete the illustration. Each column of the table represents an 'activity' and each row a 'commodity'. The variables $x$ indicate the levels at which the activities are to be run and the values $y$ represent the corresponding amounts of each commodity. The commodities (goods or services) are divided into final, $y_1$ and $y_2$; primary, $y_3$, $y_4$, and $y_5$; and intermediate products, $y_6$ and $y_7$. These divisions correspond

36. *Vide*, Peter Drucker, *The concept of the corporation* (John Day and Co., New York, 1946) for a discussion of the system employed by the General Motors Corporation. Gregory Brenstock, Aaron Yuzow, and Solomon Schwartz, *Management in Russian industry and agriculture*, Oxford University Press, London, 1944) describe a system used by the Soviet Government.

to the relations the variables, $y$, bear to the stipulations and to sign conventions used to distinguish between inputs and outputs. Final products ($y_1$ and $y_2$) are constrained to be non-negative, primary ones ($y_3$, $y_4$, and $y_5$) are constrained to be nonpositive and to conform to stipulated limits while intermediate products ($y_6$ and $y_7$) are zero. Within any column (in the body of the table) a negative sign attached to any coefficient designates an input to the activity and a positive sign an output.

Table 5
Activity Analysis Model

| Activities | | | | Net outputs and inputs | Stipulations |
|---|---|---|---|---|---|
| $x_1$ | $x_2$ | $x_3$ | $x_4$ | | |
| 1 | | | | $y_1$ | $\geqq 0$ |
| | 1 | | | $y_2$ | $\geqq 0$ |
| −3 | −2 | | | $y_3$ | $\geqq -12$ |
| −5 | | | | $y_4$ | $\geqq -10$ |
| −1 | −2 | | | $y_5$ | $\geqq -9$ |
| −1 | −1 | 1 | | $y_6$ | $= 0$ |
| | | −1 | 1 | $y_7$ | $= 0$ |

Koopmans' organization model may be summarized as follows: Each commodity (row) is placed in charge of a custodian and each activity (column) in charge of a manager.[37] Custodians and managers are each to maximize their own 'profits'. The issue is whether it is possible for a central office committee – a 'helmsman' in Koopmans' terminology – to devise a system of prices, or price rules, which will guarantee certain results (not necessarily optimal) to the overall entity. As has already been indicated, only limited guarantees can be offered unless further intervention is allowed. Under certain circumstances efficiency can be achieved. Moreover, as Koopmans shows, by following specified rules of pricing both 'inside' and 'outside' transactions may be comprehended by these efficiency conditions.

It is important to emphasize both the differences and similarities that exist between Koopmans and the linear programming

37. This terminology is borrowed from Koopmans, *loc. cit.* [50d] p. 93.

approaches that have previously been presented. In one interpretation an efficient program is only one that is not obviously wasteful. Thus a point $y$ with coordinates $y_i$, $i = 1, 2, \ldots$, is said to be efficient if and only if there does not exist a point $\bar{y}$, with coordinates $\bar{y}_i$, $i = 1, 2, \ldots$, which is better. The term 'better' is used in the sense of a partial ordering: No coordinate of $\bar{y}$ is less than the corresponding coordinate of $y$, and at least one coordinate is greater. Formally, $\bar{y}$ is better than $y$ if

$$\bar{y} \geqslant y, \tag{9}$$

where '$\geqslant$' means $\bar{y} \geqq y$ and $\bar{y} \neq y$. If such a point $\bar{y}$ is available, then $y$ is not efficient.

There are, to be sure, many problems which need to be considered before introducing this concept into an industrial organization. It does, however, have two virtues. First, it focuses attention on the fact (not always recognized in currently employed internal pricing systems) that (a) the maximizing objectives of any particular supervisor[38] and of the overall entity may conflict and (b) the objectives of the various supervisors may also fail to coincide. In short, the improvement secured by one may worsen the position of others. Second, there are regions in which the improvement secured by any supervisor redounds not only to his own benefit but also to the benefit of the entity and, perhaps, other supervisors as well. Thus, if $y$ is not efficient then it is possible for at least one custodian or manager (under properly conceived price rules) to improve his own position without worsening the lot of any other custodian or manager. The prices designed to produce the 'correct' behavior under these circumstances are the efficiency prices.[39] Although dynamics of these price arrangements have not been fully worked out, it is possible to ensure, under certain circumstances, that custodians and managers dealing with each other will not be foregoing benefits which they might otherwise obtain by dealing with sources outside the entity.

38. The term supervisor is here used to refer to both custodians and managers.

39. A more general formulation would specify other kinds of information, or 'misinformation', to be supplied as a means of correcting potential misbehavior by supervisors. This kind of extension is being studied by the authors in collaboration with Martin Shubik of the General Electric Co.

Koopmans has made one start on problems which are important in cost allocations as well as in organization theory. In dealing with the question of multiple objectives it was necessary for him to alter features of the usual linear programming model. The usual objective, scalar optimization of a single quantity (e.g. total profits or costs) is replaced by a problem in vector optimization. As will be shown in the appendix the activity analysis approach can be reconciled with linear programming. It replaces one linear programming problem by a series of such problems and their duals.

It is conceivable that incorporption of hierarchical[40] and hierarchoid arrangements into the models of activity analysis may provide a start toward adjusting them for industrial applications. But the activity analysis approach is important in its own right. The relations between linear programming and zero-sum two-person games are well known. It is possible that the activity analysis approach may provide a similar bridge for other types of games as well. The so-called Pareto–Nash[41] equilibrium points in non-cooperative game solutions suggest an affinity and common origin with Koopmans' approach. Extended versions of delegation models may also offer a means of dealing with some of the difficult problems of sub-optimization [38] that are often faced in applied work. In particular, it should be possible to evolve methods for imputing prices (initially or finally) to omitted elements of the system. These possibilities alone would seem to warrant the further research required for industrial applications.

## 6 Conclusion

It has been possible within the scope of this paper only to touch on a variety of topics. Other, perhaps equally important, topics have perforce been either omitted or treated too lightly. The work of Bellman and others[42] in dynamic programming has been

40. *Vide* [60] for a simplified example and further references.
41. Cf. [16], [64], and [68].
42. Cf. [45]. The arrays which Dantzig [26], following W. Jacobs, calls 'block triangular' will probably be important special types in dynamic programming. The horizon concepts described in [20] provides another class of general approaches.

too slightly treated and the same is true of recent work in quadratic programming,[43] sequencing [44], line balancing [16], inventory control [84], and other areas as well. The title assigned to this paper can serve as an excuse but not as a justification, for omitting any reference to reported studies in farm management,[44] engineering design [69, 72], and other topics closely allied to industrial programming.

The conjectural nature of some of the topics covered in this talk, especially those dealing with the idea of basic model types, should be underscored. As will be illustrated in the appendix, however, these concepts are useful in any event as a guide to approximations.

Having proceeded thus far into the realm of conjecture it is perhaps as well to proceed a step farther. This will at least help to close the discussion on a more positive note and to sharpen the potential relevance of such work for progress in management science. It is sometimes stated that this science (or body of sciences) is lacking in parameters analogous to, say, gravitational constants, etc, which have played such critical roles in other disciplines. This criticism, though relevant, need not be decisive at this stage of development. Possible differences in management and these other sciences must be allowed for. It may be, as the discussion throughout this paper suggests, that no such isolated (or isolable) constants will ever be discovered. It appears more likely that such parameters, if they exist, will make their appearance in the form of systems or even constellations of systems. If this be true then progress in management science depends critically on (a) the evolution of appropriate methods of systems analysis and (b) the development and identification of basic management models which can comprehend such constellations in understandable form. Linear programming has provided one avenue for a start in this task, especially in the field of industrial applications. Doubtless other avenues are (or will be) opened by other approaches as well.

43. [4], [33], and [59].
44. Cf. [75] for a source.

## Appendix: Introduction

This appendix extends the examples and discussion of the main text. First, the transportation approximation of Tables 3 and 4 are carried to completion. This is followed by an example of oil field exploitation in order to show (a) how solutions may be secured by an interpretation of the bounded variables routines [22] and (b) how the concept of model approximations may be used for guidance. Finally, Table 5 is studied further in order to interpret activity analysis models in terms of linear programming and to provide an expedient method of computation for securing all efficient points and efficiency prices.

*Part one*

Table 3 (p. 320) was, it will be recalled, scaled to an approximate transportation model. If it be assumed that the scalings have resulted in values which are sufficiently close to unity (see Table 4, p. 323) the arrangement shown in Table 4-A (p. 324) may be used for guiding the calculations. This table is in transportation format with the machines as origins and the products as destinations. Infeasible routings are shown by cells which are assigned the forbiddingly large penalty rate of $\$(-M)$ per unit. A slack row, $M_\phi$, and a slack column, $\pi_\phi$, have also been added (at $\$0$ per unit) because the original problem was stated in terms of inequalities. Since the standard transportation model requires that the total of the requirements and the total of the availabilities be equal the amounts 825 and 1,686 are inserted as additional row and column stipulations under $\pi_\phi$ and $M_\phi$ respectively.[45] The remaining data (rounded to the nearest whole number) are drawn from Table 4 in the text of the article.

Table 4-B contains a trial solution with the routed amounts enclosed in circles, here called 'stepping stones' [13]. Adding these values across any row or column shows that all rim requirements are satisfied.

To determine whether this program is an optimum the 'row-column sum method' of Dantzig [50b] may be used. Row

45. The totals, 825 for $\pi_\phi$ and 1,686 for $M_\phi$, are rounded upwards by one unit each to adjust for errors of approximation in the scalings.

numbers, $R_i$, and column numbers $K_j$ are determined as follows:

Rule (i): Set $R_i + K_j = c_{ij}$ for each cell in which a routing (stepping stone) appears.

Here $c_{ij}$ is the return per unit shipped, as shown by the value enclosed within a square in each cell.[46] Ordinarily an initial $R_i$ or $K_j$ is arbitrarily chosen to start the process of solving the equations in Rule (i). For reasons which will shortly become apparent, however, the following modification will be advantageous:

Rule (i-a): If positive slack is scheduled for any cell set the corresponding $R_i$ and $K_j$ equal to zero.

Determination of the values $R_i$ and $K_j$ are therefore initiated by setting $R_\phi = 0$, as shown in the column labelled 'row numbers' of Table 4-B, and by setting $K_1 = K_5 = K_7 = K_8 = K_9 = K_{10} = K_\phi = 0$ at the top. The remaining row and column numbers are then determined by solving the equations set forth in Rule (i) so that, e.g. $R_1 = 81$ in order to satisfy $R_1 + K_1 = 81$, etc.

The value of this program, \$7,202,000, may, of course, be obtained by multiplying the programmed amount for each cell by its corresponding return per unit and summing. It may also be obtained from the sum

$$\sum_{i=1}^{m} R_i a_i + \sum_{j=1}^{m} K_j b_j \tag{10}$$

secured by multiplying each origin amount, $a_i$, by its corresponding row number and each destination amount, $b_j$, by its corresponding column number.

It is now necessary to determine whether the program of Table 4-B is an optimum. For this purpose, let

Rule (ii): $R_i + K_j = z_{ij}$ for each unoccupied cell. Only if $z_{ij} \geqq c_{ij}$ in each such cell can the program be regarded as an optimum.

The $R_i$ and $K_j$ used in Rule (ii) are, of course, the previously obtained row and column numbers.

46. The values $c_{ij} = \$(-M)$ are not shown since these cells will (ordinarily) not be used for routings.

Checking the values $R_\phi + K_4 = 0 - 10 = z_{\phi 4}$ against the value $c_{\phi 4} = 0$ it is seen that the condition specified in Rule (ii) is not satisfied. An advantage can be secured by bringing the cell indicated by a check mark ($\surd$) into the program.

In passing from the program of Table 4-B to the one shown in Table 4-C the stepping stone routine of [13] is brought into play. Starting on the stepping stone in the sixth row and first column the 'rook's tour' (with the alternate plus and minus signs shown in Table 4-B) is performed which terminates on the stepping stone in the third row and fourth column. The following rules for effecting program alterations may then be used:

Rule (iii): Include all stepping stones not covered in the rook's tour at the same programmed amounts in the new solution.

Rule (iv): Delete the positively signed stepping stone which has the smallest numerical value and assign it to the new cell which offers the promised improvement.

Rule (v): To each cell covered in the rook's tour note the sign given to it during the tour:

(a) If the sign is positive, subtract the amount which was contained in the deleted cell.

(b) If the sign is negative, add the amount which was contained in the deleted cell.

In this manner the program of Table 4-C is secured from the one shown in Table 4-B. The 48 units shown in the fifth row and second column of the latter table are transferred into the cell occupying the sixth row and fourth column of the latter. This same amount is subtracted from all stepping stones which received a '$+$' sign and added to all which received a '$-$' sign on the tour. (See Table 4-B.) All other stepping stones are simply transferred at their previous amounts into Table 4-C.

New values, $R_i$ and $K_j$, are now determined by Rules (i) and (i-a) and inserted in their proper row and column positions in Table 4-C. Applying Rule (ii) this program is found to be an optimum with $z_{ij} \geqq c_{ij}$ for all $i$ and $j$. The value, \$7,250,000, shown at the top of Table 4-C was calculated from Eq. (10).

Since this model was only an approximation the following

questions arise: (1) How can this solution be adjusted to the actual (exact) requirements, (2) is the resulting fit an optimum, (3) can the exact solution, if not optimal, be bounded or otherwise controlled, and (4) what expedient procedure, if any, is available for improving the exact solution when required?

Further extension to the row-column sum method is required to answer these questions. For this purpose, consider the schema of a transportation model shown in Fig. 3 of the text. The dual to this problem minimizes Eq. (10) subject to the restrictions[47]

$$
\begin{aligned}
R_i + K_j &\geqq c_{ij} \\
R_i, K_j &\geqq 0 \\
i &= 1, 2, \ldots, m \\
j &= 1, 2, \ldots, n.
\end{aligned}
\tag{11}
$$

It is therefore necessary to handle only one pair of variables at a time. Moreover, since

$$
\sum_{i=1}^{m} a_i = \sum_{j=1}^{m} b_j
$$

the value of one of these variables may be selected arbitrarily in order to initiate the process.

An interpretation of the calculation procedures may be devised by considering a series of relaxed duals formed from Eq. (11) in the following manner. Select, in accordance with Rule (i), those dual restrictions which correspond to nonzero values of the direct program variables and satisfy them at the lowest possible levels – i.e. as equations.[48] This is the minimum value of this relaxed dual. It is equal to the value of the direct program at that stage so that the latter may, when desired, be secured by simply applying Eq. (10) in the indicated manner. Rule (ii) may then be regarded as a test of whether the remaining dual restrictions in Eq. (11) are also satisfied. When $z_{ij} \geqq c_{ij}$ then all inequalities hold

47. If the direction problem is initially stated in the form of equations, as in Fig. 3, the nonnegativity requirements on $R_i$ and $K_j$ are eliminated.

48. For this purpose the nonnegativity requirements are also ignored. The theorem of the alternative [80] requires that dual variables which correspond to positive slack must, at an optimum, be zero (i.e. the indicated excess 'capacities' are 'free goods') so that it is convenient to commence with this condition which must, eventually, be satisfied.

and since this is a minimum for a relaxed dual it must also be a minimum for the full array in Eq. (11).[49]

Notice that this interpretation makes it possible to bound the optimum at any stage. The direct program (or its corresponding relaxed dual) provides a lower bound. Adjusting the calculated $R_i$ and $K_j$ so that all of the conditions in Eq. (11) are satisfied, an upper bound is also available since the value of any solution to the dual must be at least as great as the value of every solution (including the optimum) to the direct problem. Hence an upper bound is also obtained by making the indicated adjustments.[50]

When, as in the present case, the nonzero elements of the transportation model are replaced by arbitrary constants, $a_{ij}$ for origin constraints and $b_{ij}$ for destinations, the following extensions of Rules (i) and (ii) may be employed:

Rule ($\alpha$):  Set $a_{ij}R_i + b_{ij}K_j = c_{ij}$ for each cell in which a routing (stepping stone) appears.

Rule ($\alpha$ . 1): If positive slack is scheduled for any cell set the corresponding $R_i$ and $K_j$ equal to zero.

Rule ($\beta$):  Let $a_{ij}R_i + b_{ij}K_j = z_{ij}$ for each unoccupied cell. Only if $z_{ij} \geqq c_{ij}$ in each such cell can the program be regarded as an optimum.

These rules may, of course, be used from the outset without respect to the approximating assumption of rough proportionality in the coefficients. It may be advantageous, however, to use an approximate model for an advanced start on the exact solution. Any such solution provides a basis with a special kind of linear independence which arises from the position of the nonzero elements in transportation-type models.

The notation [13] may be used in order to clarify these remarks. Let $\hat{P}_{ij}$ represent any vector in a transportation model. From the schema of Fig. 3 it is clear that each such vector may be expressed as the sum of two unit vectors – viz.,

$$\hat{P}_{ij} = U_i + V_j, \tag{12}$$

49. If the direct problem contains inequalities the corresponding dual variables must also be nonnegative so that an additional adjustment may be required in order to satisfy all restrictions in Eq. (11).

50. This method of bounding can also be used in linear programming models which are not of the transportation variety.

where $U_i$, $i = 1, 2, \ldots, m$ is a unit vector form from the $i^{th}$ origin and $V_j$, $j = 1, 2, \ldots, n$ is a unit vector with the position of the unity element determined by the $j^{th}$ destination. A linearly independent collection of $m + n - 1$ such vectors is used to provide a basis for expressing all program possibilites at any stage in transportation calculations. Clearly, this property of linear independence is not affected when each $P_{ij}$ is replaced by a vector $P_{ij}$ with the unity elements replaced, respectively, by arbitrary constants $a_{ij}$ and $b_{ij}$. That is, the new vectors

$$P_{ij} = a_{ij}U_i + b_{ij}V_j \qquad (13)$$

also form a basis with general addition of one vector.

These interpretations may be put to use in constructing Table 3-A. The data in the rims are drawn from Table 3 in the text. Also drawn from that table are the unit profits shown in the rectangles of each square and the decimal figures used for the machine processing times. (Since all $b_{ij} = 1$, these values need not be introduced explicitly. It need only be remembered that the program values entered in each column must foot to the amount shown at the bottom.)

The circles of Table 4-C are next transferred to identical positions in Table 3-A and 'filled up' by reference to the rims. For each row values $x_{ij}$ are ascertained so that the expressions

$$\sum_{j=1}^{n} a_{ij}x_{ij} = a_i \qquad (14)$$

are satisfied for each row $i = 1, 2, \ldots, m$, and the expressions

$$\sum_{i=1}^{m} x_{ij} = b_j \qquad (15)$$

are satisfied for each column, $j = 1, 2, \ldots, n$.

Most of the figures are readily ascertained. For example, $\pi_1$ assigned to $M_1$ yields $x_{11} = 12,854$ in order to satisfy $.534\ x_{11} = 6,864$. The assignment of $\pi_1$ to $M_4$ and $M_5$ are similarly ascertained by reference to the row stipulations and the amount assigned to $M_\phi$ is obtained by subtracting the total

$$12,854 + 13,701 + 27,902 = 54,457 \text{ tons}$$

from the maximum demand, 126,151 tons, for this product.

The remainder of Table 3-A is determined in the same manner

so that the tonnages in each column total to the amount at its foot and the times utilized in each row sum to each machine's capacity. (Slack time, if any, on each machine is entered in the column labelled $\pi_\phi$ with unit processing time.) After all such figures are ascertained the figure for $\pi_\phi$ on $M_\phi$ is entered as a balancing amount.[51]

With Eqs. (14) and (15) satisfied the question of optimality may be examined by means of Rules ($\alpha$) and ($\beta$) with all $b_{ij} = 1$. Positive slack is programmed in the $M_\phi$ row so $R_\phi = 0$ as well as $K_1, K_4, K_5, K_7, K_8, K_9, K_{10}$, and $K_\phi$. Since $a_{11} = .534$ and $K_1 = 0$ the value $R_1 = 152$ is readily ascertained from the expression $.534 R_1 = 81$. Repeated application of Rule ($\alpha$) in this fashion yields the row and column numbers shown in Table 3-A.[52]

To determine whether this program is an optimum Rule ($\beta$) is applied. Upon examining the checked cell for $\pi_1$ on $M_2$ it is found that $z_{21} = a_{21}R_2 + K_1 = .511 \times 129.3 = 66$ which is lower than the value $c_{21} = 71$, shown in this cell. This program fails to pass the optimality test.

Two additional calculations may now be made in order to determine bounds on a possible optimum value. The program value $7,240,961$, listed at the top of Table 3-A, establishes a lower bound.[53] To obtain an upper bound it is necessary only to raise the $R_i$ and $K_j$ that have already been calculated so that all of the dual restrictions, including non-negativity, in Eq. (11) are satisfied. This is accomplished, in the present instance, by raising $R_2$ from 129.3 to 137.1. The sum, $7,300,598$, which is then obtained

51. This step may be omitted, if desired, and a blank circle simply entered in this cell. The value $34,320 = 5 \times 6,864$ hours at the foot of $\pi_\phi$ is, of course, the total machine capacity while the 174,228 tons assigned to $M_\phi$ is the maximum demand totalled over all products. The value 85,378 'tons' of $\pi_\phi$ assigned to $M_\phi$, as shown in Table 3-A, is the amount needed to balance out the $M_\phi$ row to its rim total. The 'time', $.401 = 34,320 \div 85,378$, is calculated residually. It may be interpreted (if desired) as an average time requirement for this unproduced demand.

52. From time to time it may be necessary to solve relatively small systems of simultaneous equations.

53. This value is approximate. [It is determined in this case by multiplying the programmed amounts by the corresponding unit returns; it may also be determined by the rim multiplications for Eq. (10).] To the indicated approximation the profit is some $10,000 lower than the total shown at the top of Table 4-C.

(to slide rule accuracy) by inserting the adjusted $R_i$ and $K_j$ in Eq. (10) provides an upper bound.

Suppose the difference \$59,637 = \$7,300,598 − \$7,240,961 between the program value and the upper bound is deemed sufficient to warrant further calculations to secure improvement. Such an improvement can be secured by entering a stepping stone for $\pi_1$ on $M_2$ – see the checked cell in Table 3-A – and removing one of the vectors in the current basis. For this purpose Rules (iii), (iv), and (v) are modified in the light of the discussion leading up to Eq. (13).

Let $P_{ij}$ represent the collection of vectors in the basis shown in Table 3-A and $P_{st}$ a new vector which is to be inserted in place of one already present. Then

$$P_{st} = \sum_{i \in I} \sum_{j \in J} y_{ij}(s, t) P_{ij} \qquad (16)$$

expresses this new vector (uniquely) in terms of the current basis.[54] Here $P_{st} = P_{21} = a_{21} U_2 + V_1$ and $P_{ij} = a_{ij} U_i + V_j$ so that Eq. (16) becomes

$$P_{21} = \sum_{i \in I} \sum_{j \in J} y_{ij}(2, 1) P_{ij}$$

or, $\qquad \alpha_{21} U_2 + V_1 = \sum_{i \in I} \sum_{j \in J} y_{ij}(2, 1)(a_{ij} U_i + V_j). \qquad (17)$

An extended version of the rook's tour[55] can be used to secure the coefficient values $y_{ij}(2, 1)$ for this purpose. Starting in the second row, third column of Table 3-A and assigning the indicated alternate plus and minus signs to the stepping stones on the tour shown therein the following extended expression is secured or Eq. (17):

$$a_{21} U_2 + V_1 = \frac{a_{21}}{a_{23}} [a_{23} U_2 + V_3] - \frac{a_{21}}{a_{23}} [a_{33} U_3 + V_3]$$

$$+ \frac{a_{21} a_{23}}{a_{23} a_{34}} [a_{34} U_3 + V_4] - \frac{a_{21} a_{33}}{a_{23} a_{34}} V_4 + V_1 \qquad (18)$$

$$= \frac{a_{21}}{a_{23}} P_{23} - \frac{a_{21}}{a_{23}} P_{33} + \frac{a_{21} a_{33}}{a_{23} a_{34}} P_{34} - \frac{a_{21} a_{33}}{a_{23} a_{34}} S_9 + S_6$$

54. See [13] from which this notation is adapted.
55. In some cases the tour must be extended beyond the usual terminal column position employed for exact transportation models. Doubts may always be resolved by reference to Eq.(16), which is controlling.

where $S_9 = V_4$ and $S_6 = V_1$ are the slack vectors associated with amounts programmed below maximum demands for $\pi_4$ and $\pi_1$, respectively. These ratios, formed from the $a$'s, are the nonzero coefficients $y_{ij}(2, 1)$ in Eq. (17).

To determine the amount $x_{21}$ to be inserted in the checked cell of Table 3-A and to designate the vector to be removed only the positively signed steps in the tour are considered. The smallest ratio

$$\theta = \frac{x_{ij}}{y_{ij}(2, 1)}, \qquad y_{ij}(2, 1) > 0, \tag{19}$$

where the values $x_{ij}$ are the amounts shown in positive stones on the tour and the $y_{ij}(2, 1)$ are obtained from the corresponding ratios of the $a$'s in Eq. (18), provides the value $x_{21} = \theta$ and indicates the vector $P_{ij}$ to be removed. The value

$$\theta = 2,624 \div \frac{.511}{.473} \doteq 2,429 \tag{20}$$

drawn from the coefficient of $P_{23}$ in Eq. (18) is this smallest ratio.[56]

Rules (iii), (iv), and (v) are now replaced by the following:

Rule ($\gamma$): Transfer all stepping stones not covered in the extended rook's tour at their previously programmed amounts.

Rule ($\delta$): Delete the positively signed stepping stone which yields the smallest value of $\theta$ in Eq. (19) and assign this amount to the cell which offers the promised improvement.

Rule ($\epsilon$): Transfer the remaining stones in the tour and enter the amounts required to conform to the rim stipulations.[57]

56. The ratio $\theta(c_{21} - z_{21}) = 2,429\ [71 - .511 \times 129.3] = \$11,965$ indicates the improvement which may be expected from the program change which will be effected. That is, a new level of profit slightly in excess of $7,252,000 may be anticipated when Table 3-A is changed to Table 3-B.

57. It is possible to supply formulas for this purpose but in this case (as usually happens) it is simpler to adjust these cells relative to the rims. Note, for example, that only $M$ produces $\pi_3$ in the new program. The amount assigned to this cell must therefore total to the figure at the foot of this column. This new assignment of $\pi_3$ to $M_3$ requires the other amounts in this row to be adjusted. But, by Rule ($\gamma$), 3,410 tons of $\pi_6$ have already been transferred to the $M_3$ row from a non-tour cell. The required reduction can

A direct application of these rules translates Table 3-A to Table 3-B.[58]

The value of this new program, $7,252,844, is secured from the direct functional

$$\sum_{i \in I} \sum_{j \in J} c_{ij} x_{ij}.$$

It exceeds the amounts shown in Tables 3-A and 4-C but falls short of the upper bound, $7,300,598, established in connection with the former program. An application of Rules ($\alpha$) and ($\beta$) shows that the program of Table 3-B is optimal. All of the dual restrictions (including nonnegativity) are satisfied so that the $R_i$ and $K_j$ are also evaluators for the corresponding rim stipulations. Every machine but only three products will return an increased profit if they are altered upwards. Moreover, any increase in machine capacity will return a greater profit than any increase in product demand. The greatest single increase per unit alteration can be secured from $M_5$ which will return (over current variable cost) some $321 for each hour's increase in its capacity after all adjustments to a new optimum are effected.

Additional information can also be secured from further scrutiny of Table 3-B. For example, this program is a unique optimum since $z_{ij} > c_{ij}$ for all vacant cells. If desired, the profit data may also be examined in order to ascertain the possible repercussions of inaccurate estimates by considering the values

---

only be secured, therefore, from the amount of $\pi_4$ assigned to $M_3$. An additional 2,624 tons of $\pi_3$ having been assigned to $M_3$ the value (.424 ÷ .376) 2,624 ≐ 2,960 indicates (to a slide rule approximation) the required reduction. Hence the $\pi$ assignment on this machine is reduced from 4,334 tons (Table 3-A) to 1,374 tons (Table 3-B). This reduction must next be compensated by adding the same 2,960 tons to slack on $\pi_4$. Finally, the 69,265 tons assigned to slack on $\pi_1$ in Table 3-B reflects the reduction from its previous level of 71,694 tons in order to compensate for the 2,429 tons of additional $\pi_1$ production which emanates from the assignment of this product to $M_2$.

58. The 84,847 'tons' of $\pi_\phi$ assigned to $M_\phi$ is calculated residually, as before, by securing the difference between total $M_\phi$ assignments and the row total of 174,228 tons and the figure .404 hours per ton is the multiplier required to reduce this amount to the 34,320 hours shown at the bottom of the $\pi_\phi$ column. These calculations may be omitted, but are shown here for completeness.

$z_{ij} = \hat{c}_{ij}$ necessary to bring in a possible alternate optimum. The closest margin is supplied by $c_{23}$.[59] Raising this unit profit by $4 from $91 to $95, or a relative error of only 4.4 per cent, this cell might become a candidate for an alternate optimum. Other profits which might be questioned in this manner are $c_{31}$ which need be low by only 5.3 per cent to produce this result, and $c_{51}$ and $c_{15}$ with error margins of 9.25 per cent and 9.5 per cent, respectively. If these profits noted on these particular routes are accurate, the program may reasonably be regarded as a 'true' optimum. The remaining unit profits are wide of the mark in terms of any potential effects. Either in absolute or relative terms their error tolerance is sufficiently high (many of them allowing 50 per cent or better errors, without any effect) that it is hardly likely that data refinement will prove worthwhile.

Additional analysis can be employed to determine the relative tolerances of all such errors, including, for example, the unit profits in the stepping stone cells. This would, of course, require the calculation of new values for the $R$ and $K_j$. Finally, a full-scale sensitivity analysis might be conducted to cover (e.g. minimal allowable) patterns of error in the $a_{ij}$ as well as the $c_{ij}$.[60]

## Part two

It was suggested that the concept of approximate models can be used for guidance in simplifying computations and analysis. An illustration can be provided with an example which further extends the techniques discussed in part one of this appendix.

Exhibit I is representative of a model for a problem in oil field exploitation.[61] The example is a hypothetical one, covering four reservoirs, with one well per reservoir.[62] Each 'block triangular' array of decimal coefficients reflects well-flow pressures adjusted

---

59. Slide rule accuracy only is used.

60. Further explanations will be offered in a research report which the authors have under way with H. A. Simon.

61. This example is based on models developed by J. Aronofsky and S. Lee of Magnolia Petroleum Company. See [2].

62. These data, supplied by Mr Carl Guenther of Arabian American Oil Co., are artificially contrived simply to illustrate certain kinds of problems. The authors are indebted to Mr Guenther and his associates, Messrs C. Harris, R. Dickson, and H. Wager, as well as J. Aronofsky and S. Lee for background material and guidance.

for the maximum withdrawals, noted under $P_0$, in four successive time periods. The 'echelons' of unity elements, one echelon under each triangle, restrict total withdrawals to the recoverable oil in place in each reservoir. The diagonals (of ones) under each echelon reflect the pipeline capacity available in each time period. Unit profits are listed above each column ($P_1, \ldots, P_{16}$) in dollars per barrel. The problem is to determine the most profitable pattern of production over the four time periods.[63]

The bottom portion of Exhibit 1 is an exact transportation model. The upper portion contains mixed hierarchical elements. Using these criteria as guides it is apparent that the 'dominances' within the triangles should be used, if possible, to guide the model approximation[64] without altering the transportation model at the bottom. This will be done in a way which, by an appropriate interpretation, provides access to the bounded variables techniques [11].

For this purpose the constraints can be either loosened or tightened. Suppose, therefore, that the constraints are tightened by assuming that in each succeeding period a maximum drawdown (and hence pressure drop) occurred in the preceding one.

The first four restrictions in the upper portion of Exhibit 1 may be used for illustration. They are:

$$
\begin{aligned}
.01677\, x_1 &\leqq 900 \\
.00057\, x_1 + .01677\, x_2 &\leqq 900 \\
.00033\, x_1 + .00057\, x_2 + .01677\, x_2 &\leqq 900 \\
.00023\, x_1 + .00033\, x_2 + .00057\, x_3 + .01677\, x_4 &\leqq 900
\end{aligned}
\tag{21}
$$

The first expression yields

$$
x_1 \leqq \frac{900}{.01677} \doteq 53.7 \times 10^3,
$$

63. See [2] for more detailed discussions.

64. The upper portion can also be regarded approximately as part of a generalized warehousing model. Under other circumstances (e.g. pressure maintenance as well as pressure drops) one of the extended versions of the warehousing model (see [11]) might have been used as a guide.

Exhibit 1

## A Four-field Pipeliner Model, 1 Well per Field

| Rows | C $P_0$ | .80 $P_1$ | .76 $P_2$ | .72 $P_3$ | .65 $P_4$ | .76 $P_5$ | .72 $P_6$ | .68 $P_7$ | .60 $P_8$ | .72 $P_9$ | .67 $P_{10}$ | .60 $P_{11}$ | .50 $P_{12}$ | .60 $P_{13}$ | .58 $P_{14}$ | .56 $P_{15}$ | .54 $P_{16}$ |
|---|---|---|---|---|---|---|---|---|---|---|---|---|---|---|---|---|---|
| 1 | 900 | .01677 | | | | | | | | | | | | | | | |
| 2 | 900 | .00057 | .01677 | | | | | | | | | | | | | | |
| 3 | 900 | .00033 | .00057 | .01677 | | | | | | | | | | | | | |
| 4 | 900. | .00023 | .00033 | .00057 | .01677 | | | | | | | | | | | | |
| 5 | 1,200 | | | | | .04855 | | | | | | | | | | | |
| 6 | 1,200 | | | | | .00177 | .04855 | | | | | | | | | | |
| 7 | 1,200 | | | | | .00096 | .00177 | .04855 | | | | | | | | | |
| 8 | 1,200 | | | | | .00072 | .00096 | .00177 | .04855 | | | | | | | | |
| 9 | 1,300 | | | | | | | | | .10650 | | | | | | | |
| 10 | 1,300 | | | | | | | | | .00400 | .10650 | | | | | | |
| 11 | 1,300 | | | | | | | | | .00230 | .00400 | .10650 | | | | | |
| 12 | 1,300 | | | | | | | | | .00150 | .00230 | .00400 | .10650 | | | | |
| 13 | 1,800 | | | | | | | | | | | | | .00152 | | | |
| 14 | 1,800 | | | | | | | | | | | | | .000048 | .00152 | | |
| 15 | 1,800 | | | | | | | | | | | | | .000028 | .000048 | .00152 | |
| 16 | 1,800 | | | | | | | | | | | | | .000021 | .000028 | .000048 | .00152 |
| 17 | 27,700 | 1 | | | | | | | | | | | | | | | |
| 18 | 11,100 | | | | | | 1 | 1 | 1 | | | | | | | | |
| 19 | 33,000 | | | | | | | | | 1 | 1 | 1 | | | | | |
| 20 | 483,300 | 1 | | | | | | | | | | | | 1 | | | |
| 21 | 20,000 | | | | | | | | | 1 | | | | 1 | 1 | | |
| 22 | 20,000 | | 1 | | | | | | | | 1 | | | | | 1 | |
| 23 | 20,000 | | | 1 | | | | | | | | 1 | | | | | |
| 24 | 20,000 | | | | 1 | | | | | | | | 1 | | | | 1 |

to slide rule accuracy. Substituting this value, the maximum period 1 withdrawal, in the second expression yields

$$x_2 \leqq \frac{900 - .00057 \times 53.7 \times 10^3}{.01677} \doteq 51.9 \times 10^3.$$

Continuing in this manner the expressions in Eq. (21) are replaced by the conditions:

$$
\begin{aligned}
\hat{x}_1 &\leqq 53.7 \times 10^3 \\
\hat{x}_2 &\leqq 51.9 \times 10^3 \\
\hat{x}_3 &\leqq 50.8 \times 10^3 \\
\hat{x}_4 &\leqq 50.1 \times 10^3,
\end{aligned}
\tag{22}
$$

a statement in bounded variables form.

Note that the approximating assumption conforms to one possible mode of production. Hence, the solution attained will be feasible, even if not optimal. An upper bound can be established, of course, either by loosening the constraints, recourse to the dual, etc.

Exhibit 2 provides a working format for the calculations, reservoirs (by number) being listed in the stub and time periods in the captions. The row sums are reservoir capacities.[65] The column sums are pipeline capacities in each period. $\phi(T)$ is reservoir slack.[66] The row labelled $\phi(C)$ is pipeline slack, or unused pipeline capacity. The rectangle in each cell contains the unit profit in dollars per barrel. The figures in the right triangles of the upper left-hand corners are the bounds (upper limits)[67] on each variable obtained by the approximating assumption such as the ones shown in Eq. (22).

Suppose now that the 'northwest corner rule' [13] is used to secure the initial basis shown in Exhibit 3.[68] Commencing in row 1, column 1, the rule is applied in the usual fashion until

65. Up to oil-water interfaces in each reservoir.
66. Unrecovered oil.
67. The method to be described can be extended to cover lower bounds as well.
68. More efficient methods are available, but the northwest corner rule is used here in order to secure a longer series of iterations and thus illustrate various contingencies which might occur.

row 3, column 3, is encountered. Here the upper bound (noted in the upper left-hand corner of the cell) takes precedence over the rims. Only 7.43 units can be assigned. The cells both to the right

Exhibit 2

Working Format for Combined Transportation and Bounded Variables Techniques

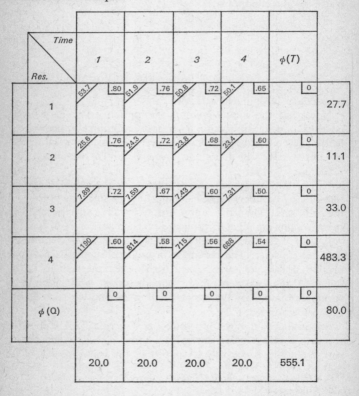

| Time / Res. | 1 | 2 | 3 | 4 | $\phi(T)$ | |
|---|---|---|---|---|---|---|
| 1 | 53.7 / .80 | 51.9 / .76 | 50.8 / .72 | 50.1 / .65 | 0 | 27.7 |
| 2 | 25.6 / .76 | 24.3 / .72 | 23.8 / .68 | 23.4 / .60 | 0 | 11.1 |
| 3 | 7.89 / .72 | 7.59 / .67 | 7.43 / .60 | 7.31 / .50 | 0 | 33.0 |
| 4 | 11.90 / .60 | 8.14 / .58 | 7.15 / .56 | 6.88 / .54 | 0 | 483.3 |
| $\phi(Q)$ | 0 | 0 | 0 | 0 | 0 | 80.0 |
| | 20.0 | 20.0 | 20.0 | 20.0 | 555.1 | |

and below this one must therefore be brought into play. At 12.57 units the latter fulfills the requirements of column 3. In row 3, column 4, however, the variable is again effectively constrained by the bound of 7.31 units so that the adjacent cells to the right and below must again be brought in. Finally, the table is completed by assigning the 80 units shown in row 5, column 5.[69]

Exhibit 3

Initial Table

| | | 1 | 2 | 3 | 4 | 5 | |
|---|---|---|---|---|---|---|---|
| | $K_j$ | .71 | .67 | .56 | .54 | 0 | |
| | $R_i$ | | | | | | |
| 1 | .09 | 53.7 / .80<br>20 | 51.9 / .76<br>7.7÷ | 50.8 / .72<br>✓ | 50.1 / .65 | 0 | 27.7 |
| 2 | .05 | 25.6 / .76 | 24.3 / .72<br>11.1 | 23.8 / .68 | 23.4 / .60 | 0 | 11.1 |
| 3 | 0 | 7.89 / .72 | 7.59 / .67<br>1.2– | 7.43 / .60<br>$\overline{7.43}$ | 7.31 / .50<br>$\overline{7.31}$ | 0<br>17.06÷ | 33.0 |
| 4 | 0 | 1190 / .60 | 814 / .58 | 715 / .56<br>12.57÷ | 688 / .54<br>12.69 | 0<br>458.04– | 483.3 |
| 5 | 0 | 0 | 0 | 0 | 0 | 0<br>(80.0) | 80.0 |
| | | 20.0 | 20.0 | 20.0 | 20.0 | 555.1 | |

Only those cells in which the variables do not bump up against their bounds are counted as stepping stones. The bars over 7.43 and 7.31 indicate that these bounded values are not available for

69. The conventions employed here differ from those in Part 1 of this appendix. The circle indicates that this value will not be changed, a condition which is apparent from the nature of the problem.

tours. Hence, there are exactly $m + n - 1 = 5 + 5 - 1 = 9$ stones available,[70] as required for a basis.

Since a stepping stone appears in row 5, column 5, the values $R_5 = K_5 = 0$ are used to initiate the calculations of row-column sum numbers. Ignoring $\overline{7.43}$ and $\overline{7.31}$ the remaining $R_i$ and $K_i$ are calculated by reference to Rules (i) and (ii) of Part 1.

Applying the optimality test it is seen that the value $c_{13} = \$.72$, in the checked cell, exceeds the corresponding $z_{13} = R_1 + K_3 = \$.65$, so that this program fails to pass as an optimum.[71] The alternate plus and minus signs starting in row 1, column 2 and ending in row 4, column 3 – skipping over the cells in which bounded values appear – indicate the tour from which Exhibit 4 is constructed. The smallest positive value is 7.7 in row 1, column 2. Before this value is transferred to the checked cell, however, it must be tested against the bound by adding the same amount to all negative steps in the tour. Reference to the relevant sum, $1.2 + 7.7 = 8.9$, in row 3, column 2, shows that this would violate the bound. The greatest addition that this cell will tolerate is $\overline{7.59} - 1.2 = 6.39$. Hence this value is entered in row 3, column 1, and then added to the programmed amount for each negative cell and subtracted from the positive ones. All cells not included in the tour are, of course, simply transferred from Exhibit 3 without altering their values.

Exhibit 4 results from carrying out these instructions. The new value, 6.39, appears in row 1, column 3. Crossing out the amount 1.2 and entering $\overline{7.59}$ in row 3, column 3 eliminates this cell from the basis – it is, effectively, the source of the transfer. Non-tour values are entered without adjustment from Exhibit 3. A stroke is drawn through the old values on the tour and the new values are entered directly above them. These new values result, of course, from subtracting 6.39 from the old ones in the cells marked '+' and adding it to the ones marked '−'. A bar is drawn above the value 7.59 in row 3, column 2, to indicate that this variable is at its bound and is therefore not in the basis.[72]

70. Including three slack vectors in the last column.

71. The cells with barred values are ignored for this purpose until a later stage, as will shortly be explained.

72. Essentially, the bounded variables technique uses information provided by the simplex tableau in order to ascertain what is happening in these extra dimensions. The variables are simply 'carried along' for this purpose.

The old values for $R_i$ and $K_j$ are shown in Exhibit 4 and a stroke drawn through all those which change prior to inserting the new ones.[73] The first failure,[74] in applying Rule (ii), is

Exhibit 4

Second Table

| | | 1 | 2 | 3 | 4 | 5 | |
|---|---|---|---|---|---|---|---|
| | $K_j$ | .64 / .71 | .60 / .67 | .56 / .56 | .54 / .54 | 0 / 0 | |
| $R_i$ | | | | | | | |
| **1** | .16 / .09 | 53.7 \| .80 <br> 20.0+ | 51.9 \| .76 <br> 1.31 / 7.7 | 50.8 \| .72 <br> 6.39− | 50.1 \| .65 | 0 | 27.7 |
| **2** | .12 / .05 | 25.6 \| .76 | 24.3 \| .72 <br> 11.1 | 23.8 \| .68 | 23.4 \| .60 | 0 | 11.1 |
| **3** | 0 / 0 | 7.89 \| .72 <br> ✓ | 7.59 \| .67 <br> 7.59 / 7.2 | 7.43 \| .60 <br> 7.43 | 7.31 \| .50 <br> 7.31 | 0 <br> 10.67+ / 17.06+ | 33.0 |
| **4** | 0 / 0 | 11.90 \| .60 | 8.14 \| .58 | 7.15 \| .56 <br> 6.18+ / 12.57+ | 6.88 \| .54 <br> 12.69 | 0 <br> 464.43− / 458.04− | 483.3 |
| **5** | 0 / 0 | 0 | 0 | 0 | 0 | 0 <br> (80.0) | 80.0 |
| | | 20.0 | 20.0 | 20.0 | 20.0 | 555.1 | |

73. In large-scale calculations it may be worthwhile stating an explicit rule to indicate which $R_i$ and $K_j$ are to be altered in proceeding from one tableau to its successor.

74. In large-scale calculations the first failure rather than the greatest difference, $z_{ij} - c_{ij}$, is used. The next tableau is devised relative to this cell in order to save calculating time and possible errors of computation.

encountered in the cell associated with row 3, column 1 – as indicated by the check mark. The tour for this cells starts in row 3, column 5, and terminates in row 1, column 1, as indicated. The

Exhibit 5
Third Table

| $K_j$ | 1 | 2 | 3 | 4 | 5 | |
|---|---|---|---|---|---|---|
| | .72 .64 .71 | .68 .60 .67 | .64 .56 .56 | .54 .54 .54 | 0 0 0 | |
| $R_i$ | | | | | | |
| **1** .08 .16 .09 | 53.7 / .80 13.82+ 20.0+ | 51.9 / .76 1.31 7.7 | 50.8 / .72 12.57 6.39 | 50.1 / .65 ✓ | 0 | 27.7 |
| **2** .04 .12 .05 | 25.6 / .76 | 24.3 / .72 11.1 | 23.8 / .68 | 23.4 / .60 | 0 | 11.1 |
| **3** 0 0 0 | 7.89 / .72 6.18– | 7.59 / .67 7.59 1.2 | 7.43 / .60 7.43 | 7.31 / .50 7.31 | 0 4.49+ 10.67+ 77.06+ | 33.0 |
| **.4** 0 0 0 | 11.90 / .60 | 8.14 / .58 | 7.15 / .56 6.18 12.57+ | 6.88 / .54 12.69+ | 0 470.61– 464.43– 458.04– | 483.3 |
| **5** 0 0 0 | 0 | 0 | 0 | 0 | 0 ⟨80.0⟩ | 80.0 |
| | 20.0 | 20.0 | 20.0 | 20.0 | 555.1 | |

smallest positively signed value, 6.18, is found in row 4, column 3. Checking the addition of this amount to all negative steps no bound is encountered. Therefore this adjustment is effected by the usual transportation model rules and Exhibit 5 emerges. The value 6.18 in row 4, column 3, is crossed out and this amount inserted in row 3, column 1. The other tour cells are adjusted, as indicated, by drawing a stroke through their previous value and entering the new amount directly above them.[75] Non-tour cells are, of course, simply transferred from Exhibit 4 to 5.

The check mark in row 1, column 4, shows where the new $R_i$ and $K_j$ fail to cover a $c_{ij}$. The smallest positive amount, 4.49, in the tour encounters a bound when added to the value 6.18 in row 3, column 1. Hence only $1.71 = 7.89 - 6.18$ can be placed in the checked cell.[76] When this is done, and all necessary adjustments effected, Exhibit 6 emerges.

The program in this exhibit returns a profit of $53,645. Ignoring the cells with barred values it is found that the dual constraints are satisfied. The program is therefore optimal – or a semi-optimum[77] – for this 'transportation-stage' of the calculations.

Cells which contain barred values are now examined to see whether further improvement can be secured by *reducing* one of these variables. The usual $z_{ij} - c_{ij}$ criterion is therefore reversed. If $R_i + K_j > c_{ij}$ in any of these cells the (barred) program value in this cell can profitably be reduced.

Row 3, column 3, provides the first such encounter. Here $c_{33} = \$.60$ and $R_3 + K_3 = z_{33} = \$.61$. The amount assigned to this cell should be reduced in order to secure further improvement. The cells to be adjusted in order to compensate for this reduction are discovered by the usual stepping stone tour. Since a

75. These data are preserved for checking, keeping track of the state of affairs, and because valuable byproduct information can be secured in this manner. If cells in the original worksheets are made sufficiently large, all this can be done without transcribing 'Cut-out' cells, to be pasted on, plastic cover sheets, etc., can also be used to save transcribing time and errors.

76. Note: If more than one such bound is encountered, the *smallest* difference is entered in the checked cell. Ties result in degeneracy, which is resolved in the usual manner. See [13].

77. It is not, of course, a true transportation optimum since the cells with barred amounts have values $R_i + K_j < c_{ij}$. (These values will be considered at the next stage of calculations.) A bound to the possible improvement can, of course, be secured by raising $K_1$ and $K_2$ to .72 and .67, respectively, in order to satisfy the dual constraints. Multiplying the $R_i$ and $K_j$, thus altered, against their corresponding rim stipulations shows that the improvement will be at most $979 = \$54,624 - \$53,645$. Succeeding calculations are therefore executed only for exposition purposes.

*reduction* is being programmed, however, the adjustment rule is reversed. The smallest *negatively* signed amount on the tour, 1.71, is selected and subtracted from $\overline{7.43}$. It is also added to

**Exhibit 6**
**Fourth Table**

| | 1 | 2 | 3 | 4 | 5 | |
|---|---|---|---|---|---|---|
| $K_j$ | .69 .72 .64 .71 | .65 .68 .60 .67 | .61 .64 .56 .56 | .54 .54 .54 .54 | 0 0 0 0 | |
| 1 .11 .08 .16 .09 | 53.7 \| .80  12.11 13.82 20.0 | 51.9 \| .76  1.31 7.7 | 50.8 \| .72  12.57+ 6.39 | 50.1 \| .65  1.71− | 0 | 27.7 |
| 2 .07 .04 .12 .05 | 25.6 \| .76 | 24.3 \| .72 | 23.8 \| .68  11.1 | 23.4 \| .60 | 0 | 11.1 |
| 3 0 0 0 0 | 7.89 \| .72  7.89 6.18 | 7.59 \| .67  7.59 1.2 | 7.43 \| .60  ✓ 7.43 | 7.31 \| .50  7.31 | 0  2.78+ 4.49+ 10.67+ 17.06+ | 33.0 |
| 4 0 0 0 0 | 1190 \| .60 | 814 \| .58 | 715 \| .56  6.18+ 12.57 | 688 \| .54  10.98+ 12.69 | 0  472.32− 470.61− 464.63− 458.04− | 483.3 |
| 5 0 0 0 0 | 0 | 0 | 0 | 0 | 0  (80.0) | 80.0 |
| | 20.0 | 20.0 | 20.0 | 20.0 | 555.1 | |

every positively signed stone and subtracted from every negatively signed one on the tour.

This eliminates the cell at row 1, column 4, from the basis and brings in row 3, column 3, at 5.72 units. (The latter value is now below its bound.) The number of stones required for a basis is therefore preserved. After all cells in the tour have been adjusted in the indicated manner and those not in the tour are transferred at their previous values, the program of Exhibit 7 is obtained.

Exhibit 7

New Table after Adjusting Bounded Variables

| $R_i$ \ $K_j$ | 1 | 2 | 3 | 4 | 5 | |
|---|---|---|---|---|---|---|
| | .68 .69 .72 .64 .71 | .64 .65 .68 .60 .67 | .60 .61 .64 .56 .56 | .54 .54 .54 .56 .54 | 0 -0- -0- -0- -0- | |
| 1 .12 .11 .08 .16 .09 | 53.7 .80 12.11 13.82 20.0 | 51.9 .76 1.31 7.7 | 50.8 .72 14.28 12.57 6.39 | 50.1 .65 1.71 | 0 | 27.7 |
| 2 .08 .07 .04 .12 .05 | 25.6 .76 | 24.3 .72 11.1 | 23.8 .68 | 23.4 .60 | 0 | 11.1 |
| 3 0 -0- -0- -0- -0- | 7.89 .72 7.89 6.18 | 7.59 .67 7.59 1.2 | .743 .60 5.72 7.43 | 7.31 .50 7.31 | 0 4.49+ 2.78 4.49 10.67 17.06 | 33.0 |
| 4 0 -0- -0- -0- -0- | 1190 .60 | 814 .58 | 715 .56 6.18 12.59 | 688 .50 12.69+ 10.93 12.67 | 0 470.61− 472.32 470.61 464.43 458.06 | 483.3 |
| 5 0 -0- -0- -0- -0- | 0 | 0 | 0 | 0 | 0 (80.0) | 80.0 |
| | 20.0 | 20.0 | 20.0 | 20.0 | 555.1 | |

New values for $R_i$ and $K_j$ are secured in the usual manner after this 'bounded variables adjustment' is made. These values are shown in the stub and caption of Exhibit 7.

It is now necessary to check the result for a transportation 'semi-optimum' by applying rule (ii).[78] This test is passed, but not the one for the bounded variables: $R_3 + K_4 = .54$ while $c_{44} = .50$. A gain can therefore be obtained by reducing the value

Exhibit 8

Optimality Check

| | | 1 | 2 | 3 | 4 | 5 | |
|---|---|---|---|---|---|---|---|
| | $K_j$ | .68 .69 .72 .64 .71 | .64 .65 .68 .60 .67 | .60 .61 .64 .56 .56 | .54 .54 .54 .54 .54 | 0 0 0 0 0 | |
| $R_i$ | | | | | | | |
| 1 | .12 .11 .08 .16 .09 | 53.7 \| .80 ; 12.11 ; 73.82 ; 20.0 | 51.9 \| .76 ; 1.31 ; 7.7 | 50.8 \| .72 ; 14.28 ; 12.57 ; 6.39 | 50.1 \| .65 ; 1.71 | 0 | 27.7 |
| 2 | .08 .07 .04 .12 .05 | 25.8 \| .76 ; A | 24.3 \| .72 ; 11.1 | 23.8 \| .68 ; A | 23.4 \| .60 | 0 | 11.1 |
| 3 | 0 0 0 0 0 | 7.89 \| .72 ; 7.89 ; 8.18 | 7.59 \| .67 ; 7.59 ; 1.2 | 7.43 \| .60 ; 5.72 ; 7.43 | 7.31 \| .50 ; 7.31 | 11.80 4.49 2.78 4.49 10.67 17.06 \| 0 | 33.0 |
| 4 | 0 0 0 0 0 | 1190 \| .60 | 814 \| .58 | 715 \| .56 ; 6.18 ; 12.59 | 688 \| .54 ; 20.00 ; 12.69 ; 10.98 ; 12.69 | 463.30 470.61 472.32 470.61 464.43 458.95 \| 0 | 483.3 |
| 5 | 0 0 0 0 0 | 0 | 0 | 0 | 0 ; 80.0 | 0 | 80.0 |
| | | 20.0 | 20.0 | 20.0 | 20.0 | 555.1 | |

$\overline{7.31}$ appearing in row 3, column 4. There is only one negative stone in the three-step tour necessary to surround this cell. It has the value 470.61 shown in row 4, column 5. Hence 7.31 can be

78. Ignoring, of course, the cells which contain barred values.

subtracted from it without trouble and added to the two positive stones (in the tour) which appear at row 3, column 5, and row 4, column 4.

**Exhibit 9**

An Optimum Program

| | | 1 | 2 | 3 | 4 | 5 | |
|---|---|---|---|---|---|---|---|
| | $K_j$ | .68 | .64 | .60 | .54 | 0 | |
| **1** | $R_i$ .12 | 53.7 \ .80 12.11 | 51.9 \ .76 1.31 | 50.8 \ .72 14.28 | 50.1 \ .65 | 0 | 27.7 |
| **2** | .08 | 25.6 \ .76 | 24.3 \ .72 11.10 | 23.8 \ .68 | 23.4 \ .60 | .0 | 11.1 |
| **3** | 0 | 7.89 \ .72 7.89 | 7.59 \ .67 7.59 | 7.43 \ .60 5.72 | 7.31 \ .50 | 0 11.80 | 33.0 |
| **4** | 0 | 1190 \ .60 | 814 \ .58 | 715 \ .56 | 688 \ .54 20.00 | 0 463.30 | 483.3 |
| **5** | 0 | 0 | 0 | 0 | 0 | 0 (80.00) | 80.0 |
| | | 20.0 | 20.0 | 20.0 | 20.0 | 555.1 | |

The entire amount in row 3, column 4, of Exhibit 7 is therefore eliminated and the tour stones adjusted by adding this amount to the positive steps and subtracting it from the negative ones. Exhibit 8 is then secured and the new values for $R_i$ and $K_j$ shown there are obtained, as before, by applying Rules (i) and (ii).

All $R_i + K_j \geq c_{ij}$ in the cells which do not contain bounded values. The test of transportation semi-optimality is thus passed.[79] The cells with barred values have $R_i + K_j < c_{ij}$ so that the bounded variables criterion for an optimum is also satisfied. Both tests being successful the program is an optimum for the full (approximation) model.

Transferring this program to Exhibit 9, for simplicity of exposition, the optimum value $\sum \sum c_{ij} x_{ij} = \$53,955$ is readily calculated. The improvement over the program in Exhibit 6, $\$310 = \$53,955 - \$53,645$ is rather small.

This optimum holds, of course, only for the approximate model. It should therefore be bounded to discover if a significant departure from the exact optimum is possibly present. The programs of Exhibits 9 and 6 both provide feasible programs for the transportation component of Exhibit 1. The latter program (Exhibit 6) provides the better solution to this component, considered alone. The bound established for that program, $\$54,624$, can therefore be used for the transportation component of the exact model as well. This is justified by noting that the transportation component of the exact model, considered alone, cannot have a lower optimum than the full model with all restrictions considered. The difference, $\$669 = \$54,624 - \$53,955$, is not worth the trouble of further calculation. Moreover (as previously noted), the approximating optimum program is also feasible in the exact case. Hence further adjustments are not necessary. The problem is regarded as solved by the program of Exhibit 9.

*Part three*

Table 5 of the text was used to illustrate some of the constructs of activity analysis. A major purpose of this approach to programming concerns the analysis of rules which might be employed to guide the activities of an entity under a decentralized management regime. The objectives of each official in such an entity may assume a variety of forms relative to the objectives of other officials, and the entity itself. They may conflict or complement one another, or they may be entirely neutral. (The economic model of a free price economy illustrates the possibilities.) The

79. The cells marked $A$, in row 3 are alternate optima since $R_i + K_j = c_{ij}$ in these cells.

358

purpose of the rules (e.g. efficiency pricing) in activity analysis is to ensure that certain levels of attainment (e.g. efficient points) will be secured when each official is allowed to pursue his own objectives.

How can multiple objectives, such as these, be restated in order to make this problem amenable to the methods of linear programming? The purpose of this appendix is to reformulate the models of activity analysis so that this can be done and then to develop computational procedures for locating all efficient points and efficiency prices.[80]

Recall that the matrix $A$ of coefficients[81] in any activity analysis model may be partitioned into three major sectors – viz.,

$$A_F, \text{ for final commodities}$$
$$A_I, \text{ for intermediate commodities} \qquad (23)$$
$$A_P, \text{ for primary commodities.}$$

A vector $y' = (y_F', y_I', y_P')$ of 'commodities' can then be similarly partitioned and associated with each such array of coefficients, by a vector $x$, of activity levels, defined so that

$$Ax = y$$
$$x \geqq 0, \quad y_F \geqq 0, \quad y_I = 0, \quad -y_P \leqq -\eta_P \quad \eta_P \leqq 0. \qquad (24)$$

Among the possible vectors $y$ are subsets called efficient points. These points are distinguished by the property that it is not possible to improve any component (within the limits allowed by the restriction) without worsening at least one (and possibly more) of the others.

The following necessary and sufficient conditions of efficiency are established by Koopmans:[82] A vector $y$ is efficient if and only if there exists a vector $p$[83] with

$$p'y = 0$$
$$p'A \leqq 0 \qquad (25)$$
and $\qquad p_F > 0, \quad p_{P=} \geqq 0, \quad p_{P>} = 0,$

80. Also called 'shadow prices' and 'accounting prices'. See Koopmans [50d, p. 65].

81. E.g. Table 5 in the text. Such matrices are called 'technology matrices'. *Vide, loc. cit.*, p. 37.

82. Theorem 5.4.1, p. 82, *loc. cit.*

83. This will be called a price vector, following Koopmans, although (as he shows) it may also be related to the concept of marginal rates of substitution. Cf. *loc. cit.*, pp. 66 ff.

where $p_F$ and $p_P$ are prices of final and primary commodities, respectively. $p_{P=}$ indicates those primary commodities (e.g. factors of production) which are utilized to capacity and $p_{P>}$ those which are not.

In order to construct a class of special linear programming problems for locating such $y$'s and $p$'s, it is useful to introduce the concept of 'antecedents' of efficient points and prices. These antecedents can be interpreted as activity vectors with special properties. They are here characterized as optimal solutions to dual linear programming problems so constructed that they can be associated with solutions to the problem in vector optimization stated by Koopmans. Means which are available for determining all optimum extreme point solutions[84] to any linear programming problem can then be used to determine all efficient points. An easy extension provides solutions to the corresponding duals. Thus all efficient points and the corresponding efficiency prices can be readily ascertained by linear programming techniques.

The sets of all antecedents of efficient points are unions of convex polyhedral sets. In general, such unions do not form convex sets. Also, since the linear image of a convex set is convex, the sets of all efficient points are unions of polyhedral convex sets and the same holds for the efficiency prices.

The linear programming problem to be considered may now be stated in matrix form as

$$\max v^{0\prime} A_F x$$

subject to
$$-A_P x \leqq -\eta_P$$
$$-A_I x = 0$$
$$x \geqq 0 \tag{26}$$
$$v^0 > 0$$

with its dual
$$\min w_P{}'(-\eta_P)$$

subject to
$$v^{0\prime} A_F \leqq -w_P{}' A_P - w_I{}' A_I$$

or
$$v^{0\prime} A_F + w_I{}' A_I + w_P{}' A_P \leqq 0, \tag{27}$$

with
$$w_P{}' \geqq 0 \text{ and } w_I{}' \text{ unrestricted.}$$

84. E.g. by the use of 'Tarry data' for the labyrinth problem. See [9]. There is no loss of generality in confining attention to extreme point optima since all others can be secured from them. See [16].

*Theorem:* If

$$(y_F', y_I', y_P') = (x^{*\prime}A_F', x^{*\prime}A_I', x^{*\prime}A_P') \text{ and } x^* \quad (28)$$

is an optimum solution to Eq. (26) then $y$ is necessarily an efficient point, and

$$p' = (p_F', p_I', p_P') \equiv (v^{0\prime}, w_I^{*\prime}, w_F^{*\prime}) \quad (29)$$

the corresponding efficiency prices where, of course, $w_I^*$ and $w_P^*$ are parts of an optimal solution to the dual, Eq. (27).

*Proof:* It is necessary only to show that these optimum solutions conform to the Conditions (25). Constructive procedures for locating all such optima will then be supplied. These solutions provide all efficient points and prices. The condition $p'A \leqq 0$ is, of course, equivalent to Eq. (27) since

$$v^{0\prime}A_F + w_I'A_I + w_P'A\mathring{P} = p'A.$$

Also,

$$p'y = v^{0\prime}A_Fx^* + w_I^{*\prime}A_Ix^* + w_P^{*\prime}A_Px^*$$
$$= v^{0\prime}A_Fx^* + w_P^{*\prime}\eta_P \quad (30)$$

since $A_Ix^* = 0$. Moreover, by the theorem of the alternative [80] $(w_P^*)_r = 0$ whenever $-(A_Px^*)_r < (-\eta_P)_r$. Hence $(A_Px^*)_k = (\eta_P)_k$, $k \neq r$, so that

$$w_P^{*\prime}A_Px^* = w_P^{*\prime}\eta_P.$$

It therefore follows that

$$p'y = v^{0\prime}A_Fx^* + w_P^{*\prime}\eta_P = w_P^{*\prime}(-\eta_P) + w_P^{*\prime}\eta_P = 0 \quad (31)$$

since, by the dual theorem, $v^{0\prime}A_Fx^* = w_P^{*\prime}(-\eta_P)$.

The first two conditions in Eq. (25) are thus established. The remaining properties, $p_F > 0$, $p_{P=} \geqq 0$, and $p_{P>} = 0$, on the price vector, are also obtained. The condition on $p_F$ is true by the assumptions on $v^0$. The properties of $w_P^*$ used in establishing Eqs. (30) and (31) are precisely those exhibited in Eq. (25) – viz., $(w_P^*)_r = 0$ whenever $(A_Px^*)_r > (\eta_P)_r$ and $(w_P^*)_k \geqq 0$ for $k \neq r$.

The proof is therefore complete. Any $y$ which has $x^*$ as its antecedent is efficient and $p' = (v^{0\prime}, w_I^{*\prime}, w_P^{*\prime})$ is the corresponding vector of efficiency prices.

To determine all efficient points and prices it is sufficient to program parametrically [35] over the set of prices

$$\sum_{r=1}^{n} (v^0)_r = 1 \qquad (32)$$

with $(v^0)_r \geqq \epsilon > 0,$

for $\epsilon$ arbitrarily small. The $x^*$ and $w^*$ obtained by tracing out the labyrinthine path over all such extreme point optima provide the required efficiency prices and efficient points.[85] The procedure is as follows: Start with an optimal solution to $(v^0)_r = \epsilon$. Next, parametrically vary $v^0$, obtaining new optimal tableaus until such tableaus have been obtained for all[86]

$$v^0 \text{ in } \left\{ v^0 \,\middle|\, \sum_r (v^0)_r = 1, \quad (v^0)_r \geqq \epsilon > 0 \right\}. \qquad (33)$$

Then for each such optimal tableau develop the alternate basic optima (e.g. by the labyrinth traversal method) [9] noting the dual basic optima as well. When this procedure is completed the efficiency prices will be available along with the antecedents (extreme points) of the efficient points.

85. The perturbation procedure provided in [9] resolves all ambiguity with respect to degeneracy or alternate optima that may be encountered in these 'wanderings'.

86. In general a tableau will remain optimal for a complete convex subset of the $v^0$. For, consider a basic solution $x^*$ associated with expressions $P_j = \sum_{i \in I} P_i y_{ij}$. Since the solution is optimal, $z_j = \sum_{i \in I} c_i y_{ij} \geqq c_j$. For present purposes $c_j > 0$. Fixing the $y_{ij}$ and allowing the $c_k$'s to be variable, then the inequalities $\sum_{i \in I} c_i y_{ij} - c_j \geqq 0$ define the intersection of $n$ halfspaces. This intersection is non-empty and convex. Its further intersection with $\sum_j c_j = 1, c_j \geqq \epsilon > 0$ is a bounded, closed convex set and, thus, a polyhedral convex set.

It follows that the set

$$\left\{ v^0 \,\middle|\, \sum_{r=1}^{n} (v^0)_r = 1, \, v_r \geqq \epsilon > 0 \right\}$$

will be swept out in a finite number of parameter variations (each sufficient to induce a change from the previous basic solution) because:

(1) Every optimal set corresponding to a $v^0$ vector contains at least one basic solution.

(2) There are only a finite number of basic solutions.

Reverting to Table 5 of the text for an illustration, let $v^{0\prime} = (1, \alpha)$, $\alpha > 0$, then the linear programming model to be used for this example of activity analysis is

$$\text{max. } v^{0\prime}A_F x = {}_x x_1 + \alpha x_2 + 0x_3 + 0x_4$$

subject to:

$$-A_I x = 0: \begin{cases} -x_1 & -x_2 + x_3 & = 0 \\ & -x_3 + x_4 = 0 \end{cases}$$

$$-A_P x \leqq -\eta_p: \begin{cases} 3x_1 + 2x_2 & \leqq 12 \quad (34) \\ 5x_1 & \leqq 10 \\ x_1 + 2x_2 & \leqq 9 \end{cases}$$

with $x \geqq 0$. For simplex solutions, or variants thereof [12], this is all that is really needed. The solutions $x \geqq 0$ provide the extreme point antecedents of the corresponding efficient $y$'s. Solutions to the dual are read from the $z_j - c_j$ row immediately under the slack vectors or their artificial counterparts [16]. The values $w_I{}^*$, $w_P{}^*$, and $v^{0\prime}$ are the corresponding efficiency prices. By varying $v^{0\prime}$ parametrically, in the parameter $\alpha$, all such solutions may be obtained.

Inserting artificial and slack vectors, as required in Eq. (34), the arrangement shown in Table 5-A is secured.[87] For $0 < \alpha < \frac{2}{3}$ the tableau of $V - B$ is a unique optimum with the activity levels $x_1 = 2$, $x_2 = 3$, $x_3 = 5$, $x_4 = 5$ appearing under $P_0$ and the unit value appearing opposite $S_5$ (in the stub) indicating that one unit of slack is programmed on the receiving facility. These are the antecedents of the efficient point $y$ with final commodities $y_1 = 2$, $y_2 = 3$, and primary commodities $y_5 = 12$, $y_6 = 10$, and $y_7 = 8$,[88] so that both machines are programmed to capacity, but the receiving facility is not. The corresponding efficiency prices may be obtained from $v^{0\prime}$ and from the values for $z_j - c_j$ shown under $I_1$, $P_4$, $S_3$, $S_4$, and $S_5$ in Table 5-B. Therefore, for any

87. The artificial vector is $I_1$, a unit vector with nonzero component in the first row. The slack vectors are $P_4 = S_2$ and $S_3$, $S_4$, $S_5$ where the subscript indicates the row in which the nonzero component appears in these unit vectors.

88. These signs may be altered, if desired, to denote input–output relations as defined by Koopmans [50d]. The intermediate commodities $y_3$ and $y_4$ need not be written down since they must always equal zero.

## Table 5 A–D Efficient Point Calculations

### A: Initial Tableau

|  |  | $P_0$ | $I_1$ | $P_4$ | $S_3$ | $S_4$ | $S_5$ | $P_1$ | $P_2$ | $P_3$ |
|---|---|---|---|---|---|---|---|---|---|---|
| | | | $-M$ | | | | | $1$ | $\alpha$ | |
| | $I_1$ | 0 | 1 | | | | | $-1$ | $-1$ | 1 |
| | $P_4$ | 0 | | 1 | | | | | | $-1$ |
| | $S_3$ | 12 | | | 1 | | | 3 | 2 | |
| | $S_4$ | 10 | | | | 1 | | 5 | | |
| | $S_5$ | 9 | | | | | 1 | 1 | 2 | |
| | | | | | | | | | | |
| | $Z_j - c_j$ | | | | | | | $-1$ | $-\alpha$ | |

### B: Optimum Tableau — for $0 < \alpha < \frac{2}{3}$

|  |  | $P_0$ | $I_1$ | $P_4$ | $S_3$ | $S_4$ | $S_5$ | $P_1$ | $P_2$ | $P_3$ |
|---|---|---|---|---|---|---|---|---|---|---|
| 1 | $P_1$ | 2 | | | | $\frac{1}{5}$ | | 1 | | |
| $\alpha$ | $P_2$ | 3 | | | $\frac{1}{2}$ | $-\frac{3}{10}$ | | | 1 | |
| | $P_3$ | 5 | 1 | | $\frac{1}{2}$ | $-\frac{1}{10}$ | | | | 1 |
| | $P_4$ | 5 | 1 | 1 | $\frac{1}{2}$ | $-\frac{1}{10}$ | | | | |
| ← | $S_5$ | 1 | | | $-1$ | $\frac{2}{5}$ | 1 | | | |
| | $Z_j - c_j$ | $2 + 3\alpha$ | $M$ | 0 | $\alpha/2$ | $\frac{2}{10} - \frac{3}{10}\alpha$ | 0 | 0 | 0 | 0 |

### C: Optimum Tableau — for $\frac{2}{3} < \alpha < 2$

|  |  | $P_0$ | $I_1$ | $P_4$ | $S_3$ | $S_4$ | $S_5$ | $P_1$ | $P_2$ | $P_3$ |
|---|---|---|---|---|---|---|---|---|---|---|
| ← 1 | $P_1$ | $\frac{3}{2}$ | | | | $\frac{1}{2}$ | | $-\frac{1}{2}$ | 1 | |
| $\alpha$ | $P_2$ | $\frac{15}{4}$ | | | | $-\frac{1}{4}$ | | $\frac{3}{4}$ | 1 | |
| | $P_3$ | $\frac{21}{4}$ | 1 | | | $\frac{1}{4}$ | | $\frac{1}{4}$ | | 1 |
| | $P_4$ | $\frac{21}{4}$ | 1 | 1 | | $\frac{1}{4}$ | | $\frac{1}{4}$ | | |
| | $S_4$ | $1\frac{5}{2}$ | | | | $-\frac{5}{2}$ | 1 | $\frac{5}{2}$ | | |
| | $Z_j - c_j$ | $\frac{3}{2} + \frac{15}{4}\alpha$ | $M$ | 0 | | $\frac{1}{2} - \frac{1}{4}\alpha$ | 0 | $-\frac{1}{2} + \frac{3}{4}\alpha$ | 0 | 0 |

### D: Optimum Tableau — for $\alpha > 2$

|  |  | $P_0$ | $I_1$ | $P_4$ | $S_3$ | $S_4$ | $S_5$ | $P_1$ | $P_2$ | $P_3$ |
|---|---|---|---|---|---|---|---|---|---|---|
| | $S_3$ | 3 | | | 1 | | | $-1$ | 2 | |
| $\alpha$ | $P_2$ | $\frac{18}{4}$ | | | | | | $\frac{1}{2}$ | $\frac{1}{2}$ | 1 |
| | $P_3$ | $\frac{18}{4}$ | 1 | | | | | $\frac{1}{2}$ | $-\frac{1}{2}$ | 1 |
| | $P_4$ | $\frac{18}{4}$ | 1 | 1 | | | | $\frac{1}{2}$ | $-\frac{1}{2}$ | |
| | $S_4$ | 10 | | | | 1 | | 0 | 5 | |
| | $Z_j - c_j$ | $\frac{18}{4}\alpha$ | $M$ | 0 | 0 | 0 | | $\alpha/2$ | $\alpha/2 - 1$ | 0 |

'prices'[89] 1, $0 < \alpha < \frac{2}{3}$, established for the final products the corresponding prices on the intermediate ones are zero[90] while those for the primary commodities are $\alpha/2$, $\frac{2}{10} - \frac{3}{10}\alpha$, and 0, respectively.

Table 5-B remains uniquely optimal until $\alpha = \frac{2}{3}$. At this point an alternate optimum is apparent with $S_4$ in place of $S_5$. The resulting substitution (indicated by the arrows in 5-B) yields the alternate shown in $V - C$. For $\frac{2}{3} < \alpha < 2$ the latter is uniquely optimal with activity levels $x_1 = \frac{3}{2}$, $x_2 = \frac{15}{4}$, $x_3 = x_4 = \frac{21}{4}$ and $\frac{5}{2}$ units of slack on $M_2$. The corresponding program is, final commodities: $y_1 = \frac{3}{2}$, $y_2 = \frac{15}{4}$, intermediate ones zero and primary ones $y_5 = 12$, $y_6 = 7\frac{1}{2}$, and $y_7 = 9$. Now the second machine and receiving facility have exchanged positions so that slack appears on the machine but not the receiving facility. This new program is also efficient with final 'prices' 1, $\frac{2}{3} < \alpha < 2$, intermediate ones at zero and primary prices of $\frac{1}{2} - \alpha/4$, 0, and $-\frac{1}{2} + \frac{3}{4}\alpha$.[91]

When $\alpha = 2$ an alternate optimum is again made available with $S_3$ in place of $P_1$, as shown in Table 5-D. This table completes the possibilities since it remains uniquely optimal for all $\alpha > 2$. For all such cases $x_1 = 0$, $x_2 = 4\frac{1}{2}$, and $x_3 = x_4 = 4\frac{1}{2}$. The value opposite $S_4$ indicates that the second machine is used by no activity. The receiving facility is now utilized to capacity and slack appears on both machines. Hence the efficiency prices, for final commodities are 1, $\alpha$ on $y_1$ and $y_2$, respectively; all intermediate and primary products, with the exception of the receiving facility, receive imputed values of zero and the receiving facility a price of $\alpha/2$ for all $\alpha > 2$.

This completes the exposition. Further understanding of what is involved can be secured by adding the appropriate constraints (and dimensions) to Figs. 1 and 2 of the text. Alternatively this

89. 'Prices', 'net profits', or other measures of relative desirability. If 1, $\alpha$, are profits then any prices which yield these net results may be used. When 'outside trading' is allowed, however, the prices must be established with these possibilities in mind. *Vide* Koopmans, *loc. cit.* pp. 91 ff.

90. I.e. the values for $z_j - c_j$ shown under $I_1$ and $P_4$ in Table 5-B. For this purpose the penalty rate, $M$, associated with the artificial vector, $I_1$, is ignored.

91. At $\alpha = \frac{2}{3}$, or $\alpha = 2$, trouble is caused by the presence of alternate optima so that the price information may not be sufficient for guidance.

additional information can be secured from the above tableaus. As has already been noted, these efficiency prices can be related to marginal productivities and the marginal rates of substitution of economic theory. They can therefore also be brought to bear in indicating the levels at which the relevant substitutions will be made and thus used to establish sensitivity limits of the kind discussed in Section 4 of the text.

## References

1. ANTOSIEWICZ, H. A. (ed.) (1955) *Second symposium on linear programming* (2 vols.) U.S. Department of Commerce, National Burau of Standards, Washington.
   (a) Bellman, R. 'Dynamic programming and multi-stage decision processes of stochastic type'.
   (b) Dantzig, G. B. 'Developments in linear programming'.
   (c) Radner, R. 'The linear team: an example of linear programming under uncertainty'.
   (d) Salveson, M. E. 'The assembly line balancing problem'.
   (e) Schell, E. D. 'Distribution of a product by several properties'.
2. ARONOFSKY, J. S., and LEE, A. S. (1950) 'Linear programming: a new tool for the reservoir engineer', *J. Pet. Tech.*
3. BARNA, T. (ed.) (1956) *The structural interdependence of the economy.* Wiley, New York.
   (a) Markowitz, H. 'Industry wide multi-industry and economy-wide process analysis'.
4. BEALE, E. M. L. (1955) 'On minimizing a convex function subject to linear inequalities', Symposium on Linear Programming, *Roy. Stat. Soc.*, B, 17, No. 2.
5. BELLMAN, R. (1955) 'Bottleneck problems, functional equations and dynamic programming', *Econometrica*, 23, No. 1.
6. BELLMAN, R. (1956) 'On the theory of dynamic programming – a warehousing problem', *Management Sci.*, 2, No. 3.
7. BOLDYREFF, A. W. (1955) 'Determination of the maximal steady state flow of traffic through a railroad network', *J. Operations Res. Soc. Am.*, 3, No. 4.
8. CAHN, A. S. (1948) 'The warehouse problem', *Bull. Am. Math. Soc.*, 54.
9. CHARNES, A. (1952) 'Optimality and degeneracy in linear programming', *Econometrica*, 20, No. 2.
10. CHARNES, A. (1953) 'Constrained games and linear programming', *Proc. Nat. Acad. of Sci.*
11. CHARNES, A. and COOPER, W. W. '(1955) 'Generalizations of the warehousing model', *Operational Res. Quart.*, 6, No. 4.
12. CHARNES, A. and COOPER, W. W. (1956) 'Non-linear power of

adjacent extreme point methods in linear programming', *Econometrica*.

13. CHARNES, A. and COOPER, W. W. (1954) 'The stepping stone method of explaining linear programming calculations in transportation problems', *Management Sci.*, **1**, No. 1.

14. CHARNES, A., COOPER, W. W., and FARR, D. (1953) 'Linear programming and profit preference scheduling for a manufacturing firm', *J. Operations Res. Soc. Am.*, **1**, No. 3.

15. CHARNES, A., COOPER, W. W., and FERGUSON, R. (1955) 'Optimal estimation of executive compensation by linear programming', *Management Sci.*, **1**, No. 2.

16. CHARNES, A. COOPER, W. W., and HENDERSON, A. (1952) *An introduction to linear programming*. Wiley, New York.

17. CHARNES, A., COOPER, W. W., and MELLON, B. (1952) 'Blending aviation gasolines – a study in programming interdependent activities in an integrated oil co.', *Econometrica*, **20**, No. 2.

18. CHARNES, A., COOPER, W. W., and MELLON, B. (1955) 'A model for optimizing production by reference to cost surrogates', *Econometrica*, **23**.

19. CHARNES, A. (1954) 'A model for programming and sensitivity analysis in an integrated oil co.', *Econometrica*, **22**, No. 2.

20. CHARNES, A., COOPER, W. W., and SYMONDS, G. H. (1955) 'A certainty equivalent approach to stochastic programming applied to heating oil, *Management Sci.*

21. CHARNES, A. and LEMKE, C. E. (1952) 'A modified simplex method for control of round-off error in linear programming', *Pro.*, Assoc. for Computing Machinery.

22. CHARNES, A. (1954) 'Computational theory of linear programming I: the bounded variables problem', ONR Research Memorandum No. 10 (mimeo). Carnegie Inst. Tech., Graduate School of Industrial Administration, Pittsburgh.

23. CHARNES, A. and MILLER, M. (1953) 'A model for optimal programming of railway freight train movements', *Management Sci.*

24. COOPER, W. W. (1955) 'Research on the business firm (discussion)', *Papers and Proc. 67th Annual Meeting*, *Am. Econ. Rev.*, **45**, No. 2.

25. DANTZIG, G. B. (1955) 'Linear programming under uncertainty', *Management Sci.*, **1**, Nos. 3–4.

26. DANTZIG, G. B. (1955) 'Upper bounds, secondary constraints and block triangularity in linear programming', *Econometrica*, **23**, No. 2.

27. DANTZIG, G. B. and FULKERSON, D. R. (1955) 'Computation of maximal flows in networks', *Naval Res. Log. Quart.*, **2**, No. 4.

28. DANTZIG, G. B., FULKERSON, D. R., and JOHNSON, S. (1954) 'Solution of a large scale travelling salesman problem', *J. Operations Res. Soc. Am.*

29. DANTZIG, G. B. and ORCHARD-HAYS, W. (1954) 'The product form for the inverse in the simplex method', *Mathematical Tables and Other Aids to Computation*, **8**, No. 45.

30. EISEMANN, K. (1955) 'Linear programming', *Quart. Applied Math.*, **13**, No. 3.

31. FLOOD, M. M. (1956) 'The travelling salesman problem', *Operations Res.*, **4**, No. 1.

32. FORD, L. R. JR, and FULKERSON, D. R. (1956) 'Notes on linear programming XXXIII: solving the transportation problem', RAND Report RM-1736. (mimeo) The Rand Corporation, Santa Monica.

33. FRANK, M. and WOLFE, P. (1956) 'An algorithm for quadratic programming', *Naval Res. Log. Quart.*, **3**, Nos. 1 and 2.

34. GARVIN, W. W., CRANDALL, H. W., JOHN, J. B., and SPELLMAN, R. A. (1954) 'Application of linear programming in the oil industry', *Management Sci.*

35. GASS, S. I. and SAATY, T. L. (1955) 'The computational algorithm for the parametric objective function', *Naval Res. Log. Quart.*, **2**, Nos. 1 and 2.

36. GOLDSMITH, R. W. (ed.) (1955) *Input-output analysis: an appraisal*, Studies in income and wealth, **18**, Conference on Research in Income and Wealth, National Bureau of Economic Research. Princeton University Press, Princeton.

37. HENDERSON, A. and SCHLAIFER, R. (1954) 'Mathematical programming: better information for better decision making', *Harvard Business Rev.*

38. HITCH, C. (1953) 'Sub-optimization problems', *J. Operations Res. Soc.*, **1**, No. s,

39. HITCHCOCK, F. L. (1941) 'The distribution of a product from several sources to numerous localities', *J. Math. Phys.*, **20**.

40. HOLT, C. C., SIMON, H. A., and MODIGLIANI, F. (1955) 'Linear decision rule for production and employment scheduling', *Management Sci.*, **2**, No. 1.

41. HURWICZ, L. (1952) 'The Minkowski-Farkas lemma for bounded linear transformations in banach spaces', Cowles Commission Discussion Papers, Math. No. 415 and 416 and Econ. No. 2109 (mimeo).

42. JACOBS, W. (1956) 'Applying linear programming' (mimeo), Headquarters, U.S. Department of the Air Force, DCS Comptroller, Washington.

43. JACOBS, W. (1954) 'The caterer problem', *Naval Res. Log. Quart.*, **1**, No. 2.

44. JOHNSON, S. M. (1954) 'Optimal two- and three-stage production schedules', *Naval Res. Log. Quart.*, **1**, No. 1.

45. KARLIN, S. (1955) 'The structure of dynamic programming models', *Naval Res. Log. Quart.*, **2**, No. 4.

46. KELLEY, J. E. JR (1955) 'A dynamic transportation model', *Naval Res. Log. Quart.*, **2**, No. 3.

47. KLEIN, L. R. (ed.) (1955) *Short term economic forecasting*, Vol. 17 in Studies in income and wealth, conference on research in income and wealth, Nat. Bur. Econ. Res., Princeton University Press.

(a) Modigliani, F. and Sauerlender, O. H., 'Economic expectations and plans of firms in relation to short-term forecasting'.

(b) Cooper, W. W. and Simon H. A. 'Commentary'.

48. KOHLER, E. L. (1956) *A dictionary for accountants*. Prentice-Hall, New York.

49. KOOPMAN, B. O. (1956) 'Fallacies in operations research', *Operations Res.*, **4**, No. 4.

50. KOOPMANS, T. C. (ed.) (1951) *Activity analysis of production and allocation*. Cowles Commission for Research in Economics, Monograph No. 13. Wiley, New York.

(a) Dantzig, G. B. 'Maximization of a linear function of variables subject to linear inequalities'.

(b) Dantzig, G. B. 'Application of the simplex method to a transportation problem'.

(c) Gale, D., Kuhn, H. W., and Tucker, A. W. 'Linear programming and the theory of games'.

(d) Koopmans, T. C. 'Analysis of production as an efficient combination of activities'.

(e) Koopmans, T. C. and Reiter, S. 'A model of transportation'.

51. KOOPMANS, T. C. (1949) 'Optimum utilization of the transportation system', *Econometrica*, Supp., **17**.

52. KOZMETSKY, G. and KIRCHER, P. (1956) *Electronic computers and management control*. McGraw-Hill, New York.

53. KUHN, H. W. (1955) 'The Hungarian method for the assignment problem', *Naval Res. Log. Quart.*, **2**, Nos. 1 and 2.

54. KUHN, H. W. and TUCKER, A. W. (eds.) (1953) *Contribution to the theory of games*, **2**. Study 28 in Annals of Mathematics Studies. Princeton University Press.

(a) von Neumann, J. 'A certain zero sum two-person game equivalent to the optimal assignment problem'.

55. KUHN, H. W. and TUCKER, A. W. (eds.) (1956) *Linear inequalities and related systems*. Study 38 in Annals of Mathematics Studies. Princeton University Press.

(a) Duffin, R. J., 'Infinite programs'.

56. LEMKE, C. E. (1954) 'The dual method of solving the linear programming problem', *Naval Res. Log. Quart.*, **1**, No. 1.

57. LEONTIEF, W. W. (1951) *The structure of the American economy*, 1919–1939, 2nd ed. Oxford Univ. Press.

58. MANNE, A. S. (1956) 'A linear programming model of the U.S. petroleum refining industry'. RM-1757 (mimeo) Rand Corporation, Santa Monica.

59. MARKOWITZ, H. (1956) 'The optimization of a quadratic function subject to linear constraints', *Naval Res. Log. Quart.* **3**, Nos. 1 and 2.

60. MILLS, H. D. (1955) 'Organized decision making', *Naval Res. Log. Quart.*, **2**, No. 3.

61. MODIGLIANI, F. and HOHN, F. (1956) 'Solution of certain problems of production planning over time illustrating the effect of the inventory constraint', *Econometrica*.

62. MORSE, P. M. (1955) 'Where is the new blood?', *Operations Res. Soc. Am.*, 3, No. 4.

63. NEYMAN, J. (ed.) (1951) *Proceedings of the second Berkeley symposium on mathematical statistics and probability*. Univ. Calif. Press.
   (a) Kuhn, H. W. and Tucker, A. W. 'Nonlinear programming'.

64. NASH, J. F. (1951) 'Non-cooperative games', *Annals of Math.*, **54**.

65. ORCHARD-HAYS, W. (1956) *Evolution of linear programming computing techniques*, Rand Report P-900. Rand Corporation, Santa Monica.

66. ORDEN, A. (1956) 'The transhipment problem', *Management Sci.* **2**, No. 3.

67. ORDEN, A. and GOLDSTEIN, R. (eds.) (1951) *Symposium on linear inequalities and programming*. Project SCOOP, Comptroller, Headquarters, U.S. Air Force, Washington.
   (a) Dantzig, G. B. and Orden, A. 'A duality theorem based on the simplex method'.
   (b) Orden, A. 'Applications of the simplex method to a variety of matrix problems'.
   (c) Votaw, D. F. and Orden, A. 'The personal assignment problem'.

68. PARETO, VILFREDO (1927) *Manuel d'economie politique*, 2nd edn. Appendix pp. 617 ff. Alfred Bonnet, Marcel Giard, Paris.

69. PRAGER, W. (1953) 'Limit analysis design', *J. Am. Concrete Inst.*, **25**, No. 4.

70. PRAGER, W. (1956) 'On the caterer problem', *Management Sci.*, 3, No. 1.

71. ROSENBLATT, D. (1951) 'A note on communication in organizations' (mimeo), USDAF Research Project on Intra Firm Planning and Behavior, Carnegie Inst. Tech., Pittsburgh.

72. SCHRAGE, R. W. (1954) 'Optimizing a catalytic cracking operation by the method of steepest ascents and linear programming' (mimeo), Esso Standard Oil Co., New Jersey.

73. SHUBIK, M. (1955) 'The use of game theory in management science', *Management Sci.*, **2**, No. 1.

74. STIGLER, G. J. (1945) 'The cost of subsistence', *J. Farm Econ.*, **27**, No. 2.

75. SWANSON, E. R. (1955) 'Solving minimum cost feed-mix problems', *J. Farm Econ.*

76. SYMONDS, G. H. (1955) *Linear programming: the solution of refinery problems*. Esso Standard Oil Co., New York.

77. THORNDYKE, R. L. (1950) 'The problem of classification of personnel', *Psychometrika*, **15**.

78. THRALL, R. M. (ed.) (1956) *Introduction to management science* (mimeo), Univ. Michigan.
   (a) Crane, R. W., 'Applications of operations research to industry'.

79. TINTNER, G. (1955) 'Programmazione lineare stocastica con applicazioni a problem di economia agraria', *G. Econ. Annali di Economica*, Luglio-Agosta.

80. TUCKER, A. W. (1955) *Game theory and programming*, Nat. Sci. Foundation Summer Math. Inst. Notes. Dep. of Math. Oklahoma Agric. and Mech. Coll.

81. VAJDA, S. (1956) *The theory of games and linear programming*. Wiley, New York.

82. VAZSONYI, A. (1954) 'The use of mathematics in production and inventory control', *Management Sci.*, **1**, No. 1.

83. VAZSONYI, A. (1955) 'The use of mathematics in production and inventory control-II', *Management Sci.*, **1**, Nos. 3–4.

84. WHITIN, T. (1954) 'Inventory control research: a survey', *Management Sci.*, **1**, No. 1.

# 11 R. A. Howard

Dynamic Programming

R. A. Howard (1966) 'Dynamic programming', *Management Science*, **12**, 317–48.

## Introduction

Dynamic programming is a mathematical technique for solving certain types of sequential decision problems. We characterize a sequential decision problem as a problem in which a sequence of decisions must be made with each decision affecting future decisions. We need to consider such problems because we rarely encounter an operational situation where the implications of any decision do not extend far into the future. For example, the best way to invest funds this year depends upon how the proceeds from this year's investments can be employed next year. The maintenance policy we should use for our machinery this year depends upon what we intend to do with this machinery in the future. The examples are as numerous as the fields of man's endeavor.

### The structure of dynamic programming

Dynamic programming is based on only a few concepts. Some it shares with other models; some are unique. The first concept that we must understand is that of a state variable. The state variables of a process are variables whose values completely specify the instantaneous situation of the process. The values of these variables tell us all we need to know about the system for the purpose of making decisions about it. The designation of system descriptors as state variables is quite arbitrary. For example, in the investment problem we might require as a state variable only the total amount of our present investment. Or we could define two state variables to describe income and investment growth. Or we might require one for investment in each industry, or even in each company. Although the number of state variables can theoretically be made as large as we please, the difficulty of solving the problems we face increases dramatically with the number of state variables involved. Thus it is to our advantage to minimize the number of state variables we use until any further simplification would destroy the utility of our model. In general, it is better to start simply and then complicate rather than to proceed in the reverse order. We usually speak of the values of all state variables as specifying the 'state' of the system.

Having defined the state variables of the problem we introduce the concept of a decision as an opportunity to change these state variables, perhaps probabilistically. For example, the decision to sell a certain amount of one stock and buy another in the investment problem would lead to a change in state variables. However, because of the vagaries of the market, the net change in the state variables over some time period is subject to considerable uncertainty.

But why bother to make decisions affect the state? Because we can realize a profit or equivalently avoid a loss by having the state variables change in different ways. We imagine that each change of state has associated with it a reward, which may be negative. The rewards generated by each decision depend only on the starting and ending states for that decision and therefore may be added for a sequence of decisions. Our job is to make decisions that will make the total reward we shall achieve as high as possible.

Finally, we suppose that our ability to make decisions about the system occurs only at certain points of time which we shall call stages. At each stage we make a decision, change the state, and therefore make a reward. At the next stage we must make another decision using the values of the state variables that resulted from the preceding decision, and so on. Using these terms we can state our goal more precisely as a desire to maximize the expected total reward we shall receive when the number of stages available and the initial values of the state variables are fixed. In terms of the investment problem this might mean maximizing expected profit over a 10-year interval using a starting capital of $1,000.

We shall make all these ideas more precise in later sections, but first let us describe how dynamic programming solves such a problem and illustrate the procedure with some examples.

## The solution concepts of dynamic programming

Perhaps the most interesting idea used in dynamic programming is that when we desire to maximize a function, the maximum value it can attain depends only on the constraints on the maximization and not on the procedure used to determine the maximum value. This is an idea best illustrated by examples. Suppose that we have available an artillery piece with a fixed muzzle velocity and that our job is to hurl the projectile as far as possible on level ground. The point is this: the maximum range we can achieve depends only on the muzzle velocity we are allowed. Those who studied basic physics know that if air resistance can be neglected, then the maximum range can be achieved by firing at an inclination of 45°. The actual range achieved will, of course, depend on the inclination angle used, but it will be a maximum only at the inclination 45°. Therefore if we picture ourselves as the sponsors of the gun-firing contest, we know that the only factor limiting the *maximum* range is the muzzle velocity we allow. The actual range achieved by any contestant will depend on this muzzle velocity and also on his intelligence in selecting the inclination angle. Thus we have illustrated that the *maximum* value of the function (range) depends only on the constraints (muzzle velocity) and not on the technique used to achieve it (inclination angle).

Perhaps another example will help. We all remember the problem of the farmer who wanted to enclose the maximum rectangular area with a fixed amount of fencing. We know that he will achieve the maximum area by using his fencing to surround a square plot. We might have solved the problem by trial and error, but more probably by calculus. Now suppose that we hold a fencing contest among farmers, supplying to each the same perimeter of fencing. We know that the maximum area anyone can enclose is determined only by the amount of fencing we provide and that it will be achieved only by a square design. Individual farmers may try a wide variety of rectangular solutions, with the one who comes closest to the square doing best. Here again we see that the *maximum* of the function (area enclosed) depends only on the constraints (fencing perimeter supplied) and not on the technique used to achieve it (shape of rectangle).

Since we have found that the best anyone can do in a decision problem depends only on the constraints, we find it worthwhile to postulate a portable genius. A portable genius is a person smart enough actually to achieve the maximum in a decision problem. The portable genius is a valuable resource – he knows that guns should be fired at a 45° inclination to achieve maximum range on level ground and that square plots have the maximum area of all rectangular plots with the same perimeter. We find it hard to hire people with this capability, but fortunately we shall find that we don't have to.

Once we have a portable genius we use him in solving a sequential decision problem by defining a function that is the total reward he could achieve if he were faced with a certain number of remaining stages and certain starting values of state variables. Since he can solve the problem, he can provide this total reward or value as we shall call it upon request. We are now ready to solve the sequential decision problem. In this problem we must first make one decision at the beginning of a long sequence of decisions. The problem is difficult because you and I as mere mortals seem to have no way of evaluating the influence of our present decision on the future. After all, how can we tell what is going to happen as a result of making this decision if we still don't know what we are going to do in the future? This is where we use our portable genius to break our multiple stage decision problem into single stage decision problems. We reason this way. In the present state we have available to us a number of different decisions that we could make. Each of these decisions would create some reward and place the system in some new state for the next stage. Now we call on our portable genius to tell us what we shall make in the future if we are now in this new state with one fewer stage remaining. He tells us, we add it to the reward from this stage, and thus obtain the total future profit from making this decision. Similarly we compute the total future profit from each other possible decision and then compare them. The decision with the highest total future profit is the one to choose.

Thus when we have the portable genius there is no difficulty in solving sequential decision problems where the profits are additive because he can tell us the implications for the future of any present action. If he tells us the value of being in each state with $n$ stages remaining, then we can figure out what to do when we have $n + 1$ stages remaining. Thus if he tells us how we shall make out when there is only one stage remaining, we can compute the best decisions when there are two stages remaining. Now that we have evaluated what to do with two stages remaining we can compute for three stages remaining and so on. Therefore we need the portable genius only for the case when there is only one stage remaining. But we do not need him even here, because when there is only one stage remaining, there are no future decisions and the present decision can be based only on the profit that it will directly generate. Therefore, we do not need the portable genius at all, although he was a useful crutch in developing our thinking about sequential decision problems.

Therefore, sequential decision problems are solved by induction using the concept of values supplied by the portable genius, a genius who turns out never to be needed. We call this solution process dynamic programming, although as you can see, a better name might be recursive programming because of the form in which the solution is generated. Dynamic programming is quite different in form and concept from linear programming. Dynamic programming is conceptually more powerful and computationally less powerful than linear programming. An approximate analogy might be that dynamic programming is like calculus while linear programming is like solving sets of simultaneous linear equations. However, let us postpone further general comments on dynamic programming until we have achieved more feeling for the process through examples.

## A Production Scheduling Example

Suppose that a company must produce a total quantity $S$ in $k$ monthly periods. We shall let $n$ be the index for months remaining at any time and use $p_n$ for the quantity that will be produced in the $n^{\text{th}}$ month from the end of the $k$-month-long production period. Figure 1 illustrates a possible production plan. There are many production plans that meet the requirements

$$\sum_{n=1}^{k} p_n = S \qquad p_n \geqq 0 \qquad (1)$$

Therefore, to make the problem definite, we assign a non-negative weighting factor $w_n$ to the square of production in the $n^{\text{th}}$ month from the end of the allowable time, and then require that the production plan minimize the sum of the weighted squares of production over the $k$-month period. The effect of the

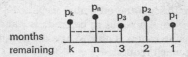

Figure 1 A possible production plan.

weighting factor would be to allow management to penalize production in some months more than others. We shall not discuss the merit of such a control procedure, but simply accept the result as an instructive example. Thus our problem is to

$$\text{Min}_{p_n} \sum_{n=1}^{k} w_n p_n^2 \qquad (2)$$

subject to the constraints in Eq. (1).

We could solve this problem in many ways that range from trial and error to the calculus of variations. We choose to use dynamic programming and therefore proceed to cast the problem in dynamic programming terms. Our first task is to identify the state variables of the process. We see that if we enter the process in the middle of a production plan, we cannot affect the production levels that have already occurred – we can only influence the amounts to be made in each month in the future. What determines the weighted sum of squares of production we shall achieve in the future is the total amount $s$ that remains to be made and the number of months $n$ that are left in which to make the amount $s$. We can consider both $n$ and $s$ as the state variables of the process, or alternatively and for convenience we can call $n$ the stage variable and $s$ the state variable of the process. This terminology is reasonable because stages are the times at which decisions can be made and every remaining month is an opportunity to set a production level for that month.

Suppose that the weights $w_n$ are fixed. If we present anyone with this problem and tell him $n$, the number of production periods he is allowed and $s$, the total amount he has to make, then in the

377

light of our previous discussion we have already established the minimum weighted sum of squares that he will be able to obtain. Of course, he will not come up with a production plan to attain this minimum unless he is intelligent and diligent, but he can do no better than the minimum determined by $n$ and $s$. We call this minimum $v(s \mid n)$, the value of being in state $s$ with $n$ stages remaining. It represents the minimum weighted sum of squares obtainable if the total amount to be made is $s$ and $n$ periods remain. Our portable genius is able to attain this minimum and to tell us its value when requested.

We also need a terminology for the decision in order to specify the production plan that will be our answer. We let $p(s \mid n)$ be the amount to be produced in the $n$th period from the end if a quantity $s$ remains to be made in $n$ monthly periods. If we knew this function, we would find it very easy to construct a production plan.

Let us now consider the situation where we have an amount $s$ to be made in $n$ months. If we make an amount $p_n$ in the present month, then we shall have to make a total quantity $s - p_n$ in the remaining $n - 1$ months. The contribution to the weighted sum of squares of making $p_n$ in the present month is $w_n p_n^2$. The minimum weighted sum of squares that can be achieved in the remaining $n - 1$ months starting with a quantity $s - p_n$ to be produced is reported by our portable genius to be $v(s - p_n \mid n - 1)$. Therefore the total weighted sum of squares we shall achieve by making $p_n$ now and doing the best anyone can do in the remaining months is $w_n p_n^2 + v(s - p_n \mid n - 1)$. Of course, we want to choose $p_n$ so as to make this total weighted sum of squares as small as possible. If we do, then we can say that this quantity is $v(s \mid n)$, the best that can be done with a total quantity $s$ to produce in $n$ months. We therefore have the equation

$$v(s \mid n) = \text{Min}_{0 \leq p_n \leq s}\{w_n p_n^2 + v(s - p_n \mid n - 1)\},$$
$$s \geq 0, \; n = 2, 3, 4, \ldots \quad (3)$$

Note that we restrict the quantity $p_n$ that can be made in the present month to be nonnegative and to be no more than $s$, the total quantity to be made throughout the $n$ month period. Of course the value of $p_n$ that minimizes the sum in Eq. (3) is $p(s \mid n)$, the amount that should be made in the $n$th month from the end of an $n$-month period in which a total quantity $s$ is to be produced so as to minimize the weighted sum of squares of production. Notice that the sum is composed of two parts, the immediate effect of the decision to make $p_n$, $w_n p_n^2$, and the long run effect of the decision, $v(s - p_n \mid n - 1)$. This structure is typical of the dynamic programming approach: it provides the correct balance of short and long run consequences.

Well, we have solved the problem if we have a portable genius, but we don't have him. What do we do? We say that when only one month remains we don't need him and that Eq. (3) then shows us how to dispense with him when more than one month remains. Let us consider the situation when there is only one month in which to make a total quantity $s$. Then there is not much choice – the total quantity $s$ must be produced in this month and the weighted sum of squares incurred will be $w_1 s^2$,

$$p(s \mid 1) = s$$
$$v(s \mid 1) = w_1 s^2. \tag{4}$$

Thus the problem becomes trivial when only one month remains.

But now that we know what to do with one month remaining we can figure out what to do with two months remaining by writing Eq. (3) with $n = 2$,

$$v(s \mid 2) = \text{Min}_{0 \le p_2 \le s} \{ w_2 p_2^2 + (s \, v - p_2 \mid 1) \}. \tag{5}$$

Since we already know the function $v(\cdot \mid 1)$ from Eq. (4), the minimization is clearly identified. We have many techniques that can be applied to perform this type of minimization. The easiest one to use in this case is differentiation of the expression and setting the result equal to zero. When we differentiate the quantity in braces with respect to $p_2$ and set it equal to zero, we obtain

$$\partial \{ \ \} / \partial p_2 = 2 w_2 p_2 - v'(s - p_2 \mid 1) = 0. \tag{6}$$

From Eq. (4) we observe

$$v'(s \mid 1) = 2 w_1 s \tag{7}$$

so that we can write Eq. (6) as

$$2 w_2 p_2 - 2 w_1 (s - p_2) = 0 \tag{8}$$

or

$$p_2 = p(s \mid 2) = w_1 s / (w_1 + w_2). \tag{9}$$

Thus if we have two months in which to make a total quantity $s$ we should make a fraction $w_1/(w_1 + w_2)$ of the quantity in the present month to assure that the weighted sum of squares will be a minimum.

We find $v(s \mid 2)$, the minimum weighted sum of squares that we can obtain in producing a total quantity $s$ in a two-month period by evaluating the quantity in braces in Eq. (5) at the minimizing value of $p_2$ given by Eq. (9). We obtain

$$v(s \mid 2) = \{w_2 p_2{}^2 + v_1(s - p_2)\}_{p_2 = w_1 s/(w_1 + w_2)}$$
$$= w_2(w_1/(w_1 + w_2))^2 s^2 + v_1(w_2 s/(w_1 + w_2))$$
$$= w_2 w_1{}^2 s^2/(w_1 + w_2)^2 + w_1 w_2{}^2 s^2/(w_1 + w_2)^2$$
$$= w_1 w_2 s^2/(w_1 + w_2). \tag{10}$$

This is, of course, just the weighted sum of squares that will result from making $w_1 s/(w_1 + w_2)$ in the present month and $w_2 s/(w_1 + w_2)$ in the last month.

Eq. (9) yields the policy to follow at the second stage, the amount that should be produced at present to insure that the decision will be the best possible as far as future decisions are concerned. Eq. (10) provides the value, the expected profit that will result by taking the optimum present decision and also following an optimum course in the future.

Now that we have evaluated what to do when 1 or 2 months remain we can continue to the case where three months remain. Then Eq. (3) takes the form

$$v(s \mid 3) = \text{Min}_{0 \le p_3 \le s}\{w_3 p_3{}^2 + v(s - p_3 \mid 2)\}. \tag{11}$$

We again perform the minimization by differentiation and write

$$\partial\{\ \}/\partial p_3 = 2w_3 p_3 - v'(s - p_3 \mid 2) = 0. \tag{12}$$

Eq. (10) shows that the derivative of the function $v(s \mid 2)$ with respect to its argument is

$$v'(s \mid 2) = 2w_1 w_2 s/(w_1 + w_2). \tag{13}$$

When we substitute this result into Eq. (12), we find

$$2w_3 p_3 - 2w_1 w_2(s - p_3)/(w_1 + w_2) = 0,$$
$$p_3(w_1 w_2 + w_1 w_3 + w_2 w_3) = w_1 w_2 s \tag{14}$$

or $\qquad p_3 = p(s \mid 3) = w_1 w_2 s/(w_1 w_2 + w_1 w_3 + w_2 w_3). \tag{15}$

380

The amount that should be made at present if three months remain in which to make a total quantity $s$ is a fraction of $s$ equal to the product of the weights in the last two months divided by the sum of the products of all possible pairs of weights for the three months.

If we substitute this value for $p_3$ into Eq. (11), we obtain $v(s \mid 3)$, the minimum weighted sum of squares obtainable throughout the three-month period,

$$
\begin{aligned}
v(s \mid 3) &= \{w_3 p_3{}^2 + v(s - p_3 \mid 2)\}_{p_3 = w_1 w_2 s/(w_1 w_2 + w_1 w_3 + w_2 w_3)} \\
&= \{w_3 p_3{}^2 + w_1 w_2 (s - p_3)^2/ \\
&\qquad (w_1 + w_2)\}_{p_3 = w_1 w_2 s/(w_1 w_2 + w_1 w_3 + w_2 w_3)} \\
&= w_1 w_2 w_3 s^2/(w_1 w_2 + w_1 w_3 + w_2 w_3). \qquad (16)
\end{aligned}
$$

Thus Eq. (15) provides the policy or what to do and Eq. (16) provides the value or how much we shall profit by doing it for the case when three months remain.

We could continue to use the recursive Eq. (3) to solve the problem for higher and higher numbers of months or stages remaining. However, what we have already done is sufficient to see the form of the solution. For the policy we observe that

$$
p(s \mid n) = \frac{1/w_n}{\sum_{i=1}^{n} 1/w_i} s, \qquad n = 1, 2, 3, \ldots \qquad (17)
$$

is consistent with the results of Eqs. (4), (9), and (15). It is clear that the reciprocals of the weights appear more naturally in the problem than do the weights themselves. Similarly, for the value we see that

$$
v(s \mid n) = s^2/\sum_{i=1}^{n} 1/w_i \qquad (18)
$$

is a general form for the results of Eqs. (4), (10), and (16). Furthermore, if we substitute the policy and value results from Eqs. (17) and (18) directly into Eq. (3), we find that Eq. (3) is satisfied. Therefore Eqs. (17) and (18) constitute a complete solution to the problem.

A word is in order about the form in which the solution has been generated. Although we seek a production plan for a specific total quantity $S$ to be made in a time period specified to be $k$ months long, we have in fact solved a more general problem.

The more general problem is that of finding how much to make in the present month for any amount to be produced $s$ and months remaining $n$. We can not only solve the specific problem proposed, but also the whole class of problems. This generality provided and required by the dynamic programming procedure is called imbedding the problem in a larger class of problems. As you might expect, imbedding is a very good idea when you would like to have a general solution. However, it may also lead to higher computational requirements than would be needed if the specific problem posed were solved directly. The point is that in dynamic programming you always get more than you bargained for, even if you don't want it.

Note that when we finally get around to solving a specific problem, we must interpret our general solution as a rule for generating and evaluating optimum production plans rather than as a production plan itself. The policy tells us how much to make in the present month if we know the total amount to be made and the number of months remaining. Once we take this action, we then proceed to the next decision point with a lesser quantity to be made and one less month remaining. The policy for this stage again tells what to make in the present month, and we continue to generate the production plan in this way. However, at any stage and state the value function tells us the minimum sum of squares we shall be able to obtain into the future, even though at this point we have not yet found the explicit production plan that will be followed in the future. In other words, the value function tells our farmer contestant the maximum rectangular area he will be able to enclose even before it tells him the dimensions to use. Thus the policy and value functions provide powerful, if somewhat unusual, aid in solving decision problems.

Perhaps the structure of the solution appears most clearly in the case when all weights are equal, and for simplicity, let us say equal to unity. Then the policy of Eq. (17) becomes

$$p(s \mid n) = s/n, \qquad n = 1, 2, 3, \ldots \qquad (19)$$

This equation states that when $n$ months remain in which to make a total quantity $s$, an amount $s/n$ should be made in the present month. We know from the symmetry of the problem that when all weights are equal, equal amounts should be produced in each of the remaining months. Eq. (19) presents this result in implicit rather than explicit form. For example, suppose that three months remain to make a total quantity $S$. Then according to Eq. (19), $\frac{1}{3}S$ should be made in the present month. Next month a quantity $\frac{2}{3}S$ will remain; Eq. (19) shows that one half of it or $\frac{1}{3}S$ should be produced next month. That will leave $\frac{1}{3}S$ to be produced during the last month, and Eq. (19) states, of course, that all of it must be produced in that month. The net result is that we have produced $\frac{1}{3}S$ in each of the three remaining months by applying the result of Eq. (19) recursively.

Eq. (18) shows that the value function for the case of equal unity weights is

$$v(s \mid n) = s^2/n, \qquad n = 1, 2, 3, \ldots \tag{20}$$

For the production schedule we have just developed the weighted sum of squares is

$$(\tfrac{1}{3}S)^2 + (\tfrac{1}{3}S)^2 + (\tfrac{1}{3}S)^2 = \tfrac{1}{3}S^2, \tag{21}$$

which is the result of Eq. (20) when a total quantity $S$ must be made in three months. The interpretation of a policy as a decision rule rather than as a specific plan and the interpretation of the value function as an overall measure of policy rather than of any part of it are fundamental to the dynamic programming approach.

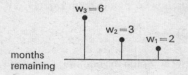

Figure 2 Weighting factors for the example.

## Numerical results

Suppose that we want to minimize the weighted sum of squares of production of a three-month period in which we must make 9 units. Thus $k = 3$, $S = 9$. The weighting factors for the three months are $w_1 = 2$, $w_2 = 3$, $w_3 = 6$ and are shown in Fig. 2.

We begin by deciding how much to make in month 3 (from the end). From Eq. (17),

$$p(9 \mid 3) = \frac{1/w_3}{1/w_1 + 1/w_2 + 1/w_3}$$

$$(9) = \frac{\frac{1}{6}}{\frac{1}{2} + \frac{1}{3} + \frac{1}{6}} (9) = 1.5. \quad (22)$$

We find that we should make 1.5 units in the present month when three months remain. Manufacturing 1.5 units might be a problem if our products were automobiles, but we shall assume that it is a bulk product for the moment and return to the quantization problem later.

From Eq. (18) we compute the value of being in state 9 with three stages left,

$$v(9 \mid 3) = \frac{1}{1/w_1 + 1/w_2 + 1/w_3}$$

$$(9)^2 = \frac{1}{\frac{1}{2} + \frac{1}{3} + \frac{1}{6}} (81) = 81. \quad (23)$$

Thus the minimum weighted sum of squares we shall be able to obtain is 81. We have not yet specified what our production plan will be (except for the first month and we have not used the result of that calculation) and still we can predict how well we shall do by following it.

Now we come to two months remaining with a total quantity $9 - 1.5 = 7.5$ yet to be produced. The amount of production for this middle month we compute from Eq. (17) as

$$p(7.5 \mid 3) = \frac{1/w_2}{1/w_1 + 1/w_2} (7.5) = \frac{\frac{1}{3}}{\frac{1}{2} + \frac{1}{3}} (7.5) = 3. \quad (24)$$

From Eq. (18) we compute the minimum weighted sum of squares for the last two months,

$$v(7.5 \mid 3) = \frac{1}{1/w_1 + 1/w_2} (7.5)^2 = \frac{1}{\frac{1}{2} + \frac{1}{3}} (56.25) = 67.5. \quad (25)$$

Notice that since our production of 1.5 units in the third month from the end contributed $w_3 p_3^2 = 6(1.5)^2 = 13.5$ to the weighted sum of squares, the predictions of Eqs. (23) and (25) are consistent.

In the last month remaining we have left to produce $9 - 1.5 - 3 = 4.5$ units, and of course Eq. (17) states that they all must be produced in this month,

$$p(4.5 \mid 1) = 4.5. \tag{26}$$

Equation (18) then shows that the contribution to the sum of squares of this last month is

$$v(4.5 \mid 1) = \frac{1}{1/w_1} (4.5)^2 = 2(20.25) = 40.5. \tag{27}$$

The complete production plan along with the weighted squares of production for the plan appears in Fig. 3. We observe that the

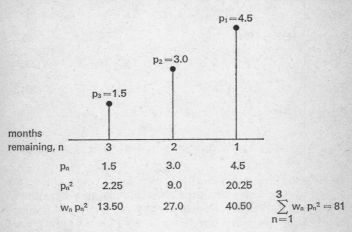

| months remaining, n | 3 | 2 | 1 | |
|---|---|---|---|---|
| $p_n$ | 1.5 | 3.0 | 4.5 | |
| $p_n^2$ | 2.25 | 9.0 | 20.25 | |
| $w_n p_n^2$ | 13.50 | 27.0 | 40.50 | $\sum_{n=1}^{3} w_n p_n^2 = 81$ |

Figure 3 The best production plan.

predictions of Eqs. (23), (25), and (27) about the sum of squares to be obtained in the future of the plan at different stages are substantiated by these results. The sum of squares for the entire plan is 81 as predicted initially by $v(9 \mid 3)$. No other production plan can achieve so low a weighted sum of squares.

## The variational approach

We observe that the best production plan has the property that the product of the production and weighting factor in any month is the constant 9. We can explain this behavior by solving this same problem using a variational approach. Thus to perform the minimization of Eq. (2) subject to the constraints of Eq. (1) we would first form the quantity

$$\sum_{n=1}^{k} w_n p_n^2 + \lambda(\sum_{n=1}^{k} p_n - S) \tag{28}$$

and then differentiate it both with respect to $p_n$ and with respect to $\lambda$. We obtain for these differentiations

$$2w_n p_n + \lambda = 0 \tag{29}$$

and

$$\sum_{n=1}^{n} p_n = S. \tag{30}$$

Then

$$p_n = -\lambda/2w_n \tag{31}$$

and we use Eq. (30) to find $\lambda$,

$$\sum_{n=1}^{k} p_n = S = -(\lambda/2) \sum_{n=1}^{k} 1/w_n \tag{32}$$

or

$$\lambda = -2S/\sum_{n=1}^{k} 1/w_n. \tag{33}$$

Finally we substitute this result into Eq. (31) to produce the solution

$$p_n = \frac{1/w_n}{\sum_{n=1}^{k} 1/w_n} S, \qquad n = 1, 2, \ldots, k. \tag{34}$$

Happily the production quantities turn out to be positive so we do not have to worry about the constraint that they be positive.

Equation (31) shows immediately that the product of production quantity and weighting factor in any month will be a constant. Eq. (33) shows further that this constant is just the total quantity to be produced divided by the sum of the reciprocals of the weighting factors of the months involved, and we have therefore checked our numerical example.

However, the important thing to note in the variational solution is that Eq. (34) describes the production quantity for each month rather than a rule for constructing the production quantity when the amount yet to be made is known. The solution is explicit rather than in the recursive form of Eq. (17). Since both expressions look virtually identical, they differ only in interpretation, but the difference is critical. If we evaluate the weighted sum of squares of production for this production plan, we find

$$\sum_{n=1}^{k} w_n p_n{}^2 = \sum_{n=1}^{k} w_n \frac{(1/w_n)^2}{(\sum_{n=1}^{k} 1/w_n)^2} S^2 = \frac{1}{\sum_{n=1}^{k} 1/w_n} S^2,$$

(35)

in agreement with Eq. (18) when $S$ must be produced in $k$ months.

It is clear that solving the production problem by variational methods is simpler than solving it by dynamic programming. We chose the less efficient route initially because it is a good way to illustrate the dynamic programming process. Yet if variational methods are better, why do we need dynamic programming? The answer is that dynamic programming provides a convenient approach to problems that are difficult to treat by variational methods. For example, the requirement that the production quantities must be positive is difficult to incorporate in the variational approach. We were fortunate that this constraint was not violated in the present problem. But what if it had been? The dynamic programming approach can easily handle this type of difficulty. At most it would mean that we could not use the differentiation method for finding the minimum of the quantities in braces in Eqs. (5) and (11); however, other methods are available. Similarly, we can use dynamic programming to treat the case where there are limits on the production in each month. But perhaps the most dramatic illustration of the advantage of dynamic programming arises when we require that the amount of production in each month be an integer.

## The production problem with integer constraints

Let us consider the same example of producing 9 units in three months so as to minimize the weighted sum of squares of production using the weights of Fig. 2. Only now we shall require that the number of units made during each month be integral. The only change that we have to make in our previous analysis is that the values of $p_n$ considered in carrying out the minimization in Eq. (3) must be limited to the integer values 0 through $s$; that is,

$$v(s \mid n) = \mathrm{Min}_{p_n = 0, 1, 2, \ldots, s}\{w_n p_n{}^2 + v(s - p_n \mid n - 1)\},$$
$$s = 0, 1, 2, \ldots, n = 2, 3, 4, \ldots \quad (36)$$

Since the quantity to be made must always be specified as an integer, Eq. (4) still applies,

$$p(s \mid 1) = s,$$
$$v(s \mid 1) = w_1 s^2. \tag{37}$$

Consequently, Eqs. (36) and (37) constitute a complete formal statement of the problem of finding the best integral production schedule.

Table 1
Computation of Integral Production
Problem at First Stage

| $s$ | $p(s \mid 1) = s$ | $v(s \mid 1) = w_1 s^2 = 2s$ |
|---|---|---|
| 0 | 0 | 0 |
| 1 | 1 | 2 |
| 2 | 2 | 8 |
| 3 | 3 | 18 |
| 4 | 4 | 32 |
| 5 | 5 | 50 |
| 6 | 6 | 72 |
| 7 | 7 | 98 |
| 8 | 8 | 128 |
| 9 | 9 | 162 |
| 10 | 10 | 200 |

We begin writing $p(s \mid 1)$ and $v(s \mid 1)$ in Table 1 for values of $s$ ranging from 0 through 10. We choose 10 simply to illustrate that we are not solving a particular problem, but rather a class of problems.

We continue now to the second stage and write Eq. (36),

$$v(s \mid 2) = \text{Min}_{p_2 = 0, 1, 2, \ldots, s} \{ w_2 p_2^2 + v(s - p_2 \mid 1) \}$$
$$s = 0, 1, 2, \ldots \tag{38}$$
$$= \text{Min}_{p_2 = 0, 1, 2, \ldots, s} \{ 3 p_2^2 + v(s - p_2 \mid 1) \}.$$

For $s = 0$,

$$v(0 \mid 2) = \text{Min}_{p_2 = 0} \{ 3 p_2^2 + v(-p_2 \mid 1) \} = v(0 \mid 1),$$
$$\tag{39}$$

an obvious result. For $s = 1$,

$$v(1 \mid 2) = \text{Min } _{p_2=0,1}\{3\,p_2{}^2 + v(1 - p_2 \mid 1)\}$$

$$= \text{Min}\begin{cases} p_2 = 1: & 3 + v(0 \mid 1) = 3 + 0 = 3 \\ p_2 = 0: & 0 + v(1 \mid 1) = 0 + 2 = 2 \end{cases}$$

$$= 2 \text{ at } p_2 = 0. \tag{40}$$

Therefore when one unit must be made in two months, it should not be made in the present month, but made in the last month. The weighted sum of squares so incurred will be 2.

For $s = 2$,

$$v(2 \mid 2) = \text{Min } _{p_2=0,1,2}\{3\,p_2{}^2 + v(2 - p_2 \mid 1)\}$$

$$= \text{Min}\begin{cases} p_2 = 2: & 12 + v(0 \mid 1) = 12 + 0 = 12 \\ p_2 = 1: & 3 + v(1 \mid 1) = 3 + 2 = 5 \\ p_2 = 0: & 0 + v(2 \mid 1) = 0 + 8 = 8 \end{cases}$$

$$= 5 \text{ at } p_2 = 1. \tag{41}$$

Therefore when there are two units to be made in two months, one should be made in each month; a weighted sum of squares of 5 will be achieved.

We could continue in this way to compute all values of $v(s \mid 2)$ from $v(s \mid 1)$, but let us examine the general procedure we have been following. Suppose $s = 3$. Then we are constructing a column $3p_2{}^2$ for $p_2 = 3, 2, 1, 0$ and adding to each entry the value of $v(4 - p_2 \mid 1)$ from Table 1, thus,

| $p_2$ | $3p_2{}^2$ | | $v(4 - p_2 \mid 1)$ | | |
|-------|-----------|---|---------------------|---|-----|
| 3 | 27 | + | 0 | = | 27 |
| 2 | 12 | + | 2 | = | 14 |
| 1 | 3 | + | 8 | = | 11 |
| 0 | 0 | + | 18 | = | 18. |

$$\tag{42}$$

The smallest value of the sum is 11, occurring when $p_2 = 1$. Therefore if 3 units must be made in two months, one should be made in the present month and two in the last month. The total weighted sum of squares will then be 11.

Thus a simple way to construct $v(s \mid 2)$ would be to construct a paper strip with a column containing entries $p_2$ and $3\,p_2{}^2$. This strip could be moved beside the column $v(s \mid 1)$ from Table 1 and the value of $3 p_2{}^2 + v(s - p_2 \mid 1)$ could be computed mentally through row $s$ of Table 1. The smallest value of this quantity would be $v(s \mid 2)$; the value of $p_2$ at which it occurred would be $p(s \mid 2)$. Then the strip would be moved down one space and the computation would be repeated for the next higher value of $s$, and so on. By proceeding in this way with a paper strip the calculation

Table 2
Result of Three Stages for Integral Production Problem

| $s$ | $p(s \mid 1)$ | $v(s \mid 1)$ | $p(s \mid 2)$ | $v(s \mid 2)$ | $p(s \mid 3)$ | $v(s \mid 3)$ |
|---|---|---|---|---|---|---|
| 0 | 0 | 0 | 0 | 0 | 0 | 0 |
| 1 | 1 | 2 | 0 | 2 | 0 | 2 |
| 2 | 2 | 8 | 1 | 5 | 0 | 5 |
| 3 | 3 | 18 | 1 | 11 | 0, 1 | 11 |
| 4 | 4 | 32 | 2 | 20 | 1 | 17 |
| 5 | 5 | 50 | 2 | 30 | 1 | 26 |
| 6 | 6 | 72 | 2 | 44 | 1 | 36 |
| 7 | 7 | 98 | 3 | 59 | 1 | 50 |
| 8 | 8 | 128 | 3 | 77 | 1 | 65 |
| 9 | 9 | 162 | 4 | 98 | 1, 2 | 83 |
| 10 | 10 | 200 | 4 | 120 | 2 | 101 |

of $v(s \mid 2)$ from $v(s \mid 1)$ becomes straightforward. When we continue on to calculate $v(s \mid 3)$ from $v(s \mid 2)$, we use the same procedure, but use a paper strip containing the values of $p_3$ and $6 p_3{}^2$ since $w_3 = 6$. The values on this strip are added mentally to the values of $v(s - p_2 \mid 2)$ already obtained to perform the optimization at the third stage. Since we can continue this process indefinitely, we can find $v(s \mid n)$ for any value of $n$ we like.

Table 2 shows the result of following this computational procedure for the first three stages. The table provides a solution for any number of months remaining through 3 and any quantity to be produced through 10. To see how to use this table, suppose we determine the production plans corresponding to the requirement of producing 9 units in three months. From the table we observe $p(9 \mid 3) = 1, 2$. That is, when we have three months remaining and 9 units to make, we have a choice of making either 1 or 2 in the present month. The choice arises because we find in determining the minimum value of $v(9 \mid 3)$ in the computational procedure that two different values of $p_3$, 1 and 2, produce the same minimum value of 83. Suppose that we decide to make 1 unit in month 3. Then 8 units must be made in the last two months. Since $p(8 \mid 2) = 3$, we find that we must make 3 units in month 2. That leaves $9 - 1 - 3 = 5$ units to be made in month 1, and, of course, $p(5 \mid 1) = 5$.

If on the other hand we choose to make 2 units in month 3, then $9 - 2 = 7$ units remain to be made in the last two months. Since $p(7 \mid 2) = 3$, again we make 3 units in month 2. That leaves $9 - 2 - 3 = 4$ units to be made in month 1, and $p(4 \mid 1) = 4$. Therefore we have our choice of two production plans:

$$
\begin{array}{llll}
\text{Plan 1} & p(9 \mid 3) = 1 & p(8 \mid 2) = 3 & p(5 \mid 1) = 5 \\
\text{Plan 2} & p(9 \mid 3) = 2 & p(7 \mid 2) = 3 & p(4 \mid 1) = 4 \quad (43)
\end{array}
$$

We can make the 9 units in the order 1, 3, 5 or in the order 2, 3, 4. The monthly contributions to the weighted sum of squares for each plan are:

|  |  | $n = 3$ | $n = 2$ | $n = 1$ | Total |
|---|---|---|---|---|---|
| Plan 1 | $w_n p_n^2$ | 6 | 27 | 50 | 83 |
| Plan 2 | $w_n p_n^2$ | 24 | 27 | 32 | 83 | (44) |

We see that both plans produce a weighted sum of squares of 83. We observe that $v(8 \mid 2) = 77$ gives the correct prediction of the weighted sum of squares in the last two months for plan 1 and that $v(7 \mid 2) = 59$ gives the corresponding correct prediction for plan 2.

Thus we have seen that the requirement that the amount of production in each month be integral has caused the minimum weighted sum of squares to increase by two units from the value of 81 we observed in Eq. (23) for the case where this constraint was not imposed. This points up the general result that adding a constraint in a problem can never help and may hinder the attainment of the maximum or minimum value obtainable without the constraint. The effect of adding constraints has philosophical as well as mathematical implications.

Finally, we should note that the value function must be unique, but the policy function need not be. The value function is unique because it represents the results obtainable from our portable genius – the best anyone could do. Clearly the best cannot have two different values. However, the policy need not be unique. As in this problem, there may be two or more different sets of decisions that lead to the same optimum solution of the decision problem. Many roads of equal length may lead to Rome. We should regard this possibility with gratitude because it allows us in some situations a set of policies that are equally good from a formal point of view, but within which we may be able to exercise a preference on some second order basis, like ease of explanation. Of course, we could also include more and more of these second order considerations into the formal statement of the problem and ultimately make the optimum policy unique. Rarely, however, is such an approach necessary or desirable.

## An Action-timing Problem

As a further example of dynamic programming we consider what we shall call an action-timing problem. This is a problem in which a certain action may be taken only once and the question is when it should be taken. The problem we shall solve could serve as a useful model for a wide variety of situations. For example, suppose that we are riding in an automobile and will soon enter a turnpike. We are low on gasoline, and decide to fill up. However, we know the gasoline on the turnpike is expensive and that the stations before the turnpike vary in their gasoline prices. The problem is if we know the number of stations remaining and observe the price at the present station, should we or should we not fill up here? The same problem could arise in hiring if we were allowed to interview 10 applicants for a single vacancy but had to reach an irrevocable decision not to hire each one after he was interviewed before we could interview the next applicant. Or we might encounter the problem in a commodity market where we had to make a purchase before a certain deadline and we wanted to know whether today's price is sufficiently low to make the purchase. Even in amateur photography can we find an application. Suppose that we have only one frame of film left and no possibility of obtaining any more. How do we determine whether a given scene is worthy of a shot when we have only expectations about the scenes we have remaining? Finally, the problem of getting married can be posed in these terms, but perhaps it is not wise to pursue that example further.

We shall develop a model general enough to allow considering all these possibilities. A known number of opportunities for action will be presented to us. At any of them we can take action and thereby terminate the problem. We can observe the utility of each opportunity before deciding whether or not to act. However, we do not know the utilities of future opportunities. We assume that

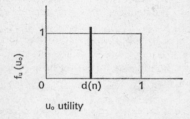

Figure 4 The density function for the utility presented at each opportunity.

the utility of each opportunity is measured on a scale ranging from 0 to 1 with 0 being the lowest possible utility and 1 the highest. Thus the utility of one corresponds to the cheapest possible gasoline, the most capable employee, the best possible commodity bargain, the unforgettable picture, and the ideal wife. We assume further that the utilities $u$ presented on successive opportunities are selected independently from the same probability distribution. Our initial choice for this distribution is the uniform distribution of Fig. 4. All values of utility between 0 and 1 are equally likely to be presented at each opportunity.

We shall let $n$ represent the number of opportunities remaining at any time; in our previous terminology $n$ is a stage variable. The essential problem is this: if we have arrived at a point where we have $n$ opportunities remaining and have not yet acted, should we accept the present utility and act now? What we would really like to have is a decision criterion $d(n)$ for accepting the utility $u$ offered with $n$ opportunities remaining. That is, we would like to know a number $d(n)$ such that if $u$ is less than $d(n)$ we shall not act now, while if $u$ equals or exceeds $d(n)$ we shall act now. If we denote acting by $A$ and not acting by $A'$, then at any $n$

$$u < d(n) \quad \text{implies} \quad A'$$
$$u \geq d(n) \quad \text{implies} \quad A. \tag{45}$$

To calculate $d(n)$, we begin by noting that the decision maker must be in one of two states at any time. If we let $i$ be the index of his state, then we can assign $i = 1$ to the situation where he has not already taken the action and $i = 2$ to the situation where he has already acted. We define $v_i(n)$ as the value or expected utility of being in state $i$ when $n$ opportunities remain. It is often convenient as it is here to specify the state of the system by a subscript. Since there is no value of being in state 2 beyond that received when the action was taken, we have

$$v_2(n) = v_2(n-1) = \ldots = v_2(0) = 0. \tag{46}$$

However, there is an expected utility to be derived from being in state 1 when $n$ opportunities remain. If the decision maker sets the criterion level $d(n)$ at some value, then he will take action if $u$ is at least as large as $d(n)$ and otherwise not act. Since the utility $u$ that will be presented is a random variable, the probability that he will act when $u$ is revealed is the probability that $u$ will equal or exceed $d(n)$. If he does act, then he will obtain the expected utility of a draw conditional on the draw's not being less than $d(n)$. He will also receive the value of being in state 2, but as we have said this position has no value in itself. The probability that he will not take action is 1 minus the probability that he will take action. In this case he finds himself once more in state 1, but this time with one fewer opportunity remaining. The value of this situation is $v_1(n-1)$, and must be supplied by the portable genius. Of course, the problem of the decision maker is to select the $d(n)$ that will yield the highest expected utility from the process. Therefore we have the recursive equation,

$$v_1(n) = \text{Max}_{d(n)}\{p(A \mid d(n))[(\text{expected utility} \mid A,$$
$$d(n)) + v_2(n-1)] + [1 - p(A \mid d(n))]v_1(n-1)\}$$
$$= \text{Max}_{d(n)}\{p(u \geq d(n))\langle u \mid u \geq d(n)\rangle \tag{47}$$
$$+ [1 - p(u \geq d(n))]v_1(n-1)\}, \qquad n = 1, 2, 3, \ldots$$

The value $v_1(0)$ of being in state 1 with no opportunities remaining must be specified as part of the problem statement. However, once $v_1(0)$ is known, Eq. (47) can be used to find $v_1(n)$ for $n = 1, 2, 3, \ldots$ and thereby we can avoid using the portable genius.

We shall now specialize our results to the particular density function for $u$ shown in Fig. 4. It is clear that the probability that $u$ will exceed $d(n)$ is just the area under this density function between $d(n)$ and 1 or $1 - d(n)$. The expected value of $u$ given that $u$ is greater than or equal to $d(n)$ is just half-way between $d(n)$ and 1 or $\frac{1}{2}[1 + d(n)]$. Therefore Eq. (47) becomes simply

$$v_1(n) = \text{Max}_{d(n)}\{[1 - d(n)]\tfrac{1}{2}[1 + d(n)] + d(n)v_1(n - 1)\}$$
$$= \text{Max}_{0 \le d(n) \le 1}\{\tfrac{1}{2}[1 - (d(n))^2] + d(n)v_1(n - 1)\}, \quad (48)$$
$$n = 1, 2, \ldots$$

The problem is now to find the value of $d(n)$ between 0 and 1 that maximizes the quantity in braces when $v_1(n - 1)$ is known. Once more differentiation is an efficient procedure. We differentiate the quantity in the braces with respect to $d(n)$ and set the result equal to zero,

$$-d(n) + v_1(n - 1) = 0 \qquad (49)$$
$$d(n) = v_1(n - 1), \quad n = 1, 2, \ldots$$

From the second derivative we confirm that this solution represents a maximum rather than a minimum. We have therefore found that we should set the criterion level when $n$ opportunities remain equal to the value of not having taken action when $n - 1$ opportunities remain: the form of the policy is very simple.

We find how well we shall do under this policy by evaluating the quantity in braces in Eq. (48) at the value of $d(n)$ given by Eq. (49),

$$v_1(n) = \{\tfrac{1}{2}[1 - (d(n))^2] + d(n)v_1(n - 1)\}_{d(n) = v_1(n-1)}$$
$$= \tfrac{1}{2}[1 - (v_1(n - 1))^2] + (v_1(n - 1))^2$$
$$= \tfrac{1}{2}[1 + (v_1(n - 1))^2], \quad n = 1, 2, 3, \ldots \quad (50)$$

The expected utility to be derived from not having acted in a process when $n$ opportunities remain is equal to $\frac{1}{2}$ of 1 plus the square of the expected utility when $n - 1$ opportunities remain, but only, of course, if the optimum policy specified by Eq. (49) is followed.

Two special cases are of interest. The first is where $v_1(0) = 1$. This means that the highest utility is assured even if one never takes advantage of any of the opportunities. In this case Eqs. (49) and (50) show that

$$v_1(n) = d_1(n) = 1, \qquad n = 0, 1, 2, \ldots \qquad (51)$$

Because $d_1(n) = 1$, no action will ever be taken at any opportunity. Because $v_1(n) = 1$, the decision maker is assured of achieving the highest possible utility by following this policy. It is reassuring that even in this very unusual case the formulation provides the appropriate result.

Table 3
Results for a Uniform Distribution of Opportunity Utility

| Opportunities remaining $n$ | Decision criterion $d(n) = v_1(n-1)$ | Value $v_1(n) = 0.5 + 0.5(v_1(n-1))^2$ |
|---|---|---|
| 0 | — | 0 |
| 1 | 0 | 0.50000 |
| 2 | 0.50000 | 0.62500 |
| 3 | 0.62500 | 0.69531 |
| 4 | 0.69531 | 0.74173 |
| 5 | 0.74173 | 0.77508 |
| 6 | 0.77508 | 0.80037 |
| 7 | 0.80037 | 0.82030 |
| 8 | 0.82030 | 0.83644 |
| 9 | 0.83644 | 0.84982 |
| 10 | 0.84982 | 0.86110 |
| 11 | 0.86110 | 0.87074 |
| 12 | 0.87074 | 0.87910 |
| 13 | 0.87910 | 0.88641 |
| 14 | 0.88641 | 0.89286 |
| 15 | 0.89286 | 0.89860 |
| 16 | 0.89860 | 0.90374 |

However, a more interesting case arises when $v_1(0) = 0$. This value for $v_1(0)$ means that the decision maker is assured of the lowest possible utility if he does not take advantage of any opportunity. The values of $d(n)$ and $v_1(n)$ generated for this case using Eqs. (49) and (50) appear in Table 3. As we would expect, the criterion level when only one opportunity remains is 0 – we are forced to act. However, the criterion level increases gradually with $n$, showing that we are getting more and more selective as the number of opportunities available to us increases. Furthermore, the expected utility that would be gained by following the optimum policy increases with the number of opportunities $n$. The rate of increase is greater when $n$ is small than it is when $n$ is large. The quantities $d(n)$ and $v_1(n)$ approach 1 and each other asymptotically as $n$ becomes larger and larger. Thus we can become arbitrarily choosy about accepting an opportunity and very optimistic therefore about how well we shall do in expected utility provided that a large enough number of opportunities remain.

Note that the policy is very easy to implement. All we need is a card showing the decision criterion $d(n)$ for each $n$. The first time we encounter an opportunity whose utility equals or exceeds the corresponding $d(n)$, we act. Thus implementation would be practical even for the truck driver buying gasoline.

## A non-optimum policy

To convince ourselves that we have found the optimum policy for this problem, let us consider another policy: Act the first time the utility of an opportunity is better than average unless only one opportunity remains, in which case act regardless of the utility presented. This policy requires

$$d(1) = 0; \quad d(n) = 0.5, \quad n = 2, 3, 4, \ldots \quad (52)$$

We observe that Eq. (48) allows us to evaluate any policy, even non-optimal ones, if we use the actual values of $d(n)$ rather than the optimizing values of Eq. (49). We therefore have

$$v_1(n) = \tfrac{1}{2}[1 - (d(n))^2] + d(n)v_1(n - 1),$$
$$n = 1, 2, 3, \ldots \quad (53)$$

Using the policy of Eq. (52) we find

$$v_1(1) = 0.500$$
$$v_1(n) = \tfrac{1}{2}[1 - (0.5)^2] + 0.5\, v_1(n - 1)$$
$$= 0.375 + 0.5\, v_1(n - 1),$$
$$n = 2, 3, 4, \ldots \quad (54)$$

Table 4 shows the values of $v_1(n)$ computed from Eq. (54). We must remember that $v_1(n)$ is now the value of being in state 1 with $n$ opportunities remaining when we are using the policy of Eq. (52). By comparing Tables 3 and 4 we observe that when $n = 1$ or 2 the expected utility from the process under both

Table 4
Evaluation of a Non-optimum Policy

| Opportunities remaining $n$ | Decision criterion $d(n)$ | Value $v_1(n) = 0.375 + 0.5v_1(n - 1)$ |
|---|---|---|
| 0 | — | 0 |
| 1 | 0 | 0.50000 |
| 2 | 0.5 | 0.62500 |
| 3 | 0.5 | 0.68750 |
| 4 | 0.5 | 0.71875 |
| 5 | 0.5 | 0.73438 |
| 6 | 0.5 | 0.74219 |
| 7 | 0.5 | 0.74610 |
| 8 | 0.5 | 0.74805 |
| 9 | 0.5 | 0.74903 |
| 10 | 0.5 | 0.74952 |
| 11 | 0.5 | 0.74976 |
| 12 | 0.5 | 0.74988 |
| 13 | 0.5 | 0.74994 |
| 14 | 0.5 | 0.74997 |
| 15 | 0.5 | 0.74999 |
| 16 | 0.5 | 0.75000 |
| | | $\vdots$ |
| | | 0.75 |

policies and in fact the policies themselves are identical. However, when $n$ exceeds 2, then the expected utilities for the optimum policy shown in Table 3 always exceed the expected utilities for the present policy shown in Table 4 for the same value of $n$. Moreover, the asymptotic expected utility when $n$ is large under the present policy is 0.75 rather than 1. The present policy does not provide the appropriate balance of birds in the hand and birds in the bush. Note, for example, that when 16 opportunities remain the decision maker will obtain an increase of about 0.15 in expected utility by following the optimum policy rather than the policy of Eq. (52).

*Grafting optimum policies*

Suppose that for some reason we are forced to use a non-optimum policy for some portion of our sequential decision process. How should we make decisions beyond this unfortunate region? Imagine that the non-optimum policy of Eq. (52) must be followed only when 8 or fewer opportunities remain. What should we do when more than 8 opportunities remain? We already know the answer. Eq. (49) states that regardless of where $v_1(n-1)$ came from, the best thing to do is to make $d(n) = v_1(n-1)$. Table 5 shows the result of this idea. The portion of the table for $n \leq 8$ is the same as the corresponding part of Table 4 for the non-optimum policy. However, when $n = 9$ we know that we should make $d(9) = v_1(8)$, no matter how $v_1(8)$ was produced. Since we are now operating under the optimum policy, $v_1(9)$ is computed from $v_1(8)$ using Eq. (50). Thus the rows in Table 5 corresponding to $n = 9$ through 16 are obtained by applying Eqs. (49) and (50) from the point where the non-optimum policy stopped. We observe that both $d(n)$ and $v_1(n)$ will once more approach 1 asymptotically when $n$ is large.

However, it is important to note that the values for $d_1(n)$ and $v_1(n)$ in the rows from $n = 9$ through 16 in Table 5 are *not* the same as the corresponding policy and value numbers in Table 3 where the optimum policy could be followed throughout. The difference is not too large when $n = 16$, but it exists and is important. We could easily compute that using the values for $d_1(n)$, $n = 9, 10, \ldots, 16$ given by Table 3 would lead to lower values of $v_1(n)$ than do the values of $d_1(n)$, $n = 9, 10, \ldots, 16$ indicated in Table 5. It is just not true that if we are forced to use a non-optimum policy for the final stages of the decision process, then we should use for decisions beyond that point the same decisions we would have made if we had been able to follow an optimum policy throughout. However, the decision rule for the optimum policy does apply in this event; it serves well in computing the appropriate decision criteria to use in the range for $n$ where the policy is allowed to be anything we please. The nature of a dynamic programming solution is perhaps better evidenced by the question of grafting on an optimum policy than by any other single topic we have discussed.

Table 5

Results for the Case of an Optimum Policy Grafted onto a Non-optimum Policy

| Opportunities remaining $n$ | Decision criterion $d(n)$ | Value $v_1(n)$ | |
|---|---|---|---|
| 0 | | 0 | |
| 1 | 0 | 0.50000 | |
| 2 | 0.5 | 0.62500 | Non-optimum |
| 3 | 0.5 | 0.68750 | |
| 4 | 0.5 | 0.71875 | $v_1(n) =$ |
| 5 | 0.5 | 0.73438 | $0.375 + 0.5\, v_1(n-1)$ |
| 6 | 0.5 | 0.74219 | |
| 7 | 0.5 | 0.74610 | |
| 8 | 0.5 | 0.74805 | |
| 9 | 0.74805 | 0.77979 | |
| 10 | 0.77979 | 0.80404 | Optimum |
| 11 | 0.80404 | 0.82324 | |
| 12 | $d_1(n) =$ 0.82324 | 0.83886 | $v_1(n) =$ |
| 13 | $v_1(n-1)$ 0.83886 | 0.85184 | $0.5 + 0.5\,(v_1(n-1))^2$ |
| 14 | 0.85184 | 0.86282 | |
| 15 | 0.86282 | 0.87223 | |
| 16 | 0.87223 | 0.88039 | |

*A triangular utility distribution*

We might be interested in how much the nature of our results depend on the uniform distribution of utility of Fig. 4. Let us therefore suppose that the utility distribution is the triangular distribution of Fig. 5. The effect of this change is to make higher utilities more prevalent than before. We still assume that the utilities presented at successive opportunities are independently selected from this triangular distribution. The two quantities that we need to provide in Eq. (47) are the probability that $u$ will equal or exceed $d(n)$ and the expected value of $u$ given that it does. The probability that $u$ will equal or exceed $d(n)$ is the area under the triangular probability distribution between $d(n)$ and 1, an area readily found to be $1 - (d(n))^2$. The density function

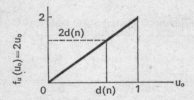

Figure 5 A triangular density function for the utility presented at each opportunity.

for $u$ conditional on $u$ equalling or exceeding $d(n)$ is then $2 u_0/[1 - (d(n))^2]$ for $d(n) \leqq u_0 \leqq 1$. Consequently the expected value of $u$ given that $u$ equals or exceeds $d(n)$ is

$$\langle u \mid u \geqq d(n) \rangle = \int_{d(n)}^{1} u_0 2u_0/(1 - (d(n))^2)\, du_0$$
$$= \tfrac{2}{3}[1 - (d(n))^3]/(1 - (d(n))^2). \quad (55)$$

When we substitute these results into Eq. (47) we obtain

$$v_1(n) = \text{Max}_{d(n)}\{[1 - (d(n))^2]\tfrac{2}{3}[1 - d(n))^3]/[1 - (d(n))^2]$$
$$+ (d(n))^2 v_1(n - 1)\}$$
$$= \text{Max}_{0 \leqq d \leqq (n) \leqq 1}\{\tfrac{2}{3}[1 - (d(n))^3] + (d(n))^2 v_1(n - 1)\}, \quad (56)$$
$$n = 1, 2, 3, \ldots$$

We observe that the denominator of the conditional expectation is just the probability that $u$ equals or exceeds $n$. Therefore the contribution of the first term within the braces is just the integral of $u_0 f_u(u_0)$ from $d(n)$ to 1, a partial expectation. We again find the maximizing value of $d(n)$ by differentiating the quantity in braces with respect to $d(n)$ and setting the result equal to zero,

$$-2(d(n))^2 + 2d(n)v_1(n - 1) = 0,$$
$$d(n) = v_1(n - 1). \quad (57)$$

Mathematical Programming

We have found once again that the decision criterion $d(n)$ when $n$ opportunities remain should be the expected utility to be derived from the process when $n - 1$ opportunities remain. The policy rule is exactly the same as before.

Table 6
Results for a Triangular Distribution of Opportunity Utility

| Opportunities remaining $n$ | Decision criterion $d(n)$ | Value $v_1(n) = \frac{2}{3} + \frac{1}{3}(v_1(n-1))^3$ |
|---|---|---|
| 0 | — | 0 |
| 1 | 0 | 0.6667 |
| 2 | 0.6667 | 0.7654 |
| 3 | 0.7654 | 0.8161 |
| 4 | 0.8161 | 0.8478 |
| 5 | 0.8478 | 0.8698 |
| 6 | 0.8698 | 0.8860 |
| 7 | 0.8860 | 0.8985 |
| 8 | 0.8985 | 0.9084 |
| 9 | 0.9084 | 0.9165 |
| 10 | 0.9165 | 0.9233 |
| 11 | 0.9233 | 0.9290 |
| 12 | 0.9290 | 0.9339 |
| 13 | 0.9339 | 0.9382 |
| 14 | 0.9382 | 0.9419 |
| 15 | 0.9419 | 0.9452 |
| 16 | 0.9452 | 0.9481 |

However, the computation of the value function $v_1(n)$ produces a different result. When we substitute the optimizing value of $d(n)$ from Eq. (57) into the recursive Eq. (56), we find

$$
\begin{aligned}
v_1(n) &= \left\{\tfrac{2}{3}[1 - (d(n))^3] + (d(n))^2 v_1(n-1)\right\}_{d(n)=v_1(n-1)} \\
&= \tfrac{2}{3}[1 - (v_1(n-1))^3] + (v_1(n-1))^3 \\
&= \tfrac{2}{3} + \tfrac{1}{3}(v_1(n-1))^3.
\end{aligned} \tag{58}
$$

Thus the procedure for constructing $v_1(n)$ from $v_1(n-1)$ is changed from the one prescribed by Eq. (50).

Table 6 shows the decision criteria and expected utilities computed from Eqs. (57) and (58) for the case of the triangular utility distribution. By comparing these results with those of Table 3 we find that for a given number of opportunities remaining the triangular distribution of utilities requires a higher decision criterion and also predicts a higher expected utility from the process. This is not surprising because in the triangular distribution case, higher utilities are more prevalent and therefore the decision maker can be more selective with the expectation of obtaining a better result.

*A general utility distribution*

Finding the same rule for establishing decision criteria for both the uniform and triangular distributions of utility presented leads us to inquire if this rule might not apply to any arbitrary utility distribution. We know that for any utility distribution $f_u(\cdot)$, the expected contribution to utility from acting now is just the partial expectation of the utility between $d(n)$ and 1. Furthermore, we shall obtain $v_1(n-1)$ with the probability we do not act, a probability that is the area of the utility density function between 0 and $d(n)$. Therefore, for a general utility density function we can write Eq. (47) as

$$v_1(n) = \text{Max}_{d(n)} \left\{ \int_{d(n)}^{1} u_0 f_u(u_0)\, du_0 + v_1(n-1) \int_0^{d(n)} f_u(u_0)\, du_0 \right\}. \quad (59)$$

We now find the optimizing value of $d(n)$ by differentiating the quantity in braces with respect to $d(n)$ and setting the result equal to zero. To perform this differentiation we must recall the rules for differentiating with respect to a variable appearing in the limits of an integral. We obtain

$$\partial\{\ \}/\partial d(n) = -d(n)f_u(d(n)) + v_1(n-1)f_u(d(n)) = 0. \quad (60)$$

Therefore our policy rule is

$$d(n) = v_1(n-1), \quad (61)$$

provided only that the density function is not zero at the point $d(n)$. Of course, when the density function is zero, then there is no possibility of a utility arising in that region and no difficulty can result. Therefore we have shown that regardless of the probability density function for the utilities presented at each opportunity, the optimum rule for establishing decision criteria is to make each decision criterion equal to the expected utility to be obtained from the process when one fewer opportunity remains.

Of course, when we consider Eq. (61) for a while we see that the result is just what we would expect. If $n$ opportunities remain and we pass up our present opportunity, then what we can expect in the future is $v_1(n-1)$. We would be silly to accept any utility for the present opportunity that was lower than $v_1(n-1)$, and equally silly to refuse any that was higher. Therefore we should establish our decision criteria just as Eq. (61) prescribes.

We obtain an equation for the value $v_1(n)$ for a general utility distribution by evaluating Eq. (59) at the value of $d(n)$ indicated by Eq. (61).

$$v_1(n) = \int_{v_1(n-1)}^{1} u_0 f_u(u_0)\, du_0 + v_1(n-1) \int_0^{v_1(n-1)} f_u(u_0)\, du_0. \tag{62}$$

This equation will not be very easy to evaluate if $f_u(\cdot)$ assumes a complicated form. This is just one instance of a result we often find in dynamic programming: it may be far easier to specify what to do than it is to determine how profitable following the best policy will be. We can generally calculate optimum policies more readily than value functions.

If we substitute the value of the lower limit $v_1(n-1)$ for the quantity $u_0$ in the integrand of the first integral in Eq. (62), we develop an interesting inequality,

$$v_1(n) \geqq \int_{v_1(n-1)}^{1} v_1(n-1) f_u(u_0)\, du_0 + v_1(n-1) \int_0^{v_1(n-1)} f_u(u_0)\, du_0,$$

$$v_1(n) \geqq v_1(n-1)\left[ \int_{v_1(n-1)}^{1} f_u(u_0)\, du_0 + \int_0^{v_1(n-1)} f_u(uo)\, du_0 \right],$$

$$v_1(n) \geqq v_1(n-1)\left[ \int^1 f_u(u_0)\, du_0 \right],$$

$$v_1(n) \geqq v_1(n-1). \tag{63}$$

Thus the value of having $n$ opportunities remaining must be monotonically non-decreasing in $n$. This is a property we have observed in our examples and one that we would expect to hold for even a general density function of utility.

404

## *Generalizations*

The action timing problem we have analyzed can be generalized in some ways at little cost and in others only by incurring great difficulty. For example, suppose that the density function for utility presented was different for each opportunity. This would cause almost no increase in complexity over the problem we solved. The decision rule would still be given by Eq. (61). All that would change is that the utility density function necessary in Eq. (62) for computing the value function would have to have a subscript to indicate that it was the utility density function for the $n^{\text{th}}$ opportunity. Otherwise the analysis is unchanged. Since the assumption of the same utility density function for all opportunities is the criticism most easily levelled at the model we considered, we are fortunate that changing this requirement causes no difficulty whatsoever.

However, if we desired to generalize the problem by allowing the utilities of successive opportunities to be not only uncertain, but dependent on one another (as might be the case, for example, if the gasoline service stations were having a price war), then we have made the problem considerably more difficult. The state of the system would have to specify not only whether or not the action had been taken, but also the utilities observed at the opportunities not taken in the past. There would have to be a strong incentive for solving this model before the effort could be justified.

Finally, suppose that the number of opportunities remaining is not known exactly but is itself uncertain. The result in this case is simplicity itself. We already know how to compute the value $v(n)$ of having $n$ opportunities remaining. All we do is weight this function with respect to the probability distribution we assign for the number of opportunities remaining to obtain an expected profit $\bar{v}$. If the opportunity currently presented has a higher utility than $\bar{v}$ then we accept it; otherwise we reject it. If no further opportunities are presented, then of course we are finished. However, if another opportunity appears then we construct a new distribution for the number of opportunities remaining and repeat the process. This new distribution will usually be the original distribution renormalized over one fewer opportunity. Thus the problem of uncertainty in the number of opportunities remaining introduces no new difficulty.

To summarize, we can usually allow a dynamic programming problem to be very general in the dependence of its variables upon the stage of the process without incurring any serious computational difficulty. As soon as the variables of the process become dependent from one stage to the next or when the concept of stage itself becomes confused, then we should expect stormy weather.

## The Dynamic Programming Formulation

We began by describing the general theory of dynamic programming in rough terms and then proceeded to a pair of examples that indicated the types of problem to which the theory is applied. Now we are ready to present the subject of dynamic programming in more formal terms to establish the generality of the concept.

Suppose that we wish to describe a system by $M$ state variables $s_i$. The composite state of the system at any time can then be represented by an $M$-component state vector $\mathbf{s}$ with components $s_i$,

$$\mathbf{s} = \{s_1, s_2, \ldots, s_M\}. \tag{64}$$

Depending on the model we construct, the components of the state variable could represent pressure or temperature, voltage or energy, investments or accounts receivable.

We can visualize every state vector $\mathbf{s}$ as a point in the $M$-dimensional state space $\mathscr{S}$ shown in Fig. 6. The representation is

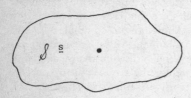

Figure 6

unique: every state vector corresponds to a point in the state space and every point in the state space corresponds to a state vector. If the values of the state variables change, then the position of the corresponding state vector $\mathbf{s}$ in the state space changes.

Suppose now that we have available a box of 'transformations'. Each transformation when applied to a state vector will change it into another state vector in the state space. A transformation in a physical problem might be an application of heat or the firing of a rocket. In a business problem it might represent a change in investment portfolio or the purchase of stock for inventory. Every transformation in the box is labeled with a number $k$ for identification; thus $T^k$ is the $k^{th}$ transformation. If $T^k$ is applied to the system when it is described by the state vector $\mathbf{s}$, the new state vector afterwards will be $T^k(\mathbf{s})$, another point in the state space $\mathscr{S}$. Figure 7 shows the box of transformations and a few

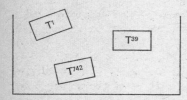

Figure 7 The box of transformations.

transformations with their labels. The number of transformations in the box may be finite or countably infinite.

Suppose now that we choose $n$ transformations from the box of transformations. We can choose the same transformation again and again as we like – there is no need that the transformations be different. Then we apply the $n$ transformations in some order to the system. The transformations and their order could look like

$$T^{23}, T^{59}, T^{12}, T^{59}, T^{231}, \ldots, T^{77}. \tag{65}$$

We shall call the first transformation applied to the system $T_1$, the second $T_2$, etc. We must remember to distinguish between the identification number of a transformation and the number that indicates the order in which it is applied.

We shall specify that the system is originally described by the state vector $\mathbf{s}$, and denote its state vector after the first transformation $T_1$ is applied by $\mathbf{s}_1$, after the second transformation $T_2$ by

407

$s_2$, etc. The sequence of state vectors for the system therefore satisfies the successive equations,

$$s_1 = T_1(s)$$
$$s_2 = T_2(s_1)$$
$$s_3 = T_3(s_2)$$
$$\vdots$$
$$s_n = T_n(s_{n-1}). \tag{66}$$

This sequence of state vectors establishes a trajectory in the state space, a trajectory shown in Fig. 8. The particular trajectory that

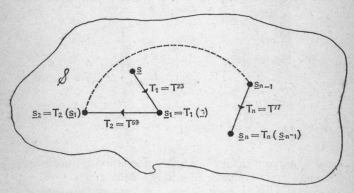

Figure 8 Trajectory in state space.

will be produced depends on the initial state vector $s$, the $n$ transformations selected from the box, and the order in which they are applied.

To make trajectories interesting to us we assume that associated with the $k^{th}$ transformation in the box there is a reward function $r^k(s)$ that specifies the reward (money, fuel, power, etc.) that will be gained by applying the $k^{th}$ transformation to the system when it is described by the state vector $s$. Rewards may, of course, be either positive or negative. Each trajectory of the system will therefore have an associated set of rewards. For the particular trajectory we illustrated in Fig. 8 the sequence of rewards is

$$r^{23}(s), \ r^{59}(s_1), \ r^{12}(s_2), \ \ldots, \ r^{77}(s_n). \tag{67}$$

We denote this sequence by

$$r_1(s), r_2(s_1), r_3(s_2), \ldots, r_n(s_{n-1}) \tag{68}$$

in accordance with our notation for the sequence of transformations.

Figure 9 shows the box of transformations, each with an

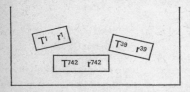

Figure 9 The box of transformations with associated rewards.

associated reward function. Figure 10 shows the system trajectory and the rewards generated by the application of each transformation. We now add one last feature to the model. We associate with each state vector s in the state space a terminal reward func-

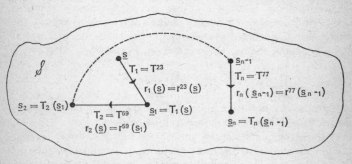

Figure 10 The system trajectory with rewards.

tion $r_0(s)$ that specifies the additional reward to be gained if the system has state vector s after all transformations have been applied. We require such a function because in many problems no reward is paid while transformations are applied but only after they cease. We call these problems terminal value problems; they are good approximations to a broad class of control problems including the guidance of lunar probes. A more mundane need for terminal rewards is to include the effect of scrap value in machinery replacement problems.

Let us use $P$ to indicate the policy represented by a particular set of transformations and a particular order of applying them. The total reward $r(s \mid n, P)$ from being allowed to choose $n$ transformations depends on the policy $P$ and the starting state vector $s$. Thus for a particular policy,

$$r(s \mid n, P) = r_1(s) + r_2(s_1) + \ldots + r_n(s_{n-1}) + r_0(s_n). \quad (69)$$

We can now imagine a game where the starting state vector $s$ and the number of transformations allowed $n$ are specified and we have to decide what transformations to use in what order so as to maximize the total reward from the trajectory that results. That is, we must find the best policy.

As we have said before, some of us will be better at this game than others and will be able to achieve higher total rewards. However, the maximum total reward that anyone can achieve is a function only of the starting state vector $s$ and the number of transformations allowed $n$ – these are the ultimate constraints on performance. Our portable genius knows how to achieve the maximum; we define the value function $v(s \mid n)$ as the total reward he will obtain, the best anyone can do. Formally,

$$v(s \mid n) = \text{Max } p^n(s \mid n, P) \quad (70)$$

where the maximization is carried out over all possible policies that can be constructed with $n$ transformations.

Now we begin the solution for the best policy. If the system has state vector $s$, we have $n$ transformations to use and we use the $k^{th}$ transformation now, we shall obtain the reward $r^k(s)$ and produce a new state vector $T^k(s)$ for the system. Our problem is to find what it is worth to have the system described by a state vector $T^k(s)$ when we have $n - 1$ transformations left to use. We consult the portable genius; the answer is $v(T^k(s) \mid n - 1)$. When we add this future reward to the present reward $r^k(s)$ we have obtained the total future reward to be expected from applying transformation $k$ now. We examine all transformations $k$ in this way to see which produces the highest total future reward – the one that does is selected as the first transformation we apply. These results are summarized in the recursive equation,

$$v(\mathbf{s} \mid n) = \text{Max}_k\{r^k(\mathbf{s}) + v(T^k(\mathbf{s}) \mid n-1)\}, \qquad n = 1, 2, 3, \ldots$$
$$T_1 = T^k; \qquad r_1(\mathbf{s}) = r^k(\mathbf{s}). \tag{71}$$

Figure 11 indicates the sequential nature of the result. If the value function is available when $n-1$ transformations remain, we can find it when $n$ remain. Of course, we must realize that this evaluation must be performed for every possible state vector in the state

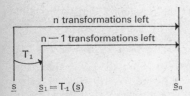

Figure 11 The sequencing relationship.

space. This computation can be prohibitively difficult if the number of possible state vectors is very large. However, at least theoretically Eq. (71) shows us how to solve the problem if only someone will specify the function $v(\mathbf{s} \mid 0)$. Yet this is just the reward to be gained by having the system described by the state vector $\mathbf{s}$ when no transformations remain; therefore it is equal to the terminal reward,

$$v(\mathbf{s} \mid 0) = r_0(\mathbf{s}). \tag{72}$$

Thus we have been able to eliminate the necessity for the portable genius. The sequence of functions $v(\mathbf{s} \mid n)$ and the optimum policy are computable directly from the specifications of the problem.

This completes our formalization of the solution principle of dynamic programming. The principle is called the 'principle of optimality' and results in recursive equations with the form of Eq. (71). We see in the general formulation that the value function must always be unique, while the policy function need not be.

There is one last point we should mention on the general formalism. In some situations the results of applying transformations to the system may not be deterministic. Rather the new state vector, the reward generated, or both, may have to be described by random variables. However, we can define an expected total future reward $\bar{v}(\mathbf{s} \mid n)$ by analogy with Eq. (70) and then realize that since the expected value of a sum is the sum of the expected values, we can write a recursive relation for $\bar{v}(\mathbf{s} \mid n)$ directly from Eq. (71),

$$\bar{v}(\mathbf{s} \mid n) = \text{Max }_k\{\bar{r}^k(\mathbf{s}) + \bar{v}(T^k(\mathbf{s} \mid n - 1))\}, \qquad n = 1, 2, 3, \ldots$$
$$T_1 = T^k; \qquad \bar{r}_1(\mathbf{s}) = \bar{r}^k(\mathbf{s}). \qquad (73)$$

Here we have used $\bar{r}^k(\mathbf{s})$ to designate the expected reward received by applying transformation $k$ to the system when it is described by state vector $\mathbf{s}$. To allow for the possibility that the terminal reward $r_0(\mathbf{s})$ may be a random variable, we replace Eq. (72) by

$$\bar{v}(\mathbf{s} \mid 0) = \bar{r}_0(\mathbf{s}). \qquad (74)$$

Equations (73) and (74) now serve to find the policy that maximizes the expected value of total future reward. However, since the solution rests on the linearity of the expectation operator, we should not find it surprising that using other criteria (as in finding the policy with the minimum reward variance) may be very difficult.

## Conclusion

We have now seen both the general structure of dynamic programming and its application to two fairly representative examples. From our discussion it is clear that applying dynamic programming requires considerable insight on the part of the analyst if he is to avoid creating a computationally infeasible problem. Therefore, dynamic programming is an approach most likely to be used by the professional analyst rather than by a manager directly. This situation stands in contrast to the widespread usage of linear programming.

As we can see from our examples, the number of points that must be evaluated in the recursive procedure increases rapidly with the number of state variables and the number of levels each state variable can assume. If there are $a$ state variables, each assuming $b$ levels, then we must consider $ba$ points in the state space. This number clearly becomes prohibitive very quickly for even the largest computers. By being clever in the evaluation process we can often reduce the amount of computation below the above requirements; however, any major reduction requires further assumptions about the structure of the problem.

One assumption on problem structure that produces computational simplifications is that the optimum trajectory is a continuous or nearly continuous function in the state space. This means that regardless of which transformation is applied to the system when it has a certain state vector, the state vector resulting from the transformation will be close in some sense to the original state vector. The assumption is most often justified in physical as opposed to business control systems. For example, an airplane subject to drag and propulsive forces will change its state arbitrarily little if the time for the change is small enough. However, an inventory system subject to large batch orders can, at least on paper, experience a sudden drastic change of state. Yet even in systems whose trajectories do contain discontinuities we can often identify regions of continuous operation. The continuity assumption simplifies computation because it limits the number of possible state vectors that must be evaluated.

Several attempts have been made to construct general dynamic programming formulations that were suitable as models for broad classes of even discontinuous problems and yet retained computational feasibility. The most important formulation of this type is the decision model based on the Markov process. In this formulation we model the problem as a finite-state Markov process that earns rewards as it makes transitions from state to state. The reward earned can be particular to the transition made. If the process is allowed to make a very large number of transitions, then it will earn some average amount of reward per transition, a number that we call the gain of the process.

The opportunity for making decisions arises whenever the process enters a state. We can select from a number of alternatives the alternative we want to govern the system's behavior until it leaves that state. Each alternative specifies both the probabilistic structure and the reward structure that the system will be subject to until it enters another state. The most usual decision problem in such a process is to determine which alternatives should be used in each state so as to maximize the gain of the process. Special algorithms exist for solving this problem; moreover, some linear programming techniques are suitable for performing the computation.

The dynamic programming formalism based on the Markov process has found application in a wide variety of practical situations. These include maintenance and repair, financial portfolio balancing, inventory and production control, equipment replacement, and directed marketing. The list grows steadily as more and more enterprises see the advantage of a formal representation of their sequential decision problems. The Markovian formulation is a natural starting point because its computability is assured.

Thus dynamic programming is a concept that gains practical implications as its domain of application is narrowed. It shares this property with all other mathematical concepts that have ever been proposed. The challenge of dynamic programming is thus a challenge to our ability to apply a very interesting concept to the solution of practical problems.

*References*

1. BELLMAN, R. (1957) *Dynamic programming*. Princeton University Press.
2. BELLMAN, R. and DREYFUS, S. (1962) *Applied dynamic programming*. Princeton Univ. Press.
3. HOWARD, R. (1960) *Dynamic programming and Markov processes*. M. I. T. Press, Cambridge, Mass.

# Further Reading

ANSOFF, H. I. (1965) *Corporate strategy.* McGraw-Hill.

BASS, F. M. *et al.* (eds.) (1964) *Mathematical method and models of marketing.* Irwin, Homewood.

BATTERSBY, A. (1966) *Mathematics in management.* Penguin.

BAUMOL, W. J. (1959) *Business behavior, value and growth.* Macmillan, New York.

BAUMOL, W. J. (1961) *Economic theory and operations analysis.* Prentice-Hall.

BEER, S. (1959) *Cybernetics and management.* Wiley.

BELLMAN, R., and DREYFUS, S. (1962) *Applied dynamic programming.* Princeton University Press.

BIERMAN, H., Jr., and SMIDT, S. (1966) *The capital budgeting decision,* 2nd. ed. Macmillan, New York.

BONINI, C. P. (1963) *Simulation of information and decision systems in the firm.* Prentice-Hall.

BROWN, R. G. (1959) *Statistical forecasting for inventory control.* McGraw-Hill.

BUFFA, E. S. (1963) *Models for production and operations management.* Wiley.

BUSH, R. R., and MOSTELLER, F. (1955) *Stochastic models for learning.* Wiley.

CHARNES, A., and COOPER, W. W. (1961) *Management models and industrial applications of linear programming.* Wiley.

CHURCHMAN, C. W., ACKOFF, R. L., and ARNOFF, E. L. (1957) *Introduction to operations research.* Wiley.

CLARKSON, G. P. E. (1962) *Portfolio selection: a simulation of trust investment.* Prentice-Hall.

CLARKSON, G. P. E. (1963) *The theory of consumer demand: a critical appraisal.* Prentice-Hall.

CYERT, R. M., and MARCH, J. G. (1963) *A behavioral theory of the firm.* Prentice-Hall.

DAVIDSON, D., and SUPPES, P. (1957) *Decision making: an experimental approach.* Stanford University.

DEAN, J. (1951) *Capital budgeting.* Columbia University.

FARRAR, D. E. (1962) *The investment decision under uncertainty.* Prentice-Hall.

FEIGENBAUM, E. A., and FELDMAN, J. (1963) *Computers and thought.* McGraw-Hill.

GORDON, M. J. (1962) *The investment, financing and valuation of the corporation.* Irwin.

## Further Reading

GRANT, E. L., and IVESON, W. G. (1960) *Principles of engineering economy*, 4th ed. Ronald, New York.

HADLEY, G. (1962) *Linear programming*. Addison-Wesley, Reading.

HADLEY, G., and WHITIN, T. M. (1963) *Analysis of inventory systems*. Prentice-Hall.

HOLT, C. C., MODIGLIANI, F., MUTH, J. F., and SIMON, H. A. (1960) *Planning production, inventories and work force*. Prentice-Hall.

HOWARD, R. (1960) *Dynamic programming and Markov processes*. M.I.T., Press Cambridge, Mass.

KEMENY, J. G., SNELL, J. L., and THOMPSON, G. L. (1957) *Finite mathematics*. Prentice-Hall.

KEMENY, J. G., and SNELL, J. L. (1958) *Finite Markov chains*. Van Nostrand.

LUCE, R. D., and RAIFFA, H. (1958) *Games and decisions*. Wiley.

LUTZ, F. A. (1961) *The theory of capital*. St Martin.

MARCH, J. G., and SIMON, H. A. (1958) *Organizations*. Wiley.

MARCH, J. G. (1965) *Handbook of organizations*. Rand McNally, Chicago.

MARKOWITZ, H. M. (1959) *Portfolio selection: efficient diversification of investments*. Wiley.

MASSE, P. (1962) *Optimal investment decisions: rules for action and criteria for choice*. Prentice-Hall.

MUTH, J. F., and THOMPSON, G. L. (1964) *Industrial scheduling*. Prentice-Hall.

RAIFFA, H., and SCHLAIFFER, R. (1962) *Applied statistical decision theory*. Harvard University.

SCHLAIFFER, R. (1959) *Probability and statistics for business decisions*. McGraw-Hill.

SIMON, H. A. (1965) *The shape of automation*. Harper and Row.

SOLOMON, E. (1964) *The theory of financial management*. Columbia University.

TONGE, F. M. (1961) *A heuristic program for assembly-line balancing*. Prentice-Hall,

WEINGARTNER, H. M. (1963) *Mathematical programming and the analysis of capital budgeting problems*. Prentice-Hall.

# Acknowledgements

Permission to reproduce the material published in this volume is acknowledged from the following sources:

Reading 1   Herbert A. Simon and the American Economic Association
Reading 2   Columbia University Press
Reading 3   H. Igor Ansoff and the Institute of Management Sciences
Reading 4   Frank Harary and the Operations Research Society of America
Reading 5   Richard M. Cyert, H. Justin Davidson, Gerald L. Thompson and the Institute of Management Sciences
Reading 6   Daniel Tiechroew, Alexander Robinchek, Michael Montalbano and the Institute of Management Sciences
Reading 7   H. Martin Weingartner and the Institute of Management Sciences
Reading 8   Bernard P. Dzielinski, Charles T. Baker, Alan S. Manne and the Institute of Management Sciences
Reading 9   Kenneth R. MacCrimmon and the Operations Research Society of America
Reading 10   A. Charnes, W. W. Cooper and the Institute of Management Sciences
Reading 11   Ronald A. Howard and the Institute of Management Sciences

# Author Index

421

# Subject Index

# Penguin Modern Economics

*Other titles available in this series are:*

## Economics of Education 1
*Ed. M. Blaug*

The quality of the labour force and the methods of training it have recently attracted the attention of economists. The education system is an important factor in economic growth, the degree of mobility of labour and the distribution of income. These important issues are considered in this volume of articles. A second volume, also edited by Professor Blaug, will examine the internal efficiency of schools and the relations between the costs of education and methods of financing these costs. These Readings will be widely welcomed by educationists, sociologists and political scientists as well as economists. X56

## The Labour Market
*Ed. B. J. McCormick and E. Owen Smith*

'Workers cannot be bought and sold, and people cannot be disassociated from their services.' This is the starting point for an analysis of the workings of the labour market. Wages are a means of allocating labour and a source of income, and considerations of efficiency frequently clash with equity criteria. This volume of Readings throws light on the efficiency of the wage system as an allocator of labour, the effects of trade unions and the role of the labour market in the problem of inflation. X55

## Public Enterprise
*Ed. R. Turvey*

The public sector as a consumer of resources and a producer of goods and services is apparent. But the methods of ensuring efficiency in public corporations are not obvious. Public enterprises may aim at social as well as commercial ends in conjunction with a private sector which is all too often imperfect in structure and behaviour. This volume of Readings is deliberately and provocative in an area where there is much confusion and disagreement. X59

## Regional Analysis
*Ed. L. Needleman*

Appalachia, Northern Ireland and Mezzogiorno are witnesses to the uneven geography of economic development. Indeed they may seem part of an 'underdeveloped' world. The application of the tools of economic analysis to regional problems has only just begun: the editor offers here a full range of regional work on one of the most interesting and exciting areas of economic enquiry. X60

## Transport
*Ed. Denys Munby*

'There is no escape from transport.' 'Almost every transport decision is a public issue.' These two challenging statements form the prelude to a collection of articles devoted to the economics of transport. The quality of the analysis and prescriptions is dictated by Dupuit's article and proceeds through Lewis, Vickrey, Walters, Meyer and Foster. All demonstrate the important contribution economists can make to the analysis of transport problems and the formulation of appropriate policies. X58

*Secular*

# LYRICS

## of the
## XIVth and XVth
## Centuries

# *Secular*

# LYRICS

## of the

## XIVth and XVth Centuries

EDITED BY

## Rossell Hope Robbins

SECOND EDITION

# OXFORD

## At the Clarendon Press

*Oxford University Press, Amen House, London E.C.4*

GLASGOW  NEW YORK  TORONTO  MELBOURNE  WELLINGTON
BOMBAY  CALCUTTA  MADRAS  KARACHI  KUALA LUMPUR
CAPE TOWN  IBADAN  NAIROBI  ACCRA

FIRST EDITION 1952
SECOND EDITION PRINTED LITHOGRAPHICALLY IN GREAT BRITAIN
AT THE UNIVERSITY PRESS, OXFORD
FROM CORRECTED SHEETS OF THE FIRST EDITION
1955
REPRINTED 1961

# PREFACE TO SECOND EDITION

In this second edition I have added a few pertinent references which have appeared in the last four years, and corrected a number of errors in the numerical references in the Glossary. Otherwise, with very few changes, this edition reproduces the first. I would like to repeat my gratitude to those scholars who in various ways have aided this work and its revision, and to thank very sincerely the Delegates of the Clarendon Press for their generous patience. As always, I am indebted to my wife, Helen Ann Mins Robbins, for her scholarly comradeship.

R. H. R.

KATSBAAN ONDERHEUGEL, SAUGERTIES, NEW YORK
*August* 1954

# FROM THE PREFACE TO THE
# FIRST EDITION

THE appearance of this collection of secular lyrics brings nearer to completion the assembling of the texts of Middle English lyric poetry begun by my teacher and friend, Carleton Brown. Like his works, it is based on a first-hand examination of the source materials. Before the publication of his anthologies (in 1924, 1932, 1939) Brown had spent many years preparing the two-volume *Register of Middle English Religious and Didactic Verse* (1916, 1920). No such register of the secular and political verse was available, however, until our joint work, *The Index of Middle English Verse*, was published in 1943. The study of the manuscripts, which *The Index* necessitated, laid the foundation for this present anthology, which, I believe, includes the most representative and most attractive of the later Middle English secular poems.

*Secular Lyrics of the Fourteenth and Fifteenth Centuries* presents, among the 212 items from 114 manuscripts, 57 poems not heretofore published, and 17 poems from hitherto unpublished variants. A further 7 previously unpublished poems and 10 unpublished variants are printed in the Notes or Introduction. Only 17 are from the fourteenth century (Nos. 15–18, 40, 60, 61, 76, 77, 103, 116–18, 141, 142, 147, 149), and, apart from fragments, there are few other secular lyrics certainly composed then. The fourteenth century is, however, comparatively rich in political poems.

In making this anthology, I have accepted Brown's definition of a lyric as any short poem, but departed from the general rules by which he excluded all poems by well-known authors (Chaucer, Lydgate, Hoccleve); poems of low literary value; and poems already printed in good and accessible editions (such as *The Early English Text*

*Society*). In general, I have tried to include poems which would illustrate, irrespective of poetic merit, all the various types of Middle English secular lyrics; all lyrics outstanding either for their literary value or for the tendencies they represent, even if they have been previously printed; the lyrics most current in Middle English —the standard of currency being the number of texts preserved—irrespective of their appeal as literature to the modern reader; and, finally, a few lyrics by known authors (except Chaucer), so as to permit a comparative survey in the compass of one volume.

R. H. R

*August* 1950

# CONTENTS

# Contents

## II. PRACTICAL VERSE

### CHARMS

### THE ALMANACK

# *Contents*

# INTRODUCTION

THE most significant feature of the Middle English secular lyric is its subordinate position in relation to the religious. For every secular lyric there are three or four religious. This ratio holds for all Middle English poetry: of the 123 texts (listed in the *Index*),[1] each of which appears in more than 8 manuscripts, only 33 are non-religious. I do not think that the destruction of manuscripts accounts entirely for this disparity; it is simply that religion dominated the scene, and all problems and conflicts had a religious frame of reference. It is only towards the end of the fifteenth century, when the ideas of the Renaissance began to ferment in England, that secular poems became more popular.

The predominance of religious poems is clearly seen in the manuscripts. The couple of thousand shorter Middle English poems of all types are preserved in about 450 manuscripts, of which 35 contain 75 per cent. of all 'lyrics'. These 450 manuscripts may be classified into 10 major groups. A very brief survey will illustrate the absence of fourteenth-century secular materials, and will also show the basis for the division of the poems in this anthology into 'Popular' and 'Courtly'.

1. *The Friar Miscellanies*. These manuscripts are the Golden Treasuries or Oxford Books of Verse of the thirteenth century. There are about 100 religious, secular, and political lyrics with a definite poetical form in half a dozen manuscripts: 2 are Dominican,[2] and 3 are Franciscan.[3] Harley MS. 2253, although compiled by

---

[1] Carleton Brown and Rossell Hope Robbins, *The Index of Middle English Verse*, The Index Society II, New York 1943, App. V, pp. 737-9.
[2] MSS. Digby 86 and Trinity Coll. Camb. 323.
[3] MSS. Digby 2; Jesus Coll. Oxford 29 (and its sister MS. Cotton Caligula A. ix); Harley 913.

monks at Leominster, clearly contains work by friars, since half its poems are duplicated in manuscripts belonging to friars. Many of these poems show considerable French influence, and MSS. Digby 86 and Harley 2253 both contain poems in French. These lyrics are the greatest achievement of all Middle English poetry, but earlier critics' justifiable concentration on them has led to the erroneous belief that *all* Middle English lyrics were written under French influence. This group, with a few preachers' tags from manuscripts of sermons, provided most of the contents of Brown's *English Lyrics of the Thirteenth Century* (56 out of 91 texts).

2. *Sermons and Sermon Note-books*. These manuscripts, most numerous in the fourteenth century, contain Latin sermons and notes to be used as occasion arose by the religious and secular clergy. Some of the sermons contain fragments of English verse, either composed by the sermon-writer or currently popular. During his sermon a preacher might repeat such a little tag in the hope that its rhythm and rhyme would help his congregation remember some moral or tenet. Tags might serve another purpose: their shortness and pithiness would help the preacher himself to remember the heads of his sermon. If English, they were seldom translated into Latin, so that their homely appeal would not be lost. Because of the subject-matter, they are almost all religious; the few secular ones, however, show what sort of poetry was popular among the broad mass of the people.

There are over 300 English tags in some 50 manuscripts; but about 200 occur in 5 major collections, all reflecting the tastes and temper of the period before the Black Death (1350). Most important is the *Fasciculus Morum* (found in 22 manuscripts), a Franciscan compilation, with about 30 English scraps, which shows an organized attempt to use English verse for practical instruction. Another manuscript is John Grimestone's commonplace book of pulpit material, arranged alphabetically in 143 topics, with over a hundred short pieces.[1] Of the 135 items in Brown's *Religious Lyrics of the Fourteenth Century*, 33 come from these manuscripts.

3. *Mystical and Devotional Works.* Most of the material in these manuscripts belongs to the second half of the fourteenth century, although the cult of mysticism continued and in fact became more intense towards the end of the fifteenth century. Many of the poems are associated with the name of Rolle. All are distinguished by love-longing or passion-longing, and were written, like their prose counterparts, to arouse devotion to Christ or the Blessed Virgin Mary. One item (*Index*, No. 2250) is introduced thus:

I wil þat 30w neuer be ydel, bot ay owthir speke of God, or worke som notabil warke, or thynk on hym principaly, þat þi thoght be ay hauand hym in mynde. And thynk oft on his passyon.

There are about 200 poems written for such a purpose, notably in the important Vernon MS. and the related Simeon MS. (B.M. Addit. 22283), and in four other manuscripts.[2]

There are striking similarities between the mystical pieces in this group and the secular love lyrics. Many poems of the Vernon MS. profess love to the Virgin in

[1] The other 3 manuscripts are: Merton Coll. Oxford 248, over 30 tags in material collected by Bishop Sheppey; Harley 2316, written in the second half of the fourteenth century, probably made for Dominican use; Harley 7322, according to Furnivall, who edited most of its contents (*EETS* 15, revised 1913), 'evidently intended for the use of preachers'.

[2] MSS. Camb. Univ. Dd. 5. 64 (Rolle); Arundel 285; B.M. Addit. 37049; Lincoln Cath. 192 (Thornton).

terms which could well be applied to a very earthly young lady; furthermore, the terminology is that of the pseudo-chivalric poems 'to his mistress' which became so popular in the fifteenth century. For example, *Index*, No. 2607, goes from

> So hertly I haue I-set my þouȝt
> Vppon þat buyrde of buyrdes best.

to

> Loue me haþ in bales brouȝt
>   For on such þat I suppose,
> Þat is so studefast in hire þouȝt,
>   Þat couþe neuere gabbe ne glose;
> Hose hire loueþ he schal not lose,
>   For ȝit be-giled heo neuer no wiht
> I likne þat ladi to þe rose—
>   I-blessed beo þat buirde briht!

The Virgin becomes

> Þat princesse is peerles of prys;
> So feir, so clene, so good, so wys,
> And þerto trewe as eny steel.

She is described:

> Heo is of colour and beute
> As fresch as is þe rose in May.

This treatment continues in the fifteenth century, for example, in H. Bowesper's single stanza (*Index*, No. 2824):

> Ryht godely, fressh flour of womanhode,
>   My lyues Ioy, myn hertes plesance,
> Example of trouth and rote of godelyhode,
>   And verayly my lyues sustenance—
>   And, with al þe hool, feythful obeisance
>     That seruant can thenk or deuyse,
>   To you þat haue myn herte in gvuernance,
>     Me recemande in all my best wyse.

As early as the thirteenth century, however, the secular style was borrowed for religious purposes, and Brown believed that the author of at least one religious poem 'was himself engaged in transposing the secular song'; and further noted 'two independent attempts to convert this secular song into a religious lyric'.[1] By the fifteenth century the convention had become established, and no doubt one and the same poet (for example, Lydgate) would write similar poems to the 'queene of Heuene' and to Queen Margaret.

4. *The Closet Hymns*. These translations of Latin hymns, or independent attempts at hymns for the liturgical seasons, were intended for private reading or for recitation from a pulpit. There are about 250 such poems in 5 fourteenth- and fifteenth-century manuscripts, with 4 authors known by name: William Herebert and James Ryman, both Franciscans; William Shoreham, a parish priest; and John Audelay, a chantry priest.[2]

None of these manuscripts contains secular lyrics.

The preceding four groups of manuscripts are almost the sole sources for our knowledge of Middle English verse to the end of the fourteenth century. There is no major source for secular lyrics in that century. After Harley MS. 2253 there is a lapse of a hundred years—the whole of the fourteenth century—until similar poetry anthologies appear. The continuity of the secular lyric must be inferred from fragments and hints.

In the fifteenth century the volume of writing increased by leaps and bounds. Brown put almost all the

[1] Carleton Brown, *English Lyrics of the XIIIth Century*, Oxford 1932, p. 236.
[2] MSS. Phillipps 8339 (Herebert); Camb. Univ. Ee. 1. 6 (Ryman); B.M. Addit. 17376 (Shoreham); Douce 302 (Audelay); B.M. Addit. 34193 (hymnal).

significant poems of the thirteenth century—religious and secular—into a single volume. His *Religious Lyrics of the Fourteenth Century* was made up largely of poems from only half a dozen important collections,[1] in all, a total of 85 out of 135 texts. But in the fifteenth century Brown could choose from a large number of suitable lyrics. 'For the volume of extant fifteenth-century poetry', he said in his introduction,[2] 'contrary to the impression which one receives from handbooks of literature, is many times larger than that of the preceding century'. Brown continued: 'Indeed, from the material available, a collection ten times the size of the present volume would have been possible.' My own study of the lyrics confirms the observation of my teacher, George G. Coulton, who once remarked to me that for every page of English written in the thirteenth century, there would be 3 in the fourteenth and 10 in the fifteenth century.

While there is much more secular lyric poetry preserved from the fifteenth than from the fourteenth century, there is not the rich and varied choice which the religious poems offer. If Chaucer, Lydgate, and Hoccleve are omitted, it would be difficult to extend the present anthology of secular lyrics by more than a bare hundred texts —even if all the secular carols not printed here were to be included. The reasons for this paucity of secular material, even in the fifteenth century, will be manifest with the further manuscript groups, where the religious items still predominate.

5. *Prayer Books.* About 200 items were written as specific devotions for the literate upper-class laity, espe-

---

[1] Herebert (14); Bishop Sheppey (7); John Grimestone (22); Rolle (10); Vernon (26); and Harley MS. 2253 (6), which he later classified as thirteenth-century material.

[2] Carleton Brown, *Religious Lyrics of the XVth Century*, Oxford 1939, pp. xvii, xviii.

cially the women. Their rubrics reveal their practical nature, like the mystical poems:

> In seiynge of þis orisoun stynteth & bydeth at euery cros & þynketh whate ye haue seide. For a more deuoute prayere fond I neuer of the Passioun who-so wolde deuoutly say hitte. (*Index*, No. 1761.)

or

> This praer here folwyng schold be sayd bifore the leuacion dewouteli kneling. (*Index*, No. 2512.)

Many of the prayers are found repeated in half a dozen manuscripts, indicating a wide circulation; they are generally added to Latin *Horae*, in collections of Latin and English private devotions, or on prayer rolls.[1] With two exceptions, all the *Horae* are fifteenth century.

6. *The Aureate Collections*. These large, well-written and often illuminated manuscripts of formal verse, mainly moral and religious, by Chaucer and especially by Lydgate, or their imitators, or by the Scottish Chaucerians, are for the fifteenth century what the Friar Miscellanies were for the thirteenth century. The manuscripts belonged to some noble or rich citizen, rather than to a religious house, and sometimes were compiled by request. Thus, dedicatory verses to the patron are added, or an occasional miniature. In this respect, these volumes of miscellaneous shorter poems resemble the more common volumes containing one long item.[2]

The poets who wrote at the request of some nobleman

---

[1] Such manuscripts include Rawlinson liturg. g. 2; Camb. Univ. Ii. 6. 43; B.M. Addit. 27924; Lambeth 559. See further, Robbins, 'Private Prayers in Middle English Verse' in *Studies in Philology*, xxxvi. 465–75.

[2] Such as Arundel MS. 38, Hoccleve's *De Regimine Principum* (a presentation copy to King Henry V); or Harley MS. 2278, Lydgate's *Life of St. Edmund* (a presentation copy to King Henry VI).

introduced a Latinized or 'aureate' vocabulary, in an effort to create a 'noble' style for their 'noble' readers. Hawes, for example, in his *Pastime of Pleasure*, scoffed at the common tongue, and described his aim to

> . . . clarify
> The dulcet speche from the langage rude,
> Tellyng the tale in termes eloquent:
> The barbary tongue it doth ferre exclude,
> Electynge words which are expedyent,
> In Latin or in Englyshe, after the entente,
> Encensyng out the aromatyke fume,
> Our langage rude to exyle and consume.

As a result, many of these courtly love lyrics of the middle and late fifteenth century retained the tyrannical convention of 'noble rhetoric'.[1] The style spread downwards and, in the semi-official verse used at public ceremonies, became even more tiresome.[2] The reader will find for himself that the polite verse is at its best when it relies for its adornment upon simple alliteration and dignity of phrase.

These Aureate Collections were the medieval equivalent of 'gift' copies, prized possessions to be shown occasionally to one's friends; for the manuscripts themselves show little evidence of use. Those written for semi-public circulation in Shirley's scriptorium, the major source for manuscripts of this type, are not worn like the manuscripts of romances. Furthermore, these large and bulky manuscripts could not be carried about easily or used for frequent reference.

There was even more duplication of texts within the Aureate Collections than there was within the Friar Miscellanies. Altogether, there are between 300 and 400

---

[1] See Nos. 130, 131, 177, 178, 205.
[2] See Nos. 120, 121, 123.

poems in upwards of 70 manuscripts, but only a mere hundred unique texts. In the 6 Shirley manuscripts,[1] out of between 250 and 300 poems, only a couple of dozen are unique texts.

For several manuscripts, Shirley wrote long rubrics describing the poems; and it is on this evidence that many pieces are ascribed to Lydgate. Ashmole MS. 59 and Trinity Coll. Cambridge MS. 600 are both rich in these descriptive prefaces; some are interesting for their light on the circumstances of Lydgate's composition: for example (*Index*, No. 3718):

> And now here begyÿnneþe a comendable balade by Lydgate Daun Iohan at þe reuerence of my Lady of Holand, and of my Lord of Gloucestre, to-fore þe day of þeyre maryage in þe desyrous tyme of þeyre truwe lovyng.

But a more interesting rubric is the little stanza which served as a sort of book plate for the Shirley manuscripts (*Index*, No. 4260):

> Yee þat desyre in herte and have plesaunce
>    Olde stories in bokis for to rede,
> Gode matiers putt hem in remembraunce,
>    And of þe oþer take yee neuer hede;
>    Bysechyng yowe of your godelyhede,
>       Whane yee þis boke have overredde and seyne,
>       To Iohan Shirley restore yee it ageine.

Shirley himself wrote two quasi-doggerel lists of contents, probably to allow the friends and patrons who borrowed his books to see quickly whether they wished to read the manuscript.[2] In one such list in B.M. Addit. MS. 29729 (but not intended for this manuscript), Shirley alludes to

---

[1] MSS. Ashmole 59; Trinity Coll. Camb. 600; Harley 2251; Harley 7333; B.M. Addit. 16165; B.M. Addit. 34360.
[2] *Index*, Nos. 1426, 2598.

> . . . many a roundell and balade
> whiche þe Munke of Bury hath made
> and sayd them with hys sugred mouthe
> in straunge metres so vnkouthe,
> of morall mater and holynesse,
> of salmes and of ympnes expresse,
> of loue and lawe and of pleyinges,
> of lordes, of ladyes, of qwenes, of kynges . . .

The sixteenth-century antiquarian, John Stowe, collected some of Shirley's manuscripts,[1] and copied poems from some others.[2] There is a further group of about 30 miscellaneous manuscripts containing poems by Lydgate and others in that tradition.[3] In addition, there are the manuscripts of the later Scottish Chaucerians, most of whose poetry is, however, outside our limits.[4]

7. *The Minstrel Collections*. The three extant manuscripts (which I believe were used by minstrels) belong to the middle of the fifteenth century, and contain about 200 poems; there is some repetition of texts  The main collections of carols appear in these manuscripts.[5] The Sloane MS. measures approximately 6 by 4½ inches, a convenient size to carry. Among its 74 items are several (such as Nos. 4 and 5) which stamp the book as that of a 'minstrel'—one who got his living by singing from place to place. He was no chapman who got bogged down in the 'fowle weyis' with a heavy pack (No. 7). In addition,

---

[1] Such as MSS. Trinity Coll. Camb. 600; B.M. Addit. 34360.

[2] Stowe's MSS. include Trinity Coll. Camb. 599 and 601; Harley 367; B.M. Addit. 29729; Lambeth 306.

[3] Such as MSS. Laud Misc. 683; Bodley 638; Fairfax 16; Tanner 346; Rawlinson C. 86; Rawlinson C. 813; Jesus Coll. Camb. 56; Cotton Caligula A. ii; Harley 2255.

[4] Such as MSS. Pepys 2553 (Maitland); Advocates 1. 1. 6 (Bannatyne); Advocates 34. 7. 3 (Gray); Laing 149 (Makculloch); Asloan.

[5] MSS. Eng. poet. e. 1; St. John's Coll. Camb. 259; Sloane 2593.

this manuscript is represented here by Nos. 21 (with its sophisticated punning), 27, 41, 43, 45 (still a favourite today), 46, and 47.

MS. Eng. poet e. 1 comes about 30 years later (1480), and contains 76 songs and carols; it is the same size, 6 by 4½ inches. The Bodleian Catalogue simply states 'for the use of a professed minstrel', and Wright says: 'This manuscript has in all probability belonged to a professed minstrel.'[1] Although, as Greene indicates,[2] 'there is no external evidence' that it was so used, there is, nevertheless, some slight internal evidence (No. 8). The third collection, St. John's Coll. Cambridge MS. 259, is, unfortunately, incomplete: only 20 carols remain; the size is about the same, 6 by 4 inches. It is represented in this collection by No. 24.

The majority of poems in these manuscripts are religious: there are, for example, over 50 carols on the Nativity, 30 moralizing songs of admonition, and 15 carols in praise of the Blessed Virgin Mary.

8. *The Song Books.* Similar to the Minstrel Collections are the song books with musical notation. Bodleian MS. Arch. Selden B. 26 (mid fifteenth-century) has over 50 carols and part songs in English and Latin, with music in two, three, and four parts. Trinity Coll. Cambridge MS. 1230 is a roll of 12 carols (including the 'Agincourt Song'), all with music; and a third collection of songs appears at the end of a Carthusian manuscript of Latin sermons and tracts in Addit. MS. 5943 of Cambridge University Library (Nos. 22, 30, 31, 62). These three manuscripts and the three Minstrel Collections supply 270 of Greene's 474 carols. These Song Books with their music are a

---

[1] Thomas Wright, *Songs and Carols of the Fifteenth Century*, Percy Society xxiii, London 1847, p. v.

[2] Richard Leighton Greene, *The Early English Carols*, Oxford 1935, p. 338.

reminder that the popular carols were for singing, a fact not evident in the carols of the Minstrel Collections.[1]

These fifteenth-century Song Books later developed into the Tudor song books,[2] but here the music was given greater prominence than the words; and for the first time in English literary history secular songs outnumbered religious.

9. *Commonplace Books*. Many of the manuscripts so far discussed are in fact 'commonplace' books, collections of pieces which interested the compiler or collector sufficiently for him to write in a book. Trinity Coll. Cambridge MS. 323, the Friar Miscellany, might be considered the institution's commonplace book, in which any member entered what interested him. The sermon collection in Advocates MS. 18. 7. 21 is generally called 'Grimestone's Commonplace Book'. But in these instances there was a more important purpose than that of mere collecting.

The commonplace books proper are of two kinds: those belonging to a citizen and those belonging to a religious community or one of its members. All are simply notebooks of facts or references for the owner, and the inclusion of poetry is accidental.

The commonplace books of citizens are not found until the end of the fifteenth century, and may be taken as a sign of the increasing power and education of the bourgeoisie. Harley MS. 2252 (early sixteenth century) is a scrapbook of John Colyn, a mercer of London during the reign of Henry VIII. It contains, in several hands, peti-

---

[1] Of the carols in this anthology, only two (No. 19 and No. 163, probably non-popular) have music; but several others have directions for singing: for example, the name of the tune is given (No. 23). Another Song Book is Egerton MS. 3307.

[2] Such as MSS. B.M. Addit. 5464 (Fairfax), which includes eleven named composers, and sets to music much of the formal Lydgate-type verse; B.M. Addit. 5665 (Ritson); B.M. Addit. 31922; Royal Appendix 58.

tions, lists of events and places connected with London, nine short poems (mainly moral instructions), and romances. There are also a couple of medical receipts, three sets of prognostications for the fortunes of the coming year, and the names of the mayors of London to 1528, with the wards and churches. No. 137 is from this manuscript. The book's value lies in the indication it gives of the interests of a townsman at the turn of the century. Tanner MS. 407 (from which comes No. 176) belonged to Robert Reynys of Acle in Norfolk; it includes a charm for bloodletting, many gnomic lines, some miracles of the Blessed Virgin, prognostications and geographical notes, and several doctrinal poems. Egerton MS. 1995 has only four short poems of moral teaching; and there are some Latin prognostications; the main contents are London chronicles by Gregory Skynner, and two romances. The Brome MS. is partly written 'in the small neat hand of the professional writer',[1] in contrast to the other commonplace books which apparently are chiefly written by the owners themselves. Its contents again reveal the middle-class interests of the later fifteenth century (*c.* 1470–80): poems of moral advice, doctrinal poems (such as the Fifteen Signs of Doomsday), gnomic saws, a few carols, some romances, and a passage from a play. Balliol Coll. Oxford MS. 354 belonged to a Richard Hill; it is a long narrow book of nearly 300 folios, at the beginning taken up with useful information—receipts for medical and household use, lists of distances and so forth; romances (its *Seven Sages* and *Siege of Rouen* are both found in other commonplace books); and doctrinal and instructional verse, including Lydgate's 'Stans puer' and a 'Boke of Curtasie'.

These books have this much in common: in addition to

[1] Lucy Toulmin Smith, *A Commonplace Book of the Fifteenth Century*, London 1886.

practical items they generally contain a few romances (for light reading), moral precepts in verse (to help bring up the children), and a few proverbial sayings. This is just what might be expected from a volume that provided directions for day to day emergencies and leisure reading.

The religious commonplace books are likewise of the very late fifteenth century. Sloane MS. 747 is a Register of Missenden Abbey with many English tags scattered throughout the Latin (No. 65). Sloane MS. 1584 (*c.* 1520) was written in the House of the Premonstratensian canons at Newbo in Lincolnshire by John Gysborn (No. 206).

10. *Fly-leaf Poems.* There is one final group of quite diverse manuscripts containing poems added to the fly-leaves. This practice already existed in the thirteenth century, but became especially prevalent in the fifteenth with secular lyrics. Many gentlemen or middle-class owners tried their hands at composing, or recording à favourite proverb on a fly-leaf.

The fly-leaf addenda provide as authentically popular pieces as do the Sermons. Six of the most charming of the Popular Songs of the first section are written on blank pages (corresponding to fly-leaves) in a very miscellaneous Latin collection of deeds and treatises in Caius Coll. Cambridge MS. 383 (Nos. 19, 23, 28, 29, 33, 37). Other popular poems, all unique texts, from such sources include Nos. 12, 20, 26, 34, 40, 42, 48, and 60.

On the other hand, the popular pieces in the second section, Practical Verse, which are often found on fly-leaves, have generally survived in several versions. Thus No. 74, from a collection of receipts, medical and agricultural notes, is found in 14 other manuscripts; No. 83 occurs on the fly-leaf of Peter Idle's *Instructions* and in 5 other manuscripts; No. 85 is added after a Passion Gospel, and is found in 7 other manuscripts.

Much of the Occasional Verse of the third section, designed for more wealthy (and often more literate) persons, is preserved in a similar way. For example, No. 107, a single stanza from Lydgate's *Fall of Princes*, occurs separately in 11 texts, 5 of which are on fly-leaves.[1] Four of the 5 texts of No. 111 are fly-leaf items. Those pieces which would logically be placed at the beginning (or end) of a manuscript also appear on fly-leaves: book mottoes Nos. 89 and 90 are added in 5 and 4 manuscripts respectively. On the other hand, those pieces which are the work of an individual owner attempting composition are naturally unique texts: individual book mottoes found on fly-leaves are Nos. 91–5; poems on deceit, similar in subject-matter to the stanza extracted from Lydgate, occur on fly-leaves in Nos. 108 and 109; and Nos. 125 and 126, both epitaphs, are also on fly-leaves. The list could be extended; the notes for the poems in this section give further details.

In the fourth section, Courtly Love Lyrics, many of the poems are obviously attempts at composition by non-professional poets. The two pieces from the former Capesthorne MS. are good examples (Nos. 193 and 194). But where a man did not have his commonplace book at hand, he would use fly-leaves. Thus a number of love lyrics are so written: No. 136, on an Old Testament History; Nos. 139 and 140 (*Confessio Amantis*); No. 144 (Vegetius, *De Re Militari*); No. 148 (a sermon collection); No. 158 (*Pricke of Conscience*); No. 178 (*Life of St. Edmund*); No. 181 (Stanzaic Life of Christ); No. 196 (Chaucer); and No. 202 (Lydgate's *Life of Our Lady*). Most of these texts are of the later fifteenth century.

The fly-leaf poems sometimes have the author's name

[1] MSS. Hatton 73; Douce 45; Trinity Coll. Camb. 600; Sloane 1825; Morgan 775.

signed or scribbled on the same page; in this way are preserved the names of a few fifteenth-century writers. There is, for example, one H. Bowesper (quoted above, p. xx). A Nycholas Wikes composed two stanzas in rhyme royal with the refrain 'Slypper it is to grype one whome is no holde' (*Index*, No. 2132) on the fly-leaf of a Hoccleve manuscript, adding underneath a list of his sons and daughters, and copying out the little moral tag (No. 85):

> He that in yought to no vertew himselfe applieth,
> In age to amende him badd costome deniethe.

William Coullicke addressed his mistress on a fly-leaf (*Index*, No. 675). In the early sixteenth century Thomas Lower added lines from Walton's *Consolation of Philosophy* to a manuscript of Latin decretals, and a moralizing couplet (*Index*, No. 1421):

> yf Luste or anger do Thy mynde assaylle,
> Subdu ocasyon and Thou shalte sone prevaylle.

A William Huchen signed an orison to the Virgin in a Wycliffite version of the Psalms. These are typical instances. Including the better-known figures, it is possible to list about fifty such names, but for the most part the authors of the lyrics remain unidentified.

The superiority of such writers as Chaucer, Lydgate, Gower, and Hoccleve may be seen from the poems in this anthology, a superiority recognized by their contemporaries, to judge by the adulation given them. And the fact that no other poets receive a like adulation suggests that there were no no other major writers, or at least none known to the public at large. George Ashby, for example, opens a poem, *Index*, No. 2130, with a prologue to

> Maisters Gower, Chauucer, & Lydgate,
> Primier poets of this nacion.

*Index*, No. 564 (late fifteenth century) praises Chaucer the archetype:

> And gif that worthy Chaucere wer on lyve,
> Quilk was of poetis the honour and the glore.

And a poem in Fairfax MS. 16, *Index*, No. 4043, bemoans its limited style:

> Or els that I coud with wordys of rethoryke
> Sumwhat descryue wher-to she ys lyke.
> Cum on Tulius, with sum of thy flouris!
> Englesshe Geffrey, with al thy colourys,
> That wrote so wel to Pope Innocent;
> And mayster Chauser, sours and fundement,
> In Englysshe tunge swetely to endyte,
> Thy soule God hath with virgynes white;
> Moral Gower; Lydgate, rether and poete;
> Ouide; Stase, Lucan, of bataylle grete . . .

An examination of these ten groups of manuscripts will reveal that the majority were written for (and in some cases by) the upper classes. The verse literature of the rest of the population is not immediately discernible. It is possible, however, to garner such poetry (often very attractive, to judge from the existing texts and fragments) by selecting from those manuscripts written for the mass of the people—the Minstrel Collections—and by searching the commonplace books, sermon collections, and fly-leaves for those trivial popular pieces which were held unworthy of permanent record.

These are the two big sub-divisions of Middle English poetry, the courtly and the popular—reflecting the stratification of medieval society. This division is revealed most clearly in the religious poetry; the upper-class was encouraged to make use of devotional literature; the lower classes were discouraged. A sermon-writer opposes the conventional view that such restriction of knowledge was desirable:[1]

> ffor manie of hem seyn that it is not lefful lewide men to knawe the blesside lawe of the Gospel of Oure Lorde Ihesu Crist, but oneli prestes and clerkes; but it sufficeth to hem to kunne her pater noster and to beleeve wel.

The first two sections of this anthology, then, illustrate the poems circulated among the 'lewd'. In the Popular Songs, 21 items are taken from the Minstrel Collections.[2] Of the remaining 39 texts, 7 are from a commonplace book (Balliol 354), and 6 come from scattered pages of English in the midst of Latin sermons and homilies (Caius Coll. Cambridge MS. 383). Five items (Nos. 9, 15–18) are on a little scrap of vellum, Rawlinson D. 913 (which, along with Nos. 40 and 60, are the only fourteenth-century specimens in this section); 2 are added to a Welsh manuscript (Nos. 3 and 6); and 5 are added on fly-leaves (Nos. 12, 34, 42, 48, and 60). These texts were preserved only because the manuscript, to which they were incidental, was preserved. On the other hand, the more formal courtly love lyrics, because they were written by and for people of wealth, were preserved for their own supposed worth. The majority of those pieces are found in large carefully written collections.

These poems of the first section are the songs which would be sung at popular gatherings in the hall, in the inn, on the green, on the road. Of the 60 texts, 24 are in the strict carol form. This is the typical popular form, a quatrain including refrain, and a two-line burden sung at the beginning of the poem and at the end of every

[1] B.M. Addit. MS. 41321, quoted by G. R. Owst, *Literature and Pulpit in Mediaeval England*, Cambridge 1933, p. 190, footnote 4.

[2] St. John's Coll. Camb. MS. 259 (1); MS. Eng. poet. e. 1 (10); Sloane MS. 2593 (10).

stanza. The carol is one of the four major types of
medieval poetic form, and is traceable back to the early
fourteenth century.

The *Red Book of Ossory*, containing the Acts of the
Synods and Dublin diocesan transactions, was started by
the Franciscan, Richard de Ledrede, Bishop of Ossory,
in 1316, and continued by his successors into the sixteenth
century. On 15 double-column pages of the manuscript
are about 60 Latin songs, among which appear a few
scraps of vernacular verse—9 English and 2 French.
A Latin rubric explains the reason for the presence
of these early-fourteenth-century songs. The clergy of
Ossory had picked up, from contact with the local people,
various *cantilene teatrales turpes*. The Bishop, hesitating
to prohibit what was enjoyed, substituted pious words
for the secular, and thereby reproduced in Latin the
original form of the vernacular pieces. So that his clergy
would recognize the tune for the new Latin verses, Ledrede headed some of his sacred parodies with lines of the
corresponding vernacular song. These lines are either the
opening lines of the English song or the 'refrain' (technically, the 'burden'), just as it was a refrain, 'Swete
lemman dhin are', and not a particular line among the
stanzas, that the absent-minded mass-priest remembered.[1] An inspection of these Latin songs shows in some
the form of their popular prototypes—a fixed stanza
form and a burden connected with the last line of each
stanza by rhyme, and repeated throughout, but outside
the regular metrical scheme of the stanzas. Here is the
opening of a 'Cantilena de Nativitate Domini':

> Verbum caro factum est,
> De Virgine Maria.

[1] See Carleton Brown, *English Lyrics of the XIIIth Century*,
p. xi.

Cujus nomen est qui est,
Verbum caro factum est,
Ab eterno natus est,
    De patrio vsia.                    [οὐσία: *essence*

    Verbum caro, &c.

Cujus mater virgo est,
Verbum caro factum est,
Deus humanatus est,
    Felix genelogia.

    Verbum caro, &c.

Of the seven English fragments[1] attached to this group
of 25 Latin Christmas songs, three are burdens. One is
incomplete, 'Haue God day my lemon, &c.'; and two are
paralleled by four-line Latin burdens:

    Do, do, nyghtyngale synges wel mury;
    Shal y neure for thyn loue lenger karie      [*report*

and

    Hey, how the cheualdoures      [*entertainers*
    woke al nyght.                 [*kept a wake*

As for the fragments which stand with burden-less Latin
forms, 'Haue mercie on me, frere, Barfote that y go'
seems to be the first two lines of a quatrain; 'Maydyn in
the mor lay' confirms the metrical pattern of No. 18 by
a similar Latin roundel; and

    Gayneth me no garlond of green,      [*is suitable*
    Bot hit ben of wythoues ywrought      [*willows*

heads a Latin poem decrying trust in worldly goods. The
most interesting is a five-line stanza, repeated exactly in
Latin, apparently an English *chanson de mal mariée*:

    [1] R. L. Greene, 'The Songs of the Red Book of Ossory', *MLA*,
Group English II, 29 December 1952.

> Alas, hou shold y syng—
> y-loren is my playinge ?
> How shold y wiþ þat olde man
> To leuen, and let my leman,
> Swettist of al thinge ?

These are among the earliest English popular lyrics, and they leave their imprint on later songs.

If a late fourteenth- or early fifteenth-century text (for example, No. 23 or No. 29) is compared with a late fifteenth- or early sixteenth-century poem (such as Nos. 24, 25, 26), there is no difference visible in the form and very little difference in subject-matter or treatment. The majority of the popular love songs deal with the customary progress of young love, and frequent were the plaints of betrayed maidens (Nos. 21, 23–29).

About 80 per cent. of all carols have burdens of 2 short lines, and nearly 200 of them preserve the four-line stanza.[1] Repetition of the burden after every stanza is found in over 100 texts where the first few words are written out following each stanza (Nos. 19, 23, 29, and 38).

Of the other metrical forms represented in the first section, there are 13 poems in quatrains (in addition to the carols) and 5 in couplets. There is 1 eight-line stanza and there are 11 other types (five-line, irregular, &c.). Of the other main type of popular verse, the tail-rhyme stanza, there are only 4 examples: six-line (Nos. 36 and 58), eight-line (No. 1), and ten-line (No. 53). The staple form, then, of the popular song is the quatrain, 32 out of 60 items.

Placing these lyrics as popular or courtly with any certainty is sometimes difficult: Wilson, for example, considers Nos. 145, 147, 148 'popular'.[2] I explain my

---

[1] 'The Burden in Carols', *Modern Language Notes*, lvii. 16–22.
[2] R. M. Wilson, 'Lost Literature in Old and Middle English', *Leeds Studies in English*, v. 36–49.

disagreement in the notes. On the other hand, No. 142 might well go with a popular group. There is some interchange between popular and courtly; and the stylized diction of the thirteenth-century courtly poetry might well have become the stereotypes of fifteenth-century popular poetry. In the same way, pastoral situations, probably at one time actual, later became literary conventions. No. 29 with the girl's concern to 'mylkyn in þis payl' is unsophisticated; No. 20, where the banished lover wants to drink from 'ronnyng stremes' and to eat acorns, is stylized and self-conscious. Another example is *Index*, No. 1312;[1] here the two-part music and its appearance in a manuscript with other courtly poems indicate a non-popular origin:

> Ie haue so longe kepe schepe on the grene,
> Wilkyne, that alle 30were hert ys so for-hew
> so gracius þat somme wolde y wene,
> Wilkyne, how þat 3e wex were vntrewe.
>
> 3e may, Wilkyn, wyt rye strawys twyne,
> & pypy as 30w lyst;
> on 30wre songe sayth 3e loue me best,
> y-wys, & moste on 30were þow3t.
>
> But that 3e seye 3e wol for loue dye,
> Arys vppon þe morne and lust for to pleye.
> thys may ryme wel but hyt acorde nou3t.

In the same way, the single quatrain from the sixteenth-century Tudor Song Book, MS. Royal Appendix 58, often erroneously cited as a choice specimen of popular verse, is quite a sophisticated piece:

> Westron wynde, when wyll thow blow?
> The small rayne downe can rayne.
> Cryst, yf my loue wer in my armys,
> And I yn my bed Agayne.

[1] The manuscript of this text is badly faded.

Much of the popular poetry in Middle English must have been lost—even if it were ever recorded.[1] I have spoken of the number of poems written casually on fly-leaves or added to a manuscript, but of many others there are only glimpses. Some of the pieces which appear in sermons are too fragmentary to be printed formally as items in an anthology; but how tantalizing they are. A Latin sermon in Cotton Faustina A. v, for example, has:

Karissimi, bene scitis quod iste mulieres. . . . þat lulle þe child wyth þair fote & sinnges an hauld song, sic dicens:

> Wake wel, Annot,
> þi mayden boure;
> & get þe fra Walterot,
> for he es lichure.

Some manuscripts of the *Fasciculus Morum* have:

> ffor it is myry to ben a wyf,
> Dy I wyll & lese my lyf.

Another sermon in Trinity Coll. Cambridge MS. 43 quotes a 'worthless' dance song, which goes

> Atte wrastlinge, my lemman i ches;
> and atte ston-kasting i him forles.

A newly discovered text in Camb. Univ. MS. Ii. 3. 8 provides another version of this little rhyme:

> Atte ston castinges my lemman i ches,
> and atte wrastlinges sone i hym les;
> allas, þat he so sone fel;
> wy nadde he stonde better, vile gorel? [*fat fellow*

In *Index*, No. 2700, a poem by 'Farnelay' on how the

[1] See R. M. Wilson, *The Lost Literature of Medieval England*, London 1952, pp. 171–214.

Apostles made the Creed, scorn is thrown at those who do not sing holy songs, but instead sing

> . . . songe of Hey Dery Danne,
> (ne) howe þe grome gate gyrse by þe rede syde.

'Robertus seynte Mary clericus' is the subscription under some scraps in Worcester Cath. MS. Q. 50, which include

> Ne saltou neuer, leuedi,
> tuynklen wyt þin eyen.

and

> hic abbe ydon al myn youth,
> ofte, ofte, ant ofte,
> long yloued ant yerne ybeden ;
> ful dere it is a-bout.           [*paid*

One little poem has often been quoted for its first two lines; damage to the manuscript (Bodley 692) deprives us of the joy of the full text of 'Jolly shepherd of Aschell downe', but infra-red examination of the manuscript has added a few more words:

> Joly cheperte of Aschell downe
> Can more on love than al this towne
> lord wy wy &c lord where he goȝth
> a    .    .    ester þou schoperte for al thy fray
> .    .    .    .    .    my . . ke away
> for ryȝt here of getest þou notȝ
> .    .    go thy way good boy go
> .    .    .    .    .    wolt þou
> .    .    .    .    .    oure cowe
> .    .    .    .    .    .
> .    .    .    .    .    .
> .    .    .    .    .    .
> .    thy way good rowunde robyn
> .    .    .    .    .    wey go

These fragments would seen to indicate that in addition to the carol, there existed a popular lyric ; both being distinct from the popular ballad, a narrative form. Confirmation of the existence of such a genre would come from such pieces as Nos. 15–18, 21, 33, 45, 46, and 47. These may be linked to their religious equivalents, Nos. 81, 83, 99, and 116, in Brown's *Religious Lyrics of the Fifteenth Century*.

The second section of the Popular Songs, Practical Verse, consists of a number of 'folk pieces' of scant literary value. I include them because they were so popular in the Middle Ages—variants of the Christmas Day prognostications occur in 8 manuscripts; Instructions for Purchasing Land in 14 manuscripts; Lydgate's 'Dietary' in 46 manuscripts; Directions for Bloodletting in 17 manuscripts; and the Philosophers' Stone in 24 manuscripts. Of the group of gnomic tags (Nos. 82–7) there are numerous variants. A body of verse so widely circulated cannot be ignored, even though today many items would be written as prose.

Nos. 68 to 73 form a group of poems of which many are familiar to modern readers. They are the sires of a continuous line of texts, which have been written and printed year after year, coming down in one or other of the versions of the *Farmers' Almanac*. There were medieval counterparts of this modern publication: manuscripts devoted solely to weather lore and astrological reckonings. There are at least four manuscripts with nothing but verse and prose prognostications for the fortunes of the year according to the day on which Christmas (or New Year) falls.[1]

---

[1] For example, St. John's Coll. Camb. MS. 237 is a small English manuscript with a version of the *Storia Lune* (the lucky days of the month), and an incomplete text of the New Year's Day prognostications, the *Erra Pater*. Digby MS. 88 has Latin astronomical tracts and three sets of English prognostications (compare No. 72), and a series of six couplets on the occupations

There is evidence that such prognostications were seriously regarded, in Royal MS. 17. A. xvi, another book of astronomical tracts and a liturgical calendar. The owner has written in a very faint and faded hand the kind of weather experienced for the days following Christmas for some year (probably 1429) when Christmas Day fell on a Sunday. He did so doubtless for reference to these pieces which claimed to forecast the fortunes of the year by the weather. Good examples of this type of prognostication (in Latin) are to be found in Egerton MS. 1995. On a simpler scale are the weather rhymes such as that for St. Swithun's Day in Emmanuel Coll. Cambridge MS. 27 (late thirteenth century) or for St. Paul's Day (No. 71). It might be recalled that one of the objections to the revision in 1581 of the Gregorian Calendar was that the country people would not be able to rely on their weather rhymes.

At the same time, however, some of these prognostications may have been regarded lightly as Yuletide diversions. No. 72 (in the Sloane MS. version) suggests this by its conclusion of a three-line prayer to Jesus 'that we may com to thy blysse;' and more particularly by its introduction which states plainly that the poem is intended for amusement:

> If ye woll hyre ye may haue myrthe . . .
> Lordelynges I warne you by-forne.

The third section consists of 'Occasional' Verse—verse composed for some special occasion; it shows the increasing interest in form and style, as well as the various uses to which verse was put. The six book plates (Nos. 89–94), as has already been indicated, all appear on fly-leaves,

of the various months (No. 67). See further Robbins, 'English Almanacks of the Fifteenth Century', *Philological Quarterly*, xviii. 321–31.

and were no doubt added after the books had been received by their owners. On the other hand, the prologues and introductions (Nos. 100–3) are integral parts of the manuscripts and as such are found in several texts. This would be expected with a definite item such as Trevisa's *De Proprietatibus Rerum*, which has the English preface in 7 manuscripts (No. 101) ; but is surprising in No. 103, where the contents of all 10 manuscripts vary considerably, and where the verse introduction serves either as prologue or epilogue.

Nos. 110, 111, and 112 are curiosities which anticipate the better-known punctuation letter in *Ralph Roister Doister*. Another example, an attack on women, occurs in two manuscripts,[1] and must have occasioned merriment akin to that provided by No. 38, which has the 'destroying' burden:

> of all Creatures women be best,
> Cuius contrarium verum est.

The manuscripts of all these poems date from the early part of the sixteenth century, but this is probably a case of overlapping from the earlier period.

The fourth section, Courtly Love Lyrics, contains thirty-one poems hitherto unpublished, interesting for the study of the formal love lyric in the fifteenth century. As with the other sections, the fourteenth century is scarcely represented: No. 141, only a fragment, is perhaps the earliest poem in the section. No. 147, although written down later, is also of the fourteenth century, and is more pleasing than most of those from either century. Other fourteenth-century pieces are No. 142, the quatrain from the sermon collection, and No. 149, six English lines in a French love letter.

[1] See notes to No. 112.

The 86 texts occur in over 40 different manuscripts, but 31 are in 6 of these manuscripts. The Song Books and the Aureate Collections do not contribute quite as many items as might be expected, for the contents of these Song Books are largely religious; only No. 174 comes from such a source. The Lydgate-type pieces are poorly represented by the Shirley manuscripts: No. 170 along with No. 96 in the third section is the only poem from Trinity Coll. Cambridge MS. 600; and Harley MS. 2251 is represented only in the third section (Nos. 77 and 121). From the Stowe manuscripts come 5 texts from Trinity Coll. Cambridge MS. 599,[1] and 1 from Lambeth MS. 306.[2] From the miscellaneous Aureate Collections, come 5 from Bodleian MS. Rawlinson C. 813;[3] and No. 177 and 3 poems by the Duke of Suffolk (Nos. 187–9) from Fairfax MS. 16. The reason for this comparatively small number—only 17 items—is that once again the majority of texts are religious or moral; and of the secular items themselves many are over-long for an anthology of this kind; others are occasional verses like those for mummings or pageants (adequately represented by Nos. 120–3); others seem later than the fifteenth century; and still others (No. 177 is a typical example) are very mediocre and insignificant. Bodleian MS. Rawlinson C. 813, for example, was written in the early sixteenth century, and it is frequently difficult to decide which of its 51 items are contemporary and which are earlier. The 5 printed here I have taken as being late fifteenth century, because of their content, form, language, as well as their general tone.

Besides these 3 manuscripts (Trinity, Rawlinson, and Fairfax), there are 3 others, each likewise represented here by 5 or 6 poems. Bodleian MS. Ashmole 191 (*c.* 1445)

---

[1] Nos. 138, 160, 173, 191, 211.                          [2] No. 190.
[3] Nos. 129, 130, 200, 204, 207.

is a small volume containing a Calendar; on 6 leaves are 6 songs complete with music; these are printed in full (Nos. 152–6, 171), for not only are they attractive in themselves, but they stress the interdependence of music and poetry. Bodleian MS. Rawlinson poet. 36 is a slim volume of the second half of the fifteenth century which, in addition to a few religious pieces, contains some boisterous secular poems.[1] The answering poems (Nos. 208 and 209) by two lovers each abusing the other are in the best humorous satirical tradition of 'When she hath on her hood of grene' (*Index*, No. 2237) and of Skelton's 'Elynour Rummynge'. They provide a needed relief from the conventional paeans of praise. The third manuscript, Camb. Univ. Ff. 1. 6, will be discussed below.

The rest of the poems come from some three dozen different manuscripts. The Scottish Chaucerians are included, although here again their date is doubtful: Nos. 132, 133, and 212 are from the Bannatyne MS. (dated 1568). No. 196 is also a Northern text (added on the fly-leaf of a Chaucer). Charles d'Orleans, to whom are ascribed more individual poems than any other author except Lydgate, is represented by 5 poems (Nos. 182–6). His friend, the Duke of Suffolk, follows him with the 3 items already mentioned (Nos. 187–9). The large group of 36 items in the Lyrics for Singing comes from a variety of manuscripts; 14 texts have their music preserved.[2] Some are scribbled on fly-leaves.[3] No. 157 is taken from a Burgundian chansonnier, and was written down by a scribe who apparently knew very little English. No. 145 is

---

[1] Nos. 159, 175, 192, 208, 209.
[2] Nos. 146, 147, 150–8, 163, 171, 174.
[3] Such as Nos. 141, 144, 148, 158, 161, 162. No. 143 is written on a scrap of vellum; No. 146 appears in a collection of fragments; No. 147 is written on the back of a papal bull; No. 163 is written on the back of a leaf of legal notes.

another curiosity; it appears as a graffito in a disused church in Cambridgeshire.

The remaining manuscripts continue the assortment. Commonplace books provide No. 137, No. 176, and No. 206. No. 201 is bound with a collection of French poems. No. 202 is added in an early-sixteenth-century hand to a Lydgate's *Life of Our Lady*. No. 178 is added on the fly-leaf of Lydgate's *Life of St. Edmund*.

Finally, two manuscripts warrant comment. Camb. Univ. MS. Ff. 1. 6, which gives us Nos. 164 to 169, is a long compilation of 185 folios. It is an anthology, dated about 1500 (although the material is without question fifteenth century), and made by many hands at the country house of Findern, Derbyshire.[1] It contains some well-known poems by Chaucer and Lydgate—which strengthen the view that no major poem by these authors has been lost, for most of their pieces circulated in several texts. It contains also some poems not elsewhere found which are apparently specimens of love lyrics written in the prevailing fashion. The 'Findern Anthology' thus becomes an index of taste of the upper classes at the end of the fifteenth century. What is unusual about it is that some of the poems have been transcribed by women, who have signed their names after the poems and on various other pages. Altogether there are about twenty-eight different hands; and it appears that the manuscript was added to at different times and with different gatherings; poems would be copied by various members of the household from borrowed volumes, and later the pages would be bound together. The result is, of course, scrappy but has a value of its own.

The second manuscript also shows the literary tastes of the provincial gentry, and introduces a new literary

[1] Robbins, 'The Findern Anthology', *PMLA*, lxix. 610–42.

figure.[1] The manuscript, until 1947 known as the Capes-thorne MS. (so called from its location at that estate), is now Bodleian MS. Lat. misc. c. 66. Its writer is Humfrey Newton, 1466–1536. He lived in Cheshire, and was apparently of comfortable circumstances. In his commonplace book he not only copied down the best sellers of his day —de Caistre's popular hymn, 'Advice to Purchasers of Land' (see No. 74), Lydgate's Nightingale poem (*Index*, No. 931), and the gnomic tag 'When feith failes in prestes sawes'—but himself composed seventeen poems, represented here by Nos. 193 and 194. Newton is one of the few poets known whose work is not mainly religious or didactic, and whose literary efforts are not confined to one or two examples. For these reasons he is valuable; and he is valuable, too, for those occasions where he is seen at work, changing rhythms and rhymes and vocabulary, and leaving a record of his trial attempts at composition. Nevertheless, the value of his poems is not so much intrinsic as illustrative of the influence of the upper middle class on literature, growing throughout the fifteenth century as that of the church waned.

The Cambridge MS., the Newton holograph, and MS. Rawlinson C. 813 are the only three Middle English manuscripts (apart from Chaucer and Charles d'Orleans) which are predominantly secular.

I have referred to the common forms of the popular poems—the quatrain, including both the carol form and the simple cross-rhymed quatrain; the couplet; and the tail-rhymed stanza. While some of these forms are present in the third and fourth sections—there are 22 quatrains (including one, No. 163, in carol form), 14 couplets, and 5 tail-rhyme pieces—the chief forms are rhyme royal and

[1] Robbins, 'The poems of Humfrey Newton, Esquire, 1466–1536', *PMLA*, lxv. 249–81.

ballade stanza. Of the former there are 34 examples, and 25 of the latter. These 2 forms are typical of the style for courtly writing; in the first section there are no examples, and in the second only 3.[1] Any Shirley manuscript, however, designed for circulation among the upper middle classes, reveals no carols, hardly a single tail-rhyme stanza, but almost all rhyme royal or ballade stanza. On the other hand, any collection for popular use (such as Sloane MS. 2593) will show the reverse. The difference is especially striking among the religious lyrics, for here there are more numerous examples to corroborate this; in 270 typical items from the Aureate Collections, about 100 are in rhyme royal, and over 120 in ballade stanza; couplets are found in 16 items, quatrains in 6 items—and the couplet poems are all didactic or instructive (for example, Virtues of the Mass). An analysis of 70 vernacular verse prayers from prayer books shows only 6 in rhyme royal and 7 in ballade stanza, but 25 in couplets, 21 in quatrains, and 9 in tail-rhyme stanzas. The more practical the lyric, the more simple the form.

From a survey of the lyric production of the two centuries, four important conclusions emerge:

## A. *The Simplicity of Metrical Forms*

In 1932 Miss Beatrice H. N. Geary made a metrical analysis of 1,211 lyrics of the fifteenth century—791 religious and 420 secular.[2] She adopted the strict definition of 'lyric' and excluded, for example, versions of the Pater-

---

[1] No. 77, on the Complexions, a poem which comes from a Shirley MS.; No. 78, Lydgate's 'Dietary'; and No. 79, a single stanza rhyme royal on 'Doctrines of Temperate Diet' (in the same style as No. 78).

[2] Beatrice H. N. Geary, *A Study of Fifteenth Century English Lyric Verse from MSS. and Printed Editions with special reference to Metrical Form.* Thesis deposited in Bodleian Library, 1932, p. 164.

noster and Ave Maria, a fact which accounts for the small number of couplets in her tabulation. Here are her figures:

| | |
|---|---:|
| Carol stanzas of all types . . . | 348 |
| Rhyme royal stanzas . . . . | 251 |
| Ballade stanzas . . . . | 243 |
| Cross-rhymed quatrains . . . | 176 |
| Tail-rhymed stanzas . . . . | 81 |
| Couplets . . . . . | 36 |
| Ballad measure . . . . | 21 |
| Roundels . . . . . | 9 |
| Virelais . . . . . | 3 |
| Miscellaneous . . . . | 43 |

Since Miss Geary was working from the manuscripts, her total has not been appreciably increased by the entries in the *Index*. By counting every minor variation in metre, Miss Geary enumerated 156 different metrical schemes—a striking contrast to the thousand different metrical forms that Chaytor finds in troubadour poetry.[1] Yet most of the English variations exist in only one or two poems each, and in any case do not depart appreciably from the half-dozen basic stanzaic patterns. Most important, however, the chart shows that only 6 per cent. of the lyric production of the fifteenth century is outside the common types—couplets and quatrains and tail-rhymes on the one hand, and rhyme royal and ballade stanza on the other. This analysis is important because it modifies the generally accepted opinions of previous critics who have perhaps over-stressed 'the variety of experimentation'.

## B. *The Class Division of Metrical Forms*

The social level of the various groups of readers and hearers largely determines the metrical forms used. For

[1] H. J. Chaytor, *The Troubadours*, Cambridge 1912.

the court groups or the moneyed merchants or the clergy, verse is written in rhyme royal or ballade stanzas, if for pleasure; in quatrains or couplets, if for practical use, as in the devotional prayer books. For the working class, for anyone who would be unlikely to read, verse is written in quatrains or tail-rhyme stanzas.

## C. *Standardization of Forms*

In Middle English verse there is a customary form for each type of writing. The englished 'Essentials of Belief' (Paternoster, Ave Maria, Decem precepta, &c.), to be learned by everybody who hoped for Heaven, are seldom more than metrical prose, with very few exceptions written in the simplest of styles, the couplet. The formal devotional poems are generally in rhyme royal, the moralizing poems in ballade stanzas. Romances are equally divided between couplet, twelve-line tail-rhyme, and miscellaneous forms. Information poems, such as the alchemical texts, are in couplets. Popular songs favour the quatrain.

Any development of style beyond the most elementary forms and devices is confined to the 'polite' lyrics found in the Friar Miscellanies and in the very late fifteenth-century collections (particularly Skelton). Lydgate himself called rhyme royal 'this sympall metre', and tended to reject the extremes of the high style. A couplet (*Index*, No. 2757) in Harley MS. 665 maintains:

> Playn word entereth the hert;
> I-flarysched the eeres feedyt.

Once again, interest on the part of critics exclusively in these two groups of manuscripts has led to the slighting of the popular lyric. Miss Geary found 527 lyrics in rhyme royal, ballade, roundel, and similar forms; but 641 lyrics in couplet, quatrain, and tail-rhyme:[1]

> Now this, considering that the formal verse, being of greater acknowledged importance at the time of its being written, would have better chances of survival in manuscript, points conclusively to a strong body of indigenous song verse, stronger even than the polite Chaucer type which is generally taken as representative of the period.

Middle English verse was not confined to court circles; even the formal lyrics often had a popular quality. In this respect, Middle English lyric poetry is quite unlike the Provençal lyrics, which form, according to Chaytor, 'a poetry essentially aristocratic, intended for nobles and for courts, appealing but rarely to the middle classes and to the common people not at all.'[2] It is not surprising that lyric poetry should have had a broader appeal in fifteenth-century England, where the decline of feudalism led, not to the suppression but to the protection of the middle classes by the monarchy.

## D. *Unimportance of French Influence*

It is undoubtedly true that the thirteenth-century English lyrics show considerable direct French influence. But Schofield, for example, speaks of the 'mass' of English courtly lyric types in the thirteenth and *fourteenth* centuries exactly like the French poems, and of French poems which 'in a measure determined the production of Chaucer, Gower, and other English writers who at first wrote in the same style'.[3] Chaytor, the leading exponent of the French theory, says that 'the influence of the troubadour poetry upon the English lyric was consider-

---

[1] Geary, op. cit., p. 165.    [2] Chaytor, op. cit., p. 10.
[3] W. H. Schofield, *English Literature from the Norman Conquest to Chaucer*, New York 1906, p. 135.

able'.[1] But I am convinced that in any case there is not a 'mass' of such poems extant (unless a hundred items constitutes a mass), and that these statements are not true for the *whole* output of the fourteenth and fifteenth centuries. This confused evaluation arises from undue attention to a single manuscript, Harley 2253, from which, with one exception (a Lydgate-type poem), Chaytor took all his examples of French inspiration. While the lyrics of the Friar Miscellanies had some small circulation,[2] that circulation did not continue after the first years of the fourteenth century. After the Black Death, Harley MS. 2253 was forgotten; there is not a single later lyric that shows any influence of this or any other 'Friar' anthology. Harley MS. 2253 is but one part of Middle English poetry, and it is not the most enduring one: it comes without warning and leaves as suddenly. From 1300 to the Black Death, and later, there is practically no courtly secular poetry. And when the threads are picked up again (as in the shorter poems of Chaucer) they do not seem to lead back to Harley MS. 2253. Where is the French influence in the big collections of the fourteenth century? William of Shoreham's poems show little; Herebert's hymns none; and, even allowing for the strong *chanson·d'aventure* influence in the refrain poems of the Vernon and Simeon MSS., there is not much which an English writer, acquainted with France and its continental fashions in only a superficial way, could not have developed independently, perhaps assisted by a slight knowledge of the Latin literature of the church. By the fifteenth century the tricks and devices originally borrowed from France

---

[1] H. J. Chaytor, *The Troubadours and England*, Cambridge 1934, p. 134.
[2] Seven of the Harley lyrics appear in Digby MS. 86; one in each of MSS. Digby 2, Trinity Coll. Camb. 323, and Harley 913.

had become so native, that even a large body of verse showing signs of French influence would prove little; and there is no such corpus. Adornment confines itself to alliteration and refrain; and any unusual 'colores' or stylistic devices, for example, in the Aureate Collections, can best be traced to the Latin rhetoricians.[1] Even of the early English poems, Chaytor, speaking of the alleged French influence, acknowledges: 'It may also be assumed that many of them are obviously commonplaces which would occur to any lyric poet.'[2]

Nor do the special studies of artificial forms point to a strong French influence. Sandison lists only 45 *chanson d'aventure* beginnings in the religious and didactic poems.[3] There are only 2 known pastourelles, 3 virelais, and 1 aube in Middle English. Of Cohen's study of the ballade,[4] Miss Geary writes:[5]

> Miss Cohen states that a complete bibliography of all the Middle English ballades would contain about 220 items, many of which would be questionable judged from the point of view of the strict French type. This number includes ballades in the Rhyme Royal stanzas. . . . For the fifteenth century, excluding those ballade envoys which are mere summaries of the preceding work, as frequently in Lydgate's *Fall of Princes*, and poems of a similar nature, which cannot be regarded as lyric, I find a total of only 41 poems in the stanza *ababbcbc* which will come within this category.

The foregoing interpretation does not, of course, deny literary intercourse between England and France in other genres, as Chaucer, Gower, and Malory bear witness. And

---

[1] See *Index*, Nos. 520 and 1237.
[2] Chaytor, *The Troubadours and England*, p. 120.
[3] Helen E. Sandison, *The Chanson d'Aventure in Middle English*, Bryn Mawr 1923.
[4] Helen L. Cohen, *The Ballade*, New York 1915.
[5] Geary, op. cit., p. 84.

Shirley had a manuscript written in French (Royal 20.
B. xv) for circulation among his friends, and included
French ballades in Trinity Coll. Cambridge MS. 600. The
Duke of Suffolk wrote French poems as easily as English
(B.M. Addit. MS. 34360); an English poet, even in the
fifteenth century, wrote a macaronic poem in French and
English (No. 172); and often an owner scribbled French
mottoes around the pages of his book.[1]

After the Black Death the Middle English lyric seems to
start out afresh. The ruling classes were speaking English,
and using English prayers in their devotions. Thus out
of the early popular 'aspirations' grew the full flower of
English devotional verse. In the field of secular poetry,
not only did the Duke of Suffolk and the Duke of Orleans
write love lyrics, but the knights and lords in the shires.
But throughout the fifteenth century the basis of literature was broadening with the national political tendencies, namely, the growth of the rich middle classes. They
were interested not so much in artificial conventions of
love, but in what has always concerned a trading group,
eager to establish law and order—morality. Thus there is
a mass of moralizing poems of the Lydgate school in the
middle and at the close of the fifteenth century, rather
than courtly love lyrics, in the Shirley type of manuscript. At this time religious poems were losing the sin-
cerity of those of the latter part of the fourteenth and
early fifteenth centuries, and, except where found in
religious books, were for pious 'decoration'. In most
cases, these upper-class religious and moral lyrics were
divorced from music: they were meant for the eye rather
than for the ear.

In a number of ways the close of the fifteenth century

[1] See notes to No. 140.

prepares the way for the Tudor and Elizabethan lyrics with the rise of 'gentlemen' poets, the formation of literary fashions, such as the love epistle and the catalogue of charms, and the heightened interest in poems of a single stanza, which prepared the ground for the acceptance of the Italian sonnet form. The break between the Middle Ages and the Renaissance is much more evident in the religious than in the secular poems. The Reformation, while taking away little of the essentials of religious belief, did change some of the dominant forms of its expression. Thus the praise of and petition to the Virgin and saints, in which Middle English poetry is so rich, almost ceases with the Reformation to provide the stimulus to devotional verse. English poetry shows its continuity much more in the secular than in the religious poems.

Most of the poems in this anthology deal with the realities of the daily life of the period; they had a reason for existing, and were associated with many activities— drinking, begging, seducing, bringing in the boar's head. Their naturalness and simplicity come from the fact that they were meant for daily use. They lack the storm and stress and psychological conflict which come in later poetic and dramatic art, when the artist becomes a unique person; and at the same time, they are free from the pretensions and fakery which often come with more highly developed art. The best of these poems have a natural and unaffected charm, a quality which much of the poetry of later centuries has lost.

## Bodleian MSS. with Summary Catalogue numbers

Laud Misc. 683 (798); Digby 2 (1603); Digby 86 (1687); Digby 88 (1689); Bodley 638 (2078); Bodley 692 (2508); Arch. Selden B. 26 (3340); Fairfax 16 (3896); Vernon (3938); Hatton 73 (4119); Hatton 2 (4130); Ashmole 191 (6668); Ashmole 59 (6943); Tanner 346 (10173); Tanner 407 (10234); Rawl. C. 86 (11951); Rawl. C. 813 (12653); Rawl. poet. 36 (14530); Rawl. liturg. g. 2 (15834); Douce 45 (21619); Douce 54 (21658); Douce 302 (21876); Eng. poet. e. 1 (29734).

# THE TEXTS

THE texts here printed have in every case (with the exception of No. 94) been transcribed from the original manuscripts. The manuscripts have been followed in orthography and capitalization; and the Middle English characters þ, ð, and ȝ have been retained. The common manuscript contractions have been expanded without the use of italics. The punctuation of the texts is editorial, and hyphens have been introduced where components of words are separated in the manuscripts, and where modern usage demands.

Obvious scribal errors have been corrected to make the texts more intelligible; but where an emendation has been made, the original manuscript reading is recorded at the foot of the page.

# I. POPULAR SONGS

## 1. *A Minstrel's Greeting*

### Balliol Coll. Oxford MS. 354

Bon Iowre, bon Iowre a vous!         [f. 251ᵛ]
I am cum vnto this hows,
   Vith par la pompe, I say.

IS þer any good man here
  þat will make me any chere?
& if þer were, I wold cum nere
  to wit what he wold say.         4
    A, will ye be wild?
    by mary myld

    .    .    .    .

  I trow ye will syng gay.         8
    Bon Iowre.

Be gladly, masters euerychon!
I am cum myself alone
to appose you on by on.
  let se who dare say nay—         12
    Sir, what say ye?
    Syng on, lett vs see.
    Now will it be
Thys or another day?         16
    Bon Iowre.

Loo, this is he þat will do þe dede!
he tempereth his mowth, þerfore take hede.
Syng softe, I say, leste yowr nose blede,
  ffor hurt yowrself ye may!         20

16 MS. an *struck through before* or.

But by god þat me bowght,
your brest is so towght,
tyll ye haue well cowght
ye may not þer-with away.                    24
  Bon iowr.


Sir, what say ye with your face so lene?
ye syng noþer good tenowre, treble, ne mene.
vtter not your voice with-out your brest be clene,
  hartely I you pray!                    28
   I hold you excused,
   ye shall be refused,
   ffor ye haue not be vsed
  to no good sport nor play.                    32
    Bon Iowre.


Sir, what say ye with your ffat face?
Me thynkith ye shuld bere a very good bace
To a pot of good ale or Ipocras,
  truly as I you say!                    36
   hold vp your hede,
   ye loke lyke lede;
   ye wast myche bred
  euermore from day to day.                    40
    Bon Ioure.


Now will ye see wher he stondith behynde?
Iwis, broþer, ye be vnkynd.
stond forth, & wast with me som wynd,
  for ye haue ben called a synger ay.                    44
   Nay, be not ashamed;
   ye shall not be blamed,

21 MS. brow *struck through before* bowght.
44 MS. ye *inserted above line.*

ffor ye haue ben ffamed
the worst in this Contrey!                48
bon Iowr.
   Explicit.

2.   *Invitation to Festivity, I*

   Balliol Coll. Oxford MS. 354

  Make we mery bothe more & lasse,  [f. 223ᵛ]
  ffor now ys þe tyme of crystymas.

LEtt no man cum into this hall—
 Grome, page, nor yet marshall,
But þat sum sport he bryng with-all,
 for now ys the tyme of crystmas.  4

Yff that he say he can not syng,
sum oder sport then lett hym bryng,
þat yt may please at thys festyng,
 for now ys the tyme of Crystmas.  8

Yff he say he can nowght do,
Then for my loue aske hym no mo;
But to the stokkes then lett hym go,
 for now ys þe tyme of crystmas.  12
   Explicit.

3.   *Invitation to Festivity, II*

   B.M. Addit. MS. 14997

  hay, ay, hay, ay,   [f. 44ᵛ]
  make we mere as we may.

NOw ys ȝole comyn with gentyll chere,
 Of merthe & gomyn he has no pere;
In euery londe where he comys nere
 Is merthe & gomyn, I dar wele say.  4

12 yf *struck through before* ys.
No. 3. *Burden written as one line.* 1 MS. gentyll g chere.

Now ys comyn a messyngere
Of ȝore lorde, ser nu ȝere,
Byddes vs all be mere here
   And make as mere as we may.    8

Therefore euery mon that ys here   [f. 45ʳ]
Synge a caroll on hys manere;
Yf he con non we schall hym lere,
   So þat we be mere allway.    12

Whosoeuer makes heve chere,
Were he neuer to me dere,
In a dyche I wolde he were,
   To dry hys clothes tyll hyt were day.    16

Mende the fyre, & make gud chere!
ffyll þe cuppe, ser botelere!
let euery mon drynke to hys fere!
   thys endes my caroll with care awaye.    20

*4.*          *An Unwilling Minstrel*

Sloane MS. 2593

IF i synge ȝe wyl me lakke,   [f. 31ᵛ]
   & wenyn I wer out of myn wyt;
þer-for smale notes wil I crake;
   so wolde god I wer qwyt.    4

Syn me muste take þis mery toyn
   to glade with-al þis cumpany;
I rede or ony swych be don,
   for godes loue, tèy vp ȝour ky!    8

ffor-soþe I may not synge, I say—
   my voys & I arn at discord;
but we xul fonde to take a day      [f. 32ʳ]
   To tåkyn myn avys & myn acord.      12

## 5.     *A Minstrel's Begging Song*

### Sloane MS. 2593

OMnes gentes plaudite,      [f. 10ᵛ]
   I saw myny bryddis setyn on a tre;
he tokyn her fley3t & flowyn away,
with ego dixi, haue good day.      4
Many qwyte federes ha3t þe pye—
I may noon mor syngyn, my lyppis arn so drye!
Manye qwyte federis ha3t þe swan—      [f. 11ʳ]
þe mor þat I drynke, þe lesse good I can!      8
ley stykkys on þe fer, wyl mot it brenne,
3eue vs onys drynkyn er we gon henne!

## 6.     *A Plea for Another Drink*

### B.M. Addit. MS. 14997

IS tell yw my mynd, anes tayliur, dame;      [f. 39ᵛ]
   I deme we lak plesur.
loke here, dame, vn-loke your dur;
a-lacke we haue no lykur!      4

ffrende, and we ar ferr yn dette
for your fyne gode wyne, god watte,
A short gynt hase a pynt potte;
I dranke onys, I wold drinke yette.      8

No. 5. 9 it MS. is.
No. 6. 3 doore *added in later hand at side.*
8 drinke *added in later hand above line.*

7.        *The Minstrel and His Wares*

Sloane MS. 2593

We ben chapmen lyȝt of fote,                    [f. 26ᵛ]
þe fowle weyis for to fle.

WE bern abowtyn non cattes skynnys,
pursis, perlis, syluer pynnis,
smale wympeles for ladyis chynnys;             [f. 27ʳ]
    damsele, bey sum ware of me.          4

I haue a poket for þe nonys,
þerine ben tweyne precyous stonys;
damsele, hadde ȝe asayid hem onys,
    ȝe xuld þe raþere gon with me.          8

I haue a Ielyf of godes sonde,
Withoutyn fyt it can stonde;
It can smytyn & haȝt non honde;
    Ryd ȝourself quat it may be.          12

I haue a powder for to selle,
Quat it is can I not telle—
It makit maydenys wombys to swelle;
    þerof I haue a quantyte.          16

8.            *A Carefree Life*

MS. Eng. poet. e. 1
(Sum. Cat. No. 29734)

A, a, a, a,                                    [f. 23ᵛ]
ȝet I loue wherso I go.

IN all þis warld nis a meryar lyfe
þan is a ȝong man withovtyn a wyfe,
for he may lyven withovȝten stryfe
In euery place wherso he go.          4

No. 7. *Burden written as one long line.*          3 MS. wympeł.
8 þ *struck out before* ȝe.          No. 8. 1 nis MS. is.

In euery place he is loved ouer all
Among maydyns gret & small—
In daunsyng, in pypynge, & rennyng at þe ball,
   In euery [place wherso he go.]          8

Thei lat ly3t be husbondmen
Whan þei at þe ball rene,
Thei cast hyr loue to 3ong men
   In euery [place wherso thei go.]        12

þan sey maydes, 'farwell, Iacke,
þi loue is pressyd al in þi pake;
þou beryst þi loue behynd þi back,
   In euery [place wherso þou go!']        16

9.    *A Toast to His Lost Mistress*

MS. Rawlinson D. 913
(Sum. Cat. No. 13679)

WEr þer ouþer in þis toun          [Item 1, i]
   ale or wyn,
isch hit wolde bugge
   to lemmon myn.                        4
Welle wo was so hardy
   forte make my lef al blody;
þaut he were þe kynges sone
   of normaundy,                         8
3et icholde a-wreke boe
   for lemman myn.
Welle wo was me tho—
   wo was me tho—                        12
þe man that leset þat he louit
   hym is al-so.

No. 9. *Written as prose.*
2 MS. wy.

        Ne erle ne lerde  
          ne—no more i n' can!       16  
        but crist ich hire biteche  
        þat was my lemman.

### *10.*        *A Drinking Song*

(With Music)  
MS. Arch. Selden B. 26 (Sum. Cat. No. 3340)

      Verbum caro factum est     [f. 25<sup>r</sup>]  
      Et habitauit in nobis.  
    Fetys bel chere,  
    Drynk to thi fere,  
    Verse le bauere,             4  
      & synge nouwell!

### *11.*    *A Three-Part Catch for Drinking*

(With Music)  
MS. Arch. Selden B. 26 (Sum. Cat. No. 3340)

      Tappster, fille Anoþer Ale.     [f. 32<sup>v</sup>]  
        Anonne have I doo;  
    god send vs good sale.  
    Avale þe stake, Avale,  
      here ys good Ale I-fovnde!     4  
      drynke to me,  
        & I to þe,  
      and lette þe coppe goo Rounde.    8

No. 10. 5 MS. Vesse.  
No. 11. *The text is written three times, each with music:*  
Dryngker fyll A-nother Ale A-nonn god sende us good sale  
A-vale the stake A-vale here is good Ale y-founde And y to þe  
and lette þe cuppe go Rounde.  
Contra Tenor: Drynker Anonne have I do god sende vs good  
sale A-vale þe stake A-vale here ys good ale y-founde drynke to  
me & y to þe And lete þe coppe goo rounde.  
Tenor: tappster fille A-noþer Ale have I doo god send vs good sale  
A-vale þe stake A-vale here ys good Ale I-fovnde drynke to me &  
I to þe and lette þe coppe goo Rounde.

*12.* ### Good Cheer

Trinity College Dublin MS. 214

HEr I was and her I drank; [f. 1^r]
far-wyll dam, and mykyll thank.
her I was and had gud cher,
and her I drank wyll gud ber.

4

*13.* ### Bring Good Ale

MS. Eng. poet. e. 1
(Sum. Cat. No. 29734)

Bryng vs in good ale, & bryng vs in good ale; [f. 41^v]
ffore owr blyssyd lady sak, bryng vs in good ale!

BRyng vs in no browne bred, fore þat is mad of brane;
[f. 42^r]
Nor bryng vs in no whyt bred, fore þer-in is no game,
But bryng vs in good ale.

Bryng vs in no befe, for þer is many bonys; 4
but bryng vs in good ale, for þat goth downe at onys,
& bryng vs in good ale.

Bryng vs in no bacon, for þat is passyng fate;
but bryng vs in god ale, & gyfe vs I-nought of þat, 8
& bryng vs in good ale.

bryng vs in no mutton, for þat is ofte lene;
Nor bryng vs in no trypys, for þei be syldom clene,
but bryng vs in good ale. 12

Bryng vs in no eggys, for þer ar many schelles;
But bryng vs in good ale, & gyfe vs noþing ellys,
& bryng vs in good ale.

No. 12. *Written as prose.* 3 MS. he.
No. 13. *The first stanza is written last but marked with the letter*
a; *the other stanzas are marked* b *to* h.
14 MS. noþng.

Bryng vs in no butter, for þer-in ar many herys;    16
Nor bryng vs in no pygges flesch, for þat wyl mak vs
  borys,
  but bryng vs in good ale.

Bryng vs in no podynges, for þer-in is al gotes blod;
Nor bryng vs in no veneson, for þat is not for owr
  good,    20
  but bryng vs in good ale.

Bryng vs in no capons flesch, for þat is ofte der;
Nor bryng vs in no dokes flesch, for þei slober in þe mer,
  but bryng vs in good ale.    24

## *Fill Every Glass*

### Balliol Coll. Oxford MS. 354

*drink to all* how, butler, How! bevis a towt!  [f. 251ᵛ]
  ffill þe boll, Ientill butler, & let þe cup rowght!

I Entill butler, bell amy,
 ffyll þe boll by þe eye,
þat we may drynk by & by.
 with how, butler, how! bevis a towt!    4
 ffill þe boll, butler, & let þe cup rowght!

here is mete ffor vs all,
both for gret & for small;
I trow we must þe butlar call.    8
 with how, butler, how! bevis a towght!
 ffill þe boll, butler, & lett þe Cupe rowght!

No. 13.  19 MS. godes good.  20 MS. blod.  24 go
*struck through before* good.
 No. 14. *Burden* MS. butlet.

I am so dry I can-not spek,                    [f. 252<sup>r</sup>]
I am nygh choked with my mete—                 12
I trow þe butler be a-slepe.
   with how, butler, how! bevis a towght!
   ffill þe boll, butler, [& let þe cup rowght!]

Butler, butler, ffill þe boll,                 16
or elles I beshrewe thy noll!
I trow we must þe bell toll.
   with how, butler, how! bevis a towght!
   ffill þe boll, [butler, & let þe cup rowght!]  20

Iff þe butlers name be water,
I wold he were a galow-claper,
but if he bryng vs drynk þe raþer.
   with how, butler, how! bevis a towght!    24
   ffill [þe boll, butler, & let þe cup rowght!]
     Explicit.

## (15.) *The Irish Dancer*

MS. Rawlinson D. 913
(Sum. Cat. No. 13679)

Ich am of Irlaunde,                            [Item 1,g]
ant of the holy londe
oi irlande.

GOde sire, pray ich þe,
  for of saynte charite,
come ant daunce wyt me
In irlaunde.                                   4

No. 15. *Written as prose.*
1 MS. 3e.

### 16. *The Hawthorn Tree*

MS. Rawlinson D. 913
(Sum. Cat. No. 13679)

OF euerykune tre—                    [Item 1, a]
  of euerykune tre—
þe haweþorn blowet suotes
  of euerykune tre.                     4

My lemmon sse ssal boe—
  my lemmon sse ssal boe—
þe fairest of erþkinne,
  my lemmon sse ssal boe.               8

### 17. *All Night by the Rose*

MS. Rawlinson D. 913
(Sum. Cat. No. 13679)

AL nist by þe rose, rose—               [Item 1, j]
  al nist bi the rose i lay;
darf ich noust þe rose stele,
  ant ȝet ich bar þe flour away.         4

### 18. *Maiden of the Moor*

MS. Rawlinson D. 913
(Sum. Cat. No. 13679)

MAiden in the mor lay—                  [Item 1, h]
  in the mor lay—
seuenyst fulle, seuenist fulle.
Maiden in the mor lay—                   4
  in the mor lay—
seuenistes fulle ant a day.

No. 16. *Written as prose.*
      2 MS. euerykne.
No. 17. *Written as prose.*

Welle was hire mete.
wat was hire mete?
   þe primerole ant the—
     þe primerole ant the— 8
Welle was hire mete.
Wat was hire mete?
   the primerole ant the violet. 12

Welle [was hire dryng.]
wat was hire dryng?
   [þe chelde water of þe—]
     [þe chelde water of þe—] 16
[Welle was hire dryng.]
[Wat was hire dryng?]
   þe chelde water of þe welle-spring. 20

Welle was hire bour.
wat was hire bour?
   [þe rede rose an te—]
     [þe rede rose an te—] 24
[Welle was hire bour.]
[Wat was hire bour?]
   þe rede rose an te lilie fiour.

## 19.     *A Lover's Plea*
### (With Music)
#### Caius Coll. Cambridge MS. 383

þei y synge & murþus make,     [p. 210]
  it is not y wolde.

MYn owne dere ladi fair & fre,
  y pray ow in herte ʒe ruwen on me,
for al my lykyng is on þe
  Wan y on ʒow be-holde. 4
   þei y etc.

No. 18. *Written as prose.*    7 MS. wat.
No. 19. *At the head is a staff with notes described as* le bouldon; *the first bar is indicated* primus versus, *and the second & sic* deinceps secundus versus. *Written as prose.*

wer we to to-gadere beyne,
þou myst me lysse of my peyne;
y am a-gast, it wol not geyne—
    myn herte falluþ colde.                    8
        þei y syng &c.

my-self y wol myn arnde bede,
þe betur y hope forte spede;
non so wel may do myn nede—
    a womman so me tolde.                    12
        þei y &c.


20.            *The Banished Lover*

Huntington MS. EL 1160 (*olim* Ellesmere MS.)

I Must go walke þe woed so wyld,    [f. 11ᵛ]
    & wander here & there
  in dred & dedly ffere;
ffor where I trusted I am begyld,            4
    & all ffor on.

Thus am I banysshyd ffrom my blys
    by craft & false pretens,
  fautles with-out offens,                   8
as off return no certen ys,
    and all for ffer off on.

No. 19.  9 arde *deleted before* arnde.
No. 20. *Stanza 1 occurs in a different hand on f. 108ᵛ; stanzas 2 and
3 on f. 107ᵛ, and the first four lines of stanza 2 on the margins of
f. 109ʳ.*
    *The following are the readings of these repeated stanzas:*
    5 and all for your loue my dere. *And so line 15.*        6 for my
blys.        7 with; & false *not on f. 11ᵛ.*        10 and all for my
loue my dere.        19 but when that I of hur bewtye dↄ thynk.
20 and all for my loue my dere.
    *Readings of f. 11ᵛ:*
    5 *After* on *a blank space and the word* nowe.        10 *After the
line is written* thus am I.        14 MS. day by do I ffl.        15 *Inserted between lines 13 and 14.*        18 *After the line is inserted* and
all ffor on.        19 MS. thyn; of *supplied.*

my bed schall be under þe grenwod tre,
   a tufft off brakes vnder my hed,     12
   as on ffrom Ioye were fled;
thus from my lyff day by day I fflee,
   and all ffor on.

The Ronnyng stremes shall be my drynke,   16
   acorns schalbe my ffode;
   nothyng may do me good,
but when of your bewty I do thynk,
   & all ffor lowe off on.
                      20

21.

## *Love in the Garden*

Sloane MS. 2593

I Haue a newe gardyn,        [f. 11ᵛ]
   & newe is be-gunne;
swych an-oþer gardyn
   know I not vnder sunne.     4

In þe myddis of my gardyn
   is a peryr set,
& it wele non per bern
   but a per Ienet.     8

þe fayrest mayde of þis toun
   preyid me,
for to gryffyn her a gryf
   of myn pery tre.     12

quan I hadde hem gryffid
   alle at her wille,
þe wyn & þe ale
   che dede in fille.     16

& I gryffid her
    ry3t vp in her home;
& be þat day xx wowkes
    it was qwyk in her womb.                    20

þat day twelfus month,
    þat mayde I mette:
che seyd it was a per robert,
    but non per Ionet!                           24


22.                        *Careless Love*

Cambridge Univ. MS. Addit. 5943
(*olim* Lord Howard de Walden MS.)

Wolde god that hyt were so                    [f. 178ᵛ]
as I cowde wysshe by-tuyxt vs too.

THe man that I loued Al-ther-best
    In Al thys contre, est other west,
to me he ys A strange gest;
    what wonder es't thow I be woo?              4

when me were leuest that he schold duelle,
    [he maketh haste fro me to go;]
he wold no3t sey ones fare-well
    wen tyme was come that he most go.           8

In places ofte when I hym mete,
    I dar no3t speke but forth I go;
with herte & eyes I hym grete,
    so trywe of loue I know no mo.               12

No. 21. *Written in long lines.*        18 *Two small letters* (? ag)
*inserted above* ry3t; MS. honde.        24 MS. Ion.
    No. 22. *The appropriate feminine pronouns have been interlined
in another hand*: sche 1, 3, 5, 6, 7, 8, 13, 14, 16, 19, 20, 22; hyre 9,
11, 21.        6 *MS. duplicates line* 7; he wold no3t sey onys fare-
welle.        8 most *written over* wold.        10 speke but forth I
go *struck through at end of line and* I go *inserted.*

As he ys myn hert loue,
  My dyrward dyre, I-blessyd he be;
I swere by god that ys A-boue,
  Non hath my loue but only he.                    16

I Am I-comfertyd in euery syde,
  The colures wexeth both fres and newe;
when he ys come & wyl a-byde,
  I wott ful wel that he ys trywe.                 20

I loue hym trywely & no mo—
  wolde god that he hyt knywe!
And euer I hope hyt schal be so,
  Then schall I chaunge for no new.                24

## 23. *A Forsaken Maiden's Lament*

Caius Coll. Cambridge MS. 383

Were it vndo þat is y-do          [p. 210]
I wolde be-war.

Y Louede a child of þis cuntre,
  & so y wende he had do me;
now my-self þe soþe y see,
  þat he is far.                                   4
    Wer it undo þat is i-do &c.

No. 22. 15 boee (?) *struck through before* boue.    16 only
*inserted above line;* hys *struck though at beginning of line.*
  21 wolde god *struck through at end of line.*
  22 sche were trywe *interlined.*
No. 23. *The tune is indicated before the first burden*: Bryd on
brere y telle yt, to non oþur y ne dar. *Written as prose.*
  4. *The burden is written above* brid on þe þrere &c *dotted for
deletion.*

he seyde to me he wolde be trewe,
& change me for non oþur newe;
now y sykke & am pale of hewe,
    for he is far.                                    8
      Wer it undo &c.

he seide his sawus he wolde fulfille,
þerfore y lat him haue al his wille;
now y sykke & morne stille,
    for he is far.                                    12
      Wer it undo &c.

24.                          *The Wily Clerk*

St. John's Coll. Cambridge MS. 259

A, dere god, qwat I am fayn,                    [f. 2ᵛ]
for I am madyn now gane!

ÞIs enþer day I mete a clerke,
  & he was wylly in hys werke;
he prayd me with hym to herke,
    and hys cownsell all for to layne.        4

I trow he cowd of gramery,
I xall now telle a good skyll wy;
for qwat I hade siccurly,
    To warne hys wyll had I no mayn.          8

qwan he and me browt un us þe schete,
Of all hys wyll I hym lete;
Now wyll not my gyrdyll met—
    a, dere god, qwat xal I sayn?             12

No. 24. 4 MS. lene.    6 MS. kyll; telle *supplied*.    7 MS.
sicculy.    8 MS. may.        12 MS. A dere god qw ar I xal say.

I xall sey to man & page                [f. 3ʳ]
þat I haue bene of pylgrymage;
Now wyll I not lete for no rage
    With me a clerk for to pleyn.                16

## 25.    *A Betrayed Maiden's Lament*

Cambridge Univ. MS. Ff. 5. 48

I haue for-sworne hit whil I life          [f. 114ᵛ]
to wake the well-ey.

THe last tyme I the wel woke
  Ser Iohn caght me with a croke,
he made me to swere be bel & boke
    I shuld not tell [-ey.]                4

ȝet he did me a wel wors turne,
he leyde my hed agayn the burne,
he gafe my mayden-hed a spurne
    and rofe my kell [-ey.]                8

Sir Iohn came to oure hows to play
ffro euensong tyme til light of the day;
we made as mery as flowres in may—
    I was begyled-ay                12

Sir Iohn he came to our hows,
he made hit wondur copious
he seyd that I was gracious
    to beyre a childe-ey.                16

No. 24. 16 MS. pley.
No. 25. *Burden written as one line.*
    12 we were *struck through after* I was.

I go with childe, wel I wot;
I schrew the fadur þat hit gate,
with-outen he fynde hit mylke & pap
a long while-ey.                                    20

bryan hys my name iet.

26.                    *Our Sir John*

Huntington MS. EL 1160
(*olim* Ellesmere MS.)

hey noyney, I wyll loue our ser Iohn & I loue eny.    [f. 11ʳ]

O Lord, so swett ser Iohn dothe kys,
     at euery tyme when he wolde pley;
off hym-selfe so plesant he ys,
     I haue no powre to say hym nay.          4

ser Iohn loues me & I loue hym;
     the more I loue hym the more I maye.
he says, 'swett hart, cum kys me trym'—
     I haue no powre to say hym nay.          8

ser Iohn to me Is proferyng
     ffor hys plesure ryght well to pay,
& In my box he puttes hys offryng—
     [I haue no powre to say hym nay.]        12

ser Iohn ys taken In my mouse-trappe:
     ffayne wold I haue hem bothe nyght and day.
he gropith so nyslye a-bought my lape,
     I haue no pore to sa[y hym nay.]          16

No. 25.  18 childe *struck through before* fadur.    rubric MS. hyf.
No. 26. *The burden is repeated in a different form in the margin
of f. 73*ᵛ: hey troly loly hey troly loly I must loue our sur Iohn &
I loue eny o lord.
    5 MS. Iohn loue me.                9 MS. In.
    15 lape *corrected from* pape.

ser Iohn geuyth me reluys rynges,
  With praty plesure ffor to assay—
ffurres off the ffynest with other thynges:
  [I haue no powre to say hym nay.]        20

### *Jolly Jankin*

Sloane MS. 2593

'kyrie,' so 'kyrie,'                        [f. 34ʳ]
Iankyn syngyt merie,
with 'aleyson.'

AS I went on ȝol day in owr prosessyon,
  Knew I Ioly Iankyn be his mery ton.
  [kyrieleyson.]

Iankyn be-gan þe offys on þe ȝol day,      [f. 34ᵛ]
& ȝyt me þynkyt it dos me good, so merie gan he say
  kyrieleyson.

Iankyn red þe pystyl ful fayr & ful wel,
& ȝyt me þinkyt it dos me good, as euere haue I sel.   8
  [kyrieleyson.]

Iankyn at þe sanctus crakit a merie note,
& ȝyt me þinkyt it dos me good—I payid for his cote.
  [kyrieleyson.]                                       12

Iankyn crakit notes an hunderid on a knot,
& ȝyt he hakkyt hem smaller þan wortes to þe pot.
  k[yrieleyson.]

Iankyn at þe angnus beryt þe pax brede,               16
he twynkelid, but sayd nowt, & on myn fot he trede.
  [kyrieleyson.]

No. 26. 17 MS. relyus.
No. 27. *Burden written as one line.*    5 *Written as two lines.*

Benedicamus domino, cryst fro schame me schylde.
Deo gracias þerto—alas, I go with schylde!    20
  k[yrieleyson.]


## 28.    *A Midsummer Day's Dance*

Caius Coll. Cambridge MS. 383

alas, ales, þe wyle—    [p. 41]
þout y on no gyle,
  so haue y god chaunce.
ala[s], ales, þe wyle—
  þat euer y cowde daunce.

LAdd y þe daunce a myssomur day;
  y made smale trippus soþ fore to say.
iak oure haly watur clerk com be þe way,
& he lokede me vpon, he þout þat y was gay—    4
  þout yc on no gyle.

Iak, oure haly watur clerk, þe ȝonge strippelyng,
ffor þe chesone of me he com to þe ryng,
& he trippede on my to, & made a twynkelyng;    8
euer he cam ner, he sparet for no þynge—
  þout y on [no gyle.]

iak, ic wot, priyede in my fayre face,
he þout me ful worly, so haue y god grace;    12
as we turndun owre daunce in a narw place,
Iak bed me þe mouþ; a cussynge þer was—
  þout y on no g[yle.]

*Written as prose.*
  *The burden is written after stanza 1; the last two lines of the bur-
den precede stanza 1, apparently as a familiar indication of the carol:*
alas alas þe wyle þat euer y coude daunce.
  3 MS. clek.
  4 MS. *faded.*
  5 no MS. ne.

iak þo began to rowne in myn ere:    16
'loke þat þou be priuey & grante þat þou þe bere,
a peyre wyth glouus ic ha to þyn were!'
'gremercy, iacke,' þat was myn answere—
   þoute yc [on no gyle.]    20

sone aftur euensong iak me mette:
'com hom aftur þy glouus þat ic þe byhette.'
wan ic to his chambur com, doun he me sette;
from hym mytte y nat go wan we were mette—    24
   þout y [on no gyle.]

Schetus & chalonus, ic wot, were yspredde;
fore-soþe þo iak & yc wenten to bedde.
he prikede & he pransede, nolde he neuer lynne:    28
yt was þe murgust nyt þat euer y cam ynne—
   þout y [on no gyle.]

wan iak had don, þo he rong þe belle;
al nyȝt þer he made me to dwelle;    32
Oft, y trewe, we haddun yserued þe reaggeth deuel of
   helle!
Of oþur smale burdus kep y nout to telle—
   þout y [on no gyle.]

þe oþur day at prime y com hom, as ic wene;    36
Meth y my dame coppud & kene:
'Sey, þou stronge strumpeth, ware hastu bene?
þy trippyng & þy dauncyng wel it wol be sene!'
   þout y [on no gyle.]    40

Euer bi on & by on my damme reched me clot;
Euer y ber it priuey wyle þat y mouth,
tyl my gurdul a-ros, my wombe wax out;
'Euel yspunne ȝern euer it wole out'— 44
þout y on no gyle.

## 29. *The Serving Maid's Holiday*

Caius Cell. Cambridge MS. 383

Wybbe ne rele ne spynne yc ne may, [p. 41]
ffor ioyȝe þat it ys holyday.

AL þis day ic han souȝt,
spyndul ne werue ne wond y nouȝt;
To myche blisse ic am brout
aȝen þis hyȝe holyday. 4
Wybbe &c.

all vnswope ys owre vleth,
& owre fyre ys vnbeth,
Oure ruschen ben vnrepe ȝeth,
aȝen þis hy halyday. 8

yc moste feschun worton In;
þredele my kerchef vndur my khyn;
leue iakke, lend me a pyn
To þredele me þis holiday. 12

Now yt draweþ to þe none
& al my cherrus ben vndone;
y moste a lyte solas mye schone
to make hem dowge þis holiday. 16

*Written as prose.*
4 holyday *MS. damaged by holes*: lyda.
6, 7 *Transposition corrected by letters* a *and* b.

y moste mylkyn in þis payl;
Outh me bred al þis schayl,
ȝut is þe dow vndur my nayl
    as ic knad þis holyday. 20

Iakke wol brynge me onward in my wey,
Wyþ me desyre for te pleyȝe;
Of my dame stant me non eyȝe
    an neuer a god haliday. 24

Iacke wol pay for my scoth
a sonday atte þe ale-schoth;
iacke wol sowse wel my þroth
    euery god haliday. 28

sone he wolle take me be þe hand,
& he wolle legge me on þe lond,
þat al my buttockus ben of sond,
    opon þis hye holyday. 32

In he pult & out he drow,
& euer yc lay on hym y-low;
'by godus deth, þou dest me wow
    vpon þis hey holyday!' 36

sone my wombe began to swelle
as greth as a belle;
durst y nat my dame telle
    Wat me betydde þis holyday. 40

27 MS. wroth.
28 MS. halida.
30 MS. men.
31 MS. son.
38 MS. a greth.
39 MS. drurst.
  *The repetition of the burden is indicated by* W *at the end of the
second and following stanzas.*

## 30.    *Silver White*

Cambridge Univ. MS. Addit. 5943
(*olim* Lord Howard de Walden MS.)

Cantelena

i      AT the northe ende of seluer whyte,  [f. 170ᵛ]
        my lef me bat—
at the northe ende [of seluer whyte,]
  [my lef me bat] I scholde abyde.          4
    I leyde my ware, a bogeler brode,
      and euer he smote—
I leyde my ware, a bogeler brode,
    & euer he smote by syde.          8
     shalle ther neuer man iust ther-at,
      but ȝyf he can—
shalle ther neuer man iust ther-at
    but yf he can hyt smyte.        12

ii      At the suthe ende of seluer whyte,
      [my lef me bat—]
[At the suthe ende of seluer whyte,]
   [my lef me bat I scholde abyde.]     16
     leyde I my ware, a peckel wyde,
      & euer he smote—
[leyde I my ware, a peckel wyde,]
    [& eyer he smote by syde.]      20
     [shalle ther neuer man iust ther-at,]
      [but ȝyf he can—]
[shalle ther neuer man iust ther-at,]
   [but yf he can hyt smyte.]      24

*Written as prose.*
The lines supplied are indicated in the MS. as follows: 3 &c.; 4 *superfluous & after* abyde; 13 w *struck through before* suthe; &c. vt supra; 18 &c. vt supra; 26 &c.; 31 &c. vt supra; 33 &c.
  8 MS. he suy smote.
  11 MS. iusty.

iii      At the weste ende of seluer whyte,
       my lef me bade—
   [At the weste ende of seluer whyte,]
   [my lef me bade I scholde abyde.]      28
       layde I my ware, a bosshelle brode,
         & euer he smote—
   leyde [I my ware, a bosshelle brode,]
   [& euer he smote by syde.]      32
       shalle ther neuer [man] iust þer-at,
         [but ȝyf he can—]
   [shalle ther neuer man iust þer-at,]
   [but yf he can hyt smyte.]      36

*31.*        *In My Lady's Chamber*

Cambridge Univ. MS. Addit. 5943
(*olim* Lord Howard de Walden MS.)
Cantelena

MAy no man slepe in ȝoure halle,    [f. 170ᵛ]
    for dogges, madame—for dogges, madame;
but ȝyf he haue a tent of xv ynche
   with twey clogges,      4
[to dryve awey the dogges,] madame.
   I-blessyd be such Clogges,
   that ȝyuef such bogges,
   by-twyne my lady legges,      8
[to dryve awey the dogges, madame.]

May no man slepe in ȝoure halle,
for rattys, madame—for rattys, madame;
but ȝyf he haue a tent of xv enche      12
   wyt letheryn knappes,

*Written as prose; 3–4, 6–8 in margin.*
   1 sher *struck through before* slepe.     2 r *struck through be-*
*fore* dogges.     3 MS. ten tent: *a false start; and so* 12.     8
MS. my twyne.     10 slo *struck through before* slepe.

to dryve awey the rattys, madame.
  I-blessyd be suche knappes,
  that ȝyveth such swappes,             16
  vnder my lady lappes,
to dryve awey the rattys, madame.

Ma no man slepe in ȝoure [halle,]
for flyes, madame—[for flyes, madame;]     20
but [ȝyf he haue a tent of xv enche]
  [wyt . . . byes]
[to dryve awey the flyes, madame.]
  I-blessyd be such byes,             24
  that maketh such suyes,       [f. 171ʳ]
  by-tuynne my lady thyes,
to dryve awey the flyes, madame.

*32.*          *Little Pretty Mopsy*

             Canterbury Cathedral
          Christ Church Letters, ii. 173

          'I pray yow, cum kyss me,
          My lytle prety mopse,
          I pray yow, com kyss me.'

'ALas, good man, most yow be kyst?
    Ye shall not now, ye may me trust;
wherfore go where as ye best lust,
  ffor, I-wyss, ye shall not kyss me.'        4

'I-wyss, swet hart, yff that ye
had askyd a gretur thyng of me,
so onkynd to yow I wold not haue be;
  wherefore, I pray yow, com kyss me.'     8

No. 31. 16 MS. smappes.     24 byes: *initial letter obscured;
possibly* s *or* v.
  No. 32. 8 MS. where.

'I thynke very well þat ye ar kynd
whereas ye lowe and set yore mynd,
but all yore wordes be but as wynd
   wherefore now ye shall not kyss me.'    12

'I do but talke, ye mow me trust,
but ye take everythyng at the worst.'
'wherefore I say, as I sayd furst,
   I-wyss, ye shall not kyss me.'    16

'I pray yow, let me kyss yow.
Iff that I shall not kyss yow,
let me kyss yore karchos nocke;
   I pray yow let me kyss yowe.'    20

'All so I say as I furst haue sayd,
and ye wyll not therewith be dysmayd;
yet wyth that onsar ye shall be payd:
   I-wyss, ye shall not kyss me.'    24

'now I se well that kyssys ar dere,
and, yff I shold labvr all the hole yere,
I thynke I shold be neuer the nere;
   wherefore, I pray yow, cum kyss me.'    28

'neuer the nere, ye may be shewre,
ffor ye shall not so sone bryng me in vre
to consent vnto yore nyse plesure,
   nor, I-wyss, ye shall not kyss me.'    32

'I pray yow, com and kyss me,
my lytle pretty mopse,
And yff that ye wyll not kyss me,
   I pray yow, let me kyss yow.'    36

19 MS. let me loke let me kyss: *a false start.*
25 thes *struck through before* that.

'well, ffor a kyss I wylle not stycke,
so that ye wyll do nothyng but lykke;
but, and ye begyn on me ffor to prycke,
    I-wyss, ye shall not kyss me.'                    40

'now I se well that ye ar kynd;
wherefore ye shall euer know my mynd,
and euer yore own ye shall me fynd
    At all tymes redy to kyss yow.'                   44

        ffinys quod wulstane persone.


33.            *In Praise of Brunettes*

            Caius Coll. Cambridge MS. 383

SUmme men sayon þat y am blac.    [p. 190]
    yt ys a colour for my prow;
þer y loue þer ys no lac,
    y may not be so wyte as þou.                      4

blac ys a colur þat ys god—
    so say y & many mo;
blac ys my hat, blac ys my hod,
    blac ys al þat longet þer-to.                      8

blac wol do as god a nede
    as þe wyte at bord & bedde;
& þer-to also treu in dede,
    & þer-to y ley my lyf to wedde.                   12

Wynd & watur may steyne þe wyte,
    y-wys þe blac yt may not so;
þer yse þe blac ys al my delyte,
    y am yholde be schyle þer-to.                     16

No. 32.  39 me MS. m: *hole in MS.*        rubric MS. p. . . . sone:
*hole in MS.*
No. 33.  2 MS. þrow.     11 MS. indede.     14 MS. Wyn wys.

Peper wyt-oute yt ys wel blac,
  y-wys wyt-inne yt ys not so;
lat go þe colur & tak þe smac,
  þys y sey by me & mo.                           20

  god saue ale hem þat buþ broune,
    for þey buth trew as any stel;
  god kepe hem boþe in feld & toune,
    & þanne schal y be kept ful wel.           24

**34.**          *In Praise of Women*

Harley MS. 4294

I am as lyght as any roe                  [f. 81ʳ]
To preyse wemen wher that I goo.

TO onpreyse wemen yt were a shame,
  For a woman was thy dame;
Our blessyd lady beryth the name
  of all women wher that they goo.              4

A woman ys a worthy thyng—
  they do the washe and do the wrynge;
'lullay, lullay,' she dothe the synge,
  And yet she hath but care and woo.           8

A woman ys a worthy wyght,
  she seruyth a man both daye and nyght,
therto she puttyth all her myght,
  And yet she hathe bot care and woo.        12

No. 33. 21 hem *inserted above line.*
No. 34. 2 MS. da *struck through after* was.
3 Of women *written above line and struck through;* blessyd *inserted above line.*
  8 MS. bo *struck through after* hath.
  9 a *supplied.*
10 MS. nygh.

35.        *A Young Girl's Ideal*

Sloane MS. 1584

So well ys me be-gone,                    [f. 45$^v$]
   troly, lole—
so well ys me be-gone,
   troly, loly.

OFf seruyng men I wyll begyne,
   Troly, loley,
ffor they goo mynon trym,
   Troly, loley.                                          4

Off mett & drynk & feyr clothyng,
   Troly, loley,
by dere god I want none,
   Troly, loley.                                          8

His bonet is of fyne scarlett,
   Troly, loley,
With here as black os geitt,
   Troly, lolye.                                         12

His dublett ys of fyne satyne,
   Troly, lolye.
Hys shertt well mayd & tryme,
   Troly, lolye.                                         16

His coytt itt is so tryme & rownde,
   Troly, lolye.
His kysse is worth A hundred pownde,
   Troly, loly.                                          20

His hoysse is of london black,
   Troly, lolye.
In hyme ther ys no lack,
   Troly, lolye.                                         24

*Burden written as two lines (rubricated).  The refrain is written
at the end of each line.*
12 MS. Torly.          19 MS. worth A C$^l$.          21 is *supplied*.

His face yt ys so lyk a man,
 Troly, lolye.
Who cane butt love hyme than,
 Troly, lolye.   28

Wher-so-euer he bee, he hath my hert,
 Troly, lolye,
And shall to deth de-part,
 Troly, lolye.   32

  So well ys me be-gone,
   troly, loly,
   S[o] well ys me be-gone,
   Troly, lolye.

## 36. *Old Hogyn's Adventure*

Balliol Coll. Oxford MS. 354

HOgyn cam to bowers dore—  [f. 249ᵛ]
hogyn cam to bowers dore,
he tryld vpon þe pyn for love,
 hum, ha, trill go bell—  4
he tryld vpon þe pyn for love,
 hum, ha, trill go bell.

Vp she rose & lett hym yn—
vp she rose & let hym yn,  8
She had a-went she had worshipped all her kyn,
 hum, ha, trill go bell—
She had A-went she had worshipped all her kyn,
 Hum, ha, trill go bell.  12

When þei were to bed browght—
Whan thei were to bed browght,
The old chorle he cowld do nowght,
 hum, ha, trill go bell—  16
The old chorle he cowld do nowght,
 hum, ha, trill go bell.

  No 36. 11 her MS. he.

Go ye furth to yonder wyndow—
go ye furth to yonder wyndow,                    20
And I will cum to you with-in a throw,
   hum, ha, trill go bell—
& I will cum to you with-yn a throw,
   hum, ha, trill go bell.                        24

Whan she hym at þe wyndow wyst—
Whan she hym at þe wyndow wyst,
She torned owt her ars & þat he kyst,
   hum, ha, trill go bell—                        28
she torned owt her ars & þat he kyst,
   hum, ha, trill go bell.

Ywys, leman, ye do me wrong—
ywis, leman, ye do me wrong,                     32
Or elles your breth ys wonder strong,
   hum, ha, trill go bell—
or elles your breth ys wonder strong,
   hum, ha, trill go bell.                        36

      Explicit.


37.        *A Mocking Song of Love*

       Caius Coll. Cambridge MS. 383

    Care away, away, away,                    [p. 68]
    Murnyng away.
      y am forsake,
      an-oþer ys take,
    no more murne yc may.

I Am sory for her sake,
 yc may wel ete & drynke;
wanne yc sclepe yc may not wake,
  so muche on here yc þenke.                     4

    No. 37. *Written as prose.*

I am brout in suche a bale,
& brout in suche a pyne,
Wanne yc ryse vp of my bed
me liste wel to dyne.                    8

I am brout in suche a pyne,
y-brout in suche a bale,
wanne yc haue rythe god wyne
me liste drynke non ale.                 12

## 38.                *Abuse of Women*

Balliol Coll. Oxford MS. 354
of all Creatures women be best:
Cuius contrarium verum est.            [f. 250ʳ]

IN euery place ye may well see,
that women be trewe as tirtyll on tree,
Not lyberall in langage, but euer in secree,
& gret Ioye a-monge them ys for to be.    4

The stedfastnes of women will neuer be don,
So Ientyll, so curtes they be euery-chon,
Meke as a lambe, still as a stone,
Croked nor Crabbed ffynd ye none!         8

Men be more Cumbers a thowsand fold,
& I mervayll how they dare be so bold,
Agaynst women for to hold,
Seyng them so pascyent, softe & cold.    12

ffor tell a woman all your Cownsayle,
& she can kepe it wonderly well;
She had lever go quyk to hell,
Than to her neyghbowr she wold it tell!  16

*Burden headed* ffote.
*The repetition of the burden is indicated by* Cuius *after each stanza.*
3 MS. secrete.

ffor by women men be Reconsiled,
ffor by women was neuer man begiled,
ffor they be of þe condicion of curtes gryzell
ffor they be so meke & mylde.                                    20

Now say well by women or elles be still,
ffor they neuer displesed man by þer will;
to be angry or wroth they can no skill,
ffor I dare say they thynk non yll.                              24

Trow ye þat women list to smater,                   *cf · TMW*
Or Agaynst þer husbondes for to clater?
Nay, they had leuer fast bred & water
then ffor to Dele in suche a mater.                             28

Thowgh all þe paciens in þe world were drownd,
& non were lefte here on the grownd,
agayn in a woman it myght be fownd,
Suche vertu in them dothe abownd!                               32

To þe tavern they will not goo,
Nor to þe Ale-hows neuer the moo,
ffor, god wot, þer hartes wold be woo,
To sspende ther husbondes money soo.                            36

yff here were a woman or a mayd,
that lyst for to go fresshely arayed,
Or with fyne kyrchers to go displayed,
Ye wold say, 'they be prowde:' it is yll said.                  40

Explicit.

39.          *The Trials of Marriage*

MS. Eng. poet. e. 1
(Sum. Cat. No. 29734)

W Hat, why dedyst þou wynk whan þou a wyf
    toke?                                    [f. 26ʳ]
þou haddest neuer mor ned brodde to loke!
A man þat wedyth a wyfe whan he wynkyth,
But he star afterward, wonder me thynkyth!        4

40.      *Against Hasty Marriage, I*

MS. Digby 196
(Sum. Cat. No. 1797)

K Now or thow knytte; Prove or thow preyse yt.
                                          [f. 20ʳ]
   ȝyf þou know or þou knyt, þan mayst þou Abate;
   & ȝyf þou knyt er þou knowe, Than yt ys to late.
Ther-fore Avyse þe er þou þe knot knytte,          4
ffor 'had y wyst' commeth to late for to lowse yt.

(41)      *Against Hasty Marriage, II*

Sloane MS. 2593
Man, bewar of þin wowyng,             [f. 9ᵛ]
for weddyng is þe longe wo.

L Oke er þin herte be set;
   lok þou wowe er þou be knet;
& if þou se þou mow do bet,
   knet vp þe heltre & let her goo.                4

Wyuys be boþe stowte & bolde,
her husbondes aȝens hem durn not holde;
& if he do, his herte is colde,
   howsoeuere þe game go.                          8

No. 39. 4 *After* me *the letter* l *crossed out.*
No. 40. *The first three lines written as six short lines; fourth and*
*fifth bracketed at the side.*

Wedowis be wol fals, I-wys,
for þey cun boþe halse & kys
til onys purs pikyd is,
   & þey seyn, 'go, boy, goo!'     12

Of madenys I wil seyn but lytil,
for þey be boþe fals & fekyl,
& vnder þe tayl þey ben ful tekyl;
   A twenty deuel name, let hem goo!   16

## 42.    *The Tribulations of Marriage*

MS. Douce 257
(Sum. Cat. No. 21831)

A . . . . .   p   [f. 99ᵛ]
  per ys no merth yn noþir;
  A man þat haþ yteyd hym vp
  May nawht chese anoþir.    4

  A yong wyf and an arvyst-gos
  Moche gagil wiþ boþe;
  A man þat haþ ham yn his clos,
  Reste schal he wroþe.    8

## 43.    *A Henpecked Husband's Complaint, I*

Sloane MS. 2593

  how! hey! it is non les,   [f. 24ᵛ]
  I dar not sey3 quan che sey3t 'pes!'

ȜYng men, I warne ȝou euerychon:
  Elde wywys tak ȝe non;
for I my-self haue on at hom—
  I dar not seyn quan che sey3t 'pes!'   4

No. 41. 10 þey *supplied.*
No. 42. *The first line is rubbed out in the MS.*

Quan I cum fro þe plow at non,     [f. 25ʳ]
In a reuen dych myn mete is don;
I dar not askyn our dame a spon—
    I dar not [seyn quan che sey3t 'pes!']     8

If I aske our dame bred,
che takyt a staf & brekit myn hed,
& doþ me rennyn vnder þe bed—
    I dar not [seyn quan che sey3t 'pes!']     12

If I aske our dame fleych,
che brekit myn hed with a dych:
'boy, þou art not wor3t a reych!'
    I dar [not seyn quan che sey3t 'pes!']     16

If I aske our dame chese,
'boy,' che sey3t, al at ese,
'þou art not wor3t half a pese.'
    I dar not sey quan che sey3t 'pes!'     20

## 44. *A Henpecked Husband's Complaint, II*

MS. Eng. poet. e. 1
(Sum. Cat. No. 29734)

    Care away, away, away—     [f. 23ʳ]
    care away for euermore!

All þat I may swynk or swet,
  My wyfe it wyll boþ drynk & ete;
& I sey ov3t she wyl me bete—
    carfull ys my hart þerfor!     4

If I sey ov3t of hyr but good,
She loke on me as she war wod,
& wyll me clov3t abov3t þe hod—
    carfull [ys my hart þerfor!]     8

No. 43. *Burden written as one line*; non *rubbed out.* 11 MS. led.
No. 44. *Burden written as one line.*

If she wyll to þe gud ale ryd,
Me must trot all be hyr syd;
& whan she drynk I must abyd—
    carfull [ys my hart þerfor!]                    12

If I say, 'it shal be thus,'
She sey, 'þou lyyst, charll, I-wovs!
Wenest þou to ouercome me þus?'
    carfull [ys my hart þerfor!]                    16

Yf ony man haue svch a wyfe to lede,    [f. 23ᵛ]
*judgement* He schal know how <u>iudicare</u> cam in þe cred;
Of hys penans god do hym med!
    carfull [ys my hart þerfor!]                    20

45.                    *My Young Sister*
                    Sloane MS. 2593

I Haue a ȝong suster                    [f. 11ʳ]
  fer be-ȝondyn þe se,
many be þe drowryis
    þat che sente me.                              4

che sente me þe cherye
    with-outyn ony ston,
& so che ded þe dowe
    with-outyn ony bon.                            8

sche sente me þe brer
    with-outyn ony rynde,
sche bad me loue my lemman
    with-oute longgyng.                            12

how xuld ony cherye
    be with-oute ston?
& how xuld only dowe
    ben with-oute bon?                             16

No. 45. *Written in long lines.*        7 þe *supplied.*

how xuld ony brer
    ben with-oute rynde?
how xuld y loue myn lemman
    with-out longyng?                    20

Quan þe cherye was a flour,         [f. 11ᵛ]
    þan hadde it non ston.
quan þe dowe was an ey,
    þan hadde it non bon.               24

Quan þe brer was on-bred,
    þan hadde it non rynd.
quan þe maydyn haȝt þat che louit,
    che is with-out longing.           28

46.            *My Gentle Cock*

Sloane MS. 2593

I Haue a gentil cook,               [f. 10ᵛ]
    crowyt me day;
he doþ me rysyn erly,
    my matyins for to say.                4

I haue a gentil cook,
    comyn he is of gret;
his comb is of reed corel,
    his tayil is of get.                  8

I haue a gentyl cook,
    comyn he is of kynde;
his comb is of red corel,
    his tayl is of Inde.                 12

No. 45. 19 MS. on *struck through after* xuld.
No. 46. *Written in long lines.*      11 MS. scorel.

his legges ben of asor,
  so geintil & so smale;
his spores arn of syluer qwyt,
  in-to þe worte-wale.                    16

his eynyn arn of cristal,
  lokyn al in aumbyr;
& euery ny3t he perchit hym
  in myn ladyis chaumbyr.                 20

*47.*         *My Twelve Oxen*

Balliol Coll. Oxford MS. 354

I Haue XII oxen þat be fayre & brown,     [f. 178ᵛ]
  & they go a-grasynge down by the town.
  with hay, with howe, with hay!
Sawyste thow not myn oxen, þou litill prety boy.     4

I haue XII oxen, & they be ffayre & whight,
& they go a-grasyng down by the dyke.
  with hay, with howe, with hay!
Sawyste not þou myn oxen, þou lytyll prety boy.      8

I haue XII oxen & they be ffayre & blak,
& they go a-grasyng down by the lak.
  with hay, with howe, with hay!
Sawyste not þou myn oxen, þou lytyll prety boy.     12

I haue XII oxen, & they be fayre & rede,
& they go a-grasyng down by þe mede.
  with hay, with howe, with hay!
Sawiste not þou my oxen, þou litill prety boy.      16

Explicit.

No. 47.  1 tweff *struck through after*-haue.
      3 howe *struck through before second* hay.

48.            *The Fox and the Goose*

Royal MS. 19. B. iv

'Pax uobis,' quod the ffox,                [f. 97ᵛ
'for I am comyn to toowne.'                 col. ii]

I T fell ageyns the next nyght
    the fox yede to with all his myghte,
with-outen cole or candelight,
    whan that he cam vnto the toowne.        4

Whan he cam all in the yarde,
soore te geys wer ill a-ferde;
'I shall macke some of youre berde,
    or that I goo from the toowne!'          8

whan he cam all in the croofte,
there he stalkyd wundirfull soofte;
'for here haue I be frayed full ofte
    whan that i haue come to toowne.'       12

he hente a goose all be the heye,
faste the goos began to creye!
oowte yede men as they myght heye,
    and seyde, 'fals fox, ley it doowne!'   16

'Nay,' he saide, 'soo mot I the—
sche shall goo vnto the wode with me;
sche and I wnther a tre,
    e-mange the beryis browne.              20

I haue a wyf, and sche lyeth seke;
many smale whelppis sche haue to eke—
many bonys they muste pike
    will they ley a-downe.'                 24

## 49.    *The False Fox*

Cambridge Univ. MS. Ee. 1. 12

THe fals fox came vnto our croft,    [f. 80ᵛ]
 And so our gese ful fast he sought.
 With how fox, how; with hey fox, hey!
 Come no more vnto our howse to bere our gese aweye! 4

The fals fox came vnto our stye,
And toke our gese ther by and by.

The fals fox cam into our yerde,
And ther he made the gese aferde.    8

The fals fox came vnto our gate,
And toke our gese ther wher they sate.

*heard
cenfession*

The fals fox came [vn-] to our halle-dore,
And <u>shrove</u> our gese ther in the flore.    12

The fals fox came into our halle,
And assoyled our gese both grete & small.

The fals fox came vnto our cowpe,
And ther he made our gese to stowpe.    16

He toke a gose fast by the nek,
And the goose thoo began to quek.

The good-wyfe came out in her smok,
And at the fox she threw hir rok.    20

The good-man came out with his flayle,
And smote the fox vpon the tayle.

He threw a gose vpon his back,
And furth he went thoo with his pak.    24

*The repetition of the refrain is indicated in the second and follow-ing stanzas by* With how fox &c. *at the end of each couplet.* 1 *and* 33
the fals fox *written in large characters.*
  11 *Two letters erased before* to.    20 at *inserted above the line.*

The goodman swore yf that he myght,
he wolde hym slee or it wer nyght.

The fals fox went into his denne,
And ther he was full mery thenne.                    28

He came ayene yet the next weke,
And toke awey both henne & cheke.

The goodman saide vnto his wyfe,
'This fals fox lyveth a mery lyfe.'                   32

The fals fox came vpon a day,
And with our gese he made affray.

He toke a goose fast by the nek,
And made her to sey 'wheccumquek.'                   36

'I pray the, fox,' seid the goose thoo,
'Take of my feders but not of my to.'

**(50.)** *Holly and Ivy*

MS. Eng. poet. e. 1
(Sum. Cat. No. 29734)

HOlvyr and heyvy mad a gret party,          [f. 30ʳ]
Ho xuld haue þe maystre
  In londes qwer þei goo.

þan spake holuyr: 'I am frece and Ioly;            4
I wol haue þe maystre
  In londes qwer þei goo.'

þan spake heyvy: 'I am lowd & prowd,
And I wyl haue þe maystre                            8
  In londes qwer þei goo.'

No. 49. 38 *Added in a later hand.*
No. 50. 4 MS. Iol.

þan spak Holvyr, & set hym downe on his kne:  [f. 30ᵛ]
'I prey the, Ientyl heyvy, sey me no veleny
In londes qwer we goo.'                                      12

## *In Praise of Holly*

MS. Eng. poet. e. 1
(Sum. Cat. No. 29734)
Alleluia, alleluia,                          [f. 53ᵛ]
Alleluia Now syng we.

HEr commys holly þat is so gent,
to pleasse all men is his intent.
Alleluia.

But lord & lady off þis hall,                           4
Whosoeuer ageynst holly call—
Alleluia.

Whosoeuer ageynst holly do crye
In a lepe shall he hang full hye.                       8
Alleluia.

Whosoeuer ageynst holly do syng,        [f. 54ʳ]
he maye wepe & handys wryng.
Alleluia.                                                      12

## *In Praise of Ivy*

MS. Eng. poet. e. 1
(Sum. Cat. No. 29734)
Ivy, chefe off treis it is;                  [f. 54ʳ]
Veni, coronaberis.

THe most worthye she is in towne—
He that seyth oþer do amysse—
And worthy to ber the crowne.
Veni, coronaberis.                                      4

No. 50. 11 *Written as two lines in MS.*
No. 51. *Burden written as one line.*
No. 52. *Burden written as one line.*

Ivy is soft & mek off spech;
   Ageynst all bale she is blysse;
Well is he þat may hyr rech.
   Veni, coronaberis.        8

Ivy is green with colour bright,
   Off all treis best she is;
& þat I preve well now be right,
   Veni, coronaberis.        12

Ivy beryth berys black;
   God graunt vs all his blysse,
ffor there shall we nothyng lack.
   Veni, coronaberis.        16

## 53. *A Boar's Head Song*

MS. Eng. poet. e. 1
(Sum. Cat. No. 29734)

TYdynges I bryng ȝow for to tell    [f. 22$^v$]
   What me in wyld forest befell,
Whan me must with a wyld best mell—
   With a bor so bryme.        4
A bore so bryme þat me pursued,    [f. 23$^r$]
Me for to kyll sor sharply a-meved,
þat brymly best so cruell & unryd,
   þer tamyd I hym,        8
And reft fro hym both lyth & lyme.

Truly to shew ȝow þat is trew,
Hys hed with my swerd I hew,
to mak þis day to ȝow myrth new.    12
   Now etes þerof anon.

No. 53. 7 cruell . . . brymly *marked for transposition.*

Etys on, much good do yt ȝow!
Take ȝow bred & musterd þerto,
Ioy with me þat I haue þus done;                16
I pray ȝow to be glad eüerychon,
   & Ioy all in one.

54.            *A Boar's Head Carol, I*

MS. Eng. poet. e. 1
(Sum. Cat. No. 29734)
Po, po, po, po,                        [f. 29ᵛ]
loue brane & so do mo.

A T þe begynnyng of þe mete
  Of a borys hed ȝe schal hete,
& in þe mustard ȝe xal wete,
   & ȝe xal syngyn or ȝe gon.            4

Wolcum be ȝe þat ben here,
& ȝe xal haue ryth gud chere,
And also a ryth gud fare;
   & ȝe xal syngyn or ȝe gon.            8

Welcum be ȝe eüerychon,
For ȝe xal syngyn ryth anon;
Hey ȝow fast þat ȝe had don,
   & ȝe xal syngyn or ȝe gon.            12

55.            *A Boar's Head Carol, II*

Balliol Coll. Oxford MS. 354
Caput apri Refero,             [f. 228ʳ]
Resonens laudes domino.

T He boris hed In hondes I brynge,
  with garlondes gay & byrdes syngynge!
I pray you all helpe me to synge,
  Qui estis in conuiuio.                4

No. 54. 10 MS. ryth anon *written over* or ȝe go *which is struck through.*
No. 55. *The burden is marked* fote.
    *The last line of each stanza is written at the right.*

The boris hede, I vnderstond,
ys cheff seruyce in all this londe,
wher-so-ever it may be fonde,
  Seruitur cum sinapio. 8

The boris hede, I dare well say,
anon after the <u>XIIth day</u>, *Epiphany.*
he taketh his leve & goth a-way—
  Exiuit tunc de patria. 12

## 56. *A Boar's Head Carol, III*

Porkington MS. 10

Hey, hey, hey, hey! [f. 202ʳ]
þe borrys hede is armyd gay.

THe boris hede in hond I bryng,
  Witt garlond gay in porttoryng;
I pray yow all witt me to synge,
  Witt hay! 4

Lordys, knyghttis, and skyers,
Persons, prystis, and wycars—
The boris hede ys þe furst mes,
  Witt hay! 8

The boris hede, as I yow say,
He takis his leyfe, & gothe his way
Son after þe tweylffyt Day,
  Witt hay! 12

Then commys in þe secund kowrs witt mykyll pryid:
þe crannis & þe heyrrons, þe bytteris by þer syde,
þe pertrychys & þe plowers, þe wodcokis & þe snyt,
  Witt hay! 16

No. 56. *Burden written as one line.*
7 MS. furt.    11 MS. xii theylffyt.    16 MS. ha.

Larkys in hoot schow, ladys for to pyk,
Good drynk þerto, lycyvs and fyn—
Blwet of allmayn, romnay and wyin,
   Witt hay!                                        20

Gud bred, alle, & wyin, dare I well say,
þe boris hede witt musterd armyd soo gay.

furmante to potdtage, witt wennissun fyn,
& þe hombuls of þe dow, & all þat euer commis in.   24

Cappons ibake, witt þe pesys of þe roow,
Reysons of corrans, witt odyr spysis moo.


57.                *Sir Penny, I*

Sloane MS. 2593

Go bet, peny, go bet, go!                       [f. 26ᵛ]
for þou mat makyn boþe frynd & fo.

PEny is an hardy knyȝt,
   peny is mekyl of myȝt,
peny of wrong he makyt ryȝt
   In euery cuntre qwer he goo.                    4

þow I haue a man I-slawe
& forfetyd þe kynges lawe,
I xal fyndyn a man of lawe
   Wyl takyn myn peny & let me goo.                8

& If I haue to don fer or ner,
& peny be myn massanger,
þan am I non þing in dwer—
   my cause xal be wel I-doo.                      12

No. 57. *Burden written as one line.*

& If I haue pens boþe good & fyn,
men wyl byddyn me to þe wyn;
'þat I haue xal be þin,'
 sekyrly þei wil seyn so.          16

& quan I haue non in myn purs,
peny bet ne peny wers,
of me þei holdyn but lytil fors:
 'he was a man, let hym goo!'      20

58.          *Sir Penny, II*

Cotton MS. Galba E. ix
Incipit narracio de domino denario.     [f. 50ᵛ
                                          col. ii]

IN erth it es a litill thing,
 and regnes als a riche king,
 Whare he es lent in land;
Sir peni es his name calde—          4
he makes both ȝong & alde
 bow vntill his hand.

Papes, kinges, and Emperoures,
bisschoppes, abbottes, and priowres,   8
 person, prest, and knyght,
Dukes, Erles, and ilk barowne,
to serue him er þai ful boune
 both bi day and nyght.              12

Sir Peny chaunges mans mode,
and gers þam oft do doun þaire hode,
 and to rise him ogayne.
men honors him with grete reuerence,   16
makes ful mekell obedience
 vnto þat litill swaine.

No. 57. 15 MS. þi.
No. 58. 13 Peny *written above line in red.*

In kinges court es it no bote,
ogaines sir peni forto mote,                          20
   so mekill es he of myght;
he es so witty, and so strang,
þat be it neuer so mekill wrang,
   he will mak it right.                      24

with Peny may men wemen till,
be þai neuer so strange of will,
   so oft may it be sene.
lang with him will þai noght chide,          28
for he may ger þam trayl syde
   in gude skarlet and grene.        [f. 51ʳ col. i]

He may by both heuyn and hell,
and ilka thing þat es to sell,                     32
   in erth has he swilk grace;
he may lese, and he may bind,
þe pouer er ay put behind,
   whare he cumes in place.                 36

when he bigines him to mell,
he makes meke þat are was fell,
   and waik þat bald has bene.
all þe nedes ful sone er sped                    40
bath with-owten borgh and wed,
   whare peni gase bitwene.

þe domes-men he mase so blind
þat þai may noght þe right find,               44
   ne þe suth to se.
forto gif dome þam es ful lath,
þar-with to mak sir peni wrath,
   ful dere with þam es he.                     48

44 þai MS. he.

þare strif was, peni makes pese;
of all angers he may relese,
   in land whare he will lende.
of fase may he mak frendes sad,      52
of counsail thar þam neuer be rad
   þat may haue him to frende.

þat sire es set on high dese,
and serued with mani riche mese,     56
   at þe high burde.
þe more he es to men plente,
þe more ȝernid alway es he,
   and halden dere in horde.      60

he makes mani be forsworne,
and sum life and saul forlorne,
   him to get and wyn.
oþer god will þai none haue      64
bot þat litil round knaue,
   þaire bales forto blin.

On him halely þaire hert es sett,
him forto luf will þai noght let—    68
   nowþer for gude ne ill.
all þat he will in erth haue done,
ilka man grantes it ful sone,
   right at his awin will.      72

he may both lene and gyf,
he may ger both sla and lif,
   both by frith and fell.

Peni es a gude felaw;      76
men welcums him in dede and saw,  [f. 51ʳ
   cum he neuer so oft.     col. ii]

he es noght welkumd als a gest,
bot euermore serued with þe best,                    80
  and made at sit ful softe!

who-so es sted in any nede,
with sir peni may þai spede,
  how-so-euer bytide.                           84
he þat sir peni es with all
sal haue his will in stede and stall,
  when oþer er set byside.

Sir Peny gers in riche wede                          88
ful mani go & ride on stede,
  in þis werldes wide;
in ilka gamin, and ilka play,
þe maystri es gyfen ay                               92
  to peny for his pride.

Sir peny ouer all gettes þe gre,
both in burgh and in cete,
  in castell and in towre;                       96
with-owten owþer spere or schelde
es he þe best in frith or felde,
  and stalworthest in stowre.

In ilka place, þe suth es sene,                      100
sir peni es ouer al bidene,
  maister most in mode.
and all es als he will cumand,
oganis his steuyn dar no man stand,                  104
  nouþer by land ne flode.

Sir peny mai ful mekill availe
to þam þat has nede of cownsaill,
  als sene es in assise.                          108

he lenkithes life, and saues fro dede,
bot luf it noght ouer wele, I rede,
   for sin of coueityse.

If þou haue happ tresore to win,      112
delite þe noght to mekill þarin,
   ne nything þareof be;
bot spend it als well as þou can,
so þat þou luf both god and man     116
   in parfite charite.

God graunte vs grace with hert & will,
þe gudes þat he has gifen vs till
   well and wisely to spend;     120
and so our liues here forto lede,
þat we may haue his blis to mede,
   euer with-owten end.

                  Amen.

59.      *The Power of the Purse*

        MS. Eng. poet. e. 1
       (Sum. Cat. No. 29734)

MAn vpon mold, whatsoeuer þou be,   [f. 26ᵛ]
   I warn vtterly þou getyst no degre,
Ne no worshyp abyd with þe,
   but þou haue þe peny redy to tak to.     4

If þou be a ȝeman, a gentyllman wold be,
Into sum lordes cort þan put þou þe;
Lok þou haue spendyng larg & plente,
   & alwey þe peny redy to tak to.     8

       No. 58. 111 MS. fro.

If þou be a gentylman, and wold be a squyer,
Rydest ovt of cuntre as wyld as eny fyer:
I þe warn as my frend þou faylyst of þi desyr
    but þou haue [þe peny redy to tak to.]      12

If þou be a squyer, & wold be a knyȝt,
& darest no in armur put þe in fyȝt,
þan to þe kynges cort hy þe full tyȝt,
    & lok þou haue þe [peny redy to tak to.]      16

If þou be a lettryd man, to bere estat in scole,
A pilion or taberd to wer in hete or cole,
þe to besy þer-about I hold þe but a fole
    but þou haue [þe peny redy to tak to.]      20

If þou be a bachelar & wold[est ever thryve,]   [f. 27ʳ]
Prekyst out of contre & bryng[est home a wyfe;]
In much sorow & car ledyst þou þi l[yfe]
    [but þou haue þe peny redy to tak to.]      24

If þou be a marchant [to bu]y or to sell,
& ouer al þe countre wold[est bere] þe bell,
I þe connsell as a frend a[t home] to dwell
    But þou haue [þe peny redy to tak to.]      28

If þou be a ȝong man in lust þi lyfe to lace,
Abovt chyrch & market þe byshop wyl þe chace;
& yf þou mayst be get, þou getes novþer grace
    But þou [haue þe peny redy to tak to.]      32

If þou haue out to do with þe law to plete,
At london at þe parvis many on wyll þe rehete:
I warne þe com not þer but þi purse may swete,
    And þat þou [haue þe peny redy to tak to.]      36

9 MS. a squyer wold be.
21–27 *MS. torn.*

60. *On Penny*

Caius Coll. Cambridge MS. 261

SPende, and god schal sende;    [f. 234<sup>r</sup>]
   spare, and ermor care;
non peni, non ware;
non catel, non care.       4
   go, peni, go.

# II. PRACTICAL VERSE

## 61.　*A Charm by the Holy Rood*

Stockholm Kungl. Biblioteket MS. x. 90

HElpe, crosse, fayrest of tymbris three,　　[p. 146]
　　In braunnchys berynge bothe frute & flowr!
Helpe, banere beste my fon to doo flee,
　　Staf & strencthynge full of socowr!　　　　　4
On londe, on see, where þat I be,
　　Fro fyir brennynge be me by-forne,
Now Cristis tree, sygne of pyte,
　　Helpe me euir I be nowght lorne.　　　　　8

## 62.　*A Charm Against Robbers*

Cambridge Univ. MS. Addit. 5943
(*olim* Lord Howard de Walden MS.)

I Coniour hem in the name of the ffader, and sone, and
　　holy gost;　　　　　　　　　　　　　　[f. 170ʳ]
in hem ys vertu al-ther-most! ✠
In the bygynnyng & in the endyng,
And in the vertu of Al thyng　　　　　　　　4
ys, & was, & euer schal be—
In the vertu of the holy trinite—
By the vertu of euery masse,
that euer was seyde, more & lasse—　　　　　8
In the vertu of erbe, gras, ston, & tre—
And in the vertu that euer may be:
yf here come eny fon
me to robbe, other me to sclon;　　　　　　12

No. 61.　3 to *inserted above the line.*
No. 62.　12 MS. me to to robbe; sch *struck through before* sclon.

they stond as stylle as eny ston,
they haue no powere away to gon,
By the vertu of the holy trinite,
Tylle they haue lyve of me.    16
lord iesu, Graunte me þys,
as ȝe ben in heuen blys.


63.    *A Charm Against Thieves*

MS. Ashmole 1378
(Sum. Cat. No. 7798)

TO the holy goste my goodes I bequeth  [p. 77]
    that in this place be set,
To the father & the sone
    all theves for to lett.    4
And if any theves hyther come
    my goodes away to fett,
The holy goste be them before
    and make them for to let;    8
And make them to abyde
    tyll I agayne come;
Thorough þe vertu of the holy gost,
    the father, and the sonne.    12
Now I go my way—tyde what may betyd!
if any theves hyther come here I shall abyde.
I bynd yow theves
& do yow coniure,    16
So St. bartylmew bownd the Devyll
With his bearde so hoare . . .

16 coniure MS. *faded.*

## 64.        *A Charm for Travellers*

MS. Ashmole 1378
(Sum. Cat. No. 7798)

HEre I ame and fourthe I mouste,        [p. 60]
   & in Iesus Criste is all my trust.
no wicked thing do me no dare,
nother here nor Elles whare.        4
the father with me; the sonne with me;
the holly gosste, & the trienete,
be by-twyxte my gostely Enime & me.
   In the name of the father, & the sonne,        8
   And the holly goste, Amen.

             Amen.

## 65.        *A Charm Against Fever*

Sloane MS. 747

Medicina pro morbo caduco & le fevre.        [f. 57<sup>r</sup>]
In nomine patris et filii et spiritus sancti.
                Amen.

WHat manere of Ivell thou be,
   in goddes name I coungere the.
I coungere the with the holy crosse
that Iesus was done on with fors.        4
I conure the with nayles thre
that Iesus was nayled vpon the tree.
I coungere the with the crowne of thorne
that on Iesus hede was done with skorne.        8
I coungere the with the precious blode
that Iesus shewyd vpon the rode.
I coungere the with woundes fyve
that Iesus suffred be his lyve.        12

No. 64. 5 (*2nd*) me MS. the.
No. 65. *Written as prose.*

I coungere the with that holy spere
that longeus to Iesus hert can bere.
I coungere the neuer-the-less
With all the vertues of the masse,                    16
And all the holy prayers of Seynt dorathe.

In nomine patris et filii et spiritus sancti.

Amen.

## 66.   *A Charm Against the Night Goblin*

MS. Rawlinson C. 506
(Sum. Cat. No. 15353)

ffor the ny3the-mare.                          [f. 297ʳ]

Take a flynt stone þat hath an hole thorow of hys owen growyng,
& hange it ouer þe stabill dore, or ell ouer horse, and ell writhe
þis charme:

In nomine Patris &c.

SEynt Iorge, our lady kny3th.
 he walked day, he walked ny3th,
till þat he fownde þat fowle wy3th;
& whan þat he here fownde,                     4
he here bete & he here bownde,
till trewly þer here trowthe sche ply3th
þat sche sholde not come be ny3the,        [f. 297ᵛ]
With-Inne vij rode of londe space              8
þer as Seynt Ieorge i-namyd was.

St. Ieorge. St. Ieorge. St. [Ieorge.]

In nomine Patris &c.

& wryte þis in a bylle & hange it in þe hors' mane.

No. 65.  13 the *supplied*.
No. 66.  *Written as prose*.
    2 MS. noy3th.

**67.**    *Occupations of the Months*

MS. Digby 88
(Sum. Cat. No. 1689)

| | | |
|---|---|---|
| Januar | By thys fyre I warme my handys; | [f. 89ᵛ] |
| Februar | And with my spade I delfe my landys. | |
| Marche | Here I sette my thynge to sprynge; | |
| Aprile | And here I here the fowlis synge. | 4 |
| Maij | I am as lyght as byrde in bowe; | |
| Junij | And I wede my corne well I-now. | |
| Julij | With my sythe my mede I mawe; | |
| Auguste | And here I shere my corne full lowe. | 8 |
| September | With my flayll I erne my brede; | |
| October | And here I sawe my whete so rede. | |
| November | At Martynesmasse I kylle my swyne; | |
| December | And at Cristesmasse I drynke redde wyne. | 12 |

**68.**    *Days in the Months*

Harley MS. 2341

THirti dayes hath nouembir,    [f. 5ʳ]
  April, iune, and septembir;
Of xxviijᵗⁱ is but oon,
And all the remenaunt xxxᵗⁱ and j.    4

**69.**    *Months, Weeks, and Days*

Harley MS. 3362

I Wot a tre XII bowys betake,    [f. 33ʳ]
  LII nestys beþe þat vp ymad;
In euery nest beþ bryddys VII.
I-thankyd be þe God of heuene    4
And euery bryd wyth selcouth name.

70.                *To Find Easter*

Cambridge Univ. MS. Ff. 6. 8

I N merche, after þe fyrst C,                [f. 3ᵛ]
  Loke the prime wher-euer he be ;
The 3ᵈ sonday, full I-wysse,
Ester day trewly yt ys.                        4
& yf þe prime on þe sonday be,
rekyne þat sonday for one of þe thre.


71.    *St. Paul's Day Prognostications*

Dunrobin MS.

G Iff sanct Paullis day be fair and cleir,
  Than sal be-tyd ane happie yeir.
Gif it chances to snaw or rane,
Than sal be deir all kynde of grayne.          4
and giff þe wind be hie on loft,
Than weir sall vex þe kingdome oft.
and gif þe cloudis mak darke þe skye,
Boith nowte and foull that yeir sall dye.      8


72.    *Christmas Day Prognostications*

MS. Digby 88
(Sum. Cat. No. 1689)

N Ow hathe ye harde, bothe olde & yonge,    [f. 75ʳ]
  Discriuede many a dyuers thyng—
Off dremyng, off chaffarynge, of childres byrthe,
Off lettyng blode, off weddyng, & of other myrthe,   4
And off other thyngges þat ben to done
By the Rule of the moone,
And by oure forme-fadres witnes.
But I warne you, bothe more & les,            8

No. 71.   2 MS. salbe ty[d].      3 rane MS. *faded*.
          4 MS. salbe.            6 kingdome ? MS. *faded*.

þat ye be never the more bolde
For no thyng that I haue tolde
þat to done morow or eve,
But who so shall any thyng leve,                12
As I haue you made of mynde,
Bettir profyt may no man fynde
þat þis þing ys trewe Anowȝe
þat I haue of spokyne to you.                   16

But listenythe nowe, & ye shall here      Nota: of cristes-
A talkynge of the same mater                ·    messe day
That ys proved trewe by cristes byrthe;
Yf ye wyll here, ye mowne haue myrthe;          20
For you shull here dyuers maters
Wher-by you shall knowne All yerres
Fro hennis vn-to domes day:
Whiche shall be gude & harde, perfay,           24
And whiche shall be mervelous,
And whiche ben esy & plentyuous.              [f. 75ᵛ]
In thys mater ys no fable,
I shall you shewe by scylle stable,             28
By recorde of swete iesu,
And by many other vertue.
Nowe listenethe All to me;
Of thys mater here shull ye,                    32
Lordynges, I warne you be-forne.

Yf þe day that cryste on was borne
Fall vpon A Sonday,
That wynter shall be gude Ay,                   36
But grete wyndes on lofte shall be;
The somer shall be faire & drye,
Shepe & bene shull multeplie,
But other vitalles shall hastely dye            40

40 MS. drye.

Be kynde skyll, withoutyn les.
Thorowe-owte all londes shall be pease,
In gude tyme All thyng to done.
But who-so stele ou3t he shall be take soone;     44
And what childe so that day borne be
A grete lorde bene shall hee.

Yf Cristemas day on A munday be,
Grete wynter þat yere ye shull see;     48
And full off wyndes lowde & felle,
But þe somer, truly to tell,
Shull be sterne wyndes also,
And full of tempeste þer-to;     52
All vitaile shull multeplye,
But grete plente of bestes shall dye.
þat bene borne þat day, I wene,
Shull be stronge Ilkon & kene.     56
He shall be take who-so stele ou3t.
But þou3 þou be seke, þou dyeste nou3t.

Yf Cristemas day on a tuesday bee,     [f. 76ʳ]
þat yere shull dye women grete plente;     60
And the wynter shall yeve grete mervell;
Shepe shall die, A grete peraille.
That yere shall lordys & kynggis be slane,
In londe of were grete wone certeyn.     64
A dry somer that yere shall be.
All þat be borne þat day in fe
þei shall be stronge & covetous,
But thier Ende shall be dowtevous.     68
Yf þou stell ou3t, þou lesythe thy lyffe;
þou shalt dye thorow swerde or knyffe.
But þou3 þou fall seke, certeyn
þou shalt turne to lyf Agayne.     72

49 stylle *struck out after* lowde &.     59 fall *struck out after*
tuesday.     69 þou lesythe MS. yt lesythe.

Iff Cristemas day, for-sothe to say,
ffall vppon A Weddynysday,
That yere shall be harde wynter & stronge,
And many hedous wyndes Emonge;                    76
The somer gude & mery shull be.
That yere shall be whete plente.
Yinge folke shall dye also;
And shyppys on the see haue grete woo.            80
What childe so that day borne ys,
He shall be dowghty, ly3t, & wysse,
And wisse & sly Also off dede,
And fynde many on mette, At wede.                 84

If Cristemas day on A Thursday be,
A wonder wynter ye shull see;
Of weyndes & of weddres wyke,
& harde tempeste stronge & thyke;                 88
The somer shall be gude & dry;
Cornes & bestes shull multeplie.
That yere ys gude londe to tyll;        [f. 76ᵛ]
But kynges & princes shall dye by skyll.          92
What children so that day borne bene,
They shall hape well to theyn,
Of dedes þei shall be gude & stable,
Of speche wyse & of tonge Resonable.              96
Who-so that day be thefte A-bowte
He shall be shente withoute doute,
But þou3 seknes þat day be-fell,
Yt shall not longe with ye dwell.                 100

Iffe Cristemas day on A fryday be,
The fyrste of wynter harde se shall ye,
With froste, & snowe, & with flode;
But þe latter ende of wynter ys gude.             104

96 MS. Renable.

þe somer ys gude & faire also.
Folke of þar eeyn shall han grete woo.
Wemmen with children, bestes, & corne
Shull multeplye & non be lorne.                    108
The children that be borne þat day
Shall longe lyve & be licherous ay.
Who-so stele ouȝt he shall be founde;
þouȝ þou be seke, yt lastythe no stounde.          112

If Cristemas day on A Setterday fall,
That wynter we mowen drede All.
Yt shall be so full of tempeste
þat yt shall sley bothe man & beste;               116
ffruttes & cornes shall faile grete wone;
And olde folke dye many oon.
What woman that day of childe travaille,
They shall bothe be in gret peraile.               120

Amen.

Explicit &c.

73.  *The Lucky and Unlucky Days*

Bodleian MS. Add. A. 106
(Sum. Cat. No. 29003)

MAysters, þat war of craftes sers,        [f. 192ᵛ]
Numbers dayes, monethes, & ȝers.
þat is to wete in a twylmouth
Twa & twynty dayes er sel-couth,                     4
þat nedfull is to mannes lyfe;
And also er dayes fyfe,
And whoso in any of þer dayes
In any sekenes down hym lyes—                        8
Masters says, þat war full wys,
Of hys seknes schuld he neuer ryse.

And whoso in þer days er born
Sone hys lyf sall be for-lorn ;                           12
And he þat takys a lang way,
He sall neuer com agayn I say ;
And whoso sall a wyf wed,
þar sall son be stryfe in bed,                           16
Or els to part in twayn,
Or sorow led þar lyfe in.
He þat takes an erand strang
He sall noght maynten it full lang ;                     20
And bot gret grace god hym send,
He sall neuer mak gud hend.
Ianuer is þe fyrst mone,
þat fallys in þe circumsicon ;                           24
Seuen dayes er noght lythe :
þe fyrst, þe secund, þe forth, þe fyft,
The tente, þe fyftende, er full kyn ;      [f. 193ʳ]
And also er þe nentende.                                 28
And also in feuerȝere,
Thre dayes er fers & fere :
The fyrst, þe seuentend, be letter,
And þe eghtende is no better.                            32
Also fowre dayes er in may,
þat gers men syng of 'walaway' :
The seuend, þe tente, & þe seuentend,
And þe eghtend is full kyn.                              36
In Iuin is noght bot ane,
þat is þe seuend—hym alayn.
And also twa er in Iuly :
The fyftend & þe twynty.                                 40
Also in august er twa :
The nentende & þe twynty.

19 MS. a nerand.                    34 MS. gres.
41 aust *crossed out after* in.

Also two er in september:
The fyftend, þe seuentend er not tender.       44
Also þe fyrst day of october
Is full fell & nothyng sober.
Also in nouember er thre weterly:
The fyftend, þe seuen, & þe twynty.       48
In december er thre I wèn:
The sext, þe seuent, & þe fyftend.
Ilka man in þer dayes forsake
To lat hym blod, or medecyn take.       52
It is to bestes full houly,       [f. 193ᵛ]
And þer dayes namly:
The last day of aueryll
þat is both stowt & gryll;       56
The fyrst day of august is not tender;
And þe last day of december.
And who-so in þes dayes ettes fleche
Of gos, other mare or lesse,       60
The master says—I make no ly—
Wyth-in fortty dayes he sall dy.
Who-so in marche þe seuenet day,
Or þe eleuent, saneȝ delay,       64
Lattes hym blod if þat he myght,
He sall neuer lose hys syght.
And he þat in þe hend of may—
The fyrst or þe fyft day—       68
Of both hys armys lattes hym blod
He sall neuer haf þe feuer wode,
Yf he do it in goddes pety;
ffor it is proued be profecy—       72
Bede says, þat was clark cler.
þer is thre dayes in þe ȝere,

64 MS. sameȝ.

In þe qwylk for nakyn case of ned
Lyket noght to man no best to bled,                76
Ne tak any potacyon
þat is of drynkes confecon.                    [f. 194ʳ]
The last day of all aprell—
þat many a man lykes well;                      80
The fyrst day of august—
þat lettes many fro þe lust;
The last day of december beand
Passes many a man fro þer land:                84
þes er thre days for to ken
Wyth all ȝowr besenes full eueyn.
In þer thre dayes þat er ser,
Watte man or women of þe ȝer               88
Er born, so says þe prophecy,
Thurght euyle ded þai sall dy.


74.    *Instructions for Purchasing Land*

MS. Douce 54
(Sum. Cat. No. 21628)

Who-so wil be wise in purchasing,       [f. 64ʳ]
   consyder þe poyntes þat ben following:
fyrst that the land be clere
in the tytell of the seller;                     4
And that it stand in no daynger
of no womans dower.
Se whether yt be bond or free,
and se the Relese of euery fefee;           8
Se that þe seller be of age,
& yf the land be not in morgage.
Lok if any tayle may be found,
or yf yt stand in statute bounde;          12

No. 73. 88 *þe in MS. written* ȝe ; *þ otherwise always written here as* y.

And consyder the servyce þat longeth therto,
& what quyt-Rent there-owt must goo;
And yf it meve of a wedded woman,
thynke on couerd-barine then.                          16
And if þou maye in any wysse,
mak þi charter with warrantyse
To thyne heyres & assygners also,
thus shall a wysse pvrchaser doo.                      20
& in xiiij yeare, yf thow wysse are,
þou shalle agayne thy money see.

finis.

75.                   *Teeth, Bones, and Veins*

MS. Rawlinson poet. 32
(Sum. Cat. No. 14526)

XXXII teth that beþe full kene,          [f. 205ʳ]
CC bonys and Nyntene,
CCC vaynys syxty and fyve,
Euery man haþe that is alyve.                          4

76.                   *The Complexions, I*

Lambeth Palace MS. 523

ffleumaticus:                                 [f. 85ᵛ]

S Luggy & slowe, in spetynge muiche,
  Cold & moyst, my natur ys suche;
Dull of wit, & fatt, of contnaunc strange,
fflewmatyke, þis complecion may not change.          4

No. 74.  22  MS. shalbe.
No. 76.  4  MS. complcion.

Sanguineus:

Delyberall Y am, lowynge and gladde,
laghynge & playynge, full seld y am sad;
Syngynge, full fayr of collour, bold to fyght,
hote & moyst, benynge, sanguine y hyght.          8

Colericus:

I am sad & soleynge with hewynes in thoght;
I cowet ryght muiche, leue wyll y noght;
ffraudulent & suttyll, full cold & dry,
Yollowe of collour, colloryke am y.               12

Malencolicus:

Ynvyws, dysseuabyll, my sckyn ys roghe;
owtrage in exspence, hardy y-noghe;
suttyll & sklendyr, hote and dry,
Of collour pale, my nam ys malencolly.            16


77.            *The Complexions, II*

Harley MS. 2251

Sanguineus:                                    [f. 79ʳ]

O Ff yiftes large, in love hath grete delite,
      Iocunde and gladde, ay of laughyng chiere,
Of ruddy colour meynt somdel with white;
      Disposed by kynde to be a champioun,       4
      Hardy I-nough, manly, and bold of chiere.
          Of the sangwyne also it is a signe,
          To be demure, rigth curteys, and benynge.

Colericus:

The Coleryk: froward and of disceyte,            8
      Irous in hert, prodigal in expence,
Hardy also, and worchith ay by sleyght.
      Sklendre and smalle, ful light in existence,

No. 77. 7 MS. rigthet.

Right drye of nature for the grete fervence     12
Of heete; and the coleryk hath this signe,
He is comunely of colour cytryne.

fflevmaticus:     [f. 79ᵛ]

The fflewmatyk is sompnelent and slowe,
With humours grosse, replete, ay habundaunt,     16
To spitte Invenons the flewmatik is knowe,
By dulle conceyte and voyde, vnsufficiaunt
The sutill art to complice or haunt;
ffatt of kynde, the flewmous, men may trace,     20
And know hym best by whitnes of his face.

Malencolicus:

The Malencolius thus men espye:
He is thought and sette in covetise,
Replenysshith full of fretyng envye;     24
His hert servith hym to spende in no wise,
Trayterous frawde full wele can he devise;
Coward of kynde whan he shuld be a man,
Thow shalt hym knowe by visage pale and wan.28


*78.*     *Lydgate's Dietary*

MS. Rawlinson C. 86
(Sum. Cat. No. 11951)

FFor helth of body, couere for colde þyn hede;     [f. 61ʳ]
Ete no rawe mete, take good hede þerto,
Drynke holsom wyne, fede þe on lyghte brede,
With an apitite rise from þy mete also;     4
With women agid, flesshely haue not A-doo;
Vppon þy slepe, drynke not of þe cuppe;
Gladde toward bedde and at morwe boþe to;
And Vse neuer late for to suppe.     8

And yf so be þat leches do þe fayle,
  Thanne take good hede to Vse þynges thre—
Temperat dyet, temperat traveyle;
  Not malincolius for non aduersite,        12
  Meke in troubill, glad in pouerte,
    Ryche with litell, content with suffisaunce,
  Neuer grucchyng, but mery lyke þy degre;
    Yf physike lakke, make þis þy gouernaunce.    16


To euery tale, sonn, gyff not credence;
  Be not hasty nor sodenly vengeabill,
To poure folke do no violence,
  Curteys of langage; of fedyng mesurabyll,    20
  On sondry metis not gredy at þe tabill,
    In feding gentill; prudent in daliaunce;
  Close of tunge, of worde not deceyuabill,
    To sey þe best sette al-wey þy plesaunce.    24


Haue in hate mowthes þat ben doubill,
  Suffir at þy tabill neuer detraccioun,
Haue despite of folke þat ben trouble,    [f. 61ᵛ]
  Of fals rowners and adulacioun;    28
  Within þy court suffir no devisioun,
    Whych in þyn houshold shulde cause gret excesse;
  Of all welfare, prosperite, and fusoun,
    With þy neyghbours lyve in reste and pease.    32


Be clenly clad aftyr thyne estate;
  Passe not þy bondys, kepe þy promisse blyve;
With thre folkes be not at debate—
  ffirst with thy bettir beware for to strive,    36

A-geyne þy felawe no quarell do contive,
  With þy soget to striue it were shame;
Wherfor I counsell pursue all þy lyve
  To lyve in pease and gete þe A good name.          40


ffyre at morwe and toward bedde at euen,
  A-geyne mystys blake and eyre of pestelens;
Be-tyme at masse, þou shalt þe better cheve;
  ffirste at þy rysing do to god reuerence;          44
Visite þe pore with intere diligence,
  On all nedy haue compassioun,
And god shall send grace and influence
  The to encrese and þy possesioun.          48


Suffir no surfetis in þyn house at nyght,
  Ware of rere-soupers and of gret excesse,
Of noddyng hedis and of candel lyght,
  Of slougth on morow and slombryng ydelnesse,          52
Whyche of all vices is chef portresse;
  Woyde all dronkelawe, lyers, and lechours;   [f. 62ʳ]
Of all Vnthryfty exile þe mastresse,
  That is to sey, dyse pleyers and hasardours.          56


Aftir mete be-ware make no long slepe;
  Hede, fote, and stomake preserue aye from colde;
Be not to pensife, of thowth take no kepe,
  Aftir þyn Rente mayntayne þyn housholde;          60
Suffir in tyme, in þy Ryght be bolde,
  Swere no othyes no man to begyle,
In youthe be lusty, sad whanne þou art olde—
  No worldely Ioye laste but A whyle.          64

52 Of slougth MS. On slougth.
56 MS. hasadours.

Dyne not at morow Afore þyn appetyte—
  Clere ayre & walkyng maketh good digestioun;
Betwene mealys drynke not for no froward delyte,
  But thurste or traveyle geve þe occasioun;        68
  Ouer-salte metys do gret oppressioun
    To febill stomakys whanne þey cannot refrayn
ffro þynges contrarie to her complexioun;
    Of gredy handis þe stomake hath grete payn.     72

Thus in two þinges standith all þe welth
  Of soule and of body, whoso hem sue,
Moderat fode gevyth to man his helth,
  And all surfetys doth from him remewe;            76
  And charite to þe soule is due,
    This resceyte bought is at no poticarye,
Of master Antony nor of master hewe,
    To all indifferent þe rycheste dietarye.        80

                    ffinis.


79.     *Doctrines of Temperate Diet*

              Huntington MS. HU 1051
            (*olim* Ashby-de-la-Zouche MS.)

**P**Hebus fonde first the craft of medecine      [f. 49ᵛ]
    By touche of poues & vryne Inspections.
Esculapius taght the doctryne
    To know the qualities of the iiij compliccions,  4
    Of electuaries, drages, & pociouns.
      Among all other ther is no-thyng mor mete
      To the help of man then temperat diete.

        No. 78. 67 dy *struck out before* drynke.
               71 MS. ffor.
               76 MS. remeve.

## *80. On the Medicinal Properties of Leeks*

Huntington MS. HU 1051
(*olim* Ashby-de-la-Zouche MS.)

IUce of lekes with gotes galle     [f. 85ʳ]
For evyl herynge help it shalle.
Too partes of the Iuce, the third of galle,
Mellyd smal, and warme with-alle.     4
In noise or eyr where it be do,
For grete hedewark wel it slo ;
Brokyn bonys wil it knyt,
And angrey sorys wille it flyt.     8
Lekes & salt same done,
Helpys a woman to clooe son.
It is gud for dronkyn men
A raw lek to ete, & comfortyth the brayn.     12

## *81.*    *Directions for Bloodletting*

MS. Arch. Selden supra 73
(Sum. Cat. No. 3461)

MAistres! ye that vsen blode-lettynge,     [f. 25ʳ]
And therby geten youre lyuynge ;
Here May ye lerne wysdome goode,
What plase that ye shall letten blode     4
In man and in childe,
ffor euelles that ben wyked & wyld.
Veynes þer ben thirty and ij
ffor euelles many moste be vndo ;     8
Sextene in the hede full Riȝtt,
And sextene be-nethe, as I yowe pliȝt.

No. 80. 1 mylk *struck through after* gotes.
    6 MS. hedewarb.
    12 *After* ete *the abbreviation for* com *crossed out.*

In what place þei shall be founde
I shall yowe tell at this stounde.                    12
Be-side the Ere there ben ij
That on A childe mote be vndo
To kepe his hede fro euell-turnynge,
And fro scall withouten lesynge.                      16
ij at the temples ther most blede
ffor Stoppynge and Akynge, I Rede;
and i is in the myd forehed                    [f. 25ᵛ]
ffor lepre and sausfleme þat moste blede.             20
Aboue the nose forsoth is i
ffor fransy most ben vndone.
ij ther ben at the eyen ende
Yf þou be blered, hem to Amende,                      24
And for web þat comyth þorowe smokynge.
I yowe tell, no maner lesynge,
At the hole of the þrote ther ben ij
That lepre and strayte breth will vndo.               28
In the lippes foure þer ben
Goode to blede, I tell the:
ij be-nethe, above also,
As I the tell þer ben so,                             32
ffor sorowes of the mouth to blede,
And whan hit is flayne, as I Rede;
ij vndir the tonge, with-ovten lye,
Must bledyne for the Sqynsye,                         36
And whan the tonge is ought akynge,
And for euery maner Swellynge.
Nowe I haue tolde of the Sextene
That longen for the hed, as I wene.                   40
Of as many nowe I will Saye
That elles-where ben in faye.

24  MS. Amen.
34  MS. hit flayne.

In euery Arme ther ben fyf
fful goode to bleden for man and wyfe.　　44
Cephalica is i, I-wys,
The hed-veyne cleped he is;
The body abouen and the hed
He clensith well from euery qued.　　48
In the byhte of the Arme Also
A-noþer is mote ben vndo:
Basilica his name is,
Lowist he sittith þer, I-wys;　　52
fforthe he clensythe the lyuer A-Ryȝtt,
And al odir membres benethe as tyȝtt.
The myd be-tuyx þe [veynes] ij　　[f. 26ʳ]
The Corall he is cleped so,　　56
That veyne clensith withouten doute
Abouen, be-nethen, within and with-oute.
ffro basilica, as I of told,
A Branched veyne goth full bolde;　　60
To the thombe gothe that branche—
The Cardiacle hit will staunch.
The toþer bravnch full Ryȝt he goth
To the littill fynger, with-outen othe—　　64
Salue stella is his name;
He is A vayne of nobill fame;
Ther is no veyne þat clensith so clene
Stoppynge of lyuer and of Splene.　　68
Aboue the knokelles on the fete
With ij veynes there þou may mete:
Within sittith domestica,
And withouten Siluatica.　　72
Domestica clensith well
The bleddir within euery dell.

43 fyf MS. v.
53 MS. clesythe.

Siluatica, withouten doȝte,
He clensith well frome the govte.                    76
In the hammes A woman shall blede
ffor stoppynge of her flawres at nede.
A man shall bleden þer also
The emeraudes to for-do.                            80
The veynes yf þou vse, I saye,
The quarteyne þou may voyde Awaye.
All þe veynes I haue nowe tolde
That clensen men, both yonge & olde.                84
Yf þou þis vse at þi nede,
ffor evell þou dar not drede;
So þat þe lord be helpyng,
That all thyng hath in gouernynge.                  88
So mote hit be, sey nowe we,
Amen, Amen, for charite!


## 82.                *Number Maxims, I*

Magdalene Coll. Cambridge
Pepys MS. 1236

IN 8 is alle my loue                     [f. 128ʳ]
  & 9 be y-sette byfore
So 8 be y-closyd aboue          } IHC
Thane 3 is good therefore
                                                     4


## 83.                *Number Maxims, II*

Cambridge Univ. MS. Ee. 4. 37

KEpe well x And flee fro vii;            [f. 113ᵛ]
  Rule well v And come to hevyn.

No. 81. 86 dar *supplied (from Loscombe* MS.).
87–90 *Written as two long lines.*

84.  *Peace to Peace*

Cambridge Univ. MS. Ff. 1. 6

PEes maketh plente.      [f. 53ᵛ]
Plente maketh pryde.
Pryde maketh plee.
Plee maketh pouert.      4
Pouert makethe pees.

85.  *Youth and Honour*

Cambridge Univ. MS. Gg. 2. 8

HE that in yowthe no vertu wyll yowes, [flyleaf]
in aege all honor shall hym refuse.

86.  *On Nought*

Corpus Christi Coll. Oxford MS. 237

HE that spendes myche & getes nothing, [f. 1ʳ]
And owthe myche & hathe nothing,
And lokes in his porse & fyndes nothing,
he may be sorye and saie nothing.      4

Quothe K. L.

87.  *Silver and Friend*

Harley MS. 116

I had my  ⎫         ⎧ and my ⎫            [f. 170ᵛ]
I lent my  ⎬  good  ⎨  To my  ⎬ ffrend.
I askyd my ⎪         ⎪  Of my  ⎪
I lost my  ⎭         ⎩ and my ⎭            4

I made of my ffrend my ffoo:
I will be war I do no more soo.

88.        *The Philosophers' Stone*

Corpus Christi Coll. Oxford MS. 226

Pro lapide philosophorum                    [f. 57<sup>r</sup> col. i]

TAke of spayne clere light,
    Off the red gumme that is so bright,
Off the philesophir sulphur vif,
Golde I-callid with-out strif;                    4
Off thes draw out thy tyngture,
And make a matremoyne pure
Betwis the husband & his wif
I-spowsid with the spirit of lif.                    8
And that no diuisioun
Be yn the coniunccioun
Off the mone & of the sonne,
Affter the mariage be begonne,                    12
Mak of hem water clere rennyng
As cristalstone, bright, shynyng;
I-draw out of a body fyxt,
By nature priuely mixt.                    16
Of the fier the quantite
As egal phebus the bemys be,
In the monyth of Iun or Iull;
Vnderstonde & be not dul,                    20
And thou shalt see meruaillis grete—
Of collours that springyn out yn the hete,
Summe blak & sum blew & also red,
And after citrine with-out dreed;                    24
So that with-Inne houres thre
The stone perseyued shal be
Thourgh the collours that on hem light—
The whiche is a wondir sight!                    28
ffor whan the spirite is so refraynyd
And with his body so constraynyd

That noon may hym fro oþer parte,
So fore nature doth hem coarte.                      32
ffor affter thei be yn mariage knyt,
Loke neuer thi vesel by vndit
Til thei be engendrid in-to a ston,
That In the world is suche noon ;                    36
ffor he is callid rial—
Riccher then the mineral
The whiche is founde yn euery place—
Who therto myght haue grace—                         40
In the & me & ouer-al
Vegitable & bestial,
ffor on hie hilles & valeys lowe
He growith, who-so kuothe hym knowe.                 44
ffor fischis yn the depe see,
and briddis that yn the aer do fle,
By moistour of the red grape          [col. ii]
And of the white, who cowthe it take,                48
Bestis that ben sensatif,
And herb that ben vegitatif—
All these bryngyn to thi hous.
This ryche Ruby precious                             52
And the soueraygnte of this werk,
Bothe to lewid & to clerk
Lith yn good discrescioun
Off thi fier & thi coccioun.                         56
Of hem that kan seke it out
In Ens & vbi is al the dout,
Off hem that putten hem in pres
To seke genus or species,                            60
Qualitas & other quantite,
To dulle wittis it may noght be

31 MS. may fro ouer parte.
62 MS. nogh.

To brynge about at my devis
This riche Rubie, so gret of pris,                    64
hard & hevy & persyng.
Who knew euer so wonder a thyng?
I kuwthe neuer suche oon aspie
Til I fond how marie                                  68
That sister was to moyses,
She it first fond, with-out les.
ffor who it be that wil it werke,
loke he begyn noght yn the derke;                     72
ffor he may fayle for faut of light,
Al if he haue candil bright.
Avis were good or he begyne,
Or ell he shal but litil wynne.                       76

Explicit lapis philosophorum.

# III. OCCASIONAL VERSE

### 89. *A Book Plate, I*

#### Royal MS. 18. A. xvii

HE þat stelys this booke       [f. 199ʳ]
  shulbe hanged on a crooke;
He that this booke stelle wolde
sone be his herte colde:                   **4**
That it mow so be
seiþ amen, for cherite.

    Qui scripsit carmen Pookefart est sibi nomen
    Miller jingatur qui scripsit sic nominatur.

### 90. *A Book Plate, II*

#### St. John's Coll. Oxford MS. 76
#### Iesu.

THys boke ys on,            [f. 5ᵛ]
    crystys curs ys Anodyr;
he that sstellyth the ton,
    I pray good send hym þe todyr.       **4**

    quod Iohannes wryghtson.

### 91. *A Book Plate, III*

#### Cambridge Univ. MS. Kk. 6. 18

GOodman, fool, ass, lovte—     [cover]
  That tearest a Book with-out dovbte
That dooth displease thee,
By the wyse amendid mai bee;           **4**
But be it the argument is bad,
Keape it for a wittness to be had!

No. 89. *Written in long lines.*     No. 90. *Written in long lines.*

92.     *William Barbour's Book Plate*

Cambridge Univ. MS. Ii. 6. 4

WHo-so-euer thys booke fynde,          [f. 2ʳ]
     I pray hym haue thys in hys mynde
ffor hys loue that dyed on tre:
saue thys book and bryng yt to me.          4

Wylliam Barbor off new Bokenham.

93.     *Lady Scrope's Book Plate*

Clare Coll. Cambridge MS. 5
Ihesus est amor meus.          [f. 147ʳ]

HO that lust for to loke,
     or for to rede on this boke—
Be he of cyte, toun, or thrope,
Pray he for my lady scrope;          4
And thinke ȝe neuir to done amys,
But þenke on hym that gaf ȝow this;
For ihesu loue haue hym in mynde,
that this sette on ȝowre boke be-hynde.          8

94.     *Verses on a Chained Horae*

Hodsock Priory, Mellish MS.

THis present book legeble in scripture,          [f. 8ᵛ]
     Here in this place thus tacched with a cheyn,
Purposed of entent for to endure,
     And here perpetuelli stylle to remeyne          4
     Fro eyre to eyre; wherfore appone peyn

No. 94. *Lines alternately written in blue, red, and black.*

Of cryst-is curs, of faders and of moderes,
Non of hem hens attempt it to dereyne,
   Whille ani leef may goodeli hange with oder.   8

But for-as-moche that noo thyng may endure
That urthely ys, alwey, y trowe, certeyn ;
When-so-euer thys book here-aftyr in scripture
   Eyder in koueryng begynneth fause ayeyn,   12
All tho therto that diligence doth or peyn
   Hit to reforme, be they on or other,
Haue they the pardon that criste yafe magdaleyn,
   With daili blessyng of fader and of moder.   16

Gret reson wolde that euery creatur,
   Meued of corage on hit to rede or seyn,
Shuld hym remembre in prayer that so sure
   Bothe preeste and place and bokes lust ordeyn   20
At his gret cost, John Harpur, noght to leyn ;
   Wherfor in speciall his eires wyth all oder
Ar hyly bondon to pray the souereyn
   Lord of all lordes present hym to hys moder.   24

95.   *Presentation Verses with a Ring*

Royal MS. 17. D. vi

GOo, lytell ryng, to that ylke suehte   [f. 3ʳ]
   That hath my hert in hyr demaeyne,
And loke þou knell doune at hyr ffete
   besechyng hyr she wold not dysdayene   4
On hur smalle fyngerys the to streyne ;
   than I wyll you say boldly :
   'My masster wold that he wer I.'

No. 95.  4 MS. bescheyng.
       5 MS. steryne.

## 96.   *Presentation Verses with an Eagle*

### By John Lydgate

#### Trinity Coll. Cambridge MS. 600

Þis balade was gyven vn-to þe kyng henry þe vj and [p. 149]
to his moder, þe qweene Kateryne, sittyng at þe mete; vpon
þe yeris day, in þe Castell of hertford; made by Lede-
gate &c.

Þis hardy foole, þis bridde victoryous,
 þis staately foole mooste Imperyal,
Of his nature fiers and corageous,
 Called in scripture þe foole celestyal—    4
 þis yeeris day to youre estate ryal
  Lowly presenteþe t'encresce of your glorye,
  Honnour and knighthoode, conquest and victorye.

Þis staately bridde dooþe ful heghe soore,    8
 Percyng þe beemys of þe heghe sonne,
And of his kynde excelleþe euermoore
 In soryng vp above þe skyes donne;
 And for þis bridde haþe þe crowne wonne   12
  Above briddes alle, presenteþe to your glorye,
  Honnour of knyghthoode, conquest and victorye.

Þis foole is sacred vnto Iubyter,      [p. 150]
 þe lord of lordes in þe heghe heven,     16
Weel willing planete beholding frome so fer
 Aboue þe paleys of þe sterres seven
 Alle constillacyouns þat any man kan neven;
  þis saame foole presenteþe to youre glorye,  20
  Honnour of knighthoode, conquest and victorye.

Pp. 150, 151. *Heading across top of both pages* : Balade made to
þe kyng Henry and to þe qweene Kateryne.

þis is þe foole, as clerkis telle can,
   Which leete dovne falle in þe natiuyte
Of cryst Ihesu vn-to Octouyan         24
   þe grene Olyue of pees and vnytee,
    Whane þe heghe lord tooke oure humanytee;
      þis ryal Egle sendeþe to your glorye,
      Honnour of knighthoode, conquest and victorye. 28

þis is þe foole which Eȝechyel
   In his avysyoun saughe, ful yoore agoon;
He saughe foure beestis tournyng on a wheele,
   Amonges wheeche þis ryal brydde was oon,    32
    Called in scripture þ'evangelyst saint Iohan;
      þis yeeris day presenting to your glorye,
      Honnour of knighthoode, conquest and victorye.

A la Rygne

þis ryal bridde, moost peersande of hir sight,    .36
   Ageyne Phebus stremys moost shynyng fresshe and
      sheene,
Blencheþe neuer for al þe cleer light,
   Presenteþe also vn-to þe noble qweene
   þat sitteþe nowe here ful gracyous on to seene,    40
      þis yeris day dovne frome þat hevenly see,
      Helþe and welfare, Ioye and prosparytee.

þis foole also by tytle of hir nature,
   Of fooles alle is qweene and Emperesse,    44
fflyeþe heghest, and lengest may endure,
   Bating hir wynges with-oute werynesse
   To Iunoos Castel, in heven a gret goddesse— [p. 151]
      Sendeþe to you, pryncesse, here sitting in youre
      see,    48
   Helthe and welfare, Ioye and prosparytee.

47 MS. Iuvoos.

He sendeþe also vn-to youre hye noblesse,
  Of alle vertus fulsome haboundaunce,
ffredame, bountee, honnour, and gentylesse,          52
  Which wee þee mene by gracyous allyaunce
  To sette in pees England and ffraunce,
    To whas hyenesse dovne from þe hevenly see,
    Helthe and welfare, Ioye and prosparytee.       56


þis bridde in armys of Emperoures is borne,
  Which in þe tyme of Cesar Iulius
In Roome appering whane Cryst Iesu was borne
  Of a mayde moost clene and vertuous;              60
  Wherefore, O pryncesse, happy and gracyous,
    To you presenteþe þis egle as he dooþe flee,
    Helthe and welfare, Ioye and prosparytee.


þis foole with briddes haþe holde his parllement,   64
  Where as þe lady which is called Nature
Sate in hir see lyche a presydent,
  And alle yche oon þey dyd hir besy cure
  To sende to yowe goode happe, goode aventure,     68
    Alle youre desyres acomplisshed for to beo,
    Helth and welfare, Ioye and prosparytee.


                    L'envoye                  [p. 152]

Mooste noble prynce, which in especyal
  Excelle alle oþer, as maked is memorye,           72
þis day beo gif to youre estate ryal,
  As I sayde erst, honnour, conquest, victorye;
  Lyche as þis Egle haþe presented to your glorye,
    And to yowe pryncesse he wol also þer be,       76
    Helth and welfare, Ioye and prosparytee.

  50 *Seventh stanza* (43–9) *repeated, but struck through.*

## 97. *Presentation Verses with a New Year's Gift*

By William Dunbar
Cambridge Univ. MS. Ll. 5. 10

MY prince, in god gif þe guid grace,    [f. 2ᵛ]
  Joy, glaidnes, confort, and solace,
Play, pleasance, myrth, & mirrie cheir,
   In hansell of þis guid new ʒeir.    4

God gif to þe ane blissed chance,
And of all vertew aboundance,    [f. 3ʳ]
And grace ay for to perseveir,
   In hansell of þis guid new ʒeir.    8

God giue þe guid prosperitie,
Fair fortoun, & felicitie,
Euir-mair in earth quhill thow ar heir,
   In hansell of þis guid new ʒeir.    12

The heavinlie Lord his help þe send,
Thy realme to reull and to defend,
In peace & Iustice it to steir,
   In hansell of þis guid new ʒeir.    16

God gif þe blis quhair-euir þow bownes,
And send þe many fraunce crownes!
Hie liberall heart, & handis nocht sweir,
   In hansell of þis guid new ʒeir.    20

Quod Dumbar.

11 And *struck through before* Euir, *inserted above line.*
16 new *supplied.*

## 98.   *A Dedication for a* De Regimine Principum, *I*

By Thomas Hoccleve

Huntington MS. HM 111
(*olim* Phillipps MS. 8151)

Ce feust mys en le liure de monseigneur Iohan lors nommeȝ ore
Regent de France & Duc de Bedford.                    [f. 37ᵛ]

U N-to the rial egles excellence,
       I humble Clerc, with al hertes humblesse,
This book presente; & of your reuerence
      Byseeche I pardon and foryeuenesse,                4
      þat of myn ignorance & lewdenesse
         Nat haue I write it in so goodly wyse
      As þat me oghte vn-to your worthynesse.
      Myn yen hath custumed bysynesse                    8
         So daswed þat I may no bet souffyse.

I dreede lest þat my maistir Massy,
      þat is of fructuous intelligence,
Whan he beholdith how vnconnyngly                       12
      My book is metrid, how raw my sentence,
      How feeble eek been my colours, his prudence
         Shal sore encombrid been of my folie;
      But yit truste I þat his beneuolence               16
      Conpleyne wole myn insipience
         Secreetly, & what is mis rectifie.

Thow book, by licence of my lordes grace,
      To thee speke I and this I to thee seye:           20
I charge thee, go shewe thow thy face
      Beforn my seid Maistir, & to him preye,
      On my behalue, þat he peise and weye
         What myn entente is þat I speke in thee;        24
      For rethorik hath hid fro me the keye

Of his tresor, nat deyneth hir nobleye     [f. 38<sup>r</sup>]
Dele with noon so ignorant as me.

C'est tout.

## 99.    *A Dedication for a* De Regimine Principum, *II*

### Royal MS. 17. D. vi

MY lord, whan ye thys boke wolle ouyr redde,    [f. 2<sup>r</sup>]
   hast nowte to blyne—yt wolle yow more auayll.
god of hys merssy do hys sowlle mede
  þat vp-on hyme take the labbur and trauayll     4
on-to hys prynce to geue suche counssell,
    wyche ys to yow a uery memery,
    and vn-to al othyr lorddys how they schale hem gy.

Enprente hys worddys and al heye entent,         8
  to boddy and sowll he schall fynd et veyllabyl;
ffollow yt for he hathe trewlly mente;
  to god and to the world yt ys commendabbyll.
A counsseller to hys prynce ys wys & proffytabbyll  12
  to say the trowthe and no thyng to hyde;
  ye so to do, I pray god be your only gyde.

## 100.    *Prologue for an Apocalypse*

### Magdalene Coll. Cambridge MS. 5

WHo redes þis boke of ymagerie,     [f. 1<sup>v</sup>]
   Hit will hom counfort & make redie,
And vndirstonde hor witte to clere,
By þes beestis purtreyed here;         4

No. 99.  4 *After* þat *two letters apparently struck through.*
       9 to boddy and sowll *repeated but struck through.*
   13 MS. the the.

And ful knowyng of mykel treuth
þat now is hidde, hit is grete reuth;
What þei by-meenen in hor kynde,
Waytnas þo gloose & ȝe shal fynde          8
Hit is as keye þat wil vnloken
þo dore þat is ful faste stoken;
þis keye were gode men to fynde,
To make hom se þat now ben blynde;        12
God gif vs grace þat sight to haue,
To reule vs riȝt we may be saue.

                                    Amen.


*101.   Translator's Prologue to Trevisa*

Cambridge Univ. MS. Ii. 5. 41

A Cros was maad al of reede          [f. 10ʳ]
    In þe bigynnyng of my book,
þat is clepid 'god me spede,'
    In þe first lesson þat I took.          4

þanne I lerned a & b,
    And oþere lettris bi her names;
But alwei 'god spede me'
    þanne þouȝt me nedeful in alle games.    8

Wheþer I pleiede in feeld eiþer meedes,
    Stille eiþer wiþ vois,
I preiede to hym help in alle my dedes
    Of hym þat diede upon þe crois.          12

Now diuerse pleies in his name
    I shal lete passe forþe, & fare,
And auenture to pleie o long game;
    Also I schal spare                       16

No. 100.  8 MS. waytas.

Wodes, meedes, & feeldis,
  Place þat I haue pleiede inne;
And in his name þat al þing weldes
  þis game I shal bigynne;                    20

And preie help, councel, & reed,
  To me þat he wole sende;
And þis game reule & lede
  And brynge it to a good ende.               24

## 102. *Preface to a Medical Treatise*

MS. Douce 84
(Sum. Cat. No. 21658)

Ipocras þis bok sende to þe emperour sesar.      [f. 1ʳ]

Wite þou wel þat þis bok ys leche
  to alle þyng þat hit doyþ teche;
do also þis bok hym bit,
hit techeþ lechys al here wyt,                   4
of ech maner euyl what-so-euere it be,
so here aftur þou myȝt se
man or womman þat hauþ nature,
how þou schalt him take in cure.                 8
Now þou man tak good ȝeme
how þou schalt þi body ȝeme.

## 103. *Introduction to a Medical Tract*

Sloane MS. 2584

Man þat wole of lechecrafte here      [f. 13ʳ]
  Rede ouer þis booke & he may lere
Manye medycenys ben goode & trewe,
To leche sores boþe olde & newe;                 4

No. 101. 23 rede *struck through before* lede.
No. 102. *Written as prose.*      5 MS. mane.

Here-in ben medycyns with-outen fable
To hele al sores þat arn curable
Of swerde, of knyf, & of arwe—
Be wounde wyde or narow,                              8
Of spere, of quarel, or dager, or darte—
To make hem hole on eche parte
So þat þe seke wol don wisly
And kepe hem-self fro surfetrie.                      12
Be þe wounde neuer so deep
Ther-of þar hem take keep.
So þat þei drynke saue or antioche
Hem dar noȝt drede of non out-rage;                   16
Be þat 21 daies be come & gon
He schal ben hole boþe flesche & bon,
To ride & go in eche place
Thorw þe myȝht of godes grace.                        20
þus seith ypocras þe goode surgean,
And socrates & Galean,
þat wore ffilosophers alle þre
þat tyme þe best in any cuntre,                       24
in þis world were noon hure peere
As fer as any man myght here,
And practiseden medycyns be godus grace
To saue mannus lyf in dyuers place.                  28
Cryst þat made boþe est & west
Leue here soules haue good reste,
Euere-more in ioye to be
In heuen with god in trinite.                         32

Amen, for charite.

14 keep *supplied.*

*104.* *Envoy for a Commentary*

Advocates MS. 18. 8. 5

GOo, little book of commendacion, [f. 53ʳ]
   I pray to god that right wele must thowe spede ;
and shewe thy matier in contemplacion,
   the maner and ende howe men theym-silf shal leede  4
  By lawe to blesfulnesse, withowten drede,
    that neuer shall fyne but euermore endure,
  yeving rewarde to vertue for his mede
    after deserte of euery creature.    8


Thy matere is the lawe of goddes heste,
   the maner sheweth howe by commaundement,
hoo lust to walke in this wey, moost or leeste,
   it is the verrey path, as we haue ment    12
  by that lawe, to strecche to oure entent
    ffoorthright withouten lette, & not offende,
  by vertuus dedes while god vs lyff hath lent,
    and come to hym that gynnyng is and ende.   16


Vnto the iuges yef it may be thy grace
   to be accept, with fauoure the to rede,
Be not aferde in any other place
   t'appere with support of theyme forto speede,   20
  to all th'ynnes of cowrte, and sowe thi seede
    withynne the tylled landes of theire brestis,
  shewyng howe goddes lawe shall yeue theym mede
    In euer-lastyng blisse where that rest is.   24

105.    *Sotelties for the Coronation Banquet,*
*A.D. 1432*

London Guildhall MS. 3133

This that foloweth was the first cours atte the feste of the [f. 129ᵛ]
kynges coronacion. . . . A sotilte: Seynt Edward and seynt lowes
armed in Cote Armures, bryngyng yn betwene hem the kyng in
his Coote of armes with this scripture:

LO here two kynges, right parfite and right good,
    Holy seyntes Edwarde and seint lowes;
And see the braunche born of here blessed blode
    lyve amonge cristen, Moost souverain of pris,    4
    Heriter of the floure-de-lys;
        God graunte that he may, thrugh helpe of crist Jhesu,
    This sixt Herry to regne and be as wyse,
        And hem resemble in knyghthode and in vertue.  8

the secunde cours. . . . A sotilte: the Emperour and the [f. 130ʳ]
kyng that dede is, armed, and here mantelles of the garters;
and the kyng that nowe is knelyng before hem with this Reson:

Ageyn myscreauntz the Emperour Sigismounde
    Hath shewed his myght which is imperiall;
Syn henry the fyfte so noble a knyght was founde
    ffor cristes cause in actes marciall,    12
    Cherysshyng the Chirche, lollardes had a fall,
        To yeve ensample to kynges that succede,
    And to his braunche in speciall,
        While he dothe regne, to love god and drede.  16

the thrydde cours. . . . A sotilte: oure lady sittyng, and [f. 130ᵛ]
hyre childe in here lappe; and she holdyng in here honde a Croune;
And seint george knelyng on that oon side, And seint Denyse on
that other, presentyng the kyng knelyng to oure lady with this
Reson folowyng:

O blessed lady, cristes moder dere,
    And thou seint George that called art here knyght;
Holy seynt Denys, o martir moost entier,
    The sixt Henry here present in youre sight,    20

Shedeth of grace on hym youre hevenly light;
His tender youthe with vertu dothe avaunce,
Bore by discent and by title of right
Justely to regne in Englond and in Fraunce.      24


*106.*      *An Indigent Author*

By Thomas Hoccleve
Huntington MS. HM 111
(*olim* Phillipps MS. 8151)

FAdir in god, benigne and reuerent,      [f. 38ʳ]
My lord the Chanceller, with al humblesse
I your seruant, at your commandement,
Byseche vn-to your excellent noblesse      4
þat my patente bere may witnesse,
That myne arrerages been granted me
Right as your staf your warant wole expresse,
Byseeche I yow so my patente be.      8


I truste in yow, for euere or this han yee
Be my good lord, and now to stynte I gesse
Applied is nat your benignitee,
Specially syn my poore symplesse      12
Nat hath offendid your hy worthynesse
Wityngly, but myn herte is euere bent
To sheete at yowr good-wil in soothfastnesse—
There-in am I ful hoot & ful feruent.      16


O my lord, gracious, wys and prudent,      [f. 38ᵛ]
To me, your Clerc, beeth of your grace free,
Let see now cacche a lust and a talent
Me to haue in your fauour & cheertee;      20

No. 106.  15 MS. yow.

Thereon wayle I—I wayle on your bountee
    That to so manye han shewid gentillesse,
Let me no stepchyld been, for I am he
    That hope haue in yow confort & gladnesse.   24

C'est tout.

*107.*           *Deceit, I*

MS. Hatton 73
(Sum. Cat. No. 4119)

**D**Ysceyt disceyueth, and shal be disceyved;  [f. 122ᵛ]
    ffor by disceyt, who that is disceyvable,
Thouh his disceyt be nat out parceyved,
    To a disceyvour disceyt is retournable.       4
ffraude quyt with fraude is guerdone covenable,
    ffor who with fraude fraudulent is founde,
    To such defraudour fraude wele ay rebounde.

*108.*           *Deceit, II*

MS. Laud misc. 108
(Sum. Cat. No. 1486)

[A]Llas diceyte þat in truste ys nowe,    [f. 238ᵛ]
    [D]uble as fortune, turnyng as a balle,
[B]rotylle at assay lyke þe rotyn bowe,
    [W]ho trustith to truste ys redy for to falle.   4
    [S]uche gyle ys in trust allmost ouer-alle
    [T]hat yn poynte a man no frende fynde shalle;
        [W]herfore beware of trust, after my devise;
        [T]rust to þi-selfe and lerne to be wyse.   8

No. 106. 23 me MS. be.
No. 108. *The edge of the MS. is cut away.*

*109.* ### Deceit, III

MS. Rawlinson D. 82
(Sum. Cat. No. 12900)

WO hath þat conyng by wysdam or prudence  [f. 34ʳ]
    To know whether his frende be feynt or stable?
Ther ys no creature, I trow, þat hath þat science
  To know his ffrende—þe world ys so mutable,    4
And ffrenship ys double and varry disseyvable;
  The mowthe seythe ane, þe hert þinketh anoþer;
Allas to say, hit ys full lementable,
  Vnneth a man now may truste his owne broþer.    8

*110.* ### Punctuation Poem, I

Pembroke Coll. Cambridge MS. 307

TRvsty . seldom to their ffrendys vniust . [f. 197ᵛ]
    Gladd for to helpp . no Crysten creator
Wyllyng to greve . settyng all þeir ioy & lust
  Only in þe plesour of god . havyng no cvre    4
Who is most riche . with them þey wyl be sewer
  Wher nede is . gevyng neyther reward ne ffee
Vnresonably . Thus lyve prestys . parde

*111.* ### Punctuation Poem, II

Cambridge Univ. MS. Hh. 2. 6

NOwe the lawe is ledde by clere conscience . [f. 58ʳ]
    ffull seld . Couetise hath dominacioun .
In Euery place . Right hath residence .
  Neyther in towne ne feld . Similacion .    4
Ther is truly in euery cas . Consolacioun .
  The pore peple no tyme hase . but right .
Men may fynd day ne nyght . Adulacioun .
  Nowe reigneth treuth in euery mannys sight .    8

No. 110. *The punctuation is that of the MS.*
No. 111. *The punctuation is that of the MS.*
    6 *After* peple *the letters* ha *struck through.*

### 112. *Punctuation Poem, III*

Cambridge Univ. MS. Hh. 2. 6

IN women is rest peas and pacience .　　　[f. 58ʳ]
　No season . for-soth outht of charite .
Bothe be nyght & day . thei haue confidence .
　All wey of treasone . Owt of blame thei be .　　4
　No tyme as men say . Mutabilite .
　　They haue without nay . but stedfastnes .
In theym may ye neuer fynde y gesse . Cruelte
　　Suche condicons they haue more & lesse .　　8


### 113. *A Burlesque Prescription*

MS. Eng. poet. e. 1
(Sum. Cat. No. 29734)
A good medycyn for sor eyen.　　[f. 21ᵛ]

FOr a man þat is almost blynd:
　Lat hym go barhed all day ageyn þe wynd
　tyll þe soȝne be sette;
At evyn wrap hym in a cloke,　　　　　　4
& put hym in a hows full of smoke,
　& loke þat euery hol be well shett.


& whan hys eyen begyne to rope,
fyll hem full of brynston & sope,　　　　8
　And hyll hym well and warme;
And yf he se not by þe next mone
As well at mydnyȝt as at none
　I schal lese my ryȝt arme.　　　　　12

No. 112. *The punctuation is that of the MS.*
No. 113. 2 MS. agey.
　　10 mone *interlined above* morne *which is struck through.*

*114.* *When to Trust Women*

Balliol Coll. Oxford MS. 354

WHan netilles in wynter bere Rosis rede, [f. 250ᵛ]
   & thornys bere figges naturally,
& bromes bere appylles in euery mede,
   & lorelles bere cheris in þe croppis so hie,     4
   & okys bere dates so plentvosly,
     and lekes geve hony in þer superfluens—
     Than put in a woman your trust & confidens.

Whan whityng walk in forestes hartes for to chase,     8
   & herynges in parkys hornys boldly blowe,
& flownders more-hennes in fennes enbrace,
   & gornardes shote rolyons owt of a crosse bowe,
   & grengese Ride in huntyng þe wolf to ouer-throwe,     12
     & sperlynges Rone with speris in harnes to defence—
     Than put in a woman your trust & confidence.

Whan sparowys bild chirches & stepulles hie,
   & wrennes Cary Sakkes to the mylle,     16
& curlews cary clothes horsis for to drye,
   & semewes bryng butter to þe market to sell,
   & woddowes were wodknyffes theves to kyll,
     & griffons to goslynges don obedyence—     20
     Than put in a woman your trust & confidence.

Whan Crabbis tak wodcokes in forestes & parkes,
   & haris ben taken with swetnes of snaylis,
& Camelles with þer here tak swalowes & perchis,     24
   & myse mowe Corn with wafeyyng of þer taylis,
   Whan dukkes of þe dunghill sek þe blod of haylis,
     Whan shrewd wyffes to þer husbondes do non offens—
     Than put in a woman your trust & confidence.     28

Explicit quod Richard hill.

15 MS. chiches.

*115.*      *The Insects and the Miller*

Nat. Lib. of Wales
Peniarth MS. 356B

THe krycket & þe greshope wentyn here to fyȝght,

[p. 44]

With helme and haburyone all redy dyȝght;
The flee bare þe baner as a duȝty knyȝth,
The cherubud trumpyt with all hys myȝth.                4

Salamandraque cicada domitatum perereterunt,
Galiaque cum lorica presto se parauerunt;
Musca vexillum portabat vt miles egregius,
Scarabius buccinauit totis suis viribus.                8

The hare seyte a-pon þe hyll & chappynd here schone,
And swere by the knappes wich were þer a-pon,
That scho wowld not ryse ne gon
Tyll sche se xx howndes and a won.                12

Lepus super montem se ipsum collocauit,
Et suos sotulares laquitissinauit,
Et per laquitissos ipseque iurauit
De lustro surgere nec ire voluit                16
quousque vigenti canis vnum videret.

þe mylner sedet o-pon the hull
and all þe hennes off the town drew hym tyll;
The mylner sayd, 'schew, henne, schew!                20
I may not schake my bage for yow.'

Molendinarius super montem sedebat,
gallinarum ville ad se copia currebat;
Molendinarius inquit, 'sco, galina, sco!                24
Meum saccum pro uobis vrcillare non possum.'

1 MS. fyȝgh.    7 MS. potabat.    8 MS. bucbicinat.    10 MS.
knapp; wich MS. wᵗ.        11 MS. schow owld.        24 MS. scō

## *116.* *The Schoolboy's Wish*

Lincoln Cath. MS. 132

WEnest þu, huscher, with þi coyntyse, [f. 100ʳ]
   Iche day beten us on þis wyse,
  As þu wer lord of toun?
We had leuur scole for-sake,             4
& ilche of us an-oþur crafte take,
  þeri long to be in þi bandoun.


but wolde god þat we myth ones
cache þe at þe mulne stones,           8
  or at þe crabbe tre—
We schuld leue in þe such a probeyt
ffor þat þu hast us don & seyd,
  þat alle þi kyn suld rwe þe.         12


& þow sire robert, with his cloke,
Wold þe helpe & be þi ppoke,
  þe werre þu schust fare;
& for his prayer þe raþur we wold    16
ȝyuen hym stripes al un-colde,
  not for hym þe spare.


ffor ofte sore we abye
þe twynkelinges of his hye,        20
  þe maystur us to bete;
ffor he & þu are at asent,
Al day ȝyuen agagement
  to ȝyuen us strokes grete.       24

1 MS. husch.
10 þe *supplied*.

*117.*      Monologue of a Drunkard

MS. Rawlinson D. 913
(Sum. Cat. No. 13679)

D . . . dronken—                              [Item 1, 1]
  dronken, dronken y-dronken—
. . . dronken is tabart atte wyne.
hay . . . suster, walter, peter,                    4
  ȝe dronke al depe,
  ant ichulle eke!
stondet alle stille—
  stille, stille, stille—                        8
stondet alle stille—
  stille as any ston;
trippe a lutel wit þi fot,
  ant let þi body go!                          12

*118.*        The Blacksmiths

Arundel MS. 292

SWarte smekyd smeþes, smateryd wyth smoke,  [f. 71ᵛ]
  dryue me to deth wyth den of here dyntes!
Swech noys on nyghtes ne herd men neuer:
What knauene cry, & clateryng of knockes!              4
þe cammede kongons cryen after 'col, col!'
& blowen here bellewys þat al here brayn brestes.
'huf, puf!' seyth þat on. 'haf, paf!' þat oþer.
þei spyttyn & spraulyn & spellyn many spelles,        8
þei gnauen & gnacchen, þei gronys togydere,
and holdyn hem hote wyth here hard hamers.
of a bole hyde ben here barm-fellys,
here schankes ben schakeled for þe fere-flunderys;   12

No. 117. 5 MS. þe.
No. 118. *Written as prose.*

heuy hamerys þei han þat hard ben handled,
stark strokes þei stryken on a stelyd stokke.
'lus, bus! las, das!' rowtyn be rowe—
sweche dolful a dreme þe deuyl it todryue;                    16
þe mayster longith a lityl & lascheth a lesse,
twyneth hem tweyn, and towchith a treble.
'tik, tak! hic, hac! tiket, taket! tyk, tak!
lus, bus! lus, das!'—swych lyf þei ledyn!                     20
Alle cloþemerys cryst hem gyue sorwe,
may no man for brenwaterys on nyght han hys rest!


*119.*       **The Hunted Hare**

Porkington MS. 10

**B**I a forrest as I gan fare,                               [f. 81ᵛ]
    Walkyng al myselven a-lone,
I hard a mornyng of an haare,
    Rouffully schew mad here mone.                        4

Dere-worth god, how schal I leve
    And leyd my lyve in lond?
ffrov dale to doune I am I-drevfe;                            [f. 82ʳ]
    I not where I may syte or stond!                      8

I may noþer rest nor slepe
    By no wallay þat is so derne,
Nor no couert may me kepe,
    But euer I rene fro herne to herne.                   12

hontteris wyll not heyre þer mase
    In hope of hunttyng for to wend;
They cowpully3t þer howndes more & lase,
    And bryngyth theme to þe feldys ende.                 16

No. 119. 4 MS. mad he here.
       5 worth: *superior* t *over* o.

Rochis rennyn on euery syde
    In forrovs þat hoppe me to fynd;
honteris takythe þer horse and ryde,
    And cast the conttray to þe wynd.    20

Anone as þey commyth me be-hynde,
    I loke and syt ful style and love;
The furst mane þat me doth fynde
    Anon he cryit: 'so howe! so hoowe!'    24

'lo,' he sayth, 'where syttyt an haare—
    Aryse vpe, Watte, & go forth blyue!'    [f. 82ᵛ]
With sorroe and with mych care
    I schape a-way with my lyve.    28

Att wyntter in þe depe snove
    Men wyl me seche for to trace,
And by my steyppes I ame I-knowe;
    And followyȝt me fro place to place.    32

And yf I to þe toune come or torne,
    Be hit in worttes or in leyke,
Then wyl þe wyffys al-so ȝeorne
    flece me with here dogis heyke.    36

And yf I syt and crope þe kovle,
    And þe wyfe be in þe waye,
A-none schowe wyll swere, 'by cokkes sovle!
    There is an haare in my haye!'    40

Anone sche wyle clepe, 'forth, cure, knave!'
    And loke ryȝt weel wer I syte;
By-hynd sche wyl with a stave
    fful wel porpos me to hette.    44

22 MS. I loke a-lowe.    30 MS. sche.    35 MS. ȝe wyne.
39 sovle MS. *cut* sov.    41 MS. cure (?).    44 *catchword*:
Go forthe Wate.

'Go forthe, Wate, Wit crystus curse,    [f. 83ʳ]
   And yf I leve, þou schalt be take;
I have an hare-pype in my purce,
   hit schal be set al for þi sauke!'    48

Ten hath þis wyffys ij dogges grete,
   On me sche byddyt heme goe;
And as a scrowe sche wyll me þret,
   And euer sche cryit, 'go, dooge, gooe!'    52

But all way þis most I goo,
   By no banke I may a-byde;
lord god, þat me is woo!
   Many a hape hath me bytyde.    56

There is no best in þe word, I wene,
   hert, hynd, buke ne dowe,
That suffuris halfe so myche tene
   As doth þe sylly wat—go where he go.    60

ȝeyfe a genttylmane wyl have any game,
   And fynd me in forme where I syte,
ffor dred of lossynge of his name
   I wot wele he wyle not me hyte.    [f. 83ᵛ]

ffor an acuris bred he wyll me leue,
   Or he wyll let his hondes rene;
Of all þe men þat beth a-lyue
   I am most be-hold to genttyl-men!    68

As sone as I can ren to þe laye,
   A-non þe grey-hondys wyl me have;
My bowels beth I-þrowe a-waye,
   And I ame bore home on a stavfe.    72

      61 MS. gam.
      65 leue MS. *cut* le.

Als son as I am come home,
I ame I-honge hye vp-on a pyne,
With leke-worttes I am eette a-none,
And whelpes play with my skyne!                    76

120.        *A Mumming of the Seven
Philosophers*

Trinity Coll. Cambridge MS. 599
Festum Natalis Domini.                    [f. 1ʳ]

[T]Ronos celorum continens,
    whos byrthe thys day Reiterate,
Bothe god and man in exystens,
    Borne of a mayde Immaculate;                    4
Preserue your dygne and hygh estate,
    Syth ye preferre thys most hygh feste,
    In quo Redemptor natus est.

Senek the sage that kyng ys of desert,              8
    Regent and rewler of all wyldernesse,
Sendeth gretyng with all entier hert
    Vnto yow hys brother, kyng of Crystmas;
    lettyng yow wete with hertly tendyrnes          12
        What longeth now vnto youre astate royall
        That ye be now to so sodenly call.

Hyt ys perteynyng to euery prynce and kyng
    That pepyll shall haue vnder gouernaunce,       16
That he haue prudent and wyse counselyng,
    And to her counseyll geue attendaunce;
    And that your reame shall nat fall perchaunce
        Vnto Rewen for defaute of good counsell,    20
        Take hede herto, hit mayest avayle.

No. 120. 14 ye *supplied*.

ffor oute of olde feldes, as men sayth,
    Cometh all these new cornes from yere to yere;
So oute of olde expert men in feyth                    24
    Cometh all these good rules, as ye shall here;
    And by theire age they haue in thys matere
        The good rewle of verrey experience,
        Wherfore he sendeth hem to your hygh presence. 28


Attempt nothyng surmountyng your myght,     Primus
    Ne that to finissh that passeth your power;  Philosophus
ffor than ye stand foule in your owne lyght,
    And whoso doth, hymsylf shall foule a-dere      32
    With shame, and therfore thys wysdom ye lere:
        That hyt ys foly a man suche to begyn
        Which to performe hys wyttes be to thyn.


Whan that tyme ys of grete and large expence, Secundus
    Beware of waste and spende ay by mesure;
Who at suche tyme can fynde no dyfference,
    Hys goodes may nat with hym long endure;
    The olde ys that 'Mesure ys tresure',              40
        ffor in short tyme the good may slyp away
        That was gotyn in many a sondry day.


Of elther men ye shall your myrrour make,     [f. 1ᵛ]
    Conforme yow to that that may most yow auayle,  44
What ye shall do and what shall forsake;      Tercius.
    A bettyr thyng ne may ye not contryue
    Than to other mennys dedys to releue;
        To all that perteyneth yow eny thyng,          48
        Make other men rule of your leuyng.

Take good hede to youre owne estate:       Quartus.
  To rule your body with a good diete;
loke with tyme ye be nat at debate,         52
  Though thurgh youre owne mysrule and surfete
  Sekenes or sorow haue yeuyn yow an hete,
    The tyme ys good, and no dissemble there ys,
    But men hit make for they do amys.     56

To preue youre-sylf take deliberacion     Quintus.
  Be lycly coniectour what may betyde;
Aduertyse and here thys informacion
  How soone owre lord can set a state asyde;   60
  ffolowe hym, therfore, and let hym be your gyde
    That all thyng hath in hys regement,
    ffuture and past and your estate present.

Into a gret age when ye be crept,     Sextus. 64
  Hauyng gret ryches and habundaunce,
Be lyberall of the good that ye haue kept;
  Thynke that ye haue y-nough and suffisaunce;
  let nat youre good of yow haue gouernaunce,   68
    But gouerne hit and part hit with your frende;
    When ye go hens hit may nat with yow wende.

Who that lakketh rest may nat long endure;   Septimus.
  Therefore among take your ease and dysport,   72
Delyte yow neuer in besynes ne cure
  But that other whyle ye may eft resort
  To play, recreacion, and comfort;
    Ye may the better labour at the long,   76
    When ye haue myrthe your besynes among.

Lo, noble prince, ye here the counseyll     Nuncius.
  Of all the vij phylosophyrs sage,
Whyche to aduertyse hit may hap to avayle   80

55 MS. disseuable.

To let these wysdomes grow vp in your age,
And in your presence afore her passage,
   They purpose all afore yow for to syng,
   Yef to your hyghnes hit myght be plesyng.    84

            Explicit.


## *121.*   *A Dramatic Monologue by Law*

          Harley MS. 2251

THe high Astrapotent, auctor of all,      [f. 79ᵛ]
   Vnder whos clayme conciste the clymates,
Whiche from his paleys and see emperiall,
   The puissaunt prince, breker of Auremgates,    4
His owne sone, sent for werrys and debates
   Atwene hym and man al rancour to release;
   He graunt yow and yowres his precious pease.


Whiche peas oure first fadir by forfeture    8
   Enlonged from hym and his posterite,
Thurgh envye and covert couieiture
   Of the serpent, reuerser of verite;
   Vnto that tyme that divyne charite    12
   Sent embassiatours this werre shul cease
   And man restored vnto his sayde pease.


Whan the reuerent regent of reames    [f. 80ʳ]
   His peple whiche were vnder seruitute    16
Had ouer-spradde with mercyful beamys,
   The children of Israel—to thraldom Institute
   In the land of Egipte without refute—
   Moyses, thurgh goddis proteccyoun,    20
   And Aaron lad them fro this subieccioun

   No. 121. 15 *Catchwords foot of* f. 79ᵛ Whan þe reuerent.
2025.17            I

By the rede see, with divyne tuycioun—
  Scripture specifieth the circumstaunce—
Towarde the provynce of promyssioun.          24
    But now as of my matere a remembraunce
    Towchyng his lawe—I meane in substaunce:
      ffor litel they had of lawe of nature,
      Therfor nedeful it was that by scripture    28

They had of his lawe parfit instruccioun
  In voydeng the tourment of the vemous serpent,
Whiche men shuld be put to oblyvioun.
    And herfor visited hem the orient         32
    On Synai with hand most reuerent,
      Wrote expresse in tablis also doutles
      His lawe and commytted it to Moyses,

Which by theym, and goddis Informacioun,    36
  In tokene that lawe shuld synne distroye,
To Israel made playne relacioun,
    That the saide lawe, hadde in memory,
    Shuld gyde theym into eterne glory!       40
      That sych lawe so profitable is—
      Lo! here am I, lawe, of me ye may nat mys.

By me ye may atteyne Ioye celestiall,       [f. 80ᵛ]
  By me high princis rule theyr regiouns,    44
By me reigneth th'estate Emperiall,
    By me are daunted these rebelliouns;
    And shortly I chastice all transgressions
      What by spirytuel and temporal lawe,    '48
      All transgressours bene holdyn vnder awe.

## *122.* *Welcome to Prince Edward at Coventry, A.D. 1474*

### Coventry Corporation Leet Book

Memorandum: [f. 221<sup>r</sup>]
that the xxviij<sup>th</sup> day of the Moneth of Aprill cam oure lorde
prince Edward out of Walys so by Warrewik to Couentre; and
the Meire and his brethern with the diuers of Cominalte of the    d
seide Citie, clothad in Grene and Blewe, metyng oure seid
lorde Prince vpon horsbake by-yonde the Newe Crosse in a
Chare, beyng of Age of iij yere. . . . there welcomyng hym to
his Chaumbr and yevyng hym there a C mark in a gilt coppe of    h
xv ouncez, with a kerchyff of Plesaunce vpon the seid Coppe,
And then comyng in-to Citie. and at Babulake yate, there
ordeyned a stacioun, therin beyng kyng Richard with xiij
other, arrayed lyke as Dukes, Markes, Erles, Vicouns, and    l
Barons, and lordis, with mynstrallcy of the Waytes of the
Cite; and kyng Richard there havyng this speche here ffolow-
yng:

Rex Richardus:

WElcom full high and nobull prince to vs right
   speciall,
  To this your chaumbr, so called of Antiquite;
The presens of your noble person reioyseth our hartes all;
  We all mowe blesse the tyme of your Natiuite,    4
  The right lyne of the Royall blode ys now as itt
    schulde be;
    Wherfore god of his goodnes preserue you in bodily
    helth,
    To vs and your tenauntes here perpetuall ioy, and to
    all the londis Welth.

Also at the Condite a-fore Richard Braytoft the Elder, a-    p
nother stacion with iij Patriarkes there stondyng vpon the

    g *Space in the MS. after* yere.
    m MS. mystrallcy.
    3 MS. your hartes.

seide Condite, with Jacobus xij sonnes, with mynstralcy of
harpe and Dowsemeris ; & there Rennyng wyne in on place,
and there on of the seid Patriarkes havyng this speche vnder      t
writtyn :

O God, most glorious grounder and gyder of all grace,  8
 To vs iij Patriarkes thou promysed, as scripture
  maketh rehersall,
That of oure stok lynially schuld procede and passe
 A prynce of most nobull blode and kynges sonne
  Imperiall,
 The wich was full-fylled in god, and nowe referre itt we
  schall                                           12
  Vnto this nobull Prynce that is here present,
  Wich entreth to this his Chaumbr, as prynce full
  reuerent.

Also at the Brodeyate a Pagiont, and seint Edward beyng
therein with x a-states with hym, with mynstralcy of harpe
& lute ; and kyng Edward havyng this speche next foloyng :      x

NNobull prynce Edward, my Cossyn & my knyght,
 And very prynce of oure lyne com yn dissent,       16
I, seint Edward, haue pursued for your faders Imperiall
 right,                                           [f. 221ᵛ]
 wherof he was excluded by full furius Intent
 Vnto this your Chaumbr as Prince full excellent ;
  ʒe be right Welcom, thanked be crist of his sonde,  20
  ffor þat that was oures is nowe in your faders hande.

Also at the Crosse in the Croschepyng were iij prophettes
standyng at the Crosse Seynsyng, and vpon the Crosse
a-boven were Childer of Issarell syngyng and castyng out
Whete obles & ffloures and iiij Pypis rennyng wyne.            bb
Also in the Croschepyng a-fore the Pauyer a Pagent, and iij
kynges of Colen therin, with other diuers arraied, and ij
knyghtes armed with mynstralsy of small pypis, and on of
the kynges havyng this speche vnder writtyn :                  ff

 8 *After the rubric are written lines 15–16 which are struck
through.* and *struck through after* glorious.
 16 MS. comyn.

O splendent creator in all oure speculation,
   More bryghter then Phebus, excedent all ly3t,
We thre kynges beseche the with meke mediacion     24
    Specially to preserue this nobull prynce, þi knyght,
    Wich by Influens of thy grace procedeth a-right
      Of on of vs thre lynnyally we fynde,
        His Nobull Moder, quene Eli3abeth, ys comyn of þat
        kynde.        .        28

Also vpon the Condite in the Croschepyng was seint George
armed, and a kynges doughter knelyng a-fore hym with a
lambe, and the fader & the moder beyng in a toure a-boven
beholdyng seint George savyng theire doughter from the    jj
dragon; and the Condite rennyng wyne in iiij placez, and
mynstralcy of Organ pleyinge, and seint George havyng this
speche vnder writtyn:

O myghty god oure all socoure celestiall,
   With þis Royme hast geven to dowere,
To thi moder and to me George, proteccion perpetuall,
   Hit to defende from Enimies ffere & nere,       32
   And as this mayden defended was here
      Bi thy grace from this Dragon devoure,
      So lorde preserue this noble prince and euer be his
      socoure.

## *123.*    *Welcome to Henry VII at York*, A.D. *1486*

City of York, House Book VI

VII.                                             [f. 17^r]
Sevently, shalbe at the Common Hall, a Castell appeiring of
grete force, wherin Dauid, as the moost principall, shall appeir;
and he shall with wordes felowing yeld vnto the king a swerd
of his victorie. þer shalbe in that Castell, Citisyns, which after a
sight of the king and remembrance of hyme, with gude countenaunce shall appeir in clothing of white and greyne, shewing þer
trueth and hertly affection vnto the kinge.

No. 122. 23 MS. excadent.
No. 123. *rubric* MS. remembuance.

Dauid: [f. 17<sup>v</sup>]

MOst prepotent prince of power Imperiall,
  Redowtid in ich region of Cristes affiance,
Your actes victorious be notid principall,
  In maner more noble than Charlis of fraunce;   4
  Seth god so disposith of his preordinaunce,
    And right so yeue me might to devyne goodly,
    I, dauid, submitt to you my swerd of victorie.

When I reynid in Iudie I know and testify   8
  That Ebraunce the noble, which subdewid ffraunce,
In memorie of his triumph this Citie did edify,
  That the name of his noble shuld have continuance;
  I witnesh that this Citie, without variaunce,   12
    Was neuer deflorid be force ne violence,
    Wherfore I have chosyn it for my place to your presence.

Submitting it with th'afforce and trueth to your excellence,
  Beseching your highnesse, þe more for myne instance, 16
To this your inheritance tak gracious complacence,
  seth þat it is your Citie, not filid with dissavaunce;
  Treu and bold to your blode, not dreding perturbance,
    Which causid moost this Citie to be desolate,   20
    New reviving in comforth to attaine your asstate.

*124.*           *Epitaph for Rich Alan*

Harley MS. 665

Alanus caluus           [f. 295<sup>r</sup>]
iacet hic sub marmore duro;
Vtrum sit saluus,
non curauit, necque curo.

anglice:

HEre lyeth vnder þis marbyll ston,
  Riche Alane, þe ballid man;
Wheþer he be safe or noght,
I recke neuer—for he ne roght!   4

## 125. *Epitaph for the Earl of Dunbar,*
### *A.D. 1416*

B.M. Addit. MS. 37223

This is þe superscription of þe Erle of Marchis [f. 212ᵛ
toume or sepultur in his collaig of Dumbar.

HEir lyis Erle George þe brytan,
to þir iii kinges þat bair þe crowne,
wos of þair bluid & of þair kynn;
and hes gouernit þis land within            4
xlviii ʒeires spaice,
& deit þan þe ʒeir of grace

1416. Scotland, Ingland, and Denmark.


## 126. *A Tombstone Inscription*

Trinity Coll. Cambridge MS. 366

ALl ye that passe be thys holy place,     [flyleaf]
Both spirituall & temporall of euery degre,
Remembyr your-selfe well duryng tyme & space:
I was as ye are nowe; and as I, ye shalbe.     4
Wherfor I beseche you of your benygnite,
ffor the love of Ihesu & hys Mothyr Mare,
ffor my sowle to say A pater noster & An Aue.

No. 125. *Written as prose.*

# IV. COURTLY LOVE LYRICS

### *127.*     *A Catalogue of Delights*

#### Harley MS. 541

W Ith wofull hert & gret mornyng,    [f. 208ᵛ]
     In gret distresse & no lykyng,
   Mi compleynt þus I make
To that bird þat is most swete;
None but she my bales may bete,         4
     Nor my peynful sorow slake.

ffor her my hert is made al blak,
In sorow & care she doth me wrap;     8
     This is þe lyf þat I lede!
þe comlynes of her stature
Which passith reson & nature,
     Might help me only yn my nede.     12

Bothe here wisdom & womanhed,
Her gentilnes & goodlyhed,
     I wot þer nede no mending;
Her bevtey, her fayrnes—        16
Thise bryng me yn gret distresse,
     And wel ner to myn endyng.

Her heer is yelou as the gold,
Her forhed shapyn as it shuld     20
     with all þe feturs þerabout,
Her Eris ben comly & round,
Her browes with bewte bene bound;
     wel wer hym þat wynne her mouth.    24

Her lovely yen of colour gray,
Her rudy is like þe rose yn may
  with leris white as any milk,
Her Nose is set right womanly,          28
With mouth & tethe boþe so goodly,
  her lippes soft as any silk;

her chynne is round & right wel set—
No man could devise it bet,          32
  þat is yn erth lyvyng;
Of þat swettist & goodlyest Image
Thus shapyn is the visage,
  Crist geve it his der blessing!     36

Her nek is like þe holly flour
Replete with all swete odour;
  Allas, it make myn hert to breke—
Of þis swete nek if I more say,     40
Me þink my body breke yn tway,
  for sorow I may no lenger speke.

Her pappis bene godely & round,
her brest is boþe swete & sound,    44
  I know none so fair a wyght;
Her sidis ben long, her myddyl small,   [f. 209ʳ]
Her body is as gentill with-all,
  Her bak is set ful right;         48

her armes bene small, her hondes swete,
with fyngurs long with nayles mete;
  All of plesur she is wrout;
All oþer feturs of her, I-wisse,     52
Bene shapyn wel, no þyng amysse—
  so fair a wight know I nout.

Allas, my sorow now doth avaunce
ffor this garison of plesaunce,                                    56
    No mervayl I trow þat it be;
In her Erthly no faute is found;
But only daunger hath her bound
    þat she shall shaw no mercye.                    60

But þis I wat, & am full sure,
Mi sorow to her is sum plesur,
    And therof am I gladde;
And god wòlde I wold be fayn                                   64
ffor her love to suffre payn,
    ffor her no þing shuld make me sadde.

ffarwell, swet hart a thousand sithe,
ffarwell, þe fayrest þat euer was wyve,                      68
    farwel, comliest on þe ground;
ffarwel, lady, farwel, Maistres,
ffarwel, causer of myn hevynes,
    ffarwel, swettist þat euer I found.                        72

Crist þat is of hevyn kyng
you saue & kepe, my lady ying,
    And send yow evir all your wille;
Put yow yn mynde to þink on me,                              76
þat I may onys, or I dye,
    sum of your plesur to fulfille.

## (128) *The Beauty of His Mistress, I*

Cotton MS. Vespasian D. ix

O Lord of loue, here my complaynt,          [f. 189ʳ]
    And do me Ryght I the requere!
Why suffers thou me to be ataynt?
    loue in the lore, the I Requyre.                              4

No. 127.  60 MS. shaw *inserted above line.*    67 MS. a Mᴵ sithe.

Syth thou haste set me on the fyere,
  My hert to bren thou wyll not spare;
thou get me here that I desyre—
  that fygure fresch that ys so fayre.          8

So fayre she ys and also fresch,
  that all me loue ys on here set;
She is the fayreste of face and flesch,
  And here to loue y kan not let.          12
So myld a mayde neuer yet I met,
  here commely countenance caste me in care,
To that dyrlyng yt ys me deute—          [f. 189ᵛ]
  that fygure fraysch that ys so fayre.          16

Of schynyng schappes I here comand—
  here stedfast stature standes full bryght;
here cors can not all kynde amende,
  So ys she wroght, that worthe wyght.          20
when I of here may haue a syght,
  there may no payne me hert emperre;
I am all here, as yt ys Ryght—
  that fygure fresche that ys so fayre.          24

here feete, here hondys that byth full smale,
  And all that to here body longe,
of kynde the comlyste I here calle,
  full fayn wollde I, y myght here fonde.          28
But she me loue, she dose me wronge,
  And of my blyse I may by bare;
fore here y laye in paynes stronge—
  that fygure fresch that ys so fayre.          32

      *Text ends imperfectly.*
      22 MS. emperred.
      24 MS. fresched.

And when that ferly fallys in my thoght,
  full sore I sygh and say allas;
In butyr balles thus am I broght,
  And in paynes that wyll not fro me passe.    36
  In so grete wo neuer yet I was,
    And but she cewre me of me care,
  Intoloreable ys here trespasse—
    [that fygure fresch that ys so fayre.]    40


129.    *The Beauty of His Mistress, II*

MS. Rawlinson C. 813
(Sum. Cat. No. 12653)

IEsue þat ys most of myght,                    [f. 3ʳ]
  & made man aboffe all thyng,
Saue my trueloue, bothe day & nyght,
  & kepe hur well & yn good lykyng.            4

for she ys all-wey full curteysse,
  True & stydfast yn euery degree,
swete as the roose þat groeth on þe rysse,
  as true as turtyll þat syttes on a tree.     8

She ys the demurest þat I can see
  wher-as I walke by est & weste;
noo pere she hasse yn my eye,
  for off all women I loue hur beste.          12

hur lyppes ar lyke vnto cherye,
  with tethe as whyte as whalles bone,
hur browes bente as any can be,
  with eyes clere as crystall stoune.          16

hur fyngers be bothe large & longe,
  with pappes rounde as any ball,
no-thyng me-thynke on hur ys wronge,
  hur medyll ys bothe gaunte & small.          20

No. 128. 38 MS. crewe.        39 MS. In to oreable.

She hathe my harte & euer shall,
  & neuer to change hur for no newe,
butt for to loue hur terrestreall,        [f. 3ᵛ]
  & whyles I lyve to hur be true.       24

for I haue gone throughe englond on euery syde,
  brettyn, flander3, with many an oder place—
yet founde I neuer non yn the3 ways wyde
  Suche on as she ys to my purpasse.      28

wherfore I loue her with-owt lett,
  & for noo thyng I can cease;
soo feruentlye on hur my harte ys sett,
  but I dare nott putt me yn preace.      32

whoo be the whyle for my redres
  Sythen I am borne to lyve yn peyne,
& thys to be lafte all comfortles,
  To loue & be nott louyd ageyne.      36

yett throughe gouernance growethe grace,
  I haue harde men say In towne & strette,
how fortune cummethe yn-to many a place—-
  & with good fortune I trust to mete.      40

adew dere harte þat ys soo swete,
  god grante yow grace well for to doo;
I most walke forthe true loue to seke,
  In-to some place wher ytt doethe growe.      44

but on branche I wyll leve with yow:
  I pray Iesue ye may ytt well kepe,
for hereafter ye shall knowe
  wher kynde can-not goo, ytt wyll crepe.      48

wherfore as many tymes I grete yow     [t. 4ʳ]
    as clarkes can wrytte with papur & ynke,
& as monye moo as gressys grewe,
    or tonge can tell, or harte can thynke.    52

noo more I wryte to yow at thys tyme,
    butt wher-euer ye be, on lande or watter,
crystes dere blessyng & myne
    I sende yow yn grettyng of thys letter.    56
             finis.

## (130.) *The Beauty of His Mistress, III*

MS. Rawlinson C. 813
(Sum. Cat. No. 12653)

O Excelent suffereigne, most semely to see,    [f. 50ᵛ]
    bothe prudent & pure, lyke a perle of prise,
also fair of fygure & oreant of bewtye,
    bothe cumlye & gentyll, & goodly to aduertyse;    4
your brethe ys swettur then balme, suger, or lycoresse.
    I am bolde on yow, thoughe I be nott able,
    To wrytte to your goodly person whyche ys so
        ameable

                by reason.    8
      for ye be bothe fair & free,
        therto wysse & womanly,
      trew as turtyll on a tree
      with-owt any treason.    12

your fair here hengyng downe to your knee,
    with your rollyng eyes whyche ar as glasse clere,
& your strawbery lyppes as swete as honye,    [f. 51ʳ]
    with roose red yn your chekes—ye haue no pere!    16

No. 130. 14 MS. as glasse grey.

your chere ys as comfortable as blossome on brere,
   & your-selfe as swete as ys the gelyfloure,
   or any lauender sedes strawen yn a cooffer
           To smell.         20
      your necke lyke the lyllye,
        your lyppes lyke the strawberye,
      as swete as any honye
        þat cummys to sell.     24

your throte as clere as crystall stone,
   no-thyng amysse after my derectyon,
& your neke as whyte as whalles bone,
   I submytte me, fair ladye, vnder your protectyon.  28
   yf I doo yow dyspleyse, I wyll abyde your correction,
    lyke as the master yn þe scole techys the chylde,
    To doo your commandemente I wylbe meke & mylde
          and styll.        32
      for Iesus sake þat bought vs dere,
        & his moder, þat meyden clere,
      helpe to comforte my carefull chere,
        & lett me neuer spyll.    36

your loue, fair ladye, I wolde feyne wynne;
   ther ys no-thyng erthely myght mee soo well please.
wherfore I pray god, or that I be-gynne,
   that my symple wryttyng doo yow nott dyspleyse; 40
   for I am nott to blame þat I doo yow prease,
    o Rubycounde Roose, o lyllye most delycyouse,
    splendant In bewtye as a dyamond most precyouse
         In syght.      [f. 51ᵛ]
      your bryght fulgent face,
        replete full of grace,
      & your goodly pace,
        makethe my harte lyght.    48

    28 vnder *written above* after, *which is struck through.*

your loue I desyre with-owt any negatyon;
  Iff I myght ytt haue, then wolde I be feyne;
wherfore I pray yow, with-owt vareatyon,
  your hole mynde ye wyll wryte to me ageyne.    52
  yff ytt be good, then wolde I be feyne,
    & euer whyles I lyue to yow be obedyent
      To full-fyll your commandement as your humble
        seruaunt
                for-euer;                        56
              and neuer to change yow for no newe,
                but daylly for your grace to suye—
              Therfore swet-harte to me be trew,
                for I am at your plesure.         60


Thus at thys tyme thys byll shalbe concludyd
  The more breuely for to make an ende,
I trust verely I shall nott be Ill-usyde
  of yow to whome thys symple letter I sende;    64
  with loue to contynue thys I entende,
    & soo I trust þat ye wyll the same;
    cryste kepe vs bothe from bodely hurte & shame
                all-wey.                          68
              A-dew, fare-well my swete,
                tyll efte that we mete,
              my harte ye haue to kepe,
                by god that made thys day.        72
                  finis.

        67 h *struck through after* kepe.

*131.* *The All-Virtuous She*

By John Lydgate
Trinity Coll. Cambridge MS. 600
Loo, here begynneþe a balade which þat Lydegate wrote [p. 34]
at þe request of a squyer þat serued in loves court.

FFresshe lusty beaute Ioyned with gentylesse,
 Demure, appert, glad chere with gouuernaunce,
Yche thing demenid by avysinesse,
 Prudent of speeche, wisdam of dalyaunce,     4
 Gentylesse with wommanly plesaunce,
  Hevenly eyeghen, aungellyk of vysage—
  Al þis haþe nature sette in youre ymage!

Wyfly trouthe with Penelope,       8
 And with Gresylde parfyt pacyence,
Lyche Polixcene fayrely on to se,
 Of bounte beaute having þ'excellence
 Of qweene Alceste, and al þe diligence     12
  Of fayre Dydo pryncesse of Cartage—
  Al þis haþe nature sett in your ymage!

Of Nyobe þe sure perseueraunce,
 Of Adryane þe gret stedfastnesse,     16
Assured trouthe, voyde of varyaunce,
 With yonge Thesbe exsaumple of kyndenesse,
 Of Cleopatres abydyng stabulnesse,
  Meeknesse of Hester voyde of al outrage—   20
  Al þis haþe nature sette in your ymage!

Beaute surmounting with feyre Rosamounde,
 And with Isawde for to beo secree,
And lych Iudith in vertu to habounde,     24
 And seemlynesse with qwene Bersabee,
 Innocence, fredame, and hye bountee,
  fulfilled of vertu voyde of al damage—
  Al þis haþe nature sette in youre ymage!   28

7 ymage MS. visage.

What shoulde I more reherce of wommanhede?
　Yee beon þe myrrour and verray exemplayre,
Of whome þat worde and thought acorde in deed,
　And in my sight fayrest of alle fayre,　　　[p. 35]
　　Humble and meek, benyngne and debonayre,
　　　Of oþer vertues with al þe surplusage,
　　　Which þat nature haþe sette in youre ymage!

I seo no lack but oonly þat daunger　　　　　　36
　Haþe in you voyded mercy and pytee,
þat yee list not with youre excellence
　Vpon youre seruantes goodely for to see;
　Wher-on ful soore I compleyne me,　　　　40
　　　þat routh is voyde to my disavauntage,
　　　Siþe alle þees vertues be sitte in youre ymage.

L'envoye.

Go, lytel balade, and recomaunde me
　Vn-til hir pyte, hir mercy, and hir grace;　　44
But first be ware aforne þat þou weel see
　Disdayne and daunger be voyde oute of þat place;
　ffor ellys þou mayst haue leysier noon, ner space,
　　　Truwly to hir to done my message,　　　48
　　　Which haþe alle vertues sette in hir ymage.

### 132.　　　*Sweet Enslavement*

Advocates MS. 1. 1. 6

OFf lufe and trewth with lang continwans, [f. 220ᵛ]
　　all may ȝe luvaris cum leir at me;
That nevir a wicht had confort nor plesans
　In warld to think, nor ȝit behald with E,　　4
　In þat intent to turne fra hir bewty,
　　That evir I had, and hes my hairt compleit,
　　sen first I saw þat womanlie and sweit.

Nowþir for joy, nor scherp aduersitie,                8
  nor for disdane, dreid, danger, nor dispair,
ffor lyfe, for deth, for wo, for destany,
    ffor bliss, for baill, for confort, nor for cair, [f. 221ʳ]
    for chance of fortoun turnand heir and þair,      12
      fro hir sall nevir turne my plane hairt trew,
      Quhat I suffir of sorow, auld or new.

My faythfull hairt returne fra hir sall nevir
  Vnto no vddir lady vpoun life,                      16
quhilk but ganekalling I gif hir for evir
  With haill consent of all my wittis fyfe,
  quhill dethis rege vnto þe rut me ryfe,
    Thair sall no vþir in-to þis warld, but dreid,    20
    Depairt me fra þe flour of womanheid.

ffor weill I wet þat natur hes me wrocht
  to wirschep hir abone all erdlie wicht,
And for þat caus hes in þis warld bene brocht      24
  To be hir seruand fassit ay but slycht;
  Hir fresche effeir and Hevinlie bewty bricht
    To considdir and for to discrif,
    And for to luf hir leill in all my life.           28

THocht I suld de for trew lufe of þat wicht,
  I sall hir luf onlie, withowttin mo;
That for to fle my hairt it hes nocht micht,
  bot with þat wicht to byd and brist in wo;        32
  God grant þat I to graif befoir hir go,
    for of þis warld fra scho tak leif to fair,
    The joy of it fair-weill for evir mair.

11 wo *struck through before* cair.
13 MS. for.
15 seruice *struck through after* faythfull.

The lord of luf I thanke ane thowsand syiss,     36
  my faythfull hairt hes set so sad and sound
Vnto hir most fair, most womanlie & wyiss,
  That natur wrocht in-to þis warld so round;
    Weill fair þat wicht þat gaif so sweit a stound,     40
    Thairwith sic plesans in-to my hairt went
    That I neir slane wes with my awin consent.

The figurat dairt Invennomit with bliss,
  forgit with lufe and fedderit with delyt,     44
Withowttin wame hes wondit me, I-wiss;
  The harme of quhilk will nevir moir be quyt,
  quhois grundin point vnto my hairt did wryt
    In-to my mynd evir In remenbrans,     48
    off lufe and trewth with lang continwans.
           ffinis etc.

### 133.  *O Mistress Mine*

Advocates MS. 1. 1. 6

O Maistres myn, till 30w I me commend!     [f. 220ʳ]
  all-haill my hairt sen þat 3e Haif in cure,
for, but 3our grace, my lyfe is neir þe end;
  Now lat me nocht in danger me endure,     4
  off lyif lyk lufe suppois I be sure,
    quhay wat na god may me sum succur send?
    Than for 3our lufe quhy wald 3e I forfure?
    O maistres myn, till 30w I me commend.     8

The wynttir nycht ane hour I may nocht sleip,
  for thocht of 30w bot tumland to and fro;
Me-think 3e ar in-to my armys sueit,
  And quhen I walkyn 3e ar so far me fro!     12

No. 132. 40 MS. sound.     42 wes *written above* and, *which is
struck through.*     No. 133. 11 two *struck through after* armys.

allace! allace! þan walkynnis my wo,
  Than wary I þe tyme þat I ȝow kend;
War nocht gud hoip my Hairt wald birst in two,
  O maistres myn, til ȝow I me commend.    16

Sen ȝe ar ane þat hes my hairt alhaill,
  Without fenȝeing I may it nocht genstand,
ȝe ar þe bontie, bliss of all my baill,
  Bayth lyfe and deth standis in-to ȝour hand;    20
Sen þat I am sair bundin in ȝour band,
  That nycht or day I wait nocht quhair to wend,
Lat me anis say þat I ȝour freindschip fand,
  o maistres myn, till ȝow I me commend.    24
      ffinis etc.

## 134.    *For Old Acquaintance Sake*

Porkington MS. 10

A Dere god! haue I deservyd this—    [f. 130ᵛ]
    This dere destyny to drede,
That thus my swete I schall myse
    Thus wondurfully, & wott neuer why?    4
  Yfe anny man haue for envy
    Witt weked wordes made her wrathe,
  ffull mekely nowe I haske mercy—    [f. 131ʳ]
    That wons was lefe let neuer be lothe.    8

Thynke on me, dere hert, & be-holde:
  So stydfast my hert ys sette;
ffor well ȝe wott, yfe þat I wolde,
  To loue yowe lelyly ȝe may not me lete!    12

No: 133. 21 MS. bunding.
No. 134. *At bottom of f. 130ᵛ catchwords* fful mekely nowe.

Witt locces of loue I am be-sette,
    That syttes me nere þen anny clothe,
There-fore, dere hert, a-wyse yowe ȝette—
    That ons was leefe let neuer be lothe.        16


ffore-sothe, furst when I yowe chese,
    To wyn youre loue euer I have wroȝte;
In serttes þat myȝt I not yowe ons dysples
    In worde, ne werke, I neuer thouȝt.          20
    And nowe I se hit is fore nouȝt,
    Hit farys as dothe þe watter-frothe,
    Let fanttysyis faull oute of youre þouȝt—
    That ons was leffe lett neuer be lothe.        24


Tho I trespas neuer so mekyll,
    To yowe southely I wyll amende;
And sethe þat youre [loue] ys full fekoll,
    In-to vnkothe londes I woll wende.            28
    Alas þat in speche was spende
    Schuld turn youre loue & worschep bothe [f. 131ᵛ]
    Fro þe tru lufe þat hathe non ende—
    That ons was leffe lett neuer be lothe.        32


Yfe so hit be þat I be fore-sake,
    And youre hert sett at youre dewys,
More wrathe ȝe may well take
    And of wytte be ware & wyse.                36
    I wrathyde yowe neuer in no wyse
    And þer-to dare I swere an othe;
    There-fore sett youre hert at youre dewyse—
    That ons was lefe let neuer be lothe.          40

    31 MS. Tho þe tru.                38 MS. a nothe.

Serttes hit wer bothe syn and schame
　　Thus sodenly þat we schuld twyne,
Ne I deserwyd neuer no blame—
　　Hit is not tyme nowe to be-gynne.　　　　44
And ȝeyfe anny be to yowe leuire,
　　ȝett schulde we be frendys bothe;
Helpe hert and þinke on euyre—
　　That ons was leffe lett neuer be lothe.　　48

But sethe hit wyll be no better,
　　I most nede þat care vn-bynde;
And witt my hondis wryȝt a letter;
　　A-bout my hede I woll hit wynde,　　　　52
Tyll sche her-selfe hit wyll vnbynde　　[f. 132ʳ]
　　I schall hit were, witt-outtyn othe;
But euer I pray yowe haue in mynde—
　　That ons wos leffe lett neuer be lothe.　　56

## Have All My Heart

Porkington MS. 10

I have my hert.　　　　[f. 154ᵛ]

HAve all my hert & be in peys,
　　And þink I lowfe yow ferwently;
ffor in good fayth, hit ys no lese,
　　I wold ȝe wyst as well as I.　　　　4
ffor now I see, bothe nyȝt and day,
　　That my lovfe wyll not sese;
Hawe mercy on me as ȝe best may—
　　Hawe all my hert and be in peyse.　　8

No. 135. *At bottom of f. 154ᵛ catchwords* When I to yow.
　　　*Title and* Amen *in red.*

Hawe all my hart where-euyre I goo—
 Hert, body, and all my my3t.
Me for-þow3t we parttyd in too,
 When I to yow had most ry3t.　　　　　　[f. 155ʳ]
 Have mercy on me, mekyll of my3t,
  ffor of my lovfe I can-not seyse,
 Thow I be syldyn in youre sy3t—
  Havfe all my hert and be in peyce.　　　16

Hit ys a þinke þat me can nye,
 But yf 3e hold þat 3e have hy3t;
ffor traytors tongis, ewyll mot þi thee,
 I say to yow, myn swyt wy3t!　　　　　　20
 Therefore I sweyre, as mot I thye,
  Yf I sayd ow3t whan 3e bade pees,
 I wyll full mekely aske mercye—
  Have all my hart and be in peyse.　　　24

3e hawe my hart as I yow hy3te;
 I pray god, ellys þat I be dede,
But I love yow witt all my my3t
 As he þat wheris a forryd hood on his hede!　28
 This songe was made, witt-outtyn drede,
  ffor yowre lovfe þat I furst chese;
 Where-soo-euyre I be in stall or stede—　[f. 155ᵛ]
  Have all my hert and be in peys.　　　32
　　　　　　Amen. Et C.

*136.*　　　　　*A Fickle Mistress*

MS. Arch Selden supra 52
(Sum. Cat. No. 3440)

THayr ys no myrth vnder the sky,　[f. 168ᵛ]
 Harpyng, lutyng, nor no mery dance,
That may put owt my swet lady
All fro my daly Remembrance.　　　　　4

No. 135. 22 MS. peces.

Yie be the birde of all Plesance,
  My lady gent with loue inbraste,
ffull comly ys youre countenance—
  Be trew, lady, for I you truste.       8

I set not by no gret tresore,
  Mony, golde, nor wardly fee,
So of my lady that I be sure
  That She caste not hire loue fro me;     12
  And yie wolde ay so stabyll be
    Me for to loue for any haste,
  Thane shuld I leyffe in Rialte—
  By trew, lady, for I you truste.      16

The doyff wyche wantes discressione   [f. 169<sup>r</sup>]
  And hasse no ressone by verray kynde,
ffro that She chesse ons hir Elleccion
  A loue most plesinge vnto hire mynde,    20
  She will not stray, os doyth the hynde,
    Anoder luffer for to taste;
  Take heyd, my swete, for yie ar kynde—
  By trew, lady, for I you truste.      24

Seyne bestes that be with-out rasson
  Cane loue with-outyne varryance,
Tharfor my hert, now for this sessone,
  Put not your loue vnto sore grevance,    28
  Wher-trught gret care myght me unhance,
    And mak my hert lyk for to bruste,
  ffor of all women yie leyd the dance—
  By trew, lady, for I you truste.      32

       14 MS. Mo.
       29 MS. inhance.
       31 of *inserted above the line.*

Loue ys strange in all degre,
  Summtyme hoyt & sumtyme colde,
Tharfor to dowt, lady, yt caussis me,
  Leyff, that yie shuld fro me foyld,          36
  And fals louers youe kepe in hold,
    Than wold my sorow . . . . . .
  With fals lovers yie be not to bolde—   [f. 169ᵛ]
    By trew, lady, for I you truste.           40

Yie are the salyfe vnto my sore,
  And medyscyne to myne infirmite;
My tonge cane not expresse tharfor
  The secunde parte of youre beaute.           44
  Ther yse no surrance that may hurte me,
    Nor no sorow bot I shall cayste,
  When I think apon your love so fre—
    By trew, lady, for I you truste.           48

(137)

## *An Inconstant Mistress*

Harley MS. 2252

O Mestres, whye          [f. 84ᵛ]
  Owtecaste am I
all vtterly
  from your pleasaunce?                         4
Sythe ye & I
or thys, truly,
famyliarly
  haue had pastaunce.                           8

And lovyngly
ye wolde aply
þy company
  to my comforte;                              12

No. 136. 38 MS. *defective.*        No. 137. 11 MS. my.

But now, truly,
vnlovyngly
ye do deny
   Me to resorte.         16

And me to see
as strange ye be,
as thowe þat ye
   shuld nowe deny,    20
or else possesse
þat nobylnes
To be dochess
   of grete Savoy.     24

But sythe þat ye
So strange wylbe
As toward me,
   & wyll not medyll,   28
I truste, percase,
to fynde some grace
to haue free chayse,
   & spede as welle!    32

*138.*         *A Heartless Mistress*

Trinity Coll. Cambridge MS. 599

NOw FRESSHE floure, to me that ys so bryght, [f. 157ʳ]
   Of your louely womanhode I pray yow of grace,
Of your fayre beawte I pray yow a syght,
   That my gret mornyng may com to solace.   4

With care and mornyng I am ouercom,
   And all my Ioyes byn ouercast;
With sore syghyng styll I morne,
   That for your loue my hert ys to-brest.   8

No. 137. 21 MS. possede.

fful sore hit greueth me when I by yow sate
  And say other better belouyd than I,
And ye in your Armes so truly hym knyt,
  And I lyke a syphyr syt yow by.                12

Thowgh they be of body both gret and strong
  And semelokyr men happyly than I,
Yet with wysdom euer among
  I hope to lyue as meryly as they.             16

ffor Caton redeth in verses by ryme,
  The moche men shuld nat the lytyll blame;
ffor hit hath be seen of old tyme
  The moche of the lytyll taketh oft shame.     20

With body and connyng I wold yow please
  ffull fayne, and I wyst how to begyn;
But your fayre glose doth me desease:
  Ye speke fayre ovtward and feyneth withyn.    24

So styll ye go and lytell hede take,
  With myrthe and ioy that ye be full lyght;
Well lytyll thynke ye myn estate
  That with styll mornyng ye cast downe ryght.  28

There was neuer woman so stedfastly set,
  That in thys world suffred moche payn—
Kateryn, Elene ne Margarete,
  That stedfast were with all her myght and mayn— 32

But and they vnderstood of my carfull morne
  And trewly in what wyse my hert ys set,
Of her stedfastnes I trow they wolde turne;
  Ther shuld no worldly Ioy be to her let.      36

ffor and I in thys wyse dyd for your sake,
  As I am lyke therto in a whyle,
The paynes of hell than can ye nat scape;
  Than may ye say that your ys the gyle.        40

And ye wyll to me be any wyse kynde
　And shew me somwhat of your gentylnesse,
Moche myrthe and Ioy than I shuld fynde,
　All maner Ioy and worldly blysse.　　　　44

And with the grace of god when I recure,　[f. 157ᵛ]
　All your gentilnes well shall I aquyte ;
And in no wyse to fayle yow neuyr, ·
　But euer to please ys my delyte.　　　　48

Now, farewell, floure to me that ys so bryght,
　Of all flowres of all bewte feyre ;
ffor your loue my deth ys dyght,
　My soule to god standeth in dyspeyre.　　52

　　　　lothe to offende.

*139.*　　　*A Pitiless Mistress*

　　　　Sloane MS. 1212

MErcy me graunt off þat I me compleyne,　[f. 1ʳ]
　to ȝow my lyfis soueraigne plesaunȝ ;
And ese ȝour seruaunt of the importabyl peyne
　þat I suffre in ȝour obeysaunȝ,　　　　4
And lete ȝour femenygne natur dissolue þe cheyne
þat me bonde thorgh oo look of ȝour eyen tweyne ;
A, þan to this fyne entende shall my compleynt.

Syth ȝow like noȝt my peynys to remedy,　　8
nor at my request to graunte me mercy,
　In ȝour seruyse to deye, and þat I neuer repent ;
ffor ȝow to obeye and serue entendith my best cure,
tyl my lyfe relese his ryȝt with-outyn forfeture.　12

A, lady nature, what meved the
or-passand beaute in hir face to steyne,
Whose herte, deuoyde of mercy and pite,
on me to rewe euer hath disdeyne.               16

But sith hope hath ȝifen me herdinesse
to lofe ȝow best, and neuer to repent
whilis þat I lyfe with al faythfulnesse
to drede and serue, þough daunger neuer assent;   20
and her-vp-on knowith wele myn entent,
How I haue vowed ffully in my mynde
to be ȝour man, þough I no mercy fynde.

ffor in myn herte enprentyd is so soore        24
ȝour shappe, ȝour forme, and eke ȝour gentilnes,
ȝour port, ȝour cher, ȝour goodnes moor and mor,
ȝour womanhode, and eke your semelynes,
ȝour trouthe, ȝour faith, and eke ȝour kendeness,  28
with alle vertewis eche sette in his degre;
ther is no lack but onely off pite.

ȝour sad demenyng, off wil noȝt variabyl,
off look benygne, and rote off al plesaunȝ,     32
and exemplary to alle þat ben stabyl,
discrete, prudent, off wisdom suffisaunȝ,
Mirour of witte, ground off gouernaunȝ,
so þat I shortly shal noȝt fayne,              36
Saue vpon mercy I can noȝt complayne.

### *140.*     *A Sovereign Mistress*

Sloane MS. 1212

MYn worldly Ioy, vpon me rewe,        [f. 1ᵛ]
  And mercyles lete me noȝt pace;
ffor life or deth I wyll yow sewe,
þough I in yow neuer fynde grace.               4

lete pite daunger out off ȝour herte race,
Ande mercy cruelte remewe.
  o bountevous lady, femenygne off face,
rewe on my peynys, þat am so trewe,       8
    And shal to ȝow be whilys I haue space;
    and trewely serue and wilfully obeye.
  I am so bounde vndir ȝour lace
    I may nor wil, þough þat I deye,     12
    ffrom ȝour seruyse myn herte reneye.


myn soueraigne lady, myn hertis princesse,
assure me mercy þat mon my woo redresse.


Alle other vertewis weryn present in place,   16
  saue pite and mercy þei were behynde;
whan natur endewed hem in ȝour face,
  I suppose þei wern out of mynde.


It sittyth noȝt mercy be putt to flyȝt,    20
  Where pite haboundith, I ȝow ensure;
ffor mercy seweth pite be riȝt,
  the one with-oute oþer may noȝt endure.


Allas, mysgouernaunce off ȝouthe and freelte,  24
  the wheche euer redy all wisdom to restraigne,
  Hath me poured to my lady soueraigne.
ȝet on my-selfe haue I noo pite—
  with dedely wounde þus am I slayne.    28
now swete flour of femynyte,
  wheche may noþer fade nor stayne,
  fforgete me noȝt: to ȝour mercy I me complayne!

     13 MS. reveye.

## 141. *Cantus Occidentalis*

Pembroke Coll. Cambridge MS. 258

MYrie a tyme I telle in may,    [f. 141ᵛ]
    Wan bricte blosmen brekeӡ on tre,
þeise foules singeӡ nyt ant day;
In ilche grene is gamen an gle.      4

## 142. *Sweet and Lovely*

Harley MS. 7322

ME þingkit þou art so loueli,    [f. 162ᵛ]
    so fair & so swete,
þat sikerli it were mi det
þi companie to lete.      4

## 143. *Gracious and Gay*

Kilkenny Castle, Ormond MS.

GRacius and gay,
   on hyr lyyt all my thoӡth;
Butt sche rew on me to-day,
    to deth sche hatt me broth.      4

Hyr feyngerys bytt long and small,
   Hyr harmus byth rown & toth,
Hyr mowth as sweth as lycory,
    Vn hyr lyytt all my toth.      8

Hyr eyne bytt feyr and gray,
   Hyr bruys bytt well y-benth,
Hyr rode as rede as roose yn may,
    Hyr medyll ys small and gent.      12

No. 143. 1–4 *Written in MS. as two lines.*    10 Hyr mowth
as sweth as lyc *is written as the next line but is struck through.*
11 Hyr MS. Ass.

Sche ys swett vnder schett;
  I low hyr and no mo.
Sche hatt myne harth to kepe,
  In londes wher sche go.      16

Sodenly tell, y pray,
  To [þe] my low ys lend;
Kysse me yn my way,
  Onys ar y wen[d].      20

## 144.   *A Lady of High Degree*

Lincoln Coll. Oxford MS. 100

MY dere an dese þat so fayr ys,   [f. 2ᵛ]
  of lufe gentyl & fre,
I kan not ly, withowtyn lese,
  my lady lele best lykes me.      4

I saw neuer Ioy lyk to þat sight
  os my fayr lady schen;
her brows þay er both brant & bright,
  with ij gray lawhyng een.      8

her syds er lang chapyn of ryght,
  þat semle er to se;
be crist, & yt wer in my myght,
  scho suld my treuluf be.      12

Scho suld be my hertes qwen
  þat is so fayr and sqwete;
alas scho dos me tray & teen—
  I may noght with her met.      16

My der on des &c.

No. 143. 14 and *supplied*.
No. 144. *Written as prose.*   13 MS. sqwen.

145.    *Joyfull Pain, An Anagram*

Graffito in St. John's Church
Duxford, Cambridgeshire

With wiel my herte is wa,
    & closyd ys with care ;
L and S sekurly
    Cause me to syth full sar.         4

I and . . .
    . . . for to smerte,
V and . . . Y withall
    . . . joy come to thin hert.     8

146.    *To Annys*

(With Music)
MS. Douce 381
(Sum. Cat. No. 21956)

With ryth al my herte now y yow grete, [f. 22<sup>r</sup>]
    With hondert syes, my dere!
swete god, ȝyf vs grace sone to mete,
    and sone to spekyn yfere.     4
        Annys, Annys, Annys, Annys, Annes!
        Annes, be now stedfaste on allewys,
        & dynke on me, my swete Annys.
        my fayre Annys, my soþe Annys,    8
        I love ȝowre . . .

147.    *Bird on Briar*

(With Music)
King's Coll. Cambridge
Muniment Roll 2 W. 32

Bryd one brere, brid, brid one brere!    [verso]
    kynd is come of loue, loue to craue.
bliðful biryd on me þu rewe,
    or greyð, lef, greid þu me my graue.    4

No. 146. *Ends imperfectly*.      8 MS. soþe ?
No. 147.  3 MS. blid.          4 MS. greyd.

Hic am so bliþe, so bryhit, brid on brere;
  quan I se þat hende in halle—
yhe is quit of lime, loue-li, trewe,
  yhe is fayr, and flur of alle.                    8

Mikte hic hire at wille hauen,
  stedefast of loue, loue-li, trewe,
of mi sorwe yhe may me sauen;
  Ioye and blisse were me Newe.            12

## 148.   *An Unfaithful Mistress*

### Lincoln Cathedral MS. 133

I Haue grete meruell off a bryd        [f. 122ᵛ]
  That with my luff ys went a-way;
Sho byldus hus in a-noþer sted,
  Ther-ffore I morne both nyght & day.       4
  I cothe neuer serffe þat bryd to pay,
    Ne ffrenchypp with hyr con I none ffynd,
  bott ffast fro me she fflys a-way—
    a-las, þat euer sho was vnkynd.          8

a-las, qui ys sho with me wroth?
  & to þat bryd I trespast noght.
ȝe, gyff sho be neuer so lothe,
  sho shall noght come owte off my thoght.    12
  Now off me sho gyffis ryght noght,
    bot byldus hus ffer vndur a lynd;
  In byttur balus sho has me broght,
    a-las, þat euer sho was vnkynd.          16

a-las, qui is þat bryd . . .
  I wen . . . luff . .

No. 147.  12  MS. were were.
No. 148. *Ends imperfectly*.        3 MS. hyr.        12 MS.
sho shall come.        15 MS. boght.

### 149.    *A Letter to Margaret*

Caius Coll. Cambridge MS. 54

HAue godday, nou, mergerete,          [f. 157ʳ]
 wiþ grete loue y þe grete!
y wolde we miȝten vs ofte mete
in halle, in chaumbre, and in the strete,          4
wiþ-oute blame of þe contre—
god ȝeue þat so miȝte hit be!


### 150.    *The Faithfull Lover*

(With Music)
MS. Douce 381
(Sum. Cat. No. 21956)

MY cares comen euer anew.          [f. 22ʳ]
 A, dere god, no bote ther nys,
for y am halden for vntrewe,
 Wythowtyn gylt, so han y blys!          4

To be trew wonyt y was;
 In ony thyng þat y myth do
y þankyt god hys grete gras;
 now yt ys y may noȝt do.          8


### 151.    *Love Without Variance*

(With Music)
MS. Ashmole 1393
(Sum. Cat. No. 7589)

LOue woll I with-oute eny variaunce,          [f. 68ᵛ]
 trewly to serue with all louelynesse;
 for yn hit is triste and gentilnesse,
And þat may man honour & a-vaunce.          4

No. 150. 6 MS. Inon y tygh.     8 MS. no wyt ys y may []oȝt
do (*hole in MS. at* noȝt).

*152.*      *Love With Variance*

(With Music)

MS. Ashmole 191
(Sum. Cat. No. 6668)

Luf wil [i] with variance,      [f. 196ʳ]
  because y drede of repentance.
ffor who-so loueth with-outyn gouernance,
Oft-tyme it doth hym grevaunce;      4
therfor with avisance
loue wil [i] with variaunce.


*153.*      *To His Mistress*

(With Music)

MS. Ashmole 191
(Sum. Cat. No. 6668)

O Kendly creature of beute perleჳ,      [f. 191ᵛ]
  glorious merrour of alle clernesse,
Sum sygne of loue, y pray you with humblenesse,
to shewe your seruant In gret distresse.      4


*154.*      *The Indifferent Lover*

(With Music)

MS. Ashmole 191
(Sum. Cat. No. 6668)

THus I complayn my grevous hevynesse    [f. 194ʳ]
  to you þat knoweth þe trewth of myn entent.
Alas, why shuld ye be merseles—
  so moch beute As god hath you sent!      4
ye may my peyn reles.
  do as ye list—I hold me content!

No. 154. 3 MS. mersles.

### 155. *The Wounds of Love*

(With Music)
MS. Ashmole 191
(Sum. Cat. No. 6668)

G O hert, hurt with aduersite,     [f. 192$^v$]
   And let my lady þi wondis see ;
And sey hir þis, as y say þe :
  far-wel my Ioy, and wel-com peyne,     4
  til y se my lady Agayne.

### 156. *Parting is Sorrow*

(With Music)
MS. Ashmole 191
(Sum. Cat. No. 6668)

A Las, departyng ys ground of woo!   [f. 195$^r$]
   oþer songe can y not synge.
but why part y my lady fro,
  Syth loue was caus of our metyng?     4
  þe bitter teris of hir wepyng
    myn hert hath pershid so mortaly,
  þat to the deth hit wil me bryng,
  but yf y se hir hastily.     8

### 157. *Parting is Death*

(With Music)
Yale Univ. Mellon Chansonnier

' A Las, alas, Alas!' is my chief song!   [f. 77$^v$]
   ffor peyne and woo none other can y syng.
In-stede of rest A sobbe y tale among,
  ffor myne hert and de alvey a long siching.     4

No. 157. *The text appears in the MS. as follows*:
    Alas alas Alas is my chief song
    ffor peyne androo none other can y syng
    In stede of rest A sobbe y tale el mong
    ffornyn onert and de alve along siching

The ground oof Wo Is al de-partyng; [f. 78ᵛ]
　The more long, the more byting the peyn.
With the trew turtil all chaunge for-svering;
　'Welchome, my deth certeyne'—myn tvne and
　　pleyne!　　　　　　　　　　　　　　　　　8

*158*.　　　　*Complaint to Fortune*
　　　　　　　　　(With Music)
　　　　　Trinity College Dublin MS. 158

**M**Y hert ys so plungyt yn greffe　[f. 92ʳ]
　　ther may no barn my balyes on-bynd,
tyll y onys may sse my leffe
　it wyll not com owt off my mynd,　　　　　4
　a-lace ffortwne, þou art on-kynd!
　　why ssuffrys þou my hart to brek yn two?
　ffor y may not my lady ffynd,
　　y wot y dey ffor greffe and wo.　　　　　8

*159*.　*On the Absence of His Mistress*
　　　　　MS. Rawlinson poet. 36
　　　　　(Sum. Cat. No. 14530)

**I** Ne haue Ioy, plesauns, nor comfortt,　[f. 5ʳ]
　　In yowre absenss, my verrey hertes quene.
What other men thynk Ioy or disportt,
　To me it nys butt angyr or tene;　　　　　4
　Yff þat I lawgh, yt ys butt on þe splene.
　　thus mak I a gladfull sory chere,
　　So noyth me þe absenss of my verrey lady dere.

No. 157 (*cont.*)
　　　The groundoof wo Ifele departing
　　　The more long the more brytyng the peyn
　　　With the trew turtil all chaunge for sveregug
　　　Welchome my deth certeynement vne and pleyne
　No. 158. 2 MS. bran . . . no byne.　　6 tuo *struck through*
*before* two.
　No. 159. 6 So *crossed through before* thus; a *inserted above the line.*

*160.*          *His Absent Mistress*

Trinity Coll. Cambridge MS. 599

M Y lefe ys faren in a lond.          [f. 154$^r$]
    Allas, why ys she so?
And I am so sore bound
    I may nat com her to.                    4
        She hath my hert in hold
    Where euer she ryde or go,
        With trew love a thousand fold!

Explicit.

*161.*     *To His Mistress for Pity*

Hunterian MS. 230

N Ow good swet hart & myn ane good mestrys [f. 7$^r$]
    I dew recumend me to yower pety;
Bececheyng yow with all my gentylnes
    зat at yowre pleysuer to thynke vpon me,          4
    what payn I suffer be gret exstremytte;
        And to pardon me off my kynd wrytyng,
        ffor with wofull harte was myn endytyng.

*162.*         *The Power of Love*

National Lib. of Wales, Peniarth MS. 26

A Las, howe schale my hert be lyght,    [f. 107$^v$]
    Wyth dart of loue when hyt ys slayn;
The stroke hyt deris me day and nyght,
    Wyth carfulle hert y me complayn.          4

No. 161. *The tune is indicated at the head of the poem by* O penfull
harte. *A later hand has completed this*: That lyes in trowbull / And
in tene luk vp merely for somer hit schall [bene.]     1 MS. my nane.
No. 162. *The stanzas are indicated by bracketing of lines, capitalization, and indentation. 8 is linked to 12, and seemingly indicates the
start of the second stanza.*

for on has ofte made me vnfayn,
    for home y lye yn heuynes—
sche may redres my hert agayn,
    When y thyng on hure gentylnes.    8


thys y goo made, for on hur face
    y darnot loke lest loue me scorne,
But yf ye grawnte me of youre grace;
    for loue, alas, my lyue ys lorne.    12
alas, for loue my lyue ys lorne,
    for spase to spek then haue y non;
Ther ys no lyde þat euer was borne
    May saue my lyfe, but sche alon.    16


To you my swete y make my mone,
    In bytter bale y am y-brent,
But y myght to you com and gon
    to tell you Myn entent;    20
Where-wyth schall y me defende,
    for y haue nothere gamyn ne gle?
We may not speke but we be schent,
    yette wyll y loue you pruvyly.    24

6–7 *Written in MS. as one line.*   9 MS. for hur loue.   18 MS. yn brent.   21 MS. Wchere.   24 *There is a following line, which may best be regarded as a false ending*: yf hyt may non owthyr wys by.

(163.)

## *Sore I Sigh*

(With Music)

Public Record Office, MS. Ex^r. Misc. 22/1/1

*Music has survived.*

Alone, I lyue alone                    [recto]
& sore I syghe for on.

NO wondre thow I murnyng make,
  for grevous syghys þat myne harte dothe take,
and all is for my lady sake.
  [alone, I lyue alone.]                    4

She þat is causer of my woo
I merwell that she wyll do so,
sithe I loue hir & no moo.
  alone, [I lyue alone.]                    8

Thys am I brought in-to louers dawnce;
I wot neuer how to fle þe chawnce;
wherefore I lywe yn great penaunce.
  alone, [I lyue alone.]                    12

My mynde ys so yt is content
with hir dayly to be present,
& yet my seruis ys there mysse-spent.
  alone, [I lyue alone.]                    16

Trow ye that I wold be glade
To seke a thynge þat wyll not be hade;
Saw I neuer man so sore be-stad.
  alone, [I lyue alone.]                    20

*Burden and first stanza written under the musical parts three
times.        Burden first part MS.* syght.        *2 first part* MS.
syghthys.        *3 second part* MS. and all for my lady sake.
*4 and 24 refrain omitted.        7* louyd *struck through before* loue.
*11* lyud *struck through before* lywe; MS. gretat.        *12, 16, and 20*
MS. alone, &c.        *13–14, 17–18, 21–22, 25–26 written as one line.*

Onis me to lowe yff she began,
No man with tong nore pen tell can
the Ioy in me þat wold be than.
    [alone, I lyue alone.]         24

now pray we hym þat may purchase
To sende ws better tyme & space,
that y may stond all in hir grace.
    alone, [I lyue alone.]         28

## *164.*     *His Mistress, His Comfort*

Cambridge Univ. MS. Ff. i. 6

AS in yow resstyth my Ioy and comfort,    [f. 28ᵛ]
   youre dissese ys my mortal payne;
Sone god send me seche reporte
   þat may comfort myn hert in every vayne.    4
ho but ȝe may me sustayne,
    Ar of my gref be þe remedy,
    but ye sone haue amendement of yowre Maledy,

Weche ys to me þe heviest remembraunce    8
   þat euer can be þouth in any creature;
Myne hert hanggyng þus in balaunce
   Tyl I haue knowlege & verely sure
   þat god in yow hath lyst done thys cure,    12
    Of yowre dyssese to haue allygaunce,
    And to be releuyd of all yowre grevaunce.

No. 163. 22 norþe *struck through before* nore.
No. 164. 7 haue *supplied*.

## 165. *Love's Sorrow*

Cambridge Univ. MS. Ff. 1. 6

THis ys no lyf, alas, þat y do lede;                    [f. 153ʳ
   it is but deth as yn lyves lyckenesse,
Endeles sorow assured owte of drede,
   Past all despeyre & owte of all gladenesse.        4
Thus well y wote y am Remedylesse,
   for me nothyng may comforte nor amende
   Tyl deith come forthe and make of me an ende.


## 166. *Desire to Serve*

Cambridge Univ. MS. Ff. 1. 6

EUer yn one with my dew attendaunce            [f. 153ᵛ]
   to serue you aboue any creature,
withowten remembraunce of heuy varyaunce,
   Schall be my ioye whylys þat my lyf maye dure ;  4
to loue you beste with-outen repentaunce,
   while þat y leue and þer-of be ye sure—
Myn owne dyre herte, yn my ffull affyaunce,
   aboue all oþer formed by nature.                    8


## 167. *A Lover's Distress*

Cambridge Univ. MS. Ff. 1. 6

ALas, alas, and Alas, why                        [f. 137ᵛ]
   hath fortune done so crewelly,
ffro me to take Away þe seyte
Of þat þat gewrt my hert lyte.                        4

Of all þyng þat in erth yse,
To me hyt was þe most blyse
Whan þat y was in þy presense
To wham my hert doth reuerense,                      8

No. 166. 7 MS. My nowne.          No. 167. 7 þy *omitted in* MS.

And euer schal, for well or woo,  [f. 138ʳ]
Or drede of frende, or lyf all-soo;
Hit schal me neuer oþer A-sterte
But ye to haue my hole hert;  12

saue whan I come to þe deth,
That nedes oute mouste þe brethe
þat kepyth þe lyfe me with-inne,
And þan fro yow most I twyne.  16

And tyll þe day hit me owre,
Ryȝt feythfully I yow ensure,
þat þer schal no erly þyng
On my part make departyng.  20

Thus ame I sett yn stable wyse
To lefe and dure in yowre seruyce,
Wyt-oute faynyng of my hert
Thow I fele neuer soo grete smert.  24


*168.*      *A Lover's Plaint, I*

Cambridge Univ. MS. Ff. 1. 6

IS in my remembrauns non but ye alone,  [f. 154ᵛ]
    Wiche me causithe bothe to sygh and playne;
I haue no comfort—wher schall y make my mone?
    so far from you, that is all my payne,  4
My dyscomfort I may hit nat refreyne
    Tyll y be sewre of youre hartys ese,
Nothing but hit may my greuys pese!

No. 168. 1 MS. As.

All-wey to endure thus in woo,                    8
    What wondyr is thow y sore complayne?
youre goodlyhed hathe peryschid myn hert soo;
    Sythe of the trowthe I schall nat fayne,
    Hit causith myn yen oft for to rayne,        12
        When y thing on you and am absent,
        ffor, alas, departyng hath my hert schent!

169.        *A Lover's Plaint, II*

Cambridge Univ. MS. Ff. 1. 6

I May well sygh, for greuous ys my payne,    [f. 20ʳ]
    Now to departe fram yow thys sodenly;
My fayre swete-hert ye cause me to compleyn;
    ffor lacke of yow y stande full pytously,    4
    Alle yn dyscomfort, wyth-owten remedy,
        Most yn my mynde, my lady souerayn—
        Alas, for woo, departyng hath me slayn!

ffare-well my myrthe & chefe of my comfort,    8
    My Ioy ys turnyd ynto heuynesse
Tyll y agayn to yow may resort;
    As for the tyme y am but recurles,
    lyke to a fygure wyche that ys hertlees,     12
        Wyth yow hyt ys, god wote, y may not fayne,
        Alas, for woo, departynge hath me slayne.

ȝyt not-wythstondynge, for all my greuaunce,
    hyt shall be taken ryght pacyently,          16
and thenke hit ys to me but a plesaunce
    ffor yow to suffre a grete dele more truly,
    Wyll neuer change but kepe vnfeynyngly
        Wyth alle my myght to be bothe true & playn— 20
        Alas, for woo, departynge hath me slayn!

No. 168. 12 MS. my nyen.
No. 169. 11 MS. recules.        19 MS. vnfeynygly.

*170.* *A Roundel*

Trinity Coll. Cambridge MS. 600

Roundell [p. 373]

FFreshest of colour and moste amyable,
Considerþe my peyne and beoþe merciable;
As to my sight I sey as þat I thenk,
Or ellys for ever I am lyche to wynk. 4
To neghe I am þe pittes brink,
And withoute your comfort sodeynly lyflesse,
þane letteþe þis compleynt with mercy in your hert synk:
Suffreþe not my trouþe to eonde þus gerdonlesse. 8
ffresshest of colour [and most amyable],
[Considerþe my peyne and beoþe merciable;]
[As to my sight I sey as þat I thenk,]
[Or ellys for ever I am lyche to wynk.] 12

*171.* *A Pledge of Loyalty*

(With Music)

MS. Ashmole 191
(Sum. Cat. No. 6668)

NOw wolde y fayne sum merthis mak, [f. 191ʳ]
Al only for my lades sak
when y her se;
but nowe y am so far fro hir 4
it wil not be.

Thow y be for out of her cith,
I am her man both day & nygth,
& so wol be. 8
Therfore wolde as y loue her
she louyd me.

No. 170. 6 MS. soeynly. 7 with mercy *inserted above line.*

Whan she is mery þan am y gladde,
Whan she is sory than am y shadde,          12
   And cause is whye—
     ffor he leuyth not þat louyd her
   so wel as y.

She seith þat she hath seyn it write          16
That 'seldyn seyn is sone for-geit.'
   yt is not so—
     ffor yn good feith saue only her
   y loue no moo.          20

Wher-for y pray, bothe nygth & day,
That she may cast alle car a-way
   And leue in rest,
     And euer-mor wher-euer she be          24
   to loue me best.

And y to her to be so trewe,
And neuer to chaung for no newe,
   vn-to my ende,          28
     And þat y may in her seruice
   euer to amend.

*172.*      *Sweeting, I Greet Thee*

MS. Douce 95
(Sum. Cat. No. 21669)

E N Iesu Roy soueraign          [f. 6ʳ]
   you lady fair and fre,
En fyne amour certain
   Als reson telleth me,          4

No. 171. 14 her *supplied.*   16 MS. hith it.   20 MS.
y loue & no moo.   21 day & nygth *transposition indicated.*

Come a mon coer demesne
   Swetyng y grete the,
Vnquore durant en peyne
   But ye may bote be.        8

Quar en foye vous die
   I holde noon your peer,
Desore en vous affie
   As in my true ffeer.        12

Tredoulce tres bien ame,
   Myn oune derlyng dere,
De vostre loial vie
   Blethly wold y here.        16

Tredoulce creature
   My hert is wonder wo,
Pur vostre longe demure
   That is so fer me fro.        20

Ore swetyng loial & pure
   lete not our loue go,
qar certain & sure
   y loue you and no moo.        24

Si ils leȝ ose dire
   That is agein skill,
Que chast coer desire
   That ye may fullfille;        28

Se vous qant ieo remembre,
   ffair so flour on hill,
Souent foitȝ supprie,
   I sigh and mourne full still.        32

Ne poet estre a taunt
  As y wolde with right,
Mais Iesu tout puissaunt
  Of you me sende a sight.      36

*173.*        *The Lover's Lament*

Trinity Coll. Cambridge MS. 599

ALone walkyng,      [f. 160ʳ]
  In thought pleynyng,
And sore syghyng,
  All desolate—      4
Me remembryng
Of my lyuyng,
My deth wyssyng
  Bothe erly and late,      8

Infortunate
Ys soo my fate,
That, wote ye whate.
  Oute of mesure      12
My lyfe I hate;
Thus desperate,
In suche pore estate
  Do I endure.      16

Of other Cure
Am I nat sure,
Thus to endure
  Ys hard, certain;      20
Suche ys my vre,
I yow ensure.
What creature
  May haue more payn?      24

My trouth so pleyn
Ys take in veyn,
And gret disdeyn
  In Remembraunce;         28
Yet I full feyne
Wold me compleyne
Me to absteyne
  ffrom thys penaunce.        32

But in substaunce,
Noon allegeaunce
Of my greuaunce
  Can I nat fynde;        36
Ryght so my chaunce
With displesaunce
Doth me auaunce;
  And thus an ende.        40

      Explicit.

174.          *A Song of Scorn*

        (With Music)

    MS. Arch. Selden B. 26
    (Sum. Cat. No. 3340)

WElcome be ʒe when ʒe goo,    Tenor [f. 33ʳ]
  And fare-wel when ʒe come!
So faire as ʒe þer be noo mo,
  As brith as bery brovne.        4
I love ʒow verryly at my too,
  Nonne so moch in al þis toune.
I am right glad when ʒe wil goo,
  and sory when ʒe wil come!        8

No. 174.  3 So faire as ʒe *supplied from second part.*

And whan ȝe be ovth fare,
  I pray for yow sertayn,
þat neuer man, horsse, ne mare,
  brynge yow to town a-geyn.                    12
To prayse youre bewte I ne dare,
  ffor drede that men wille seyn.
ffare-welle! no more for you I care,
  but pray yow of my songe have no desdeyn!  16

*175.*            *Age and Love*

MS. Rawlinson poet. 36
(Sum. Cat. No. 14530)

I-Wyss, I-wyss, I remembre me          [f. 5ʳ]
  Wher-off, In trowth, of tyme I-past . . .
A, I counsell yow, lett that be—
  ffor all preuys butt fantesyes at last.      4
Why is loue no more stedfast:
  Now in trowth what remedy?
Prese forth, in youth be not a-gast.
  Why plesyth not age with novelry?          8

*176.*    *The Trials of Old Men in Love*

MS. Tanner 407
(Sum. Cat. No. 10234)

I Am olde whan age doth apele,           [f. 38ᵛ]
  hauyng a yong thyng þat lytell settyth me by.
One such in a schyre is to many, and fele
  other than trew be; by-holde a cause why—   4
I may not as I myght on my partye.
  therefor I am for-sake! age, age, woo þou be!
Youught is a traytoure, her experiens at eye;
  Oftyn-tymes and many þe blynde etyth many a flye! 8

No. 175. 6 MS. no.        8 MS. no veryly.

## 177. *The Ten Commandments of Love*

MS. Fairfax 16
(Sum. Cat. No. 3896)

The X Commaundements of Loue. [f. 184ʳ]

CErtes ferre extendeth yet my reason
  This mater as yet should be to discryue,
But I trust your grace will in this season
  Consider howe with conning that I stryue,         4
    For in his fauour coud I neuer arriue;
      Eloquence this Balade hath in greate despite—
      The maker lacketh maner to endite.

Of Loues commaundements .x. is the nombre,      8
  As aftirward shall rudely be rehearsed.
And Louers in no wise depart asunder,
  Where as they be obserued and redressed,
    Daunger and vnkindnes bin oppressed;       12
      And that is commaunded this to make,
      Is your owne all other to forsake.

           Faithe.   1 com[maundement]

Fayth is the first; and principally to tell,
  Verye Loue requireth soch credence       16
That eche beleiue other as true as the Gospell,
  Without adulacion or flattering audience,
  In true demeaninge and trusty confidence;
    Paint not yur conning with colour ne fable,     20
    For then yur loue must nedes be vnstable.

         Entencion. 2 com[maundement]

In the second, to treate of Entencion—
  Your louer to please doe your busy cure;
For as myn aucthour Romance maketh mencion,   24

        18 MS. adlaucion.

Without entent yur loue may not endure,
As women will thereof, I am right sure,
  Endeauour with hart, will, and thought,
    To please him onely that her loue hath sought.   28

### Discretion. 3 com[maundement]    [f. 184ᵛ]

In yur dealing euer be discreate:
  Set not yur loue there as it shalbe losed;
Aduertise in your minde whether he be mete,
    That vnto him yur hart may be disclosed;   32
  And after, as you finde him then disposed,
    Pointe by discretion your howre, tyme, and place,
    Conueniently mething with armes to embrace.

### Pacience. 4 com[maundement]

Of these commaundements the 4ᵗʰ is Patience.   36
  Though by irous corage thy louer be meued,
With soft wordes and humble obedience
    His wrath may sone be swaged and releiued,
  And thus his loue obteined and atcheued   40
    Will in you roote, with greater diligence,
    Because of yur meeke and womanly pacience.

### Secretnesse. 5 com[maundement]

Secretly behaue you in your werkes,
  In shewing countenance or meuing of yur iye;   44
Though soche behauor to some folke be darke,
  He that hath loued woll it sone aspie.
  Thus yur-selfe yur counseyle may descrye;
    Make priuy to yur deling as few as yee may,   48
    For .3. may kepe counsell if twayn be away!

48 Yee *altered apparently from* wee.

### Prudence. 6 com[maundement]

Let prudence be gouernor of yur bridel-reyne;
  Set not your loue in soe feruent wise,
But that in goodly hast yee may refreine          52
  If yur louer list you to dispise.
    Romaunce, min authour, would you this aduise:
      Ty slacke yur loue, for if you doe not soe,
      That wanton list will turne you into wo.          56

### Perseuerance. 7 com[maundement]

Stablishe your loue in soe stedfast wise,
  If that yee thinke your louer will be true
As entirely as ye can deuise,          [f. 185ʳ]
  Loue him onely and refuse all newe;          60
    Then shall not yur worship chaunge his hewe,
      For certes, masteres, then is he too blame
      But if that he will quite you with the same.

### Pitie. 8 com[maundement]

Be piteous to him, as womanhode requireth,          64
  That for yur loue endureth loues smarte,
Whom so sore yur pleasant looke enfireth,
  That printed is yur beaute in his harte,
    And wounded lyeth without knife or darte;          68
      There let yur pitie spred without restreinte,
      For lacke of pitie let not yur seruant feinte!

### Measure. 9 com[maundement]

Take measure in yur talking—be not outrage,
  For this reheareseth Romance de la Rose.          72
A man endued with plenteous language
  Oftyme is denyed his purpose;
    Take wisdome in langage, measure in grose,
      For measure—as right proued is by reason—          76
      Thinges vnseasonable setteth in season.

Mercie. 10 com[maundement]

Soche danger exile him vtterly
  Ouer-all mercy to occupie his place;
To piteous complaintes yur eares apply,                    80
  And receaue yur seruante in grace;
  To him þat bound is in loues lace,
    Shew fauour, Lady, and be not merciles,
    Lest yee be called a common murderes.                 84


L'enuoye.

Whan yee vnto this balade haue inspection
  In my making holde me excusable;
It is submitted vnto your correction,
  Consider that my conning is disable        [f. 185ᵛ]
  To write to you the figure amable,
    All deuoyde of conning and experience,
    Maner of enditing, reason  and eloquence.


Trust it well; the maker is yur owne,                     92
  You to obey while his life may endure,
To doe you seruice as a man vnknowne;
  Noe guerdone desyring of yearthly treasure,
  But if it might accorde with yur pleasure              96
    For true seruice him to auance,
    And call him into yur remembrance.

Explicit the x commandements of Loue.

92 is *supplied*.

## 178. *The Lover and The Advocate of Venus*

Corpus Christi Coll. Oxford MS. 61

O Ye lovers that pletyn for youre ryght  [f. 66ᵛ
   in venus courte, as do so moche for me!  col. i]
if ther be speche of eny maner wight
   that hathe lost his ladie, say þat I am he;  4
   But to pursieu restored for to be
      I haue non haste, it stondis in soche wyse,
      let hym do right þat lord is, and iustice.

Venus list not in any wise take kepe  8
   to suche men as wolle not do theyre payn
to please, serue, and brek mony a slepe,
   loue trewly, and in nothyng fayne;
   I trow ye cowthe hir seruice neuer atayn,  12
      youre hast is smalle withowte yur cause be mor
      þan I can wit by yur writyng before.

As towchyng þe moste noble and excellent
   Princes venus, by any manere  16
I haue not agrevid, aftir myn entent,
   In word, scripture, ne litrere;
   But trewly hir seruid, & in place where
      hit is rehersid, I cowthe not ateyne  20
      my souuerain lady—þe contrarye is playne.

Agrevid yit howe shuld sho els be,
   and haue disdeyn þat ye list noght to sieu
to hir þat comfortes highe and lowe degre,  24
   lightis the hertes of euere lover trewe,
   th'avaunt of youre lady me þink ye shuld eschue,
      if ye haue fond hir kynd, be not nowe wrothe—
      þat ons was with yowe lefe, I rede, let neuer be loþe.  28

22 MS. yis.
28 *At bottom of page, added in a later hand*:
    yf ye haue fond hyr kynd be not nowe wroth
    þat ons was with yowe lefe I redde let neuer be loþe

A thus in hir name ye say what ye liste;  [col. ii]
  yit trust I so gretly to hir goodnesse,
she hathe not take it so, for I it wiste,
  the hastilier I had hied þes giltles to redrisse,  32
  Avaunted I neuer yit my maistresse;
    How be it I sayde I had hir love forlorne—
    Thyng was neuer lost but it wer had beforn.

Gretly Venus to trust I hold bot in veyne,  36
  with-out yur actes wer þe bettir hir forto please;
She comawndes yowe apere afore Iuges tweyn
  to determyne yur matir & here al your pleeis.
  Sease of yur avauntyng—it will be yur ease;  40
    Amend þat is amys—þe tyme is now holy;
    And thogh it be disservyd, discouer not yur lady.

Mistrust shal I neuer by any wise
  that highe emprice, I yowe ensure,  44
whiche me hath rewarded for my seruice,
  to be loued ageyn whilis þat I endure;
  Of myn actes ye may be right sure
    what shall be sayd I dar it wel abyde,  48
    By my lady venus or of my lord cupyde.

Rewarded for yur seruice al was it loste,
  or to be lovid ageyn petie to here,
yur writyng afore spilt al þe roste,  52
  refusyng to siewe, and list not apeire
  to þe highe presence, bot stode in a were;
    Strange wordis sendyng in maner of a bost,
    Among lovers to infecte mony of an host.  56

fforto pursieu, thogh easy war myn haste  [f. 67ʳ
  Abriged is not my dieutye nor Alegeaunce,  col. i]
ffrom the highe courte if ye will atast

Th'entent of my forewrityng & þe substance,　　60
　Ye may not me condempne for lak of aparans;
　I haue offird my-self, & yit do ageyne,
　T'abyde the iugement of al oure souuerain.


Long myght ye abide in place dilectable,　　64
　offirryng your-selfe to make yur excuce;
Right glad am I, ye be so mesurable,
　dredyng lest yur matier had ben to diffuse;
　þe highe court I pray noght you to refuse,　　68
　　Amit yowe to grace þat ye be fond digne
　　To serue in hir presence þat is full benyngne.


In placis dilectable I purpose me to abide,
　T'excuse my-selfe I wote I haue no nede;　　72
youre feyned gladnesse I dar well set aside,
　drede not so sore, my matier was ordeyned,
　ffor þe courtes availe, and for myn owne spede,
　　is, hathe, and shall be my grettest desire—　　76
　　to please & to serue þat set me furst on ffire.


Wel nowe ye be recleymed to the lure
　Al yur matier for the courtis availe,
of yur good spede sethe ye be sure　　80
　þus yur cole is kyndled by travayle,
　I feyned not yit, withoutyn faile,
　　Giltles her thof ye me blame,
　　As ye me deme ye be the same.　　84


Neuer the rather for a Iapry worde　　[col. ii]
　ffloghe I from the lure to be recleymed,
in al wrytyng travers I kept with-in bord;

75 MS. owncispede.　　　76 MS. Is hathe be and shall.

Parde in yur gladdyng ye not well ye feyned,    88
for skarste of hast first ye me cleymed,
   Sethens by avantyng and aftir t'appere,
   Conclude on o poynt myn awnser ye shal here.

ffeyned nay, I said right as I thoght,    92
   my writyng was pleyn in myn opynyon;
at yur beginnyng strangely ye wroght
   The contrary aftir in your conclusion;
Noght stedfast, but nowe vp, nowe downe,    96
   turnyng with the wynd like to a fane,
   ffor my good cownsell yet ye me blame.

## 179.  *The Clerk and the Nightingale, I*

Cambridge Univ. MS. Ff. 5. 48

IN a mornyng of may,    [f. 57ʳ]
   as I lay on slepyng,
To here a song of a fowle
   I had gret likyng.    4

I herd a nyȝtyngale syng—
   I likyd hir full welle;
She seid to me, 'a wonder thyng
   I shall tell þe euery delle.    8

'Thynk, man, for þi curtesy
   & for þine owne gode,
Stonde a while and sey me
   why þou mornyst in þi mode?'    12

'Niȝtyngale, wel I may
   & wele I wot & wene,
I morne nyȝt and day
   for on þat is so schene.'    16

No. 178. 89 MS. skaste.

'Now, clerk, for-soth þou art a fole
  þat þou mournys so depe:
þat now is hot shalbe cole;
  þat now lawȝgh oft may wepe.'                    20

'Nyghtyngale, she is so gode
  þat no thyng may telle,
ffayre and trwe, mylde of mode,
  she may me gif & sell.'                          24

'Be waere, clerk, I warne þe:
  luf þou not so depe;
When þou levyst in luf to be,
  nede þou hase to wepe.                           28

'A woman is a wonder thyng,
  þow sho be fayre & stille,
She nys trwe to knyȝt nor kyng;
  clerke, to þe she nylle.'                        32

'Nyȝtyngale, why seyst þou so?
  þou gabbust in þi tale.
Wymmen bryng men owt of woo;
  she is bote of alle bale.'                       36

'Ne art þou not to lore sete,
  and wist of olde & newe;
treue þi luf & lockyt boþe
  þat word is not trwe.                            40

'Alle woo a woman began;
  she was begynyng:
Wyttenesse adam þe formast man—
  þat is no lesyng.'                               44

*Written in long lines.*
  19 MS. colde.      31 MS. kyng nor kynȝt.      34 wille
*struck through before* tale.      35 of *supplied*.      40 MS. wors.

'Nyȝtyngale, þat wot I wele:
    a woman wroȝt a shame.
A-noþer, I telle þe euery dell,
    broȝt vs alle to game.'                          48

'Be stille, clerk, þou art vn-wyse;
    þou spekist of a mayde
þat bare þe lord of paradyse,
    þat oure foo-men frayed.                          52

'Name hir to no woman,
    to mayden nor to wyfe;
ffor þou knowist, nor I ne kan,
    non so trwe of life.                              56

'I take wyttenesse of dauyd kyng,
    & at salamon þe wyse,
þat a woman for a litull thyng
    ofte change hir seruyse.                          60

'Luf a woman as þi lyfe,          [f. 57ᵛ]
    and kepe hir all with wynne,
ffor a purse or for a knyfe,
    when on is owt anoþer is in.'                     64

'Niȝtyngale, þou gabbust me,
    wymmen be fayre & hende,
fful of game and of glee
    wher-so þei wende.                                68

'were a man in sorow broȝt,
    wymmen myȝt out hym bryng;
with a lokyng turne his thoȝt,
    and with a kysse turne his mournyng.'             72

51 lord *supplied.*

'Clerke, if þou wil riȝt begynne,
   rede and vndurstonde,
Mannes thoȝt chaungis with synne,
   wel oft þou turnyd fonde;         76

'kysse of women wyrkyth wo
   with synne mony folde;
Iudas kissed god also
   and to þe iewes he hym solde.      80

'Clerk, as þou art wyse,
   þou louyst wel hir lokyng;
When þi purse shakyn is,
   fare-wel, clerk, þi cossyng!'      84

'Nyȝtyngale, þou spekist noȝt,
   late be alle þi fare.
How sholde men be forth broȝt
   ne wymmen ware?'      88

'ther-to answer I can
   with-out any stodying:
Wymmen was for man
   kynd forth to bryng;      92

'She was made to helpe man,
   and no-thyng for to leve.
þou myȝtes þat wete at Adam,
   but þou ne wilt me leve;      96

'I sey alle wymmen ar mysse-went,
   on gode is not in londe.
Men thruȝ wymmen be shent
   and ofte broȝt in bonde;      100

91 MS. mankynd.    97 MS. mysse gon.

'ffor I fynde non so gode,
  be way nor be strete,
but a man may change hir mote,
  if his purse wey grete.'                           104

'Ny3tyngale, þou gabbist me,
  and þat is shame thyn . . .'

## 180. *The Clerk and the Nightingale, II*

MS. Rawlinson poet. 34
(Sum. Cat. No. 14528)

[Philom]ena:                                     [f. 4ᵛ]

    .     .     .     .    .

ANd a woman off hauntyng moode         [f. 5ʳ
  Blythly sche wyll be swyuyd.          col. i]

But in a lytyll whyle
  Hur wyll wyll a-way wende.                        4
Be thow I-ware off gyle
  Euer at the last ende.

ffor whan a woman wepyt most,
  And sorowyth all her fyl;                         8
Than myght þou be soryst a-gast,
  Leste þat sche be-gyle the wyl.

Clericus:

Doe wey, fole, thi blamyng,
  And ffle a-way owt of þis lond.                   12
ffor a woman ys a wel fayre thyng
  And trew for to fend;

No. 179. 106 MS. thym.
No. 180. 10 wyl *supplied*.

Bryght & schene, myld of mode,
  Off dedys good & hend— 16
Ny₃tyngale, I telle the, my fode,
  That þou darst women a-schend.


Philomena:

Be styl, clerk, & hold thi mowth,
  And let gabbyng a throwe; 20
This lesyng ys wel wyde cowde,
  That may al folk know.


Clerk, be a appyl þou myght se—
  Sownd with-owtte and grene, 24
And in the core rotyd be:
  So faryth a woman, I wene.


þou seyth þei be all hend & good,
  To doe al mannes wyll; 28

.   .   .    .    .

  An þer-for, clerke, be styl.


Clericus:

Whan þou wylt al master be,
  And thy wyl al-wey haue, 32
O thyng I be-seche þe—
  As I schall be thy knaue,


And as þou art hend and ffre,
  And Comyn off good blode— 36
How schall I, tell thow me,
  To know the trew and the good?

27–30 *In MS. three lines only.*

Philomena: [col. ii]

Clerk, ylk trew woman hath vpon,
    With-owt any lesyng,          40
A robbe of grey marbyl ston,
    And of gret cumpasyng.


Ylk a woman þat ys good
    May doe gret merveyle:        44
A-reche þe sky with hur fote
    With-owtyn any fayle;


And ȝyt sche do, þe lady good,
    With her rokkes gore         48
Sche may spred all ynglonde—
    Schyp, sayle, & eke ore.


They schul be god wan god ys dede,
    And afterward maad all new.    52
Now take, clerk, thi best rede,
    ffor women schul neuer be trewe.


Clericus:

Alas, nyȝtyngale, alas,
    Me rewyth þat ilke stownde!    56
Thow hast I-broght me on a cas;
    I wene I fal to grownde!


My hert wyll be berst;
    Alas my lyf ys to long!        60
The to smyte I ame prest;
    Hens, but þat þow be goyng!

Ne blame þou women ne more,
 ffor-soth I rede the;    64
Thow shalt aby yt fful dere,
 Hennys, but þat thow ffle!

Philomena:

Nay, clerk, for thi curtesy,
 Mys-doe thow me ryght noght.   68
I wold theym preyse by & by,
 Y wyle chaunge my thoght.

I preyse women þat be good,
 What afterward be-fall;    72
They be full of curtesy & mood,
 In bowre & eke in hall.

Haue good day, clerk ffre,
 ffro the wyll y wende;    76
Take hede what þat I haue seyd þe   [f. 5ᵛ
 ffro the bygynnyng to the ende.   col. i]

Loue where thy ert may be-happe,
 What-so-euer sche be;    80
And sche schal make a glasyn cappe,
 And to skorn lawth the.

ffare-wel, clerk, & haue goodday,
 No more wyl I spute.    84
Now wyl I fare in my way,
 I rede þou to my wordys take hede.

Explicit disputacio inter Clericum et Philomenam
 etc.

78 MS. ffor.

## 181.   *The Clerk and the Husbandman*

B.M. Addit. MS. 38666

A S I cowth walke be-cause of recreacion     [f. 174ʳ]
    Be a grene wode syde as I kane,
I herde a meruolse comynycacion
    Be-twene a clerke and a husbandeman.     4
    To talke of loue þis clerke be-gane,
      And sade, 'wethur þou wylte or non,
    I moste nede blame me noo man,
      Quia amore languio.'     8

The husbande-man to hym can say,
    Wenyng to corekt hys insolens,
'ffalse-hode in felychype wole the be-tray,
    ȝefe þou to women gyf credens;     12
    Ther-fore restrane þe fro þair presens;
      And yf þou wylte couer þi-selfe fro woe,
    Truly, I know no bettur defense
      Bot turn vp hyr haltur and let hyr goe!'     16

'How schulde I do so?' then sayd þe clerke,
    'Thay wolde me lofe with all þair mayn;
Syth I fynde no faute yn worde nor worke
    Withowte a cause I may not complayne.     20
    I moste nede loue þat louyth agayn,
      I wer not kynde bot I dyde soo;
    To turn my herte þou gabste in vane,
      Quia amore languio.'     24

     2 MS. As I kane be a grene wode syde
     6, 7 *Transposed in MS.*
    12 MS. wome.
    13 MS. resrane.
    20 MS. complante.
    23 MS. labste.

' ȝet auyse þe bettur & do be cownsell,
 And do no lengur in women tryste ;
Thow wenis þat þai be in þe gospell—
 Hyt ys nat all tru þat peryth in glasse! 28
 Women can schaw a dowbull face,
  And qwer thay say lyttyll þai thynke moe ;
 As sone as þou maste reseue þi place,
  Turn vpe hyr haltur & let hyr goo!' 32

' Parauentur,' sayd þe clerke, 'a mys-fenyng fabulle,
 A womanse godenes soo to defame,
Thou fondyst neuer womon wariabull,
 Tham to depreue þou arte to blame ; 36
 Thynke on þi modur & avoyd schame—
  By-cause of hyr loue & othur moe,
 ffor qwyll I lyf, I wyll do þe same,
  Quia amore languio!' 40

That husbande-man sayd, 'womon ys wariat :
 By daly experiens hyt may be preuyt ; [f. 174ᵛ]
ffor be a womanse false delysyn
 Mony a gode man hase byn myscheuyt. 44
 ȝyf I say trowth, be not dysgreuyt ;
  And take thys for a conclisiun þer-to,
 Thy louely leuyng schall neuer be releuyt,
  Bot þou turn vpe hyr haltur & let hyr goe!' 48

The clerke vnsward & sayd, 'in bokys I fynde
 That gode made woman for mannys relefe,
Then schoe ys turnid all agaynys kynde
 ȝef schoe be cause of mannys myschefe ; 52
 Ther-for reherse no sych myspreue,
  ffor wethur þou tell me treuth or noe,
 Thou schalte nott make me myse-beleue,
  Quia amore languio!' 56

30 MS. more.     42 MS. eperiens.     55 MS. scalte.

## 182.        *Loyalty to His Mistress*

By Charles d'Orleans

Paris Bibl. nat. MS. f. fr. 25458

SO fayre, so freshe, so goodely on-to se, [p. 312]
   So welle dymeynet in al your gouernans,
  That to my hert it is a grete plesans
Of your godenes when y remembre me;     4
And trustyth fully wher that euer y be,
  I wylle abyde vndyr your obeyssance—
So fayre, [so freshe, so goodely on-to se,
  [So welle dymeynet in al your gouernans.]   8
ffor in my thought ther is no mo but ye,
  Whom y haue seruid wythout repentance;
  Wher-fore, y pray yow, sethe to my greuance
And put osyde all myn aduersite—     12
So fayre, [so freshe, so goodely on-to se,
  [So welle dymeynet in al your gouernans.]

## 183.        *The Service of His Mistress*

By Charles d'Orleans

Paris Bibl. nat. MS. f. fr. 25458

GO forth myn hert wyth my lady,    [p. 310]
   Loke that ye spar no besynes
  To serue hyr wyth seche lowlynes
That ȝe get hyr grace and mercy;     4
Pray hyr oftymes pryuely
  That she quippe trewly hyr promes—
Go forth [myn hert wyth my lady,
  [Loke that ye spar no besynes.]    8

No. 182. 7, 13 MS. so fayre, &c.
No. 183. 7, 13 MS. Go forth, &c.

I most as a hertles body
   A-byde alone in heuynes,
   And ȝe schal dowel wyth your maistres
In plesans glad and mery—        12
   Go forth [myn hert wyth my lady,
   [Loke that ye spar no besynes.]

## *184.*   *The Beauty of His Mistress*

By Charles d'Orleans
Harley MS. 682

THe smylyng mouth, and laughyng eyen gray, [f. 94ʳ]
   The brestis rounde, and long smal armys twayn,
The hondis smoþe, þe sidis streiȝt & playne,
yowre fetis lite—what shulde y ferþer say?    4
hit is my craft when ye are fer away
   To muse þeron in styntyng of my payne—
The smylyng [mouth, and laughyng eyen gray,]
   The brestis [rounde, and long smal armys twayn.]  8
So wolde y pray yow, géf y durste or may,
   The sight to se as y haue seyne;
   fforwhi þat craft me is most fayne,
And wol ben to þe howre in which y day—    12
The smylyng [mouth, and laughyng eyen gray,]
   The brestis [rounde, and long smal armys twayn.].

## *185.*   *A Confession of Love*

By Charles d'Orleans
Harley MS. 682

MY gostly fadir, y me confesse,    [f. 88ᵛ]
   ffirst to god and then to yow
   That at a wyndow (wot ye how)
I stale a cosse of gret swetnes,    4

No. 184. *Scribbled in bottom margin*: The smylyng mouth and laughing / The smy.

    Which don was out avisynes;
      But hit is doon, not vndoon, now—
    My gostly [fadir, y me confesse,]
      First to [god and then to yow.]     8
    But y restore it shall dowtles
      Ageyn, if so be that y mow;
      And that, god, y make a vow,
    And ellis y axe foryefnes—     12
    My gostly [fadir, y me confesse,]
      First to [god and then to yow.]

## 186. *A Place in His Mistress' Heart*

By Charles d'Orleans
Harley MS. 682

Honure, ioy, helthe, and plesaunce,    [f. 141ᵛ]
  Vertu, ricches habundaunt with good vre—
The lord graunt yow, which hath most puysshaunce,
  And many a gladsom yere forto endure    4
  With loue and prays of euery creature;
    And for my loue all prevayle it shall,
  I gyve hit yow as be ye verry sewre,
    With hert, body, my litill good and all.    8

And so yow not displese with my desire,    [f. 142ʳ]
  This wolde y yow biseche that of yowre grace
Hit like yow, lo, to graunt me all þis yere,
  As in yowre hert to haue a dwellyng place    12
  Al be hit neuyr of so lite a space;
    ffor which as this the rente resceyue ye shall
  Mi loue and seruice as in euery case,
    With hert, body, my litill good and all.    16

No. 186. 6 MS. small.

And syn hit is to yow no preiudice,
  Sum litill prati corner sekis me
Within yowr hert, for parde, lo, iustice,
  If y offende hit must yowr-selven be      20
    To punysshe, liche as ye þe offensis se ;
    ffor y as name nor haue no thing at all,
  But it is sovl yowr owen in eche degre,
    With hert, body, my litill good and all.      24

What so ye will, y wil hit to obey,
  ffor payne or smert how so þat me bifall ;
So am y yowre, and shal to that y dey,
  With hert, body, my litill good and all.      28

## 187. *A Lover's Plaint Against Fortune*

By the Duke of Suffolk

MS. Fairfax 16
(Sum. Cat. No. 3896)

Compleynt      [f. 321ʳ]

O Thou, ffortune, whyche hast the gouernaunce,
  Of alle thynges kyndly mevyng to and fro,
Thaym to demene aftyr thyn ordynaunce,
  Ryght as thou lyst to graunt hem wele or wo ;    4
  Syth that thou lyst that I be on of tho
    That must be reulyd be thyn avysinesse,
    Why wyltow not wythstand myn heuynesse ?

Me-thynk thou art vnkynd, as in this case,    8
  To suffre me so long a while endure
So gret a payn wyth-out mersy or grase,
  Which greuyd me ryght sore, I the ensure ;
  And syth thou knowst I am that creature    12
    That wold be fauoured be thy gentyllesse,
    Why wyltow not wythstonde myn heuynesse ?

What causyth the to be myn aduersarye?
  I haue not done that which shulde dysplese,    16
And yit thou art to myn entent contrarye,
  Whiche makyth now my sorous to encres;
  And syth þou wost myn hert ys not in ese
    But euer in trouble wyth-out sykernesse,    20
    Why wyltow not wythstande myn heuynesse?

To the allonly this compleynt I make,
  ffor thou art cause of myn aduersyte,    [f. 321ᵛ]
And yit I wot wele thou mayst vndirtake    24
  ffor myn wel-fare, yf that thou lyst agre;
  I haue no cause to blame no wyght but the,
    ffor thys thou doost of very wylfulnesse,
    Why wyltow not wythstand myn heuynesse?  28

## 188.   *In Praise of Margaret the Queen*

By the Duke of Suffolk

MS. Fairfax 16
(Sum. Cat. No. 3896)

How þe louer is sette to serve þe floure.

MYn hert ys set, and all myn hole entent,    [f. 325ᵛ]
  To serue this flour in my most humble wyse
As faythfully as can be thought or ment,
  Wyth-out feynyng or slouthe in my seruyse;    [f. 326ʳ]
  For wytt the wele, yt ys a paradyse
    To se this floure when yt begyn to sprede,
    Wyth colours fressh ennewyd, white and rede.

No. 187. 16 MS. which that.    21 MS. wystande.
No. 188. *The title comes from the Index on f. 2ᵇ.*
    6 MS. thais.

And for the fayth I owe vn-to thys flour,        8
  I must of reson do my obseruaunce
To flours all, bothe now and euery our,
    Syth fortune lyst that yt shuld be my chaunce
    If that I couthe do seruyse of plesaunce;        12
      Thus am I set and shall be tyll I sterue,
      And for o flour all othyr for [to] serue.


So wolde god that my symple connyng
  Ware sufficiaunt this goodly flour to prayse;        16
ffor as to me ys non so ryche a thyng
  That able were this flour to countirpayse.
    O noble chaucer, passyd ben thy dayse,
      Off poetry y-namyd worthyest,        20
      And of makyng in alle othir days the best—


Now thou art gon, thyn helpe I may not haue;
  Wherfor to god I pray ryght specially,
Syth thou art dede and buryde in thy graue,        24
  That on thy sowle hym lyst to haue mercy;
    And to the monke of bury now speke I,
      ffor thy connyng ys syche, and eke thy grace,
      After chaucer to occupye his place.        28


Besechyng the my penne enlumyne
  This flour to prayse, os I before haue ment,
And of these lettyrs let thy colours shyne
  This byll to forthir after myn entent;        32
    ffor glad am I that fortune lyst assent        [f. 326ᵛ]
      So to ordeyn that yt shuld be myn vre
      The flours to chese, as by myn aventure.

22 MS. go.

Wher-as ye say that loue ys but dotage— 36
  Of verey reson that may not be trew;
ffor euery man that hath a good corage
  Must louer be—thys wold I that ye knew:
  Who louyth wele all vertu will hym sew. 40
    Wherfor I rede and counsail yow expresse,
    As for thys mater take non heuynesse.

These clerkys wyse ye say were brought full lowe
  And mad full tame for alle thair sotelte; 44
Now am I glad yt shall ryght wele be know
  That loue ys of so grete autoryte;
  Wherfor I lat yow wyt, as semeth me,
    It is your part in euery maner wyse 48
    Of trew louers to forther the seruyse.

And of women ye say ryght as ye lyst,
  That trouth in hem may but a while endure;
And counsail eke that men shuld hem not tryst 52
  And how they be vnstedfast of nature.
  What causeth this for euery creature,
    That is gylty and knowyth thaym-self coulpable,
    Demyth all other thair case semblable. 56

And be your bokys I put case that ye knewe
  Mych of this mater which that ye haue meuyd,
Yit god defende that euerything were trew
  That clerkes wryte, for then myght thys be preuyd 60
  That ye haue sayd, which wyll not be byleuyd
    I late yow wyt, for trysteth verely,
    In your conseyt yt is an eresy.

A fye! for schame! O thou envyous man!   [f. 327ʳ]
  Thynk whens thou came and whider to repayr.
Hastow not sayd eke that these women can

**58** MS. myued.    **65** MS. thom; rapayr.    **66** MS. Hastow thou.

Laugh and loue nat ? Parde, yt is not fair!
Thy corupt speche enfectyth alle the air.　　　68
　　Knoke on thy brest, repent [the] now and euer
　　Ayen ther-wyth, and say thou saydyst yt neuer.

Thynk fully this and hold yt for no fable—
That fayth in women hath his dwellyng-place,　　72
ffor out of her cam nought that was vnable,
　　Saf man that can not well say in no place.
　　O thou vnhappy man, go hyde thy face!
　　　The court ys set, thy falshed is tryed,　　76
　　　Wyth-draw, I rede, for now thou art aspyed.

It thou be wyse, yit do this after me,
　Be not to hasty, com not in presence,
Lat thyn attournay sew and speke for the,　　80
　Loke yf he can escuse thy necglygence ;
　And forthermore, yit must thou recompence
　　ffor alle that euer thou hast sayde byfore ;
　　Haue mynde of this, for now I wryte no more!　84

## 189.　　*A Letter to His Heart's Joy*

By the Duke of Suffolk

MS. Fairfax 16
(Sum. Cat. No. 3896)

Lettyr　　　　　　　　　　[f. 323ᵛ]

MYn hertys Ioy, and all myn hole plesaunce,
　　Whom that I serue and shall do faythfully
Wyth trew entent and humble obseruaunce,
　Yow for to plese in that I can treuly,　　　·　4
　Besechyng yow thys lytell byll and I
　　May hertly, wyth symplesse and drede,
　　Be recomawndyd to your goodlyhede.

No. 188. 79, 80 *Marked in MS.* b *and* a *for transposition.*

And yf ye lyst haue knowlech of my qwert,        8
  I am in hele—god thankyd mot he be—
As of body, but treuly not in hert,
  Nor nought shal be to tyme I may you se;
  But thynke that I as treuly wyll be he        12
    That for your ese shall do my payn and myght,
    As thogh that I were dayly in your syght.

I wryte to yow no more for lak of space,
  But I beseche the only trinite        16
Yow kepe and saue be support of hys grace,
  And be your sheld from all aduersyte.
  Go lytill byll, and say thou were wyth me
    Of verey trouth, as thou canst wele remembre,    20
                                              [f. 324ʳ]
    At myn vpryst, the fyft day of Decembre.


### 190.   *To His Mistress, Flower of*
### *Womanhood*

Lambeth Palace MS. 306

THat pasaunte Goodnes, the Rote of all vertve,
                                              [f. 137ᵛ]
  whiche Rotide is in your femynete,
whos stepes glade to Ensue
  ys eueri woman in their degre;        4
  And sethe that ye are floure of bewte,
    Constreyned y am, magrie myn hede,
    hartely to loue youre womanhede.

Your sade, Demewre, appert goueronance,        8
  Of eliquens prengnavnt sauns coloure,
So it Renyth in my Rememberaunce
  that dayly, nyghtly, tyde, tyme and owre,

hit is my will to purches youre fauoure;    12
  whiche wilde to Criste I myght atteyn
As ye of all floures Are my Souerayn.

Whan Reste And slepe y shulde haue noxiall,
  ·As Requereth bothe nature and kynde,    16
than trobled are my wittes all;
  so sodeynly Renyth in my mynde
  youre grete bewte; my-thynketh than y fynde
    you as gripyng in myn armes twey—    20
    Bute whan y wake, ye Are away!

Entirmet with woo And gladnes,
  bothe Ioye and sorowe in woo memorall;
for than me thynkithe y see youre likenes,    24
  hit is nat so: it is fantasticall—
  thè whiche my herte with þe swarde mortall,
    that nothinge is, save uery Dethe;
    my wette is thynne, so schortithe my breth.    28

Nowe, lady myn, in Whome Vertus All    [f. 138ʳ]
  Ar Ioyned and also comprehendide,
as ye of al women y call moste principall,
  lette my gref in youre herte be entenderd,    32
  And also my veri treueloue Rememberde;
    And for my treueloue ayene me to loue
    As welethe nature and god that setithe Above.

Go, litill bill, with all humblis    36
  vnto my lady, of womanhede þe floure,
And saie hire howe newe troiles lithe in distreȝ,
  All-onely for hire sake and in mortall langoure;
  And if sche wot nat whoo it is, bute stonde in erore,  40
    Say it is hire olde louer þat loueth hire so fre, trewe,
    hir louynge a-lone—not schanginge for no newe.

Explicit.

22 MS. Entirmet this with.      40 MS. wotnat.

## *191.   A Letter to His Heart's Sovereign*

Trinity Coll. Cambridge MS. 599

HONOUR and Ioy, helth and prosperyte,   [f. 159ᵛ]
   Be vnto yow, my hartys souuerayn!
In humble wyse I lowly Recommend me
   Vnto your good grace, for verrey certente    4
   Ye be my Ioy and comfort ayenst my peyn;
     Aboue all women feyrest in my syght,
     Whom that I serue truly both day and nyght.

Desyryng hertyly aboue all other thyng    8
   The welfare of your most goodly persone,
Whyche ys to me A gret reioysyng
   To behold your goodlynes alone;
   There ys no gold, perle, nor precious stone,    12
     That ys to me half so moche plesyng
     As ys your presence, by heuyn kyng!

And when I do your goodnes behold,
   Of myrthe and Ioy I haue habundaunce;    16
Your absence causeth my hert to fold
   That nygh doth breke with peyn and greuaunce;
   Now, fayre truloue and flour of plesaunce,
     loue your louer as hyt ys verrey ryght,    20
     As he doth yow with all hys power and myght.

And of one thyng ye be full sure:
   I lyst to loue yow euyn as my lyfe,
And at all tymes your owne seruiture    24
   So that betwene shalbe no stryfe
   As hyt ys reson duryng my lyfe;
     Wherfore, fayr loue, haue me in mynd,
     And to yowre trew loue neuer be vnkynd.    28

Now constant gemme, myn hoole comfort,
  I take my leue oonly at your good grace;
Thus I submyt vnto your grace and support;
  No more I wryte to yow for thys case.    32
  The throwes of loue doth my hert so chase
    That, truly and god, ther ys no remedy
    Without your comfort, but mercylese to dy.

            Explicit.

## *192.   A Letter Protesting His Devotion*

MS. Rawlinson poet. 36
(Sum. Cat. No. 14530)

IN my hertt is þer nothyng off remembrauns    [f. 5ᵛ]
  that to Ioy sownyth, saue only to thyng vpon yow,
þis ys contynually myn ech day vsaunce;
  And thyng ye veryly þat I sey yow now    4
  That wold god ye wyst in what wyse & how
    I leue, wyssh, couete, & desyre also,
    How yow to plese, what me ys best to doe.

How ye be my souerayne lady, I-wyss I can-not wryte,  8
  ne ffynd I þerto papyr nor yng;
Wel I wote a hole ȝere it ys to lyte
  to make yow to know so mych on yow I thynke;
  so farforth þat when I sclepe or wynke    12
    me thynkith I see yow veryly in ffygure—
    The ffeyryst þat leuyth of any creature,

To whom I recommaund me with all obeysaunce,
  my hert, my loue, my trowth, & dylygence;    16
so þat yt may be yowre hertes plesaunce,

No. 191. 29 MS. cornstaṇt.
No. 192. 17 yowre *written above* my *which is struck through.*
2025.17        O

And to yow also worchyp and reuerense,
Prayng yow the effectt of my sentense
  Ye take in gre, how þat my wrytyng be rude,   20
  To trowth yt sownyth; and so y conclude.


*193.*        *To His Mistress 'M'*

MS. Lat. misc. c. 66
(*olim* Capesthorne MS.)

Mittitur:                 [f. 93ᵛ

I Pray you, M, to me be tru,      col. ii]
  for I will be tru as longe as I lif;
I wil not change you for old ne newe,
  ne neuer lof oþer whiles þat I lif.     4
and ye be auiset þis oþer yere,
ye send me a letter of luf so dere;
I was as glad of youre writynge
as euer I was of any thynge;     8
for I was sek the day be-fore—
that letter heyled, I was sek no more!
M, in space
comes fortune & grace,     12
I trist hit so for to be,
þat it shall liȝt on you & me.
M, be stidfast & tru in thoȝt,
ffor lof is the swetter the der þat it is boȝt.   16
& M I hope securly,
there is non þat byes it so dere as we.
& in what place so euer ye be,
as oft as ye wil, ye shall me þer se;   20
þer-for be ye tru, tru—
or ellis sore I mun it rew;

No. 192. 20 MS. wrytyg.
No. 193. 11, 12; 21, 22 *Single lines in MS.*    18 MS. the.

be ye stidfast & also true,　　　　　　　　　　[col. i]
ffor y wyl not change for old ne new.　　　　　　24
and sithen as we may not to-geder spek,
be writynge we shall oure hertes breke.

194.　　　　*A Letter to His Truelove*

MS. Lat. misc. c. 66
(*olim* Capesthorne MS.)

Mittitur:　　　　　　　　　　　　　　　　　　[f. 94ʳ
　　　　　　　　　　　　　　　　　　　　　　col. ii]

G O, litull bill, & command me hertely
　　Vnto her þat I call my trulof & lady,
be this same tru tokynnynge
that sho se me in a kirk on a friday in a mornyng, 4
With a sper-hauk on my hand;
& my mone did by her stond;
& An old womon sete her by
that litull cold of curtesy,　　　　　　　　　　8
& oft on her sho did smile
to loke on me for a wile.
& yet be this an-oþer token—
to the kirke she comme with a gentilwomon;　　12
euen by-hynd the kirk dore
thay kneled bothe on the flore,
& fast thay did piter-pater—
I hope thay said matens togeder!　　　　　　　16
yet ones or twyes at the lest,
Sho did on me her ee kest;
then went I forthe preuely,
& haylsed on thaym curtesly.　　　　　　　　　20
be alle the tokens truly,
comand me to her hertely.

No. 193. 23 also *inserted above line.*
　　　　24 MS. þen sore *struck through after* ffor; for old new.
No. 194. 9 MS. her ħer.

195.    *A Letter to His Mistress*

Porkington MS. 10

HOnowre witt all mannere of heylle     [f. 154ʳ]
   Be vnto yow, ffayre damseyll;
Witt stydfast hart and lovfe soo trw
This letter now I wryt vnto yow,             4
Praying yow to have me in youre mynd,
And let me neuer fynd yow vnkynd.
Loke þat ȝe be stydfast and trwe,
ffor here love þat bare Iesu.                 8
Tell me what ȝe thynk,
As my poȝt ys to wryt witt hynke.
I lowet neuer non halfe soo welle
Witt hart trw as anne stylle;              12
Sythin my lowfe ys on yow sete,
That I may noþer drynke nor eytte.
ffor maryis sake doo ȝe me to wyett
Whedyre þat ȝe wyll grant me hyet;     16
ffor yfe ȝe say me nay þertoo,
By cryst, my-selfe I wyll for-doo      [f. 154ᵛ]
And be-com schall I a gray ffrere
And newere womman to draw nere!      20
Gret here wel a thousand fold—
My moth of sugure, my hert of gold.
By yow no more at þis tym I make,
But to Iesu cryst I yow be-take.        24

Amen. Etc.

18 ffor yf ȝe sa *indicated for expunction at beginning of line.*
21 MS. a mᵃ fold.
22 MS. My sugure of moth.

## *196. From a Caitiff Bound and Thrall*

MS. Arch. Selden B. 24
(Sum. Cat. No. 3354)

O Lady, I schall me dress with besy cure,    [f. 231ʳ]
  With hart and mynde for to do observaunce
Vnto my lady britht, I ȝow assure;
  Greting hir wull with hwmyll continaunce,    4
  In termes rud, but ȝit with esperaunce.
    This bill I wret with hart Interiall,
    Exorting hir excuss my ignoraunce,
    And to haf pite of me, catife bound [& thrall.]    8


Haf piete, lady, of me catif bound [& thrall],
  And let me neuer thus de In-to diss[pair];
San in þis world is no thing corporell
  þat ma releve my cruell paine and [sair]    12
  But sche for quhome I suffir all þis [care].
    Sche hes my hert in-to hir gouern[all];
    O lady sweit, above all wthir fair,
    Haf piete of me, cative bound & thrall.    16


And gif to me þat ys most gracious,
  In colours savyn, in hart I-represant,
I-vonded sor with darttes amorous,
  In qhit, in grene, in gold, in gowlis gent,    20
  In aȝwr blew, in blak ay permanent,
    In gray most gracious, gay, cellestiall—
    O lady fair in quhom Is myn enten[t],
    Haf piete of me, catif bound & thrall.    24

*The MS. is cut away at the sides.*
18 MS. colour.
19 MS. vonde.

. . . hert of gold yow gr . . .                    [f. 230<sup>r</sup>]
   . . . quhome I suffir panis sair
þ. . . sweit hart thence hwmyll alswa . . .
   . . . in grene growand as bird on brere          28
  Gret hir weill þat ys to me so deir
   . . . ppone my panis principell
   . . . langour þat is my hart sa neir
  [Haf] piete of me, cative bound & thrall.        32


*197.*          *From a Departing Lover*

Harley MS. 3810, Part 1

T O ȝou, hie worschip & magnificence,     [f. 16<sup>r</sup>]
  be in-cresyng grace with prosperite,
[p]reservyng ȝou ay fro all offens
  of þat lord þat sitteþ in trinite;               4
  holy to ȝou y grete me,
   desyryng to here of ȝour welfare,
  besekyng ȝou of ȝour pytee
  þe whiche may bryng me out of care.            8

In care & sorew y am all-way,
  & schal be tyl ȝe me rescue;
now louely hert, y ȝou pray,
  of my paynes þat ȝe wol rew;                    12
  & lete me euer ȝoure love pursue,
   to loue ȝou wher þat euer ȝe are,
  for ȝe may euer my Ioy renewe
  & ȝe may bryng me out of care.                  16

pyte longeþ to wommanhede,
  for it becomeþ hem to be kynde;
with ȝoure pyte ȝe may me rede
  & þer-with now ȝe may me bynde;                 20

þer-for, swete, on me haue mynde,
    & with ȝoure mercy ȝe me spare;
trewe to ȝou ȝe schal me fynde,
    for ȝe may help me out of care.     24

alas, schal y not se þat day
    þat y with ȝou my fyl may speke?
ner hope were, y dar wel say,
    in twenty pecis myn hert wold breke.     28
    but þat is for you, myn hertes souereyn;   [f. 16ᵛ]
        y hope to speke with ȝou my fylle;
    when all þis wordys be but yn feyn,
        y may but þink & holde me stylle.     32

now fare-wele, my swete, & þink on me,
    þey y be ferre out of ȝoure syȝt;
now fare-wele, but trewe þat ȝe be,
    and ȝe wil as ȝe me byhyȝt;     36
    now And y were as prest of flyȝt
        as euer was faucoun tyl his pray,
    y wolde þen with all my myȝt
        to speke with ȝou onys a day.     40

y may wryte no more a dele,
    for of no leyser sykerly;
but ofte-tymes y grete ȝou wel
    as sterris sitten on þe skye;     44
    & more often by a þousand part
        þen ony clerke may wryte with inke,
    or eny man can pryve by art,
        or mouþe speke, or hert þinke!     48

22 ȝe *inserted above line.*
45 MS. party.

but and y schulde not afende,
  a lettre y pray ȝou þat ȝe make,
& to me þat ȝe it sende,
  & to crist y ȝou bytake.                    52
fare-wel now myn hert swete,
  y morne & may no merþis make;
fare-wele, loue, tyl we mete,
  for þis tyme now my leve y take.            56


## 198.  *To His Mistress, Root of Gentleness*

Cotton MS. Vespasian D. ix

Exemplye sendynge to you, rowte of gentylnes, [f. 188ʳ]
  Bothe true and trusty stok of all nature,
the bon-ayre Replenyssyd wythe perfet clennesse;
  to you, dyere hert, vnto me hole honnoure       4
  As þe muste profondyd in womanly stature,
    to whom god hathe yeve you soueraynge Suffys-
      an[ce],
    In vertu, benevolens, & trowthe wythe-oute vay-
      riaunce.

to whom in the moste lowly wys þat euer y can or may, 8
  I recommand me and all my seruyse,
To you, me lady soueraynne, & gronde of nature;
And whylle y may my lyffe-tyme endure
  to do you seruys wythe all puere and myght,      12
And to non other but to you my trowthe I plyghte.

As towchynge to youre lettre, I haue yt well consseuyd,
  And in my trew hert trustyly assayd;
god knoythe on my parte ye be not dysseuyde,         16
  ther-fore in no wysse be not dysmayde;

No. 198. 3 MS. Replevyssyd.          6 .f *struck through before*
suffysance.          7 MS. baynaunce.

I make you surans by that lord that borne was of
    [a mayde],
   though y shulde my lyf forthe wythe you forfethe,
   y shulde do for yoie, that y may youre plasauns for
     to g[ete].         20

that yf I euer to you vntrew, or to schaming you
ffor Any newe, ye me be-seched wysse,    [f. 188ᵛ]
that by youre dyscresyon, as may suffysse
to any so symple a wyked as I,    24
that lustyth not to offende hys souerayn lady.

Now fayreste of stature formyd by nature,
  of beaute the merrour, and grond of gentylnes,
Most amyable, benyng, and constant creature,    28
    Stynter of stryfe, & causere of pesse—
     to you I complayne, my souerayne maystresse,
     haue mercy on me that byth me lyues cure,
     And thynke what payne for you I endure.    32

Bounte, beaute, and perfyte whomanhode,
  Ensampull of worchype, & Rote of lustynes,
Ryght well avysyd & prudent in euery stede,
    the well Replet of gentylnys—    36
    Vowchasafe ye now on myn hevynes,
     Sythyn ye be myn hert hole Reserthe,
     Sum drope of mercy to be my comforte.

Ryght exelent maystresse, & causere of my payn,    40
  Vpon thys nobyl and lusty may,
to you my lady, and most espesyal souerane,
    whos I haue byn, now am, & shall be ay—
    I me Recommande whyll I leue and may,    44
     me hert, loue, & all me seruys,
     In all that I can or may suffysse.

19 MS. thought.    20 youre MS. yoie.    21 MS. schamig.
23 MS. many.

O ye fayre son wythe all youre bryghte bemys,   [f. 189ʳ]
   youre beaute and youre gentylnes,                    48
haue mercy on me, & let sum of youre lyght lemys,
   Dyscend don to youre seruande that lyth in heuy[nes].
thys he made at youre lustynys
    The xvi day of the month of stedfastnys,        52
    The xxiij yere of polycy and southnes.

Penses de moy.

## 199.   *To His Mistress, Fairest of Fair*

MS. Douce 95
(Sum. Cat. No. 21669)

**F**Fair fresshest erþly creature                [f. 3ᵛ]
   that euere the sonne ouer-shone,
The best & the shapliest figure
   that kynde hath wrought of blood & bone—     4
Whos y haue bene, am, and euer shall in oon,
    With all my pore hertes lowe seruyse:
    I me recomaunde on euery humble wyse
    that tonge can tell or hert devise,          8
To you, þat all my lyves ar on.


My truthe to you y wryte,
   ass he þat is with w[o] oppressed sore,
Compleynyng, as y dare endite,                      12
   My hele þat is euermore.
All-though þese wordes rude bene & lite,

No. 198. 50 MS. that lyth byn in.
No. 199. *Written in long lines.*
    5 and MS. add.
      11 wo *second letter erased*; MS. as she.

ye be not greved with me þerfore;
 Beseche y your noble grace,    16
 And hold not your deboner face
 Defouled to se þis, when y haue space,
that bote is of my sorwe sore.


Your goodnesse also y beseche,    20
 considereth all my hertes care;
ye lete your mercy ouere me streche,
 and that causeth my misfare,
  as this lettre shall you shewe.   24
 my lyves ende, my blisse bare;
  ye vouchesafe to me to dele
  right as you list, sikenesse or hele,
  lyff or deth, wo or wele—    28
All in your grace put my fare.


The fressh beaute of your comelyhede,
 so hote set myn hert on fyre,
Whan y sawe first your maidenhede   32
 that euere sith suche desire
  haue y had to serue you
  while y may tyre;
   That euer sith with cold of hete,  36
   With hete of cold, my hert is bete.
   I ne am but dede, but ye me hete
Your love ageyn to quite my hyre!


ffro whiche ye may me releve—    40
 wolde ye vouchesafe to do so—
and from all sores myn hert reue,
 with a goodly worde or two.

  19 MS. sorwes ore.    32 MS. manhede.

myght y fele in worde or other 44
þat ye wer not my fo,
  In world a wight a thowsan dele
  Was neuer sonner brought to hele;
  for and ye loved me truly lele 48
Wold y neuer haue Ioyes mo.

ffairest of fare, this lettre lite,
  that chefe is of my paynes smerte—
all can y not well endite; 52
  let þese wordes synke in your herte
  ffor all my wele & wo y-wys.
þus y conclude in wordes shorte;
  But yif ye rued vpon my payne 56
  and bryng my bale to blysse agayne,
  Certes y can-not elles sayne,
but deþ y may not a-stert.

Explicit.

## 200. *To His Mistress, Delectable Daisy*

MS. Rawlinson C. 813
(Sum. Cat. No. 12653)

AS I my-selfe lay thys enderȝ nyght, [f. 54ʳ]
  all alone with-owten any fere,
thys dremyd I of yow, my trewloue dere,
me thought þat ye were layd me nere. 4

Then was I glade as bryde on brer,
  me thought I hade yow vnto my paye;
& yn my mynde we made good chere—
  but when I wakyde, ye were a-wey! 8

No. 199. 48 MS. hele.

Alas! alas! then can I saye,
   to wette my-selfe soo woo-be-gone;
for she þat myght my sorowe deley,
   she was depertyd full farre me frome.     12

And I lay styll my-selfe alone,       [f. 54ᵛ]
   & yn no wyse my sorow cowld slake,
but euer styll mournyng with full greate mone
   vnto the tyme that I dyd wake.     16

then was I sorowfull owt of solas;
   my wytt from me ytt was almost gone;
& euer I said, 'alas, my harte, alas!'
   for I lye styll here my-selfe alone.     20

yow ar a-wey soo farre me frome,
   that to me ytt was a full greate peane;
I pray to god þat we may soone to-geder come,
   & þen wyll I showe yow þis matter playne.     24

your loue closyd soo farre yn my hart ys,
   & euer shalbe, whyles I haue space,
besechyng hym þat ys kyng of blysse
   þat I may be receyvyd yn-to your grace.     28

ytt ys full many a day agoo
   Syth þat I wythe yow dyd last speke,
my specyall comforth & my swetyng also,
   o my dere loue, ye be wyse & meke!     32

A delectable daysye ye be to beholde,
   yow be more rycher vnto my syght
then oder precyouse stoune or golde;
   thys wyse I dremyd all þe nyght.     36

24 MS. come to geder & þen (etc.).     36 MS. was.

I haue pryntyd yow yn my harte soo depe—
 wold to god I were able your seruaunt to be,
Euery nyght yn your armes þat I myght slepe ; [f. 55ʳ]
 rewarde me with your loue: I aske non oder fee. 40

Onys ye promysyde me for to be trew,
 & we were neuer soo farre betweyne ;
& now ye haue refusyd me for a new—
 alas, my harte dothe blede with peyne.    44

no more to yow I can now saye,
 but Iesus kepe yow wher-so-euer ye goo ;
thys to yow I wryte, & also saye,
 þat partyng ys þe gronde of my woo.    48
     finis.

## 201.   *An Envoy to His Mistress*

Royal MS. 19. A. iii

O Bewtie pereles, and right so womanhod,   [f. 16ᵛ]
 ffor the grete honour and vertue in you I see—
I you beseche of your moste godelyhode
 This litill Boke it myght rehersed be    4
 Vnto suche fayre þat do excile pite,
  Whiche causeth their louers to morne with peinfull
   hert,
  And not relesse them of their peynes smerte.

Other ther be with godely countenaunce    8
 that perse menes hertes right with a sobre yee ;
Their Bewtie is suche with yke þe circumstaunce,
 Whoo can refreyn, þei most nedes loved be.
 A lady faire may not exile pite ;     12
  Where bewtie is, of right þere is pities place,
  Therfore alwey gode Doo, ye pray for grace.

No. 200. 44 peyne MS. you.

## 202.    *A Farewell to His Mistress, I*

MS. Bodley 120
(Sum. Cat. No. 27643)

FAyre-wele my Ioye, my comfort and solace, [f. 95ʳ]
 fayre-wele the floure fayrest of beute,
fayre-wele the godly feture of youre face,
 fayre-wele my gladnes and felicyte,    4
 fayre-wele my helth & my prosperyte,
  fayre-wele my herttes lyve & my plesance,
  fayre-wele disport, & fayre-wele dalyance.

## 203.    *A Farewell to His Mistress, II*

Trinity College Dublin MS. 500

FFareth wele wirchepe and goodnesse, .[f. 1ᵛ]
 ffareth wele fairhede and gentilesse,
ffareth wele swettest of al swetnesse,
ffareth wele welle of al worthynesse,    4
ffareth wele of loue ae goddesse,
with-outen pere more ore lesse,
ffor nas neuere non ne yet non esse
That myght a thosand foulde, I gesse,    8
Be liik on-to youre worthynesse:
So het my ladi gracious and glorious.

No. 202. 1 *Preceded by a line marked* A It is to me of Ioy the esperance *and further headed* Aue maria.
 Now *struck through before* fayre-wele; *after* Ioye, yke *inserted above line and then crossed out;* my *inserted above line.*
 2 *This line marked with a* B.  3 wele *inserted above line.*
 7 *Followed by a line drawn across the page, and written below:* A fayre wele confort Ioye and yke solace *as if another or final version of line* 1.

## 204.   *A Farewell to His Mistress, III*

MS. Rawlinson C. 813
(Sum. Cat. No. 12653)

FArewell now my lady gaye,                    [f. 52ᵛ]
   farewell floure most freshest of hew,
farewell sapher yn all assey,
   farewell harte of whyte & blewe,                    4
   farewell kynde, curteyse & trewe,
     farewell woman withowten any evyll,     [f. 53ʳ]
   farewell þe cumlyst þat euer I knewe—
     I take my leve agaynst my wyll.               8

farewell now my derlyng dere,
   farewell most wysyst & womanly,
farewell my loue from yere to yere,
   farewell byrall bryghtest of blee,                12
   farewell kynde, curteys & free,
     farewell þat may me save & spyll;
   how-euer I fare, well fare ye—
     I take my leve agaynst my wyll.               16

farewell goodly grond of grace,
   farewell þe well of worthynes,
farewell my comforth yn euery case,
   farewell my helpe ferthe of dystresse,       20
   farewell my werrour from all sykenes,
     farewell my lady of voyce soo shryll,
   farewell nurter & all gentylnesse—
     I take my leve ageynst my wyll.               24

farewell my wershype & my welthe,
   farewell my myrthes with-owten mysse,
farewell my hartye hope & helthe,
   farewell freshe & lustye to kysse,               28

    12 MS. lyrall.        17 MS. gronder.

farewell all welthes þat men can wyshe,
  farewell as bryght as sonne ouer hyll,
farewell, god bryng yow to his blysse—
  I take my leve a-gaynst my wyll.      32

finis.

## 205.   *A Lover's Farewell to His Mistress*

MS. Douce 95<br>(Sum. Cat. No. 21669)

E<sup>Xcellent</sup> soueraine, semely to see,   [f. 1<sup>r</sup>]
  Preved prudente, peerlees of pris,
Bright blossome of Benyngnyte,
  ffigure fairest, and fresshest of devys;    4

I recomaunde me to your rialnesse
  As lowely as y can or may,
besechyng inwardly your gentilnesse
  let neuer faynt hert true love betraye.    8

Soueraine lady, semely in sight,
  your excellence of high renoun
hath arrest me vnto your myght,
  þat kendly rest is me benome.    12

your womanly beaute delicious
  hath me hent all into his cheyne,
but ye graunte me your loue gracious
  my hert will melte as snowe in reyne.    16

In humilite lete your hert descende,
  þynke not on your excellence;
and socour to your cliant ye sende
  þat in turment abideth your presence.    20

No. 205. 5 quenes *added in margin in slightly later hand.*

A true-loue is in myn hert pight
   þat doth me wo with his reson;
Dere derworth lady bright,
   your beaute is his encheson,         24

yif ye wist my lyfe & knewe
   & of þe peynes that y feell,
y-wys ye wold vpon me rewe—
   þough your hert wer made of steell!     28

And þough ye be of high renoun,
   Let mercy enclyne your hert so fre;   [f. 1ᵛ]
To you, lady, þis is my boun,
   to graunt me grace in some degre.    32

And wrye me not þat am so trewe,
   ne dryve me to deth with your danger;
but tendrely, lady, on me rewe,
   thurgh pite & mercy of your power.    36

To your mercy wold ye me take
   yif your will were for to do;
then wold y truely for your sake
   change my chere & slake my wo.    40

your beaute grete, of riall chere,
   creature comelich, my diligence
will brynge me certes to my bere,
   for ayen loue can y no defence.    44

ffor defence though y wold make,
   your lokyng wold me peressh to the hert;
thus prisoner shuld y be take,
   & suffre mo peynes stronge & smert.    48

24 MS. beaute your        33 MS. þam.

Myn hert is set in your delite:
　　Preveþ it well be experience;
and to you my trouth y plite,
　　þat euere y drede your offence.　　52

In þis world flour so faire
　　Is non, be hym þat me dere bought,
to whom y wold so sone repaire;
　　alas, yit wissh helpeth me nought.　　56

Ofte y wyssh—so haue y blysse—
　　a bird invisible for to be,
With my wynges þat y myght flussh　　[f. 2ʳ]
　　Pryvyly to you, swetyng fre.　　60

And no-body me shuld see but ye allone,
　　till þat ye wist all my thought;
of grace þan wold y hope full sone;
　　Allas, yit wissh helpeth me nought.　　64

Whan þat y may, soueraine swete,
　　In prees of peple se your presence;
Water y wrynge & begynne to wepe,
　　sighyng my-self in softe silence.　　68

Allas, that god ne hadde,
　　be verrey reason of truthe,
In your persone properrely made
　　Half your beaute, merci and ruthe.　　72

This loveli lesson is myn to lere
　　ffor y may fynde noon other blisse,
It woll brynge me to my bere
　　ffor you, womanly wight, y-wys.　　76

ffor fortune is no-thyng my frende,
   But euere he casteth me to spille;
for loue y may no lenger lende,
   so he purposeth me to spille.        80

But sith it stant in suche degre
   and may non-other-wyse trende,
of ffarewell myn ende shall be
   To you-ward wher-euere ye wende:     84

ffarewell ladi of grete pris,
   ffarewell wys, both fair & free,
ffarewell freefull flourdelys,
   ffarewell burell bright of ble.     [f. 2ᵛ]

ffarewell saphir, souerain of assay,
   ffarewell feir, fresshest & fre,
ffarewell Rubye, rial of Aray,
   ffarewell Dyamand, dere in degre.     92

ffarewell perle, pris preisable,
   ffarewell cristall, coriouse in kynde,
ffarewell amytest, all amyable,
   ffarewell emeraude, most of mynde.     96

ffarewell goodly grounde of grace,
   ffarewell most of worthynesse,
ffarwell comfort of this caas,
   ffarewell helper of hevynesse.     100

ffarewell Rote of stedefastnesse,
   ffarewell honour, prive and still,
ffarewell norice of gentilnesse,
   ffarewell sauour swettest of smell.     104

ffarewell creature comely of kynde,
   ffarewell lanterne lussom of light,
ffarewell mynder most of my mynde,
   ffarewell souerain, semely in sight.       108

ffarewell strengthe of stablenesse,
   ffarewell fairest, with-outen fable,
ffarewell counsell of clennesse,
   ffarewell Turtill trewe triable.       112

ffarewell mirthe that y do mysse,
   ffarewell prowesse in purpull pall,
ffarewell creatur comely to kisse,
   ffarewell faucon, fare you be-fall.       116

ffarewell amerouse and amyable,      [f. 3ʳ]
   ffarewell worthy, witty and wys,
ffarewell pured pris preisable,
   ffarewell ryall Rose in the rys.       120

ffarewell fair and fre figurable,
   ffarewell womanly wight in wede,
ffarewell derworth and delitable,
   ffarewell foison, your love for to fede.       124

ffarewell myn erthly ioy and blisse,
   ffarewell my worship and my wele,
ffarewell myrthe that y do mysse,
   ffarewell harder than flynt or stele.       128

ffarewell Carboncle chosen chief;
   ffarewell gloriouse as gold y-grave,
ffarewell pured principall in prees,
   ffarewell graciouse, god you save!       132

108 MS. ffarell.

ffarewell derworth of dignite,
 ffarewell grace of gouernaunce,
how-euere y fare, ffarewell ye!
 ffarewell prymerose, my plesaunce.                    136

Explicet Amor
per ducem Eboracensis nuper factus.

206.                 *Love Longing*

Sloane MS. 1584

GReuus ys my sorowe                       [f. 85ʳ]
  Both evyne and moro,
Vnto my-selffe a-lone
Thus do I make my mowne,                      4
    That Vnkyndnes haith kyllyd me
      And putt me to this peyne;
    Alas, what Remedy
      That I cannot refreyne!                  8

Whan other men doyth sleype
Thene do I syght and weype,
All Ragius in my bed,
As one for paynes neyre ded                   12
    That vnkyndnes haue kyllyd me
      And putt me to this payne;
    Alas, what remedy
      That I cannott refreyne!                 16

My harte ytt haue no Reste
but styll with peynes oppreste,
And yett of all my Smart
Ytt grevith moste my harte                    20

That vnkyndnes shuld kyll me
and putt me to this payne;
Alas, what Remedy [f. 85ᵛ]
 That I cannott refreyne! 24

Wo worth trust vntrusty!
Wo worth love vnlovyd!
Wo worth hape vnblamyd!
Wo worth favtt vn-namyd— 28
 Thus vnkyndly to kyll me
  And putt me to this payne;
 Now, alas, what Remedy
  That I cannott refrayne! 32

Alas, I lyve to longe;
my paynes be so stronge,
for comfort haue I none!
God wott I wold fayne be gone, 36
 for vnkyndnes haith kyllyd me
  And putt me to thys payne;
 Alas, what remedy
  That I cannott refrayne! 40

Iff ony wyght be here
That byeth love so dere,
come nere, lye downe by me,
And weype for company; 44
 for vnkyndnes haith kyllyd me
  And putt me to this payne;
 Alas, what Remedy [f. 86ʳ]
  That I cannott refrayne! 48

My foes, whiche love me nott,
Be-vayle my deth, I wott;
And he that love me beste
hyme-selfe my deth haith dreste. 52

What vnkyndnes shuld kyle me
If this were nott my payne;
Alas, what remedy
That I cannott refreyne!                    56

My last wyll here I make:
To God, my soule I be-take,
And my wrechyd body
As erth in a hole to lye,                    60
    for vnkyndnes to kyle me
        And putt me to this payne;
    Alas, what remedy
        That I cannot refreyne!              64

O harte, I the bequyeth
To hyme that is my deth;
Yff that no harte haith he
my harte his schalbe;                        68
    Thovght vnkyndnes haith kyllyd me
        And putt me to this payne;
    Yett yf my body dye         [f. 86ᵛ]
        My hertt cannot refrayne!            72

'Placebo dilexi . . .'
com, weype this obsequye,
My mowrnarus, dolfully
come weype this psalmody,                    76
    for vnkyndnes haith kyllyd me
        and putt me to this payne,
    be-hold, this wrechid body
        þat your vnkyndnes haith slayne!     80

58 soule *inserted above line.*
75 MS. mowrmarus.
77 MS. of.

Now I be-sych all ye,
namely þat lovers be,
my love my deth for-gyve,
and soffer hyme to lyve—                    84
 Thovght vnkyndnes haith kyllyd me
  And putt me to this payne,
 Yett haid I rether dye
  for his sake ons agayne!          88


My tombe ytt schalbe blewe
In tokyne that I was trewe,
To bringe my love frome dovte
Itt shalbe writtynge abowtte              92
 That vnkyndnes haith kyllyd me
  and putt me to this payne,
 be-hold this wrechid body        [f. 87ʳ]
  That yor vnkyndnes haith slayne!   96


O lady, lerne by me—
Sley nott love wylfully
for fer love waxyth denty

 .  .  .  .  .  .               100
 vnkyndnes to kyle me,
  or putt love to this payne;
 I ware the better dye,
  For loves Sake a-gayne!           104


Grevus Is my Soro,
butt deth ys my boro;
ffor to my-selfe a-lone
Thus do I make my mone                    108

That vnkyndnes haith kyllyd me
And passyd is my payne.
Prey for this ded body
þat your vnkyndnes haith slayne.        112

                amen.

        ffinis.


*207.*            *To Her Lover*

MS. Rawlinson C. 813
(Sum. Cat. No. 12653)

O Resplendént floure, prynte þis yn your mynde,
                                    [f. 53ᵛ]
how as yet vnto yow I was neuer vnkynde;
    & therfore, dere harte, rote of tendernes,
        to comforth me of my care & sease my paynes stronge, 4
    shortly come speke with me of your gentylnes,
        or elles dyscomforthe shalbe my songe.

for yn your confydence my worde I haue closyde,
    bothe locke & kay ye haue yn your gouernance;    8
& to yow my mynde I haue sayssyde,
    of very pety, exyle me nott owt of remembrance!

Thys I doo fynyshe my symple byll,       [f. 54ʳ]
at owr metyng ye shall knowe more of my wyll.    12
Vnto yow I nede nott to wryte my name,
for she þat louethe yow best send yow þis same.

goo lyttle queare, & recommende me
    vnto my mastur with humble affectyon    16
besechyng hym lowly, of mercy & petye,
    of my rude making to haue compassyon.

No. 207. 6 of *struck through after* elles.

& as towchyng þis letter of translatyon
  owt of frenche, how-so-euer þe englyshe be,    20
all þis ys said vnder correctyon,
  with the supportatyon of your benyngnyte.
        finis.

## *208.*    *A Mocking Letter to Her Lover*

MS. Rawlinson poet. 36
(Sum. Cat. No. 14530)
To my trew loue and able—-     [f. 3ᵛ]
As the wedyr cok he is stable—
Thys letter to hym be deliueryd.

VNto you, most froward, þis lettre I write,
  Whych hath causyd me so longe in dyspayre ;
The Goodlynesse of your persone is esye to endyte,
  for he leuyth nat þat can youre persone appayre—  4
  So comly best shapyn, of feture most fayre,
    Most fresch of contenaunce, euyn as an Oule
    ys best and most fauoryd of ony odyr foule!

youre manly visage, shortly to declare,    8
  your forehed, mouth, and nose so flatte,
In short conclusyon, best lykened to an hare
  Of alle lyvyng thynges, saue only a catte ;
  More wold I sey yf I wyst what—    12
    That swete vysage ful ofte is be-shrewyd
    Whan I remembre of som baud so lewd.

The proporcion of your body comende wele me aught, [f. 4ʳ]
  ffro the shuldre down, behynde and beforn ;  16
yf alle the peyntours in a land togedyr were soght,
  A worse coude þey not portrey þogh alle þey had it sworn!
  Kepe wele your pacience þogh I sende you a skorne.
    your Garmentes upon you ful gayly they hynge  20
    As it were an olde gose had a broke wynge.

your thyghes mysgrowen, youre shankys mych worse;
   Whoso beholde youre knees so crokyd—
As ych of hem bad odyr Crystes curse,        24
   So go they outward; youre hammys ben hokyd;
   Such a peyre Chaumbys I neuer on lokyd!
     So vngoodly youre helys ye lyfte,
     And youre feet ben crokyd, with euyl thryfte.  28


who myght haue the loue of so swete a wyght,
   she myght be ryght glad þat euer was she born.
She that onys wold in a dark nyght
   Renne for your loue tyl she had caught a thorn,  32
   I wolde hyr no more harme but hangyd on the morn,
     That hath ij good eyen & I-chese here suche a make,
     Or onys wold lyft vp here hole for youre sake!

        Youre swete loue wyth blody naylys,
        Whyche fedyth mo lyce than quaylys.


## 209.   *The Lover's Mocking Reply*

MS. Rawlinson poet. 36
(Sum. Cat. No. 14530)

   To you, dere herte, variant and mutable,   [f. 4$^r$]
   lyke to Carybdis whych is vnstable.

O Fresch floure, most plesant of pryse,
   fragrant as fedyrfoy to mannys inspeccion,
Me semyth by youre contenaunce ye be wondyr nyce,
   you for to medyl with any retorucion;      4
   To me ye haue sent a lettre of derusion,
     Endyghted ful freshly with many coryous I-clause.
     werfore I thanke you as I fynde cause.

The ynglysch of Chaucere was nat in youre mynd,   8
  Ne tullyus termys wyth so gret elloquence,
But ye, as vncurtes and Crabbed of kynde,
  Rolled hem on a hepe, it semyth by the sentence;
  And so dare I boldly withoute ony offence   12
    Answere to your letter, as fallyth to the purpose;
    And thus I begynne, construe ye the glose.

Cryst of hys goodnesse and of hys gret myght   [f. 4ᵛ]
  fformyd many a cryator to walke on the ground;   16
But he that beholdyth you by day and by nyght
  Shal neuer haue cause in hert to be Iocound,
  Rememberyng your grete hede and your forhed round,
    Wyth Staryng eyen, visage large & huge,   20
    And eyþer of youre pappys like a water-bowge.

Youre Camusyd nose, with nose-thryllys brode,
  Vnto the chyrch a noble Instrument
To quenche tapers brennyng afore the roode,   24
  ys best apropred at myne avysament;
  your leud lokyng, doble of entent,
    wyth courtly loke al of saferon hew,
    That neuer wol fayle—þe colour is so trew!   28

your Babyr lyppys of colour ded and wan,
  wyth suche mouth lyke to Iacobys broþer,
And yelow tethe not lyk to the swan—
  Set wyde asondyr as yche cursed oþer;   32
  In al a lond, who cowde fynde suche anoþer,
    Of alle feturys so vngodly for to se,
    with brethe as swete as ys the Elder tre.

16 MS. tryator.
19 *After the first* your, h *struck through.*
20 vysage *struck through after* Staryng.
27 loke *interlined above* vwe *which is struck through.*

youre body ys formyd al in proporcion,                    36
   with hangyng shuldres wauyng with euery wynde,
Smal in the bely as a wyn toune,
   wyth froward fete, and crokyd bak behynde;
He that you wold haue alway in Mynde,                    40
    And for your loue wold breke on oure reste,
    I wold he were locched with lucifer the depeste.


And of youre atyre, shortly to devyse,
   your templers colured as þe lowcray,                    44
with dagged hood, leyd on pancake wyse,
   your bolwerkys, pectorellys, and al your nyce aray;
   Treuly me semyth ye ar a louely may!
    And namely on halyday, whan ye tryp and daunce,48
    As a wylde goos kepyng your contenaunce!


Adew, dere herte, for now I make an ende
   Vnto suche tyme that I haue better space.
The pyp and þe pose to you I recomend,                    52
   And god of hys mercy graunte you so mykyl grace
                           [f. 5ʳ]
   In paradyse onys to haue a restyng place,
    Vp by the nauel, fast by the water gate,
    To loke after passage whan it cometh late.                    56

            youre owne loue, trusty and trewe,
            you haue forsake cause of a newe.

47 louely *interlined over* nyce *which is struck through.*
50 del *struck through after* Adew; er *struck through after* an.

*210.*     *Praise of His Lady*

By Thomas Hoccleve

Huntington MS. HM 744
(*olim* Gollancz MS.)

La commendacion de ma dame.     ⌈f. 52ᵛ⌉

OF my lady wel me reioise I may:
    Hir golden forheed is ful narw & smal,
   Hir browes been lyk to dym reed coral,
And as the Ieet hir yen glistren ay;      4
Hir bowgy cheekes been as softe as clay,
    With large Iowes and substancial—
Of my lady [wel me reioise I may:
    [Hir golden forheed is ful narw & smal,      8
    [Hir browes been lyk to dym reed coral,
[And as the Ieet hir yen glistren ay.]
    Hir nose a pentice is þat it ne shal
Reyne in hir mowth thogh shee vp-rightes lay—    12
Of [my lady wel me reioise I may:
    [Hir golden forheed is ful narw & smal,
    [Hir browes been lyk to dym reed coral,
[And as the Ieet hir yen glistren ay.]      16
Hir mowth is nothyng scant with lippes gray,
    Hir chin vnnethe may be seen at al,
    Hir comly body shape as a foot-bal;
And shee syngith ful lyk a pape-Iay—      20
Of [my lady wel me reioise I may:
    [Hir golden forheed is ful narw & smal,
    [Hir browes been lyk to dym reed coral,
[And as the Ieet hir yen glistren ay.]      24

(211) *Scorn of Women*

Trinity Coll. Cambridge MS. 599

LOke well about, ye that louers be;                      [f. 207ʳ]
  lat nat youre lustes leede yow to dotage;
Be nat enameryd on all thyng that ye se—
  Sampson the fort and Salomon the sage                  4
  Deceuyd were, for all theyre gret corage;
    Men deme hit ryght that they see with ey;
    Beware, therefore: the blynde eteth many a fly.

I mene, of wemen, for all theyre cheres queynt,          8
  Trust hem nat to moche—theyre trowth ys but geason;
The feyrest owtward well can they peynt,
  Theyre stedfastnes endureth but a season;
  ffor they feyne frendlynes & worchen treson.           12
    And for they ar chaungeabyll naturally,
    Beware, therefore: the blinde eteth many a fly.

What wyght on-lyue trustyth on theyre cherys   [f. 208ʳ]
  Shall haue at last hys guerdon and hys mede;           16
ffor wemen can shaue nerer then rasours or sherys.
  'All ys nat gold that shynyth!' Men, take hede—
  Theyre gall ys hyd vndyr a sugryd wede;
    Hit ys full queynt theyre fantasy to aspy;           20
    Beware, therefore: the blynde eteth many a fly.

Though all the world do his besy cure
  To make wemen stond in stabylnesse,
Hit woll nat be, hit ys agayn nature;                    24
  The world ys do when they lak dowbylnesse;
  ffor they can lawgh and loue nat—thys ys expresse.
    To trust on theym, hit ys but fantasy;
    Beware, therfore: the blynd eteth many a fly.        28

Women of kinde haue condicions thre:
The furst ys they be full of deseyte;
To spynne also ys theyre propurte;
  And wemen haue a wondyrfull conseyte:                32
  ffor they can wepe oft, and all ys as teyte,
    And euer when they lyst, the teere ys in the ey.
    Beware, therefore: the blynde eteth many a fly.

In sothe to say, thowgh all the erthe so wanne         36
  Were parchemyne smothe, whyte and scrybabyll,
And the gret see that callyd ys the occianne
  Were tornyd into ynke, blakkyr than sabyll,
  Euery styk a penne, yche man a scryuener abyll,      40
    Nat cowde [they] then wryte womans trechery;
    Beware, therfore: the blynde eteth many a fly.
                  Explicit.

212.            *Abuse of Women*            ↄ Bann.
              Advocates MS. 1. 1. 6

O Wicket wemen, wilfull, and variable,       [f. 263ʳ]
  richt fals, feckle, fell, and frivolus,
Dowgit, dispytfull, dour, and dissavable,
  Vnkynd, crewall, curst, and covettus,                4
  Ouirlicht of laitis, vnleill, and licherus,
    Turnit fra trewth, and taiclit With treichery,
    Vnferme of faith, fulfillit of fellony!

O stowt, stif, standfra, and vnstable,                 8
  Vnmeik but mesur, and malitius,
Angry, awstern, And till all evillis able,
  skornand, skaithful, skald, and most sklandrus,
  gredy not gude, Grym, gray, and vngratius,           12
    Noyus but neid, and full of Iniquitie,
    Vngentill, Iugeit, and full of Iolesie!

No. 211. 33 MS. asteyte.

Als terne as tygir, of tung vntollerable—
  o thow violent virago vennemouss,                    16
blasterand, bald, brym, and abhominable,
  ourperte, reprevivable, peirles, and perrellous,
  Evill cristiane, vnknawin, crafty, and cawtelus,
    Vnchest, evill chosin, and all but cheretie,       20
    Mellit with misdeid, and all mensworne ar ȝe!

      ffinis quod chauceir.

# NOTES

*(All texts, unless otherwise noted, are unique.)*

## 1. *A Minstrel's Greeting*

Brown and Robbins, *Index of Middle English Verse*, No. 1609. Previously printed by Flügel, *Anglia*, xxvi. 280–1; by Dyboski, EETS, ci. 117; and by Greene, *Early Eng. Carols*, pp. 284–5.

Nos. 1–8 set the key for all the 'Popular Songs'; they were no doubt used by professional minstrels in the course of their peregrinations. Two of the three main minstrel MSS. are represented in this group: Sloane MS. 2593 by Nos. 4, 5, and 7, and Bodl. MS. Eng. poet. e. 1 by No. 8. In all, one-third of the 'Popular Songs' are from these two MSS. The third MS., St. John's Coll. Camb. 259 (mainly religious, although it contains a typical minstrel's song, *Index*, No. 4078), is represented only by No. 24. For a brief discussion of these three MSS. see my article, 'The Earliest Carols and the Franciscans', in *MLN*, liii. 244–5. Although nearly 75 per cent. of the poems of all three MSS. are unique texts, nevertheless there was some circulation of the minstrel favourites: six of the poems in Sloane MS. are found in Bodl. MS. Eng. poet.; and in Richard Hill's commonplace book, Balliol Coll. Oxford MS. 354, twelve poems have parallels in Bodl. MS. Eng. poet., and three in Sloane MS.

burden. Vith par la pompe] with ceremonial procession.

## 2. *Invitation to Festivity, I*

*Index*, No. 1866. Previously printed by Flügel, *Anglia*, xxvi. 241; by Chambers & Sidgwick, *Early Eng. Lyrics*, p. 234; by Dyboski, EETS, ci. 15; by Greene, *Early Eng. Carols*, p. 9; and others.

The carol is spoken by the minstrel in the person of the Lord of Misrule, who presided over the Christmas festivities: his authority is indicated by his orders to the marshal (l. 2, a functionary in charge of seating arrangements at feasts) and by his power to extract forfeits, e.g. confinement in the stocks for those who did not enter into the revelry (l. 11).

### 3. *Invitation to Festivity, II*

*Index*, No. 2343. Previously printed by Hammerle, *Archiv*, clxvi. 204; and by Greene, *Early Eng. Carols*, p. 9.

At the end of the carol is a rubric dating it October 4, 1500: 'In die dominica prima post festum sancti Michaelis archangeli anno regis henrici septimi post conquestum anglie sextodecimo illa res erat scripta primo.'

### 4. *An Unwilling Minstrel*

*Index*, No. 1417. Previously printed by Wright, *Warton Club*, iv. 93.

1. If the minstrel attempts to sing, because his voice is bad (perhaps because of a cold), he will be blamed; consequently, he will only 'croak' a little and hope his job will soon be over.

8. tey vp ʒour ky] tune up your instrument.

11–12. The minstrel will try to appoint a day to suit his advice and agreement (to sing later when his voice is in good form).

### 5. *A Minstrel's Begging Song*

*Index*, No. 2675. Previously printed by Wright, *Warton Club*, iv. 32.

This nonsense song seems to have been specially composed for the appeal of its last line. See also Bodl. MS. Ashmole 48 (mid sixteenth cent.) for Minstrel Sheale's 'collection' song (printed by Wright, *Songs and Ballads*, Roxburghe Club 1855, pp. 162–3). Town pageants often concluded with such an appeal: see E. K. Chambers, *The English Folk Play*, passim, for a few examples. For specimens of scribes' appeals for drinks see *Bodleian Quarterly Record*, vol. 1, No. 2, p. 58; and G. G. Coulton, *Art and the Reformation*, pp. 521–2. For a reply on behalf of a lord, offering food and welcome to the singers, see Greene, *Early Eng. Carols*, p. 10. Other nonsense songs are represented here by Nos. 113–15.

### 6. *A Plea for Another Drink*

*Index*, No. 1608. Not heretofore printed. The presence of No. 3 in this early-sixteenth-century Welsh MS. suggests that this poem too is of minstrel use, a character which might otherwise be overlooked. The only other English, apart from a few medical receipts, is *Index*, No. 2683, a schoolboy's macaronic lament.

The first stanza is a perfectly regular example of *englyn unodl union*. The complicated rhyme scheme, with its assonance and alliteration, may be indicated by diacritical marks and italic letters:

I*s* t*é*ll yw my mynd, ane*s* t*à*y*li*u*r*, d*á*me ;    [traws]
   I *dé*m*e* we lak ples*ur*.
*ló*k*e* he*r*e, d*á*me, vn-*ló*k*e* you*r* d*ú*r ;    [croes]
a-*la*c*k*e we haue no *ly*k*ur.    [traws]

The second stanza is an example of *englyn proest*. It also occurs alone in Harley MS. 3725, fol. 32ʳ (also unpublished), added in an early-sixteenth-century hand on a blank page:

ffrend, an we ar ffer In det
ffor your ffyn good wyn, god wot,
short is the Ioynt of your peynt pot ;
I drank wonis, I wold drynke yet.

Immediately preceding the two stanzas is a Welsh *englyn* ; it has, unfortunately, no relation to the English :

och trwm yw'r galon ywch traeth / wych v'anwyl /
                                                    [MS. trwrn]
   och, vinab o hiraeth!                            [f'anap]
torraf vrwynen, gwen, pe gwaeth
braw kwyn-sserch no briw kan-ssaeth.

(Tr. 'Och, heavy is the heart above the shore, my fair darling ; och, my ill-luck in longing! I shall break a rush, Gwen, if the anxiety of lamenting love is worse than the wound of a hundred arrows.')

1. Is] The enclitic form of 'I shall'. That this is correct is confirmed by the metrical rules and rhyme scheme. Tr. 'I shall be frank with you, Annis (i.e. Agnes) Taylor, madame'.

5. and] even though.

## 7. *The Minstrel and His Wares*

*Index*, No. 3864. Previously printed by Wright, *Warton Club*, iv. 76–77 ; and by Greene, *Early Eng. Carols*, p. 279. This carol shows another aspect of the minstrel, that of a pedlar. Greene (p. 436) notes Chaucer's friar with his 'tippet farsed full of knives,' and lines from *Index*, No. 2777, a song against the friars:

> Thai dele with purses, pynnes, and knyves,
> With gyrdles, gloves, for wenches and wyves;
> Bot ever bacward the husband thryves
> Ther thai are haunted tille.

See also Wyclif, *Works* (1880), p. 12: 'þei becomen pedderis berynge knyues, pursis, pynnys and girdlis for wymmen.' The constant double-entendre in this poem should be compared with that in Nos. 30 and 31.

## 8. *A Carefree Life*

*Index*, No. 1468. Previously printed by Wright, *Percy Soc.* xxiii. 27; by Chambers & Sidgwick, *Early Eng. Lyrics*, p. 210; by Cook, *Reader*, p. 430; by Bennett, *England from Chaucer to Caxton*, p. 31; and by Greene, *Early Eng. Carols*, p. 278.

The composite picture of the minstrel given us in Poems 1–8 suggests an able and educated man: he might arrange the holiday season programme and direct festivities in some large house (Nos. 1–3); he had to lead the singing (No. 4), and it might be whispered that his voice improved with a drink (No. 5); at times he might turn pedlar and sell trinkets to the women folk (No. 7). He was widely travelled (No. 8). From the presence of Latin songs (in Sloane MS. 2593 and in MS. Eng. poet. e. 1) it may be inferred that he had at least some acquaintance with Latin.

7. rennyng at þe ball] Probably stool-ball, played by men and women, a simple game resembling cricket.

13–16. Greene (p. 435): 'The bachelor of the carol is apparently a chapman or pedlar, or it may be a gay friar.'

## 9. *A Toast to His Lost Mistress*

*Index*, No. 3898. Previously printed (with some inaccuracies) by Heuser, *Anglia*, xxx. 175–6. Wells, *Manual*, p. 493, describes No. 117, A Monologue of a Drunkard, from this same MS., as 'the oldest extant English drinking song'. However, this is not a song to be sung on festive occasions, as are the six items Nos. 9–14, but a very clever literary production describing how a man feels and reacts when drunk. No. 9 is somewhat better deserving of this designation. William Sandys, in his introduction to *Percy Soc.* xxiii, has a long discussion on 'Festive Songs'.

Almost all the known M.E. drinking songs are included here. Poems on the evils of excessive drinking are to be found: a thirteenth-century tag in Corpus Christi Coll. Cambridge MS. 337 (printed by James, *Cat.* ii. 169); and a translation from Latin in Lansdowne MS. 762 (printed in *Cat.*, p. 169; and in *Reliquiae Antiquae*, i. 288); as well as less serious discussions (e.g. *Index*, No. 163). A long poem (*Index*, No. 1726), relating the formation of a Fraternity of Drinkers, is printed by me in *SP*, xlvii. 35–41; and by A. C. Baugh, *Philologica* (Malone *Festschrift*), pp. 164–6.

The general sense is clear, although some words are obscure: What would not the singer do for his love? He would search for a drink in which to toast her. He would be avenged on any man, irrespective of his rank, who was so foolhardy as to harm her. But alas, he curses himself, he has lost his love. No great man—at this point words fail him; he can say no more, and commends his love to Christ.

## 10. *A Drinking Song* (with music)

*Index*, No. 795. Previously printed by Stainer, *Early Bodl. Music*, ii. 150; and by Padelford, *Anglia*, xxxvi. 109.

5. 'Pour out the drink'? Or *vesse* = voiçi?

## 11. *A Three-part Catch for Drinking* (with music)

*Index*, No. 3259. Previously printed by Stainer, *Early Bodl. Music*, ii. 177–8; by Padelford, *Anglia*, xxxvi. 114; by Chambers & Sidgwick, *Early Eng. Lyrics*, p. 226; and by J. Copley, *Seven English Songs and Carols of the Fifteenth Century*, Univ. of Leeds Texts & Monographs, vi (1940), No. 7. The present text is a composite arranged from the three parts, each of which is written in full under its own music. Copley (p. 5) notes that this is 'a fine example of the way in which a more harmonic style is applied to three-part writing', and that 'the piece might be called a part-song in the modern sense'.

2. The tapster's answer.

4. Avale] Possibly enveil, wreathe. Cf. *Index*, No. *17,

ll. 358–61: A fayre garlond of yve grene / Whyche hangeth at a taverne dore / Hyt ys a false token as I wene / But yf there be wyne gode and sewer.

## 12. *Good Cheer*

*Index*, No. 1201. Not heretofore printed. Added on a flyleaf.

## 13. *Bring Good Ale*

*Index*, No. 549. Previously printed many times: see *Index* for details. Another text of six stanzas occurs in Harley MS. 541, fol. 214ᵛ; this has been printed, with the Bodl. text, by Wright, *Percy Soc.* xxiii. 63, 102; by Greene, *Early Eng. Carols*, pp. 285–7; and separately. Modernized versions occur frequently. Its last two stanzas are variants (veal, cider). For a full note on the error of linking the preceding music with this carol, first pointed out by Chambers & Sidgwick (pp. 370–1), see Greene (pp. 437–8).

19–20. The emendation of *godes good* to *gotes blod* by the transposition of *good* and *blod* certainly improves the sense.

## 14. *Fill Every Glass*

*Index*, No. 903. Previously printed by Flügel, *Anglia*, xxvi. 282; by Dyboski, EETS, ci. 118; by Chambers & Sidgwick, *Early Eng. Lyrics*, p. 227 and pp. 371–2, with many parallels and illustrations; and by Greene, *Early Eng. Carols*, p. 285.

burden. rowght] cf. No. 11, l. 8.

21. Pun on the name 'Walter'; cf. *2 Henry VI*, iv. i. 35: 'And told me that by water I should die.'

## 15. *The Irish Dancer*

*Index*, No. 1008. This and the following three items (as well as No. 9) are short fourteenth-century fragments written on a narrow strip of vellum, about four inches wide, bound as the first item in Bodl. MS. Rawlinson D. 913. It may originally have been a small roll; it is now excessively smeared with heavy paste. The whole series, of about a dozen scraps, has been printed by Heuser, *Anglia*, xxx. 173–9. This poem has been discussed also by Chambers & Sidgwick, *Early Eng. Lyrics*, p. 279; by Sisam. *XIV Cent.*

*Verse & Prose*, p. 166; by Wells, *Manual*, p. 493; and by
Greene, *Early Eng. Carols*, p. xxxvi, who claims it as one
of the earliest English 'carols' (first half of the fourteenth
century). See also E. K. Chambers, *Eng. Lit. at Close of MA*,
pp. 77–8.

These love poems, Nos. 15 to 32, are among the freshest
and most charming of all early English compositions. They
are genuinely popular, as is shown by their realistic content, their simple form, and their casual manner of preservation. Many of them have come down only by hazard,
being scribbled on the blank leaves of learned books. This
group forms a counterpart to the more sophisticated group
of lyrics (many with the music preserved) in Nos. 141–76.

### 16. *The Hawthorn Tree*

*Index*, No. 2622. Previously printed by Heuser, *Anglia*,
xxx. 174.

### 17. *All Night by the Rose*

*Index*, No. 194. Previously printed by Heuser, *Anglia*,
xxx. 176. A scrap in Camb. Univ. MS. Hh. 6. 11 (*Index*, No.
1279, unpublished) somewhat resembles this piece—a fair
rose plucked by a churl:

> I am Rose, wo is me,
> Sutere þat i suete þe;
> I wacs þat weylawey,
> cherles hand me þristet ay.

### 18. *Maiden of the Moor*

*Index*, No. 3891. Previously printed in *Cat. Cod. MSS.
Rawl.*, p. 137; by Heuser, *Anglia*, xxx. 175; and by Sisam.
*XIV Cent. Verse & Prose*, p. 167. The first line occurs as an
incipit to indicate the tune for a Latin religious lyric,
modelled on the same roundel form, in the *Red Book of
Ossory* (Greene, *Speculum*, xxvii. 504–6).

### 19. *A Lover's Plea* (with music)

*Index*, No. 2185. Previously printed by Greene, *Early
Eng. Carols*, p. 300.

Caius Coll. Camb. MS. 383 is a mid-fifteenth-century miscellany of Latin treatises and grammatical notes, French

deeds and accounts, and a few pages of English poems. The MS. gives documentary evidence of the manner of singing carols, for several texts have the burden copied in full (or otherwise indicated) after each stanza. Represented here are Nos. 19 and 23 (p. 210), 28 and 29 (p. 41), 33 (p. 190), and 37 (p. 68).

burden. It (my present situation) is not what I could wish for.

### 20. *The Banished Lover*

*Index*, No. 1333. Not heretofore printed. This piece is no doubt a carol, but the burden is lacking. The other poem on this folio (No. 26) is a carol with the burden preserved. Both are very late texts.

### 21. *Love in the Garden*

*Index*, No. 1302. Previously printed by Wright, *Warton Club*, iv. 35–36.

15–16. She filled me up with liquor, just as I had 'filled' or 'grafted' her.

23–24. Play on words: she had produced not a 'Ienet' (John) pear (ll. 8, 24), but a 'Robert' pear (cf. No. 116, l. 13).

### 22. *Careless Love*

*Index*, No. 3418. Previously printed by Greene, *Early Eng. Carols*, p. 306.

6. This line is that suggested by Greene.

### 23. *A Forsaken Maiden's Lament*

*Index*, No. 1330. Previously printed by Greene, *Early Eng. Carols*, p. 308. The tune indicated before the burden is not No. 147, which has the same opening words. The interchangeability of a tune for several sets of words, however, is illustrated by a note in Bodl. MS. Eng. poet. e. 1 (following *Index*, No. 3736): 'Thys is þe tewyn for þe song foloying; yf so be þat ȝe wyll haue a noþer tewyn, it may as at ȝowr plesur, for I haue set all þe song.'

### 24. *The Wily Clerk*

*Index*, No. 3594. Previously printed by James and Macaulay, *MLR*, viii. 71 ; and by Greene, *Early Eng. Carols*, p. 308.

James and Macaulay comment (p. 86): 'The text of this piece is so corrupt that it is hopeless to attempt to restore it.'

14. Cf. No. 26, ll. 17–19.

## 25. *A Betrayed Maiden's Lament*

*Index*, No. 3409. Previously printed in *Reliquiae Antiquae*, i. 1; by Hazlitt, *Faiths and Folklore*, ii. 617; and by Greene, *Early Eng. Carols*, p. 309.

For other betrayed maidens' laments, see Nos. 23, 28, and 29.

## 26. *Our Sir John*

*Index*, No. 2494. Not heretofore printed.

17. Cf. No. 28, l. 18; No. 179, l. 63. The practice of giving gifts, especially rings, was apparently common: cf. 'The Maid and the Magpie' (MS. Rawl. C. 258), printed by Halliwell, *Nugae Poeticae*, p. 42 (ll. 17–20):

> He toke then out a good golde ryng,
> A purse of velweytt that was too fyne,
> Have ye thys, my dere swetyng,
> With that ye wylbe lemman myne.

## 27. *Jolly Jankin*

*Index*, No. 377. Previously printed by Wright, *Warton Club*, iv. 100–1; by Chambers & Sidgwick, *Early Eng. Lyrics*, pp. 220–1; and by Greene, *Early Eng. Carols*, p. 309.

This poem is in the same vein as the parodies on the mass, English examples of which are the Venus Mass (*Index*, No. 4186), and 'The Book of Cupid' or 'The Cuckoo and the Nightingale' (*Index*, No. 3361), which takes the several parts of the mass as titles for its love-poems. The choice of the refrain, 'Kyrie eleyson', provides a pun on the woman's name, Alison. Chambers and Sidgwick (p. 370) quote from *Index*, No. 1091:

> And theos prude maidenes . . .
> Heo runeth togaderes
>   and speketh of derne luve,
> Hwenne heo to chirche cometh
>   to the haliday.

For this refrain in popular poetry, cf. Margit Sahlin, *Étude sur la carole médiévale*, Upsala 1940, pp. 113–31.

14. Cf. *Liber Cure Cocorum* (*Index*, No. 2361), l. 46:
'Hakke smalle þy wortis and persyl.'

## 28. *A Midsummer Day's Dance*

*Index*, No. 1849. Previously printed by Greene, *Early Eng. Carols*, pp. 307–8.

41. Euer bi on & by on] Again and again.
44. Cf. *The Proverbs of Hendyng* (*Index*, No. 1669), l. 272:
'Euer out comeþe euel sponne web.'

## 29. *The Serving Maid's Holiday*

*Index*, No. 225. Previously printed by Greene, *Early Eng. Carols*, pp. 306–7.

18. 'I ought to spread out all this bowl [full of dough].'

## 30. *Silver White*

*Index*, No. 438. Previously printed (with some inaccuracies) by L. S. M[eyer], *Music, Cantalenas, Songs*, London 1906 (edition limited to 100 copies). This, and the following 'Cantelena', occur in a collection of songs, many with music; although these songs are apparently sophisticated, nevertheless the tone of these two poems suggests a popular usage. In both cases, the poems are written as prose and are considerably abbreviated; the poems are here reconstructed with the omissions indicated by '&c.' supplied in full. Both texts pose a number of problems in interpretation; and the double entendre is marked.

There is apparently one stanza (East) lacking. The speaker of the poem is a woman, and the overt imagery is that of a tournament: ware (target), bogeler (buckler), iust (joust), etc. The double entendre follows two lines: the secondary meanings of ware, smote, with the hidden verbs in bogeler (buck), peckel, and bosshelle (buss); and the successive enlargements of the 'ware' from bogeler (?) through peck to bushel.

1. seluer whyte] Apparently some place of assignation.
8. by syde] near (the mark).

### 31. *In My Lady's Chamber*

*Index*, No. 2135. Previously printed by Meyer, *Music, Cantalenas, Songs*.

### 32. *Little Pretty Mopsy*

*Index*, No. 150. Previously printed in *HMC*, Fifth Report, App., p. 458; and by Greene, *Early Eng. Carols*, pp. 301–2. This carol dates *circa* 1500.

### 33. *In Praise of Brunettes*

*Index*, No. 3174. Not heretofore printed.
20. by me & mo] According to my way of thinking and that of others. Cf. l. 6.

### 34. *In Praise of Women*

*Index*, No. 3782. Previously printed in *Reliquiae Antiquae*, i. 275; by Chambers & Sidgwick, *Early Eng. Lyrics*, p. 197; and by Greene, *Early Eng. Carols*, p. 264. Added to MS. in an early-sixteenth-century hand.

The songs in praise of women are mainly popular, but there are a few literary pieces, e.g. *Index*, No. 1504 (Harley MS. 2253), No. 1596 (Vernon MS.), and two late Scottish texts, Nos. 228 and *20. The carol collection of St. John's Coll. Camb. MS. 259 has two items in praise of women, *Index*, Nos. 1492 and 3098; Camb. Univ. MS. Addit. 5943 (sometimes popular in tone) has *Index*, No. 4218; and Sloane MS. 2593 has *Index*, No. 4219. The tendency seems to have been to divert the praise of women in general to the particular praise of the Blessed Virgin as the exemplar of women. The poems praising a mistress have little to do with these general praises—'they do the wash and do the wring' is a conception not known in courtship and wooing.

### 35. *A Young Girl's Ideal*

*Index*, No. 2654. Previously printed by Ritson, *Ancient Songs*, 1829, ii. 8–9; by Fairholt, *Percy Soc.* xxvii. 58; by Furnivall, *Ballad Soc.* vii, p. cxxx; and by Greene, *Early Eng. Carols*, pp. 303–4.

Sloane MS. 1584, early sixteenth century, is a commonplace book of Canon John Gysborn; it includes instructions on confession, receipts, prayers in prose. From this MS. comes also No. 206.

The 'troly loly' refrain is very common at this period; and Furnivall notes a couple 'of a hundred specimens'. The phrase occurs as the alternate burden of No. 26.

## 36. *Old Hogyn's Adventure*

*Index*, No. 1222. Previously printed by Flügel, *Anglia*, xxvi. 273–4; and by Dyboski, EETS, ci. 111–12.

## 37. *A Mocking Song of Love*

*Index*, No. 1280. Previously printed by Greene, *Early Eng. Carols*, p. 317.

3. No doubt a parody; cf. Worcester Cath. MS. F. 64 fragment (*Index*, No. 1142, printed by B. Dickins, *Leeds Studies in English*, iv. 44):

> He may cume to mi lef bute by þe watere;
> Wanne me lust slepen, þanne moti wakie;
> Wnder is þat hi liuie.

## 38. *Abuse of Women*

*Index*, No. 1485. Occurs also in Bodl. MS. Eng. poet. e. 1. Both texts printed frequently; together by Greene, *Early Eng. Carols*, pp. 265–6. The only important variants are ll. 19–20 which continue the pattern of l. 18:

> ffor by women was neuer man betraied,
> ffor by women was neuer man bewreyed.

The humour of this poem, of course, lies in the employment of the burden after every verse, which changes entirely the meaning of the stanzas.

As with poems attacking marriage and poems treating of love in a mocking fashion, so here in poems of attacks on womankind, there are two main classes: popular poems and sophisticated poems. In the minstrel collection, Bodl. MS. Eng. poet. e. 1, a MS. containing the popular songs of the day, collected to meet a genuine popular demand, and not collected because they appealed to the interests of a single literate poetaster, there are many attacks on women: included here are Nos. 38, 39, 44, and 114 (also in Balliol Coll. Oxford MS. 354). Then there are the literary attacks, represented here by Nos. 209–12; and also by *Index*, No. 2029 (pseudo-Chaucer); Nos. 2237, 3656, 3744 (pseudo-Lydgate); and No. 2640 (pseudo-Hoccleve, printed here No. 210). These poems quickly developed stereotyped conventions, and the sophisticated attacks parallel the set descriptions of the beloved and of the routine love epistles.

### 39. *The Trials of Marriage*

*Index*, No. 3919. Previously printed by Wright, *Percy Soc.* xxiii. 35, as part of a 'carol' with the burden, 'Man be war or þou knyte þe fast' (*Index*, No. 2049). The 'carol' is actually four disconnected moral quatrains, the first three on the subject of marriage (*Index*, Nos. 2049, 3919, 2056, 1354). The first two lines of *Index*, No. 2049 resemble lines in the two poems following here, Nos. 40 and 41:

> Man be war or þou knyte þe fast:
> Oftyn man Rewth at þe last.

A tag (*Index*, No. 1392) in Lansdowne MS. 762 (printed in *Reliquiae Antiquae*, i. 289) also parallels this piece:

> I winked, I winked, whan I a woman toke.
> Sore me for-thinked that I so moch wynked,
> ffor had I neuer more nede than nowe for to loke.

In No. 59 is one stanza on the sorrows of marriage—without money (ll. 21–24).

### 40. *Against Hasty Marriage, I*

*Index*, No. 1829. Not heretofore printed. Occurs on the first of four small pages (bound in the MS. with miscellaneous histories, chronicles, prophecies, &c.) along with *Index*, No. 3260 and several Latin prophecies.

### 41. *Against Hasty Marriage, II*

*Index*, No. 1938. Previously printed by Wright, *Warton Club*, iv. 27; by Fehr, *Archiv*, cix. 49; and by Greene, *Early Eng. Carols*, pp. 270–1.

burden. Cf. No. 40, l. 5; and cf. also *Secunda Pastorum* (Townley Plays, xii. 91–95):

> Bot yong men of wowyng, for god that you boght,
> Be well war of wedyng, and thynk in youre thoght
> 'Had I wyst' is a thyng it seruys of noght.
> Mekyll styll mournyng has wedyng home broght,
>     And grefys.

1. The first stanza almost duplicates that of No. 40.

4. This line has the force of a proverb. 'Turn vp her halter and let her go' occurs as the refrain of No. 181 and *Index*, No. 1338.

15. Cf. *Piers Plowman*, A. iii. 126: 'Heo is tikel of hire tayl.'

### 42. *The Tribulations of Marriage*

*Index*, No. *63. Not heretofore printed in full; second stanza only has been printed in *Reliquiae Antiquae*, ii. 113. Text is added on flyleaf.

### 43. *A Henpecked Husband's Complaint, I*

*Index*, No. 4279. Previously printed by Wright, *Warton Club*, iv. 70–1; by Chambers & Sidgwick, *Early Eng. Lyrics*, p. 207; and by Greene, *Early Eng. Carols*, p. 271. This MS. contains a similar carol ('3yng men I red that ye bewar', *Index*, No. 4278).

### 44. *A Henpecked Husband's Complaint, II*

*Index*, No. 210. Previously printed by FitzGibbon, *Early Eng. Poetry*, p. 179; by Wright, *Percy Soc.* xxiii. 26–7; by Chambers & Sidgwick, *Early English Lyrics*, p. 208; and by Greene, *Early Eng. Carols*, p. 272.

burden. Cf. No. 37.

18. An almost proverbial phrase. See *Index*, No. *30, and Utley, *Med. St.*, viii. 303–9.

19. The meaning here seems to be that the husband is undergoing a 'hell on earth', and that this punishment should be credited him!

### 45. *My Young Sister*

*Index*, No. 1303. Previously printed by Wright, *Warton Club*, iv. 33–4; and by Wülcker, *AE Lesebuch*, ii. 122.

Similar paradoxes are not infrequent: cf. the 'Ballad of

Lord Roslin's Daughter' and 'The Four Sisters' in Wright, *Warton Club*, iv. 109–14, 114–15. A riddling tag occurs in Bodl. MS. Eng. poet. e. 1, fol. 20ᵛ (*Index*, No. 1354; printed, with some inaccuracies, by Wright, *Percy Soc.* xxiii. 35):

> I saw iij hedles playen at a ball,
> an hanlas man served hem all,
> Whyll iij movthles men lay & low,
> iij legles a-way hem drow.

See further the nonsense poems included here, Nos. 113–15, and especially notes to No. 114. A poem of 'impossible situations' in a religious vein occurs in Bodl. MS. Laud Misc. 108, fol. 238ʳ (*Index*, No. 496, unprinted):

> Byhalde merueylis: a mayde ys moder,
> her sone her fader ys & broder.
> lyfe fauȝt with deþe & deþe is slayne;
> Most hiȝ was lowe: he styȝe agayne.

Another riddle, 'Faire laydis I pray yow till me / Whos this ij fayre cheldren be' (7 lines), occurs on a flyleaf in a Westminster School MS. The most widely circulated poem along these lines is *Index*, No. 3943, 'Merlin's Prophecy', in at least 14 MSS. (add to *Index*, Bodl. MS. Rawl. poet. F. 32, fol. 2ᵛ; and Magdalene Coll. Camb. MS. 1236, fol. 91ʳ, printed herewith):

> When feythe fayleth in prestys sawys,
> & lordys wyll be londys lawys,
> And lechery is preuy solas,
> & robbery ys goode purchas,
> Than shall the londe of albeon
> be turned into confusion.

## 46. *My Gentle Cock*

*Index*, No. 1299. Previously printed by Wright, *Warton Club*, iv. 31; by Chambers & Sidgwick, *Early Eng. Lyrics*, p. 249; by Cook, *Reader*, p. 429; and by Sisam, *Nun's Priest's Tale*, p. 32.

## 47. *My Twelve Oxen*

*Index*, No. 1314. Previously printed by Flügel, *Anglia*, xxvi. 197; by Dyboski, EETS, ci. 104; by Chambers & Sidgwick, *Early Eng. Lyrics*, p. 250; and by Chambers, *Eng. Lit. at Close of MA*, p. 113.

## 48. *The Fox and the Goose*

*Index*, No. 1622. Printed also by Bowers, *JEGP*, li. 393–4. Occurs on the flyleaf of a French 'Sayings of the Philosophers'.

7. i.e. outwit you. See Joyce Bazire, *English St.*, xxxiv. 163.
13. all be the heye] in a twinkling. Cf. No. 14, l. 2.

## 49. *The False Fox*

*Index*, No. 3328. Previously printed by Zupitza, *Archiv*, lxxxix. 285–6; and in *Reliquiae Antiquae*, i. 4–5.

## 50. *Holly and Ivy*

*Index*, No. 1225. Previously printed by Wright, *Percy Soc.* xxiii. 44; by Chambers & Sidgwick, *Early Eng. Lyrics*, p. 237; and by Greene, *Early Eng. Carols*, p. xcix.
2. maystre] Possibly a reference to the folk games between Holly (representing the men) and Ivy (the women). See *Index*, No. 1226; and A. K. Moore, *MLN*, lxii. 553–5.
6, 9. Chambers & Sidgwick emend 'þei' to 'we'.

## 51. *In Praise of Holly*

*Index*, No. 1195. Previously printed by Wright, *Percy Soc.* xxiii. 84–85; by Chambers & Sidgwick, *Early Eng. Lyrics*, p. 238; by F. A. Patterson, *Shakespeare and the Medieval Lyric*, p. 444; and by Greene, *Early Eng. Carols*, pp. 94–95.

## 52. *In Praise of Ivy*

*Index*, No. 3438. Previously printed by Wright, *Percy Soc.* xxiii. 85; by Chambers & Sidgwick, *Early Eng. Lyrics*, p. 236; and by Greene, *Early Eng. Carols*, p. 95.
'Veni, coronaberis' (*Song of Songs*, iv. 8) is more properly found as the burden and refrain of a carol to the Blessed Virgin by James Ryman (*Index*, No. 641); and as the refrain of a Song of the Assumption (*Index*, No. 3225). This parodying of a poem in honour of the Virgin is continued by the phraseology (especially in lines 3 and 6). In *Index*, No. 2735, the popular praise of Ivy is given a religious interpretation by the acronym I (Ihesus), V (Virgin), and E (Emmanuel). 'Iuy is both fair & gren' is one of twelve carols (for St. George's Chapel, Windsor) in Egerton MS. 3307.

## 53. *A Boar's Head Song*

*Index*, No. 3735. Previously printed by Wright, *Percy Soc.* xxiii. 25–26.

## 54. *A Boar's Head Carol, I*

*Index*, No. 436. Previously printed by Wright, *Percy Soc.* xxiii. 42–43 ; and by Greene, *Early Eng. Carols*, pp. 92–93.

The importance of the boar's head in feasting is indicated not only by its appearance in medieval banquets as the first course, but by the survival of a 'sotelty'—a short poem which was attached to the dish (cf. No. 105) : *Index*, No. 3886 is a 'sotelty' for a boar's head, served as the first course of a bridal feast.

## 55. *A Boar's Head Carol, II*

*Index*, No. 3313. Previously printed many times: see *Index* for details.

The Latin burden and refrains (not found in other Boar's Head carols) indicate that this song would be sung by those with a nodding familiarity with Latin. The traditional carol sung at the still-surviving ceremony of the Boar's Head at Queen's College, Oxford, is a variant of this text. For the story of killing the boar see Appendix to J. R. Magrath, *The Queen's College*, Oxford 1921. No. 56, which has a similar opening, is the 'lewed' version of this carol.

## 56. *A Boar's Head Carol, III*

*Index*, No. 3314. Previously printed in *Reliquiae Antiquae*, ii. 30; by Wright, *Percy Soc.* iv. 3–4; by Furnivall, EETS, 32 (1868), p. 264\*; by Greene, *Early Eng. Carols*, p. 93; and others.

The first three stanzas (corresponding to No. 53) are obviously the core of the carol. The next two stanzas are merely versified quatrains of the dishes at a medieval banquet. At this point the versifier apparently lost interest in his song, and added the remainder of the catalogue in three rhymed couplets. This approach is what might be expected in a commonplace book such as Porkington MS. 10.

17. schow] Greene glosses *broth* ; Furnivall suggests 'sewe' (= *stew*).

## 57. *Sir Penny, I*

*Index*, No. 2747. Previously printed many times: see *Index* for details.

Burden. The first line of the burden occurs in *Parlement of Byrdes*, l. 148, printed by Hazlitt, *Remains*, iii. 174:

> Here is nought els with friende nor foe,
> But go bet, peny, go bet, go.

## 58. *Sir Penny, II*

*Index*, No. 1480. Previously printed by Ritson, *Ancient Popular Poetry*, 1833, pp. 103–8; by Wright, *Camden Soc.* xvi. 359; by Hall, *Eng. St.* xxi. 204; and by Fitz-Gibbon, *Early Eng. Poetry*, pp. 13–14. A shorter version (93 lines) occurs in Caius Coll. Camb. MS. 174, printed in *Reliquiae Antiquae*, ii. 108–10; and by Hazlitt, *Remains*, i. 161–7.

Two other poems (both mid-sixteenth-century) on the Power of the Purse are to be found in Pepys MS. 2253 (printed by Craigie, *STS*, n.s. vii. 399); and in Advocates MS. 1. 1. 6 (printed by Hailes, *Ancient Scottish Poems*, 1770, pp. 193–5; and by Sibbald, *Chronicle of Scottish Poetry*, 1802, iii. 227).

29. i.e. To wear low trailing gowns.
60. in horde] in the state of being hoarded.
73. i.e. Peni.

## 59. *The Power of the Purse*

*Index*, No. 2082. Previously printed by Wright, *Percy Soc.* xxiii. 35–36; and by Arber, *Dunbar Anthology*, p. 179.

21–28. Lines reconstructed.
34. parvis] The Portico of St. Paul's was a common place for lawyers to gather; cf. *Canterbury Tales*, Prologue, ll. 311–12.

## 60. *On Penny*

*Index*, No. 3209. Previously printed by James, *Cat.* i. 317; and by Greene, *Early Eng. Carols*, p. 429. On end flyleaf in a neat fourteenth-century hand.

## 61. *A Charm by the Holy Rood*

*Index*, No. 1182. Previously printed by Stephens, *Archaeologia*, xxx. 398; and by Holthausen, *Anglia*, xix. 85.

1. tymbris three] The crosses on which Christ and the two thieves were crucified.

## 62. *A Charm Against Robbers*

*Index*, No. 939. Previously printed by Meyer, *Music, Cantalenas, Songs*, p. 42. This conjuration is immediately preceded by a prayer, written as prose, with the sign of the cross at the end of each phrase:

> God & sient trinite, ✠
> as I by-lyue on the, ✠
> for thy grace & for thy my3t, ✠
> Saue me, lorde, boþe by day & ny3t ✠
> fro al enemys & ffro all tene ✠
> & fro al tho that vntrywe ben. ✠
> by the vertu of thy ry3t Arme ✠
> Save me, lorde, fro al harme.

## 63. *A Charm Against Thieves*

*Index*, No. 3771. Not heretofore printed. This poem and No. 64 are in a small MS. ($4\frac{1}{2} \times 4\frac{1}{4}$ inches), which is a kind of pocket-book of medical receipts and charms written on different pieces of vellum all bound together. No. 63 and No. 64 are both written in a late-fifteenth-century hand.

A thirteenth-century charm against thieves (*Index*, No. 993) occurs in *olim* Ashburnham MS. 120, Art. 17 (now Paris, Bibl. nat. MS. n.a.l. 693), printed in *Cat. MSS. at Ashburnham Place*, London, n.d., Appendix:

> God was iborn in bedlem,
> Iborin he was in ierusalem,
> Ifolewid in the flum iordan;
> Ther nes inemmed ne wolf ne thef.

## 64. *A Charm for Travellers*

*Index*, No. 1199. Not heretofore printed. Headed in MS. by a circle, on the circumference of which is inscribed, '✠ Alpha ✠ Et Oo ✠'.

## 65. *A Charm Against Fever*

*Index*, No. 3911. Not heretofore printed. Written in an early-sixteenth-century hand. The use of the Wounds of Christ as practical remedies, not against (as is usual) the sins, but against ill health, is interesting. A similar charm in prose occurs in Sloane MS. 1314, fol. 39ʳ.

## 66. *A Charm Against the Night Goblin*

*Index*, No. 2903. Not heretofore printed. The hand is early fifteenth century. The concluding rubric shows an extension of the practice of wearing amulets. This charm apparently continued popular, for it is found in R. Scott, *The Discoverie of Witchecraft*, 1584, Book 4, ch. 12.

## 67. *Occupations of the Months*

*Index*, No. 579. Previously printed by Förster, *Archiv*, cxxviii. 296. MS. Digby 88 is a mid-fifteenth-century collection of English and Latin verse and prose pieces on prognostications, medicines, weather, palmistry, &c. Another text occurs in B.M. MS. Addit. 22720, fol. 6ʳ (unprinted). In both MSS. the verses are attached to miniatures portraying the appropriate occupations in a Calendar. For a discussion on 'Occupations of the Months in Medieval Calendars' see J. F. Willard, *Bodleian Quarterly Record*, vii. No. 74, pp. 33–39.

MS. Addit. variants:
- 3. And with þis byll Y pare my vine
- 8. And here Y repe my wete for nede
- 11. With þis ax Y kile my swyne
- 12. O þes cuppes Y drynk boþe ale & wyn

## 68. *Days in the Months*

*Index*, No. 3571. Not heretofore printed from this MS. Occurs also in N.L.W. MS. Mostyn Welsh 129 (*HMC*, Report on Welsh MSS., 1896, i. 65); Ripon Minster MS. (Fowler, *Yorks. Arch. Journal*, ii. 401); Cooke MS. 21 (*HMC*, Sixth Report, p. 419); Huntington MS. HU 1051 (*HMC*, 1928 Report, p. 419; Wilson, *Osiris*, vi. 427). There are unimportant variants in all texts.

## 69. *Months, Weeks, and Days*

*Index*, No. 1396. Previously printed by Förster, *Anglia*, xlii. 207.

## 70. *To Find Easter*

*Index*, No. 1502. Not heretofore printed from this MS. Occurs also in eight other MSS.: Bodl. MS. Lat. misc. e. 22 (R); Camb. Univ. Ee. 4. 35, Part I; Magdalene Coll. Camb. 13; Trinity Coll. Camb. 1081 (James, *Cat*. iii. 55); Harley 3810, Part I, fol. 52ᵛ; Royal 2. A. xvii (Bishop, EETS, 109. xlix); Lambeth 545 (James and Jenkins, *Cat.*, p. 748); Brough Hall (*HMC*, Third Report, p. 255).

The MS. is an early-fifteenth-century Horae written in Flanders for use in England. The text is added on the flyleaf in an early-sixteenth-century hand.

  6. 'Count that Sunday as the first of your three.'

## 71. *St. Paul's Day Prognostications*

*Index*, No. 1423. Previously printed in *HMC*, Second Report, p. 180. The MS. is a fifteenth-century Calendar, and this text is added at the foot of the page for the month of January.

There are many Latin texts of this verse, two printed in *Reliquiae Antiquae*, i. 93 (from a transcript from Spalding Register), and ii. 10 (from Harley MS. 4043). Other variants occur in Caius Coll. Camb. MS. 444; Boston Med. Lib. MS. 20; and Trinity Coll. Camb. MS. 1450, f. 64ᵛ (unprinted):

> Clara dies Pauli tempora denotat anni:
> Si fuerint venti designat prelia genti;
> Si nix vel pluuia designat tempora chara;
> Si fuerint nebulae pereunt animalia.

For a discussion on the practical use by farmers of such prophecies see my article in *PQ*, xviii. 321–31. Archer Taylor, *The Proverb*, pp. 109, has numerous comments on weather lore in gnomic verses.

## 72. *Christmas Day Prognostications*

*Index*, No. 1905. Not heretofore printed. The four other variants are all unpublished: Bodl. MS. Ashmole 189, fol. 210ʳ (lacks first 62 lines); Trinity Coll. Camb. MS. 600,

p. 257 (a late text: 126 lines); Sloane MS. 1315, fol. 65ʳ (with 20 extra lines at end); Huntington MS. HM 64, fol. 95ʳ (considerable variation: 168 lines). Another set of variants occurs in *Index*, No. 1989. The prognostics which date from New Year's Day (*Index*, Nos. 73, 3265, 4253; 1194) are very similar, even to incorporating similar lines.

## 73. *The Lucky and Unlucky Days*

*Index*, No. 2131. Not heretofore printed. The tenacity of these prognostics is shown by very similar forecasts appearing in many newspapers and magazines today, and by the survival of medieval verses in the nineteenth and twentieth centuries in the modern 'Farmers' Almanac'. See Förster, 'Die Altenglischen Verzeichnisse von Glücks- und Unglückstagen', in *Studies in English Philology in honor of Frederick Klaeber*, pp. 258–77.

A shorter, but similar, set of prognostics, 'Nota for the Days of the Moone' (*Index*, No. 956), occurs in Bodl. MS. Digby 88, fol. 62ʳ, unprinted:

Nota for the Days of the Moone:

God made Adam the fyrst day of þe moone,
And the secunde day Eve good dedis to doon.
The iij day then was Caym borne—
Begynne not on that day tille on þe morne.⠀⠀⠀⠀⠀⠀4
The iiij^th day, as I you say, ys right good for man,
ffor Abel in certayn he was borne thanne.
The v day ys right good and selle;
And on the vj day was borne Danyel.⠀⠀⠀⠀⠀⠀8
The vij day Caym Abel sloo; þat day ys good I-nowe.
The viij day & the ix^th good dedes may be doo.
The x day goo noo pilgremage,
But the xj day do thy vyage.⠀⠀⠀⠀⠀⠀12
The xij day goo vppon noo floode,
And the xiij ys yet not so good.
The xiiij ys good to tary,
And the xv yt ys contrary.⠀⠀⠀⠀⠀⠀16
The xvj day wyth-owten stryve;
And the xvij sanke Cyteis v.
The xviij ys good all thynge to do,
And the xix ys not soo.⠀⠀⠀⠀⠀⠀20

The xx day, as I you say,
And the xxj good dedes do þou may.
The xxij & xxiij, as I rede, wyth-owte drede,    [fol. 62ᵛ]
In all good werke may men spede.    24
The xxiiij and xxv day
Thow mayste well take thy Iournay.
The xxvj day of þe Moone
Good dedys may be doon.    28
The xxvij day and xxviij begynne noo thynge,
But loke þou abyde a better tymynge.
The xxix true it ys
That thy worke shall turne to blysse;    32
And the xxx day, for to spede,
Begynne noo werke as I the rede.

Non plus.

## 74. *Instructions for Purchasing Land*

*Index*, No. 4148. Not heretofore printed from this MS.
This poem occurs in fourteen MSS., and therefore ranks as
one of the most popular items in Middle English verse.
For details of MSS. and printings see *Index*. All texts show
some variations, but they fall into two groups: (1) That in
twenty-two lines represented by Bodl. MS. Douce 54, and
found in similar form in Bodl. MS. Ashmole 61, Lansdowne
MS. 762, and Royal MS. 17. B. xlvii (with introductory
couplet); and, lacking ll. 15–16, in Lambeth MS. 306; and,
with two extra lines inserted between ll. 4 and 5, in Bodl.
MS. Rawl. B. 252; (2) That in 18 lines represented by Camb.
Univ. MS. Hh. 2. 6, a version followed by Trinity Coll.
Camb. MS. 1157 and Lansdowne MS. 470 (which adds two
extra lines between lines 15 and 16), and by *olim* Capesthorne MS. (now Bodl. MS. Lat. misc. c. 66), which adds
ll. 19–20 from the Douce MS. The Camb. Univ. text,
hitherto unprinted, reads:

Who so wille be wise in purchasyng
Consider thes poyntes that ben folowyng.
Se that the seller be of age,
And that the lond be in no morgage.    4
Se whether the lond be bond or fre,
And se the reles of euery feoffe.

> looke what quyte Rent therof out must goo,
> And what seruice longith therto.                                    8
> looke whethir it movith of a weddyd women,
> And ware well of covert de baron.
> loke whether therof a tayl may be found,                          •
> And whether it stand in statut merchaund bound.       12
> And if thow be ware & wyse,
> Se that thi chartre be made with warantyse.
> And if it be lordship lond or housyng,
> To these iij longith diuerse payinges,                              16
> And if thow wise purchasour be
> In x yere day thou shalt this mony se.

The position of this poem in the MSS. indicates that it would be carefully recorded (and perhaps memorized) and put to practical use: in Lansdowne MS. 470 it is added on a flyleaf to a list of statutes from Edward III's reign; it appears in three commonplace books, MSS. Trinity Coll. Camb. 1157, Balliol Coll. Oxford 354, and Capesthorne; in Lansdowne MS. 672 it appears among lists of weights and measures; in Bodl. MS. Rawl. B. 252 it appears in a collection of Latin records for an abbey; and in the present MS. (Douce 54) it is added in a sixteenth-century hand on the flyleaf of a medley of medical receipts and agricultural notes.

In the Capesthorne MS. (and in Bodl. MS. Rawl. B. 252) the poem is ascribed to 'fortescu', and is so accepted in *Works of John Fortescue*, 1896, i. 543.

## 75. *Teeth, Bones, and Veins*

*Index*, No. 3572. Previously printed by Förster, *Anglia*, xlii. 215, and *Furnivall Misc.*, p. 104. Written (*circa* 1470) in red on the flyleaf. The MS. contains a chronicle and moral poems chiefly by Lydgate.

## 76. *The Complexions, I*

*Index*, No. 3157. Not heretofore printed.

## 77. *The Complexions, II*

*Index*, No. 2624. Not heretofore printed. The poem also occurs in four other unprinted texts: Bodl. MS. Digby 88; Bodl. MS. Ashmole 59; Camb. Univ. MS. Ff. 1. 6; and

Trinity Coll. Camb. MS. 599 (where each stanza is preceded by corresponding lines in Latin). This text is just about one century later than No. 76 (i.e. *circa* 1450–75).

In Bodl. MS. Digby 88 is a poem in twelve quatrains on the influence of the signs of the Zodiac (*Index*, No. 1253, unprinted), beginning:

> Hote and moyste ys Aquarius as ys the Eyer, men
> tellyth vs byfore,
> And it regneth in legge and shanke Wher an hurte
> wull greve soore.
> The childe borne in Januare shalbe of wittis clere,
> But he shal haue gret harme of water and fyre.

4. Camb. and Trinity try to maintain the rhyme scheme with 'chauntere' (in place of 'champioun').

17. Camb., Trinity, and Digby: & with spyttyng of Rewmos.

18. Camb. and Digby: wytte insufficiant.

23. Trinity and Ashmole: thowthfull; Camb.: fraudfull.

## 78. *Lydgate's Dietary*

*Index*, No. 824. Not heretofore printed from this MS. Lydgate's 'Dietary' is far and away the most popular 'information' piece of verse in Middle English: it occurs in 46 MSS., a number exceeded only by the long and outstanding poems, *The Pricke of Conscience*, *The Canterbury Tales*, *Piers Plowman*, and *Confessio Amantis*. It has therefore to be considered, from the point of view of contemporary popularity, as the most outstanding poem in this anthology.

It is important for a modern reader to realize the tremendous importance of this functional or mnemonic verse in the Middle Ages. The tendency to write in verse what would now without question be written in the simplest form of prose is shown in such simple quatrains as No. 68 (which is still taught in schools), No. 69, and No. 75. But the purpose, namely ease for remembering facts, holds for the longer poems, such as Lydgate's 'Dietary'. This poem was used by school-children, for it is found along with other teaching poems in small collections to be used by children. In this respect it may be linked to the whole 'Stans puer ad mensam' tradition.

In this section of Practical Verse are included two other poems which almost equalled the popularity of the Dietary: No. 74, Instructions for Purchasing Land, again of real importance in times when the popular reputation of lawyers was low (see No. 111), found in 14 MSS.; and No. 81, Directions for Bloodletting (or 'phlebotomy'), surviving in 17 MSS. It should be noted, too, that No. 70, How to Find Easter, occurs in 8 MSS.; No. 85, a proverbial tag inculcating a moral, is found in 8 MSS.; and No 84, another tag, in 14 MSS. The final poem in this section, No. 88, on the Philosophers' Stone, is another example of the value placed on functional verse: it occurs in 24 MSS.

One further point to observe is that these functional poems are not all short: the Dietary has 80 lines; Bloodletting has 90 lines; and the Philosophers' Stone has 76 lines.

### 79. *Doctrines of Temperate Diet*

*Index*, No. 2751. Previously printed in *HMC*, 1928 Report, p. 421; and by Wilson, *Osiris*, vi. 427. These lines occur among various fifteenth-century notes and scribbles. The MS. (described *HMC*, pp. 417–30) is a fifteenth-century miscellany of medical receipts.

### 80. *On the Medicinal Properties of Leeks*

*Index*, No. 1810. Previously printed (with some inaccuracies) in *HMC*, 1928 Report, p. 422. Followed in the MS. by many prose receipts.

### 81. *Directions for Bloodletting*

*Index*, No. 3848. Not heretofore printed from this MS. Occurs in 17 MSS., which all show variants; for details see *Index*. The only text previously printed is that from the Loscombe MS. in *Reliquiae Antiquae*, i. 189–91.

13. Similar directions are common: cf. *Vicary's Anatomy* (*circa* 1450), Appendix ix, p. 229: 'Be-hynde þe eres er twa vayns þat er gude to be opynd for turnseke and for scall, & alsso for euyll sight.'

28. Ashmole 1448: þat lepir & strate breste will vndo.

33. Ashmole 391: soor-nes.

## 82. *Number Maxims, I*

*Index*, No. 717. Previously printed by James, *Cat.* iii. 11. Occurs also in Bodl. MS. Douce 257 (*Reliquiae Antiquae*, ii. 112); and Balliol Coll. Oxford MS. 354. The Balliol text gives the clue to the interpretation of the lines: the figures refer numerically to the corresponding letters in the alphabet. Thus 8 = H; set 9 (I) before; 'close' (Douce reads 'y-gert') 8 or H (apparently indicating the tilda used in the contraction); and add 3 (or C). The result spells out I̅H̅C̅. In the Balliol variant the letters are glossed above the figures, and the word reads JHESUS:

> 8 is my trew love; do beffore 9; put þerto 5, so well it will beseme; 18˙twyse told, 20 betwen. he þat redith this a right wottith what I mene. this goth by the letters of the abse as þe letters stond in nombre.

## 83. *Number Maxims, II*

*Index*, No. 1817. Not heretofore printed from this MS. The tag occurs in five other MSS., some showing slight variations: Bodl. MS. Rawl. (poet.) F. 32, fol. 55ʳ (unprinted):

> Myspend we nott fyve,
> And fle we seven;
> Kepe we wel x,
> & come to Heven.

Balliol Coll. Oxford MS. 354 (printed by Flügel, *Anglia*, xxvi. 225; and by Dyboski, EETS, ci. 140); Camb. Univ. MS. Ee. 4. 35, Part I, and Harley MS. 2252 (both early-sixteenth-century texts and both unprinted); and Harley MS. 2391, fol. 134ʳ (unprinted):

> Kepe x & leyfe vii,
> Misspend not v,
> & go to heuen.

The allusions are, of course, to the Ten Commandments, the Seven Deadly Sins, and the Five Wits (Bodily or Ghostly).

## 84. *Peace to Peace*

*Index*, No. 2742. Not heretofore printed from this MS. Occurs also in 13 other MSS., printed only in descriptive catalogues; for details see *Index*; and lengthy notes by R. Brotanek, *ME Dicht. aus hs. 432*, Halle 1940, pp. 15–33.

### 85. *Youth and Honour*

*Index*, No. 1151. Not heretofore printed from this MS., a Passion Gospel, where the tag is added on a flyleaf, and written upside down at the bottom of the page. Occurs in 7 other MSS., but printed only from Trinity Coll. Oxford MS. 49, fol. 139ᵛ (a blank page in a text of *The Canterbury Tales*) by Coxe, *Cat.*, p. 50:

> He that in youthe no gud kanne,
> In age selden ys thryfty man.

Another variant comes in Royal MS. 17. D. xviii, fol. 99ᵛ:

> He that in yought to no vertew himselfe applieth,
> In age to amende him badd costome deniethe.

This couplet is frequently incorporated into longer texts, or written along with other gnomic tags, e.g. *Index*, Nos. 1817 and 3847. For full details of MSS. see *Index*.

### 86. *On Nought*

*Index*, No. 1163. Not heretofore printed from this MS., where it is added on a flyleaf in a sixteenth-century hand, immediately following *Index*, No. 981. Occurs also in Balliol Coll. Oxford MS. 354 (printed by Flügel, *Anglia*, xxvi. 220; and by Dyboski, EETS, ci. 140); and in Harley MS. 2252 (printed in *Reliquiae Antiquae*, i. 316). The Harley text replaces the word 'nothing' by 'nought.' The Balliol text adds a second quatrain and a concluding couplet:

> He þat swerith till no man trist hym,
> & lyeth till no man beleve hym,
> & borowith till no man will lend hym,
> he may go þer no man knowith hym.

> he þat will venge euery wreth,
> þe lenger he levith þe lesse he hath.

### 87. *Silver and Friend*

*Index*, No. 1297. Not heretofore printed from this MS. Occurs in seven other MSS.: Bodl. MS. Laud Misc. 23 (printed by Brown, *Register*, i. 1); Camb. Univ. MS. Ee. 4. 35, Part I; B.M. Addit. MS. 24542 (nineteenth-century transcript); Cotton Titus MS. A. xxvi, fol. 173$^v$; B.M. Addit. MS. 37049; Advocates MS. 1. 1. 6 (printed by Ritchie, *STS*, n.s. xxii. 324; and by Kaluza, *Eng. St.* xiii. 529); and Hunterian MS. 409. In the latter MS. the text appears as a 'missing word' puzzle, thus:

> I had my ...
> And my ...

The Cotton text (not listed in the *Index*) shows some variation:

> Whan I lente I fynde a frend,
> & When I aske I am vnkynd.
> Thus of my ffrend I make my foo;
> Ther-for wyll I lene no mor.

## 88. *The Philosophers' Stone*

*Index*, No. 2656. Not heretofore printed from this MS. Occurs in at least 24 MSS. (only eight are before 1500), all texts showing considerable variations. Printed previously only in a variant text by Ashmole, *Theatrum Chemicum*, pp. 275–7.

The Philosophers' Stone has a history which extends far beyond the Middle Ages: Marlowe's *Doctor Faustus* and Jonson's *The Alchemist* are but two illustrations of the continuing interest in alchemy and the search for a substance which had the property of changing base metals into gold or silver. The actual term 'Lapis philosophorum' occurs in works ascribed to Raymund Lully (1234–1315) and Arnoldus de Villa Nova (1240–1314). The *NED* gives the first English usage as 1386, in Chaucer's Canon's Yeoman's Tale, l. 309. The piece printed here is a strange hotch-potch of chemistry and mysticism.

18. i.e. equal to Phebus.

58. Ens and vbi] The uncertainty lies in questions of Essence and Location.

74. Al if] although.

## 89. *A Book Plate, I*

*Index*, No. 1165. Previously printed in *Reliquiae Antiquae*, ii. 163; by Warner and Gilson, *Cat.* ii. 269; and by Bishop, EETS, 109. xlix. Occurs also in Pepys MS. 1760; Royal MS.

18. B. xxii (*Cat.* ii. 295); and Lambeth 259 (*Cat.* p. 405). The present text is carefully written and rubricated on the flyleaf of a collection of Homilies on the Gospels.

Generally these book mottoes were stereotyped tags adapted for the use of a particular owner merely by adding his name at the beginning or end of the poem. Thus the Royal MS. text (early sixteenth century) reads:

> John Twychener ys boke.
>
> he that stellys thys booke
> he shall be hangid a-pon a hoke,
> that wyll macke ys necke to brake,
> and that wyll macke ys neck awrye.

In the Lambeth MS. the piece is written on fol. iv^r (and again on fol. iv^v) among a great many scribbles:

> He that thys boke dothe stele
> Oure lady yeff hym an euyll hele
> othyr with rope, swerd or knyff;    quod Bentylle.
> he schall haue a schort lyfe.
> þerfor, for þe love of oure lady,
> I pray ȝow lett þis boke ly.
>
>      quod Wyłł Bentelee.

*Index*, No. 1410 (*Reliquiae Antiquae*, ii. 163) is a three-line variant:

> If ony persone stele this boke,
> He shal be hongyd by a hoke,
> Or by the necke with a rope.

Other book plates where the owner's name has been added include No. 90 (following below); *Index*, No. 3614 (Robert Curzon; seventeenth century); and *Index*, No. 3615 (William Tuck). In *Index*, No. 4138, the motto occurs with a blank space, in which the name of the owner could be inserted later:

> Ho-so on me doth loke,
> I am             boke.

## 90. *A Book Plate, II*

*Index*, No. 3580. Not heretofore printed from this MS., where it is added on the flyleaf in a very late fifteenth-century hand. Occurs also in Harley MS. 1251 (*Cat.* i. 635;

*Reliquiae Antiquae*, ii. 163); Tiverton MS. (Bishop, EETS, 109. 1); Huntington MS. HM 140 (Manly and Rickert, *Canterbury Tales*, i. 436). In the Harley MS. the lines are headed: 'Thys boke ys myne eleanour worcestar', and signed 'E. Worcester'. Bishop notes: 'These last four lines are by no means uncommon in fifteenth-century books.'

### 91. *A Book Plate, III*

*Index*, No. 1007. Not heretofore printed. Added on the cover of a Psalter, in a very late fifteenth- or early sixteenth-century hand.

### 92. *William Barbour's Book Plate*

*Index*, No. 4126. Previously printed in *Reliquiae Antiquae*, ii. 164. Added on the flyleaf of a Book of Hours; on the opposite flyleaf (fol. 1ᵛ) is written:

> Whoe-som-euer thys Boke be com,
> yt ys Wyllyam Barbors off newe Bokenham.

### 93. *Lady Scrope's Book Plate*

*Index*, No. 4104. Previously printed by James, *Cat.*, p. 7. Written in a large hand on fol. 147ʳ of a fifteenth-century *Liber Precum*. James states: 'To what foundations the book belonged I cannot say with certainty. The indications are that it was given by Lady Scrope to a monastery probably in Yorkshire where St. Honoratus of Lerins was held in veneration, and that it belonged once to a man called Edward.' The Memoria of St. Honoratus appear on fol. 137.

### 94. *Verses on a Chained Horae*

*Index*, No. 3637. Previously printed by Clark, *Cambridge Antiquarian Soc. Communications* (Quarto Series), xi. 76–77. M. R. James once said there was a similar set of verses in the Library of Caius College, but I have not been able to find it.

This MS., a Sarum Horae with Psalter, &c., was described by Bradshaw in the *Proceedings of the Society* in 1878. He is quoted by Clark: 'On the last page of the Kalendar quire the scribe has written in lines of blue, crimson, black and red, three eight-line stanzas, each having the same rhymes, about the book itself, and John Harpur, by whose orders it was written.' Clark suggests a John Harpur who endowed the church in 1444.

Clark continues (p. 76): 'The chain, of iron, is attached to the middle of the left hand board by a strong slip of brass put round the board, and kept in place by rivets. Next to this slip is the usual swivel, very like those in the chains still used in the Chapter Library at Hereford, one of which I have figured in *The Care of Books* (*ed.* ii, p. 172, fig. 79). This swivel is 4½ inches long. It is succeeded by 21 links, strong and very well made. They vary in length from 2¾ inches to 2 inches. The whole length of the chain, including the swivel, is 4 feet 2 inches.'

The present owner and location of the MS. are not known.

## 95. *Presentation Verses with a Ring*

*Index*, No. 932. Not heretofore printed. The text is very much faded.

7. Other inscriptions for rings occur in the *Fasciculus Morum* (*Index*, Nos. 798, 3273, and 3275). *Index*, No. 4203, contains inscriptions for wedding rings: 'Wit þis ring i wedde þe / & wit mi bodi i worssepe þe.' For a full discussion on rings see Joan Evans, *English Poesies and Poesy Rings*, London 1931.

## 96. *Presentation Verses with an Eagle*

*Index*, No. 3604. Previously printed by MacCracken, EETS, 192. 649–51. Occurs also in Harley MS. 2251 (Halliwell, *Percy Soc.* ii. 213–16); and in B.M. MS. Addit. 29729. This text shows Lydgate as the court poet-laureate. Lydgate wrote two other sets of presentation verses with gifts, *Index*, No. 1496, and *Index*, No. 886, both in B.M. MS. Addit. 16165 (MacCracken, EETS, 192. 424–7–9). Other New Year's Day verses (with gifts) occur in Lambeth MS. 306, *Index*, No. 1789 (Furnivall, EETS, 15. 66–7); and No. 97 (following).

Henry VI had married Margaret of Anjou in 1445, about which time hopes for a prolonged peace between England and France increased. This poem, if presented on a New Year's Day, would therefore be dated 1446. Hertford, however, had been originally designated as a castle for summer residence.

### 97. *Presentation Verses with a New Year's Gift*

*Index*, No. 2267. Previously printed by Small, *STS*, iv. 256; and in editions of Dunbar's poems.

### 98. *A Dedication for De Regimine Principum, I*

*Index*, No. 3831. Previously printed by Furnivall, EETS, lxi. 56–7; and by Hammond, *Eng. Verse Chaucer–Surrey*, p. 76. Another text occurs in Royal MS. 17. D. xviii, fol. 100ʳ.

This dedication (to John, Duke of Bedford) is followed by an Envoy (a virelai), 'O litil book who yaf thee hardynesse', addressed to Henry V (then Prince), in both MSS. The 'humble book' is probably a *De Regimine Principum*. For a discussion on this and other of Hoccleve's dedications, Hoccleve's autograph MSS., the position of Master Massy in the household of the Duke of Bedford, and evidence of Hoccleve's death as occurring in 1430, see H. C. Schulz, 'Thomas Hoccleve, Scribe', *Speculum*, xii. 71–81.

### 99. *A Dedication for a De Regimine Principum, II*

*Index*, No. 2257. Not heretofore printed. The MS. belonged to William FitzAlan, Earl of Arundel (1438–87), whose arms are found on the border of fol. 40ʳ.

### 100. *Prologue for an Apocalypse*

*Index*, No. 4096. Not heretofore printed. The piece is carefully written and rubricated on the flyleaf of an illuminated Latin text of the Apocalypse. Immediately preceding this text is another similar preface, *Index*, No. 1793, also unprinted:

Beatus qui legit et qui audit et seruat ea que in eo scripta sunt.

| | |
|---|---|
| Ion blessis hom alle þat þis boke reden | |
| Wit gode entent, and hor god dreden, | |
| Or heren hit red wit gode wille | |
| In al hor myȝt hit to fulfille; | 4 |
| ffor þis blessing iche mon shulde wirke | |
| To knowe hit & mayntene Holy [Kirke]. | *erased* |
| Hit tellis of peynes & sorowes sere | |
| þat here shal falle to cristis dere; | 8 |

þoo þat ben trewe & stiffly stonde,
þei shal be hatid þorwout þo londe—
Of deefe & blinde þat wil not se,
Ne here hor fautes heelid to be.                    12
Herefore crist counfortis his chirche
And biddes hom alle with pacience wirche.
þis way went I to teche ʒou alle
Hou ʒe shal enter to heuenly halle,                 16
þere to duelle euere in pees,
In ioye & blis þat neuer shal cees.

Amen

### 101. *Translator's Prologue to Trevisa*

*Index*, No. 33. Not heretofore printed from this MS.
(Trevisa's translation of Glanville's *De Proprietatibus Rerum*).
Occurs also in Bodl. MS. e Mus. 16 ; Harley MS. 614 (Perry,
EETS, 167. cxxix) ; Harley MS. 4789 ; B.M. MS. Addit.
27944 ; Helmingham Hall MS. ; Plimpton MS. 263 (Plimpton,
*Education of Chaucer*, pp. 34–35).

7. This stanza contains an apparently accurate description of teaching methods, and the phrase 'God speed me'
often occurs in connexion with children's books. For example,

> At my begynnyng Crist me spede
> In vertv and lernyng for to spede         [*MS. lernyg*

is twice scribbled, in an early-fifteenth-century child's
scrawl, on the flyleaf of Camb. Univ. MS. Ii. 6. 36. In Lincoln Cath. MS. 189, fol. 5$^v$, again twice scribbled, is

> In my begenning God be my spede
> in grace and vertue to procede

In Harley MS. 3362, fol. 89$^r$, are childish attempts at practice letters in a late-fifteenth-century style, and, written
several times, the first probably by a teacher and the others
by a child :

> At oure begynnyng God vs spede & w$^t$ grace & vertue .
> procede

These two lines are the opening of two poems of counsel
to children (*Index*, Nos. 430 and 432), both of which were
used for memorizing by students. There are two other
curious notes which show the learning processes of the

fifteenth century. Among flyleaf scribbles in Lambeth MS. 259, fol. 1ʳ, are, 'Ego sum bonus puer quem deus amat'. In Sidney Sussex Coll. Camb. MS. 37, Horae, on the blank leaves at the end, a mother has written:

Edmovnd Choorche ys a good son for he ys wyllyng to lern

Then in a slightly different hand (presumably that of the son) comes:

Alas Edmovnd churche his not a good baye for he has a shamd frauncis churche at the barne dore shynting (?) Alas

See further notes to No. 116 (following).

### 102. *Preface to a Medical Treatise*

*Index*, No. 4182. Not heretofore printed. MS. is a collection of medical receipts in English.

### 103. *Introduction to a Medical Tract*

*Index*, No. 3422. Previously printed by Pettigrew, *Archaeologia*, xxx. 421–2; and by G. Henslow, *Medical Works of the Fourteenth Century*, 1899, pp. 125. Occurs also in nine other MSS. (for details see *Index*, No. 3422; delete 8. Royal 17. A. xxxii), all of which show some variations. The Payne MS. has been printed by Furnivall, EETS, 15. 286–7; and by Cook, *Reader*, pp. 379–80. The text occurs both as prologue and epilogue.

15. Recipes to make saue or antioche follow on fols. 13 and 14.

### 104. *Envoy for a Commentary*

*Index*, No. 929. Not heretofore printed. The MS. is a Commentary on the Psalter.

### 105. *Sotelties for Coronation Banquet*

*Index*, No. 1929. Previously printed by Thomas and Thornley, *The Great Chronicle*, pp. 152–3. Occurs also in St. John's Coll. Oxford MS. 5 (Hammond, *Eng. St.* xliii. 23); Cotton MS. Julius B. i (Nicolas, *Chronicle of London*, 1827, pp. 168–9; MacCracken, EETS, 192. 623–4); Lansdowne MS. 285; and Morgan Lib. MS. 775, fol. 15ʳ.

A sotelty, 'a tableau, in pastry or sugar, at the close of each course in a medieval banquet' (Hammond), is an indication of the elaborate nature of medieval formal feasts. The use of verse on special occasions is found in connexion with tapestries (*Index*, Nos. 500, 2152, 2541, 2592), wall decorations (*Index*: see Wresill and Leconfeld proverbs), and stained-glass windows.

### 106. *An Indigent Author*

*Index*, No. 783. Previously printed by Furnivall, EETS, lxi. 58. For references to Hoccleve, see Maxwell Lyte, *The Great Seal*, London 1926, pp. 27, 33, &c.

### 107. *Deceit, I*

*Index*, No. 674. Not heretofore printed from this MS. Occurs also in ten other MSS., four of which have been printed; for details see *Index*. The stanza is actually from Lydgate's *Fall of Princes* (ii. ll. 4432–8), but always occurs separately.

### 108. *Deceit, II*

*Index*, No .145. Not heretofore printed. Added in an early-fifteenth-century hand on a flyleaf of a composite *South English Legendary* (*Index*, No. 3387). On the same flyleaf, in the same hand, are *Index*, Nos. 477 and 496.

### 109. *Deceit, III*

*Index*, No. 4092. Not heretofore printed. Added on flyleaf of a prose *Siege of Thebes* and a *Court of Venus*. The poem is repeated in a later hand (early-sixteenth-century) immediately following.

### 110. *Punctuation Poem, I*

*Index*, No. 3809. Previously printed by James, *Cat.*, p. 274; and by Kreuzer, *RES*, xiv. 322. The poem is written twice: first in a mid-sixteenth-century hand, and second in a somewhat later hand. It appears on the end flyleaf of a *Confessio Amantis* along with other scribblings—a location which indicates the experimental nature of the verse.

For a discussion of this type of poem capable of two

different meanings according to the punctuation adopted see Kreuzer, and my note in *RES*, xv. 206–7; also Philip Bliss, *Reliquiae Hearnianae*, London 1869, i. 250. That this type of literary tour-de-force has not been forgotten is illustrated by a poem (from the *Paris Soir*) in *The New York Times*, 16 May 1941, p. 2, an alexandrine octave, the riming verses to the left of the caesura a eulogy of England, and those to the right a damnation of Hitler, the whole being a seeming paean of the Führer.

### 111. *Punctuation Poem, II*

*Index*, No. 2364. Not heretofore printed from this MS. Occurs also in Trinity Coll. Camb. MS. 366; Harley MS. 2250; and B.M. MS. Addit. 5465; all three texts have been printed by Kreuzer, *RES*, xiv. 321–3. The Trinity MS. is also printed by James, *Cat.* i. 496; and the Addit. MS. by Fehr, *Archiv*, cvi. 54. A fifth text is found in Corpus Christi Coll. Oxford MS. 261, fol. 89$^v$ (unprinted). The variants are not important.

As with No. 110, the two poems (Nos. 111 and 112) in the Camb. Univ. MS. are both (early-sixteenth-century) additions to the original contents, in this instance a collection of legal readings in Law French. All the versions of this poem, with the exception of B.M. MS. Addit. (which has a musical setting), are 'flyleaf' poems, not part of the original contents of the MSS.

### 112. *Punctuation Poem, III*

*Index*, No. 1593. Previously printed by Robbins, *RES*, xv. 206. In addition to these three short 'punctuation' poems, is another longer poem, an attack on women by Richard Hattfield, 'All women have vertues noble & excelent' (three stanzas rhyme royal), found in B.M. MS. Addit. 17924, fol. 18$^v$ (printed by Flügel, *Neuengl. Lesebuch*, p. 39); and in Longleat MS. 258, fol. 32$^r$ (unprinted); Harington MS. (unprinted); and Pepys 2253 (1 st. only; printed Craigie, i. 433).

### 113. *A Burlesque Prescription*

*Index*, No. 813. Previously printed by Wright, *Percy Soc.* xxiii. 23. Cf. 'A good medesyn yff a mayd have lost her madened to make her a mayd ageyn', *Reliquiae Antiquae*, i. 250; and noted by F. L. Utley, *The Crooked Rib*, Columbus 1944, p. 157.

### 114. *When to Trust Women*

*Index*, No. 3999. Previously printed by Flügel, *Anglia*, xxvi. 277–8; and by Dyboski, EETS, ci. 114. Occurs also in Bodl. MS. Eng. poet. e. 1 (printed by FitzGibbon, *Early Eng. Poetry*, p. 200; by Wright, *Percy Soc.* xxiii. 66–8; and by Greene, *Early Eng. Carols*, pp. 269–70); and in B.M. IB 55242 (printed by Garrett, *Anglia*, xxxii. 358; and by Carolyn Wells, *A Nonsense Anthology*, pp. 186–8). The Balliol version consists of st. 1, 3, 5, and 6 of the Bodl. text. See further, 'When wreneys weare wodknyves Cranes for to kyll,' in Furnivall, *Ballads from MSS.*, i. 313.

3. bromes] Bodl. ges.
    Cf. *Index*, No. 4236 (Bodl. MS. Eng. poet. e. 1) ll. 19–21:

> Whan brome wyll appelles bere
> And humloke hony in feere
> Than seek rest in lond

6. lekes] B. kyskys.
10. B. & marmsattes morn in mores & in lakys.
11. rolyons] B. rokes.
12. grengese] B. goslynges.
13. sperlynges] B. sprates.
    harnes] B. armys.
15. sparowys] B. spawyns.
17. B. & curlews cary tymber howsys to dyth.
19. B. & wodkokes wer wodknyfys cranis to kyll
20. griffons] B. grenfynchys.
22. crabbis] B. crowbes tak sarmon.
24. B. & cammels in the ayer tak swalows & larkes.
25. B. & myse move movntans with waggyng of ther tayles.
26. B. & schypmen tak a ryd insted of saylles.
    Blod of haylis] The Blood of Christ was presumed to have been given to Hailes Abbey in 1270 by Richard, Earl of Cornwall.
    See notes to No. 45.

### 115. *The Insects and the Miller*

*Index*, No. 3324. Not heretofore printed. Written in a fairly late fifteenth-century hand at the end of a grammar book.

### 116. *The Schoolboy's Wish*

*Index*, No. 3895. Previously printed by Woolley, *Cat.*, pp. 93–94. The hand is later than the rest of the MS., and the poem lies between the *Accentuarius* and the *Dictionarius* of John of Garland; it is much contracted. This piece is one of the most realistic in the anthology, and gives a vigorous picture of schoolboy venom. See Bowers, *PQ*, xvi. 37.

10. Tr. 'We should leave such evidence on thee (. . . that all thy kin &c.).'

13. robert] i.e. the Devil.

19. Tr. 'For again and again we pay the penalty for him (the devil) working his eye at the master (inciting him) to beat us; for he and you are of one mind, (and) all the time make an agreement to give us severe beatings.'

### 117. *Monologue of a Drunkard*

*Index*, No. *24. Previously printed by Heuser, *Anglia*, xxx. 177. The text is very faded. See notes to No. 9. For a less inebriated song, cf. Chambers & Sidgwick, *Early Eng. Lyrics*, pp. 229–31. Here the poet is trying to represent the emotions of a drunken man, who wants everything to stand still; then, when he trips, is able to relax his body. In Camb. Univ. MS. Ii. 7. 19, fol. 177$^v$, is a scribble perhaps written by one who was drunk: 'Beleve ale men that thes ys wyllyam terry boke drynkyng wt Ry Rychard call.' M. R. James has commented (privately), 'Indeed, the hand suggests inebriety'.

### 118. *The Blacksmiths*

*Index*, No. 3227. Previously printed in *Reliquiae Antiquae*, i. 240; Lindberg, *Archiv*, ci. 395; and by Sisam, *XIV Cent. Verse & Prose*, pp. 169–70. This is a magnificent example of realism in verse, and the onomatopoeic effect of the lines is outstanding. In the MS. it is preceded by the Monk's Complaint, *Index*, No. 3819, another vigorous piece (printed in *Reliquiae Antiquae*, i. 291–2).

5. cammede] Tolkien in the vocabulary to Sisam translates as *? snub-nosed*, but ·adds that *? crooked* (from Welsh *cam*) fits the context better, although the word 'is not else recorded till later.'

17–18. Sisam (pp. 257–8) comments: 'Difficult. Perhaps "The master smith lengthens a little piece (sc. of hot iron), and hammers a smaller piece, twines the two together, and strikes (with his hammer) a treble note."'

22. brenwaterys] water-burners, i.e. blacksmiths, so called from plunging hot iron into water.

## 119. *The Hunted Hare*

*Index*, No. 559. Previously printed by Halliwell, *Warton Club*, ii. 43–6. A variant text (15 stanzas) occurs in Camb. Univ. MS. Ff. 5. 48 (printed by Hartshorne, *Ancient Metrical Tales*, 1829, pp. 165). Camb. MS. omits stanzas 3 and 14 to 19; and introduces a variant stanza between Porkington text stanzas 7 and 8, and two variant concluding stanzas.

1–4.

> ffer in frithe as I can fare,
> My self syȝand allone,
> I herd the mournyng of an hare,
> Thus delfully she made hir mone.

16. Camb. 14. Be falowe be fore me for to fynde.

28. Camb. 25–28. (New stanza.)

> Thus I am in turnament
> Be woode, be way, be more, be mede,
> And oþer while my tayle is rent;
> Alle day thus my life I ledde.

34. Camb. 34. And to lurke or to leyke (Rhyme: And dere me with her doggus grete).

37. Camb. 37. I dar not sit to croppe on hawe (Rhyme: cockes mawe).

51. Camb. 47. as a swyne.

Camb. 53–56.

> The next tyme þou comes þer in,
> be my trowthe, I the be hote,
> þo þou thorowe þe hege ren,
> þou shalbe hongut be the throte.

Camb. 57–60.

> Thus I droupe, I drede my deth;
> Alas I dye long or my day!
> ffor welle & woe away it gothe,
> And this word hit wendes away.

The sympathy with animals is a curiosity of Middle English poems. See here No. 48, and also *Index*, No. 368, 'Wyl Bucke his Testament'.

### 120. *A Mumming of the Seven Philosophers*

*Index*, No. 3807. Not heretofore printed.

The four pieces (Nos. 120–3) are a sampling of the large number of formal welcomes or ceremonial entertainments still extant. Lydgate was especially active in writing such items, e.g. *Index*, No. 3301; and *Index*, No. 2200, Pageant Verses for Queen Margaret's Entry into London.

40. The old (saw).

### 121. *A Dramatic Monologue by Law*

*Index*, No. 3376. Not heretofore printed.

These lesser poems, written in the style made fashionable by Lydgate, illustrate the dull mediocrity of formal poems written to order, as it were, by men of little talent.

### 122. *Welcome to Prince Edward at Coventry*

*Index*, No. 3881. Previously printed by Craig, EETS, lxxxvii. 115, and by Harris, EETS, 135. 391–3.

h. chaumbr] 'Royal chamber' was a common way of describing a city.

8. This sentiment originally comes from the religious lyrics to the B.V.M.; later it was transferred to secular mistresses.

cc. pauyer] In all cited references, this word means 'the one who paves', but the sense here requires the meaning 'pavement'.

### 123. *Welcome to Henry VII at York*

*Index*, No. 2214. Previously printed (with some inaccuracies) by Raine, *Surtees Soc.* lxxxv. 56–7, and again in *Yorkshire Archaeological Soc.* (Record Series), xcviii. 158; and by

A. H. Smith, *London Med. Studies* (1939), pp. 393–4. Occurs also in Cotton MS. Julius B. xii, f. 12ʳ, printed ibid., p. 396. The House Book contains the Minutes of the Proceedings of the Corporation, tempus Henry VII, 1486–90.

c. In margin: 'prince Cometh to Coventry'.

### 124. *Epitaph for Rich Alan*

*Index*, No. 1207. Previously printed in *Reliquiae Antiquae*, ii. 179, as 'On a Ballad Monger' (resulting from a misreading of *ballid*).

### 125. *Epitaph for the Earl of Dunbar*, A.D. 1416

*Index*, No. 1206. Previously printed in *Cat. Add. MSS. 1900–1905*, p. 377. Added in a fifteenth-century hand on the flyleaf of a Latin Fordun's *Chronicle*.

### 126. *A Tombstone Inscription*

*Index*, No. 237. Previously printed by James, *Cat.* i. 496–7. Added on the flyleaf of a fifteenth-century *Summa Thome de Chebham*.

There are a number of tomb texts or epitaphs found in MSS., presumably written before the death of the person eulogized. *Index*, No. 4129 is a thirteenth-century piece found in seven MSS. and used frequently as a mural or tomb inscription (Brown, *Eng. Lyrics XIII Cent.*, pp. 173–4). *Index*, No. 520 is for the Duke of Bedford, *circa* 1495 (no MS. extant; Dyce, *Skelton*, ii. 388). *Index*, No. 2411 is an elegy of eight stanzas for the tomb of Lord Cromwell (*circa* 1450), occurring in two MSS. (Brown, *Rel. Lyrics XV Cent.*, p. 243). In one instance an epitaph has had a heading added, *Index*, No. 2511, and has been printed by Greene, *Early Eng. Carols*, p. 250. A general epitaph (in an early-sixteenth-century hand) occurs among many epitaphs in Latin in Lansdowne MS. 762, *Index*, No. 765 (*Reliquiae Antiquae*, i. 268). See T. F. Ravenshaw, *Antiente Epitaphes*, London, 1878.

### 127. *A Catalogue of Delights*

*Index*, No. 4209. Previously printed by Fehr, *Archiv*, cvii. 53–55. The poem is of the second half of the fifteenth century (Henry VI–Edward IV), but has been bound with a collection of miscellaneous pieces by Stowe. In the same hand in this MS. are *Index*, No. 4181 ('Wit hath wonder' &c.) on fol. 207ᵛ; and *Index*, No. 824 (Lydgate's 'Dietary') on fol. 209ᵛ.

68. For longer farewell anaphoras see Nos. 202–5.

## 128. *The Beauty of His Mistress, I*

*Index*, No. 2491. Not heretofore printed. Preceded in the MS. by No. 198 (following).

## 129. *The Beauty of His Mistress, II*

*Index*, No. 1768. Previously printed by Padelford and Benham, *Anglia*, xxxi. 315–16. Occurs in a collection of poetry, mainly love poems, in a very early sixteenth-century hand. From this MS. come also Nos. 130, 200, 204, and 207. This poem should be considered also with the Love Epistles (Nos. 191–200).

17. In stringing together his stock phrases the poet has used without thinking 'large and longe' for fingers, which are generally praised as 'long and slender.'

33. 'Alas for any redress I am likely to get.'

## 130. *The Beauty of His Mistress, III*

*Index*, No. 2421. Previously printed by Padelford and Benham, *Anglia*, xxxi. 365–7.

The first stanza may owe something to the opening quatrain of No. 205 (following). In all these formal lyrics, however, there is abundance of clichés. The mistress is always courteous and steadfast, she is the ground of his grace and causer of his pains, she is true as the turtle-dove. Her charms are catalogued: her lips are like the cherry; her teeth white; her eyebrows arched; her eyes are like crystal or clear as glass or grey; her fingers are long and slim; her waist small; and so on.

## 131. *The All-Virtuous She*

*Index*, No. 869. Previously printed by MacCracken, EETS, 192. 379–81. Occurs also in BM. MS. Addit. 29729 (only variant is *vysage* for *ymage* in ll. 8 and 35). Added across top of pp. 34–35 as a running title, 'Balade of Love by Sir Othes of holand.'

16. In Lydgate's 'Floure of Curtesy' (*Index*, No. 1487), the roster of famous women praises 'Ariadne' for her 'discrecioun'.

### 132. *Sweet Enslavement*

*Index*, No. 2634. Previously printed by Ritchie, STS, n.s. xxiii. 270–2. This poem and No. 133 are included here to illustrate the large number of Scottish formal love poems found in this Bannatyne MS.

### 133. *O Mistress Mine*

*Index*, No. 2517. Previously printed by Ritchie, STS, n.s. xxiii. 269.

4. 'Now let me not remain in peril; suppose I am only as certain of life as I am of love—who knows whether God may not send me some succour? Then why should you wish that I perish on account of your love?'

### 134. *For Old Acquaintance Sake*

*Index*, No. 4. Printed also by Kurvinen, *Neuphil. Mitteilungen*, liv. 52–55.

### 135. *Have All My Heart*

*Index*, No. 1120. Printed also by Kurvinen, *Neuphil. Mitteilungen*, liv. 57–58. The first four lines occur as ll. 9–12 of 'My harte ys sore but yett noo forse', ff. 57ᵛ–58ʳ of MS. Rawlinson C. 813 (*Anglia*, xxxi. 376). This poem is interesting because it shows the interaction between secular and religious love poems. *Index*, No. 3805, Querimonia Cristi languentis pro amore (Brown, *Rel. Lyrics XV Cent.*, pp. 175–7) has several lines which very closely parallel this text, e.g. ll. 17–18 resemble ll. 9–10, and ll. 9–16 are actually a variant of stanza 1:

> Therefor haue alle myne herte & beon yn pees
> & þynke I love you soueranly
> ffor þat I say hit is no lese
> Wolde god ye wyste as well as I

### 136. *A Fickle Mistress*

*Index*, No. 3534. Not heretofore printed. Added on flyleaf

(Old Testament history, *Index*, No. 944) in a late-fifteenth-century hand.

### 137. *An Inconstant Mistress*

*Index*, No. 2518. Previously printed in *Reliquiae Antiquae*, i. 255–6; by Flügel, *Neuengl. Lesebuch*, p. 140; and by Chambers & Sidgwick, *Early Eng. Lyrics*, pp. 76–77.

### 138. *A Heartless Mistress*

*Index*, No. 2311. Not heretofore printed.

### 139. *A Pitiless Mistress*

*Index*, No. 2161. Previously printed by Fehr, *Archiv*, cvii. 50. The manuscript, a *De Regimine Principum*, uses for fly-leaves six pages of a mid-fifteenth-century Lydgate MS. (which includes Nos. 139 and 140). It was perhaps copied by Thomas Lucas, secretary to Jasper, Duke of Bedford (cf. Scott, *Index to Sloane MSS.*). The poem is a composite: ll. 1–16 are phrases from Lydgate's *Temple of Glas*; and ll. 17–37 = ll. 736–54 of the *Temple* (ll. 762–3 replacing the last two lines of the third stanza). The 'hir' of the original appears as 'youre', to make the poem seem a direct petition of a lover to his lady, instead of a lover's remarks to Venus (cf. H. N. MacCracken, *PMLA*, xxiii. 128–40). Ll. 24–35 are found as the opening of 'In to my Hairt enprentit is so soir', f. 220ᵛ of the Bannatyne MS. (Ritchie, *STS*, n.s. xxvi. 270).

### 140. *A Sovereign Mistress*

*Index*, No. 2188. Previously printed by Fehr, *Archiv*, cvii. 51. Also a composite; MacCracken calls it 'two tries at a love-ballade, made of Lydgatian phrases'.

### 141. *Cantus Occidentalis*

*Index*, No. 2162. Previously printed by Förster, *Anglia*, xlii. 147; by James, *Cat.*, p. 237; and by Wells, *Manual*, p. 985.

### 142. *Sweet and Lovely*

*Index*, No. 2141. Previously printed by Furnivall, EETS, 15. 237 (original edition). Harley MS. 7322 is a collection of theological and moral pieces, texts and excerpts, in Latin, evidently for the use of some preacher, possibly a friar. Interspersed among the Latin are about fifty short English religious verses (mainly single quatrains or couplets); they have been printed by Furnivall in the revised edition (1903) of EETS, 15.

### 143. *Gracious and Gay*

*Index*, No. 1010. Previously printed by Seymour, *Proc. Royal Irish Academy*, xli. 208. This is also a scrap (second half fifteenth century), written on a strip of vellum, along with a macaronic poem against pride and flaunting manners (*Index*, No. 2774).

14. Cf. No. 22, l. 21, I loue hym trywely & no mo.

17. 'Speak now, I pray; on thee my love is set' (tr. Seymour).

### 144. *A Lady of High Degree*

*Index*, No. 2232. Not heretofore printed. Written in an early-fifteenth-century hand on a flyleaf of Vegetius, *De Re Militari*.

### 145. *Joyfull Pain (an anagram)*

*Index*, No. 4206. Previously printed by Coulton, *Cambridge Antiquarian Soc. Communications*, xix. 57, and *Med. Studies*, Second Series, No. 12, p. 57; and by Wilson, *Leeds Studies in English*, v. 38.

The graffito is on the pillar under the central arch of St. John's Church at Duxford, Cambridgeshire. This church is no longer used, and services are held at the other church of St. Peter's. Coulton's readings, which I follow here, were made prior to 1914, and even then many lines were illegible. When I visited the church in 1936 the whole interior had been so heavily whitewashed that the inscription had been covered up; and in 1950, restoration of the church has hidden the lines still more.

A similar anagram, with the name of his lady, is printed by Furnivall, *Ballad Soc.* vii, p. cxii, from Alde's *Book of Riddles* (1629):

> L and V and C and I
> So hight my Lady at the Font Stone

See also *Index*, No. 3256, for an anagram of his 'dere lady';
and, for acrostics, see *Index*, Nos. 481, 737, and 2217, three
poems by Humfrey Newton; *Index*, No. 158, by Charles
d'Orleans; and *Index*, No. 2479, a pseudo-Chaucerian envoy
to Alison. An unprinted acrostic in Trinity Coll. Camb. MS.
257, fol. 9ᵛ (*Index*, No. 588), might be taken as a secular poem;
it is added, however, to the end of a prayer to Saint Kathe-
rine (also pr. by Wilson, *MLN*, lxix. 21):

> k avser of my goy, helthe & Comford,
> a wlle es in yov, my hartes lady dere.
> t reule as ye lest, ryght so y me reporte
> y our servond to be, day tyme & Ere,
> r yght as ye well; bot thes y yov rekere,
> I n way of servyse as lovle as y cane,
> n euere to change, bot take me for your man.

### 146. *To Annys* (with music)

*Index*, No. 4199. Previously printed by Stainer, *Early
Bodl. Music*, ii. 59.

### 147. *Bird on Briar* (with music)

*Index*, No. 521. Previously printed by Saltmarsh, *Anti-
quaries Journal*, xv. 3–4; and *Two Med. Lyrics*, Cambridge
1933. Saltmarsh describes the poem thus: 'The manuscript
of Bryd one brere was found last year [1932] in the Muniment Room of King's College, a text of the early fourteenth
century, inscribed, with a musical setting for one voice, on
the back of an elaborate copy of a Bull of Pope Innocent
III. This document was formerly in the possession of the
Cluniac Priory of St. James by Exeter, and there it must
have received its very irregular endorsement. But the original
of the words is earlier, and not of Devonshire. They have
been copied from an older manuscript, of the thirteenth
century and probably written before 1250; the basis of
their dialect is Midland, though some of the forms suggest
that the scribe was a Northerner.'

### 148. *An Unfaithful Mistress*

*Index*, No. 1305. Previously printed by Woolley, *Cat.*,
pp. 95–6; and by Wilson, *Leeds Studies in English*, v. 37.
Added on a flyleaf of a collection of English sermons. The

page is torn at the bottom, and other parts are obscured by stains. The diction of this piece points to a courtly rather than a popular nature, although Wilson inclines to the latter view.

15. Balus] Woolley transcribes 'balns,' but cf. No. 37, l. 5; No. 158, l. 2; and No. 162, l. 18.

### 149. *A Letter to Margaret*

*Index*, No. 1121. Previously printed by James, *Cat.* i. 48; and by Robbins, *MLR*, xxxvii. 420. Occurs in a French love letter at the end of a Latin MS. in a very late fourteenth-century hand.

### 150. *The Faithfull Lover* (with music)

*Index*, No. 2231. Previously printed by Stainer, *Early Bodl. Music*, ii. 58–59. MS. is very faded. Tenor voice indicated on fol. 22$^r$.

### 151. *Love Without Variance* (with music)

*Index*, No. 2017. Previously printed by Stainer, *Early Bodl. Music*, ii. 61–2.
Tenor voice indicated on fol. 68$^v$.

### 152. *Love With Variance* (with music)

*Index*, No. 2016. Previously printed by Stainer, *Early Bodl. Music*, ii. 73–4. Bodl. MS. Ashmole 191 consists of twenty leaves, the first six having songs and music and the remainder a kalendar. The songs are all printed here, Nos. 152–6 and No. 171.
Tenor voice written in full on fols. 195$^v$–196$^r$.

### 153. *To His Mistress* (with music)

*Index*, No. 2475. Previously printed by Stainer, *Early Bodl. Music*, ii. 67.
Tenor voice written in full on fol. 192$^r$.

### 154. *The Indifferent Lover* (with music)

*Index*, No. 3722. Previously printed by Stainer, *Early Bodl. Music*, ii. 70–1.
Tenor voice written in full on fol. 193$^v$.

### 155. *The Wounds of Love* (with music)

*Index*, No. 925. Previously printed by Stainer, *Early Bodl. Music*, ii. 68–70; and by Copley, *Seven English Songs and Carols of the XV Century*. Copley writes (p. 4):

'It is not until the fifteenth century that three-part writing appears in the vernacular. It follows the same general lines as two-part writing. At the beginning of the century a florid *discantus* is added over a tenor, and the contratenor is inserted between these two voices; it has the same compass as the tenor, and its style has affinities with that part. Later the three parts become more flowing, although the *discantus* is generally more ornate than the two other parts.

'In the best work there is that freedom of movement in each part which is characteristic of the polyphonic writers of the sixteenth century [No. 155]. The method of construction seems to have been to write the contratenor last. For instance, the discantus and the tenor of [No. 155] are in the normal two-part writing of the period, while the contratenor wanders about freely but unsteadily, filling up the harmony.'

### 156. *Parting is Sorrow* (with music)

*Index*, No. 146. Previously printed by Stainer, *Early Bodl. Music*, ii. 72–3; and by Bukofzer, *Musical Quarterly*, xxviii. 45. The tenor voice is written in full on fol. 194ᵛ. Part of this song is repeated again on fol. 194ᵛ but is struck through.

### 157. *Parting is Death* (with music)

*Index*, No. 138. Previously printed by Bukofzer, *Musical Quarterly*, xxviii. 45; and, with much interpretation, by Menner, *Mod. Lang. Quarterly*, vi. 386. In this same Burgundian chansonnier (*circa* 1470–80) are two other English songs, *Index*, Nos. 2183 and 3165, also printed by Menner, ibid. The spelling seems to indicate a scribe not familiar with English. This situation probably accounts for the forms of the words in the two-line fragment, *Index*, No. 2782, in Madrid Escorial Lib. MS. iv a. 24, fol. 114ᵛ–116ʳ (printed by Bukofzer, *Music and Letters*, xix. 120):

> Princhesse af youth and floree of god lihede
> che per fight meror of alt gentilnesse

3. Tr. 'Instead of tranquillity, all the while I talk about grief.' Menner comments that 'the scribe's *el* for a tall Middle English *a* is a natural error'.

4. Tr. 'For my heart and thee (there is) always a long (period of) sighing.' Following Menner: 'I assume that the *alve* is the French scribe's attempt to pronounce *alwey*; just as *de* is his pronunciation of *pe*.'

5. The emendation of *I fele* to *is al* follows the same pattern as *el* to *a* in l. 3, with the common confusion of *f* and *s* corrected.

8. Tr. '"Welcome, certain death!"—this is my (only) song and lament.'

### 158. *Complaint to Fortune* (with music)

*Index*, No. 2245. Not heretofore printed. Added on a flyleaf of a MS. of a *Pricke of Conscience*, followed by a list of household payments. The careless manner in which this song has been jotted down well illustrates ways in which many of the lyrics of the period have been preserved.

### 159. *On the Absence of His Mistress*

*Index*, No. 1334. Not heretofore printed. Bodl. MS. Rawl. poet. 36 is a slim collection of English poems. This text is added on an unfilled page in the same late-fifteenth-century hand.

5–6. There is a play on ideas in *splene*, regarded both as the seat of learning and as the seat of laughter. Consequently, the poet can at one time make a 'gladfull' and a 'sory' countenance.

### 160. *His Absent Mistress*

*Index*, No. 2254. Previously printed by Skeat, *Athenaeum*, 24 Oct. 1896, p. 366; and by Sisam, *The Nun's Priest's Tale*, Oxford 1927, p. 34.

This text is presumably the song referred to in Chaucer's 'Nun's Priest's Tale,' ll. 113–15 (B. 4067–9):

> But such a joye was it to here hem singe,
> Whan that the brighte sonne gan to springe,
> In swete accord, 'my lief is faren in londe.'

In the Trinity MS. the poem is introduced thus: 'And for your love evermore wepyng I syng thys song.'

3. bound] Sisam emends to *in bonde*.

### 161. *To His Mistress for Pity*

*Index*, No. 2318. [Delete *Index*, No. 2536.] Not heretofore printed. Another piece where the tune is indicated by the opening lines of another song (presumably better known) is No. 23. Also Bodl. MS. Eng. poet. e. 1, fol. 45ᵛ, 'Swet Ihesus is cum to vs' (*Percy Soc.* xxiii. 69–73), 'A song in the tune of And I were a mayd &c.' *Index*, No. 3180, which Greene prints as a carol (p. 316), is probably another case of 'burden' indicating tune. No. 161 occurs as ll. 169–75, the last st. of 'O my swete lady & exelente goddas', f. 21ᵛ of MS. Rawlinson C. 813 (*Anglia*, xxxi. 338).

### 162. *The Power of Love*

*Index*, No. 152. Not heretofore printed. Late-fifteenth-century hand. In the MS. l. 8 is the first of the second stanza, and is indented, capitalized, and bracketed with l. 12.
   20. Metre deficient.

### 163. *Sore I Sigh* (with music)

*Index*, No. 266. Previously printed by Saltmarsh, *Two Med. Lyrics*, Cambridge 1933. The musical setting (in three parts) suggests that, while this poem is in carol form, its use (as with the poems in the early Tudor song books) would be non-popular. The text printed here is that for the third voice.

Saltmarsh notes (p. 3): 'The MS. was probably written about 1530. Like that of [No. 147], it was found, with a musical setting for three parts, on the back of an official document of earlier date: a draft report on a note, made in 1457, by two of the Commission of Mr. Justice Shallow's county, now in the Public Record Office, and formerly in the King's Remembrancer's department of the Exchequer. Here too the text is not an original. There is evidence that the scribe was copying from a manuscript by another hand. Moreover, the refrain at least was well known at the time; a setting for one voice has been published by the Plainsong and Medieval Music Society from BM. Addit. 31922, a song-book which is said to have belonged to Henry VIII.'

### 164. *His Mistress, His Comfort*

*Index*, No. 383. Not heretofore printed.

### 165. *Love's Sorrow*

*Index*, No. 3613. Not heretofore printed. Followed immediately by two stanzas rhyme royal of sorrowful farewells to his mistress (beg. 'My whofull herte plonged yn heuynesse') with refrain, 'alas vnkyndenesse þus haith my herte slayne' (erroneously listed in *Index* as part of this item).

### 166. *Desire to Serve*

*Index*, No. 734. Not heretofore printed.

### 167. *A Lover's Distress*

*Index*, No. 139. Not heretofore printed.
17. 'And until the day destine (decree) that (*hit* = death) to me.'

### 168. *A Lover's Plaint, I*

*Index*, No. 380. Not heretofore printed.

### 169. *A Lover's Plaint, II*

*Index*, No. 1331. Not heretofore printed.
11. recurles] without remedy or hope of recovery.

### 170. *A Roundel*

*Index*, No. 870. Not heretofore printed. Roundels are of rare occurrence in Middle English, if those of Charles d'Orleans be excepted (represented here by Nos. 182–5). The only roundels not associated with the leading writers (Chaucer, *Index*, No. 2375; Hoccleve, *Index*, No. 3224; Lydgate, *Index*, No. 2804) are *Index*, No. 3948, printed by Brown as a religious *carol* in his *Rel. Lyrics XIV Cent.*, p. 259; and the present poem. There are three double roundels by Hoccleve, *Index*, Nos. 1221, 2640, and 3889 (the second of which is included here, No. 210), and a triple roundel by Chaucer, *Index*, No. 4282. No. 18 is a roundel type.

### 171. *A Pledge of Loyalty* (with music)

*Index*, No. 2381. Previously printed by Stainer, *Early Bodl. Music*, ii. 66; and by Copley, *Seven English Songs and*

*Carols of the XV Century*, No. 3. Occurs also in Camb. Univ.
MS. Ff. 1. 6, printed by Cook, *Reader*, pp. 416–17. *Early
Eng. Lyrics*, pp. 32–3, prints a composite text.

Camb. variants:

3. and hit wold be.
6. long out of your sight.
7. your man.
8. Wherfor.
9. that she.
13. *Omit* is.
20. *Omit* &.
22. *Omit* alle.
24. Whersoeuer.
25. to loue hir best.
26. for to be trow.
27. *Omit* to.
30. for evire Amend.

## 172. *Sweeting, I Greet Thee*

*Index*, No. 734. Previously printed, in part only, by Strutt,
*Manners and Customs*, iii. 153, who describes it thus:
'Oh, it is the tender breathing of the love sick soul!'

## 173. *The Lover's Lament*

*Index*, No. 267. Previously printed frequently, including
*Early Eng. Lyrics*, pp. 27–28. See *Index* for details. In the
MS. the poem is headed 'Chaucer'.

Virelais are even more rare in Middle English than are
roundels. Apart from a piece ascribed to Richard, Earl of
Warwick (*Index*, No. 1288), and this present text, all the
other four extant virelais are by Hoccleve: *Index*, Nos. 783,
2229 (in one text of the *De Regimine Principum*), 3402, and
3854. Skeat (*Oxford Chaucer*, vii. 554) notes: 'Not a true
virelay, as the ending *ing* does not appear in the second
stanza. . . . But it is of the nature of a virelay.' This poem
follows, however, the traditional pattern of the virelai—a
poem in short lines arranged in stanzas of two rhymes only,
the ending line of one stanza becoming the chief rhyme of
the following.

### 174. *A Song of Scorn* (with music)

*Index*, No. 3879. Previously printed by Stainer, *Early Bodl. Music*, ii. 179–80; by Padelford, *Anglia*, xxxvi. 114–15; and by Chambers & Sidgwick, *Early Eng. Lyrics*, p. 216.

The contra-tenor part is written in full.

### 175. *Age and Love*

*Index*, No. 1652. Not heretofore printed.

1. 'Indeed, I recollect about what, in fact, in times gone by. . . . Ah, I advise you, forget about that, for everything is, in the last resort, phantasy.'

### 176. *The Trials of Old Men in Love*

*Index*, No. 1278. Not heretofore printed. The MS. is a mid-fifteenth-century commonplace book; *Index*, No. 2472, a religious poem, precedes this text.

8. Cf. No. 211, l. 7, a proverb.

### 177. *The Ten Commandments of Love*

*Index*, No. 590. Not heretofore printed from this MS. Occurs also in Trinity Coll. Camb. MS. 599, which has been printed by Stowe, *Chaucer*, 1561, and reprinted by Chalmers, *Eng. Poets*, i. 560–1. In the Trinity MS. the poem is headed 'Chaucer'. Skeat, *Oxford Chaucer*, vii, p. xii, comments: 'In the Envoy, the author says, truly enough, that he is devoid of cunning, experience, manner of enditing, reason, and eloquence.' This piece, in spite of its appeal to the *Romaunt of the Rose*, is not dependent on any part of it, and only in a very general way can it be related to the commandments, there given to the man. See Chaucer, *Rom. Rose*, ll. 2136–8:

> Er ye passe hens ententifly
> Your comaundementis to me ye say
> And I shal kepe them, if I may.

There may be a slight echo in l. 49 of *Rom. Rose*, B. 5259–60:

> For tweyn in nombre is bet than three
> In every counsel and secree.

78. 'Such power of love to harm, put that away completely, so that mercy may everywhere occupy its place.'

82. Cf. No. 140, l. 11, I am so bounde vndir ʒour lace.

Trinity variants:

14. oure owne. T. omits 1 Com, and all following rubrics.

27. Endever theym with hert.

65. peynes smart.

75. Take mesure in langyng wisdom engrose.

82. loues brdre (sic).

84. a mannys murderes.

89. amyable.

### 178. *The Lover and the Advocate of Venus*

*Index*, No. 2594. Also printed by Bowers, *PQ*, xxxi. 211–14. Added on a flyleaf of a Life of St. Edmund.

28. Cf. No. 134, l. 8 (refrain).

78. Cf. *Index*, No. 1086, l. 634, They be so wel reclaymed to the lure.

### 179. *The Clerk and the Nightingale, I*

*Index*, No. 1452. Previously printed by Halliwell, *Nugae Poeticae*, 1844, pp. 37–9. This poem has only a general relationship to No. 180 as a 'gab' (l. 17, gabbust). Ending incomplete.

### 180. *The Clerk and the Nightingale, II*

*Index*, No. *5. Not heretofore printed. Unfortunately the first leaf is missing; occurs among a collection of lives of saints and *Sir Degare*. Second half fifteenth century.

41. i.e. woman is true when dead.

48. 'with the skirt of her tunic.'

81. glasyn cappe] imaginary protection. See Skeat, *Piers the Plowman* (Oxf. 1886), ii. 280–1 (B, xx. 171).

### 181. *The Clerk and the Husbandman*

*Index*, No. 344. Previously printed by Brown, *MLN*, xxxiii. 415–17. Added on flyleaf in a late-fifteenth-century hand. Brown comments (p. 415): 'The stanzas spoken by the Clerk in his defense of love are very obviously modelled upon the well-known *Quia amore langueo* lyrics in which the

Blessed Virgin or Christ pleads for the love of man. That the refrain of the Clerk's song in praise of women should have borrowed from these fervent mystical lyrics is interesting, though it will hardly surprise any one who is familiar with the interrelations of secular and religious verse.' See notes to No. 135. The refrain 'turn vp hyr haltur' appears in *Index*, No. 1338; see also No. 41, l. 4.

31. reseue þi place] 'get an opportunity'.

### 182. *Loyalty to His Mistress*

*Index*, No. 3162. Previously printed by Pierre Champion, *Charles d'Orléans*, Paris 1924, ii. 571; by Hammond, *Eng. Verse Chaucer–Surrey*, p. 222; and by Steele, EETS, 215. 222. Occurs also in the Grenoble MS., printed by Champollion-Figeac, *Les Poésies du duc Charles d'Orléans*, Paris 1842, pp. 267–8; and by MacCracken, *PMLA*, xxvi. 176–7.

Steele (p. xxxi, fn.) suggests that the six roundels of the autograph (Paris) MS., of which this is one, might be the missing roundels (94–100) of the Harley MS.

1. Cf. line 1 of *Index*, No. 3163 (Harley MS. 682): So fresshe bewte so much goodlynes. The poem itself is quite dissimilar.

Charles d'Orleans is represented here by Nos. 182–6. The chief collection of his English poems, Harley MS. 682, was published in the limited *Roxburghe Club* edition in 1827 by Watson Taylor. Apart from the reprinting of a few items, the MS. remained dormant until Dr. Robert Steele made his edition for the Early English Text Society (vol. 215) in 1941.

Harley MS. 682 contains 222 poems, including about 77 which are not translations of the Duke's French texts. Royal MS. 16. F. ii was probably written for Prince Arthur, son of Henry VIII, *circa* 1500. It has many illuminations and several full-page illustrations (including one showing Charles d'Orleans seated at a window in a tower); there are three English poems among the French. The Paris autograph MS. (Bibl. nat. fonds fr. 25456) contains nine English poems (not all by Orleans). The Grenoble MS. is a copy of the Paris MS., probably by Charles's secretary, *circa* 1448–53. Four of the English poems are duplicated on two loose pages in Bodl. MS. Rawl. K. 38, and there are four other poems (*Index*, Nos. 264, 816, 2449, 3142) in Camb. Univ. Add. MS. 2585, Art. 1 (pr. *MLN*, lxvi. 501–5).

Steele discusses at length the vexed question of the authorship of the poems in Harley MS. 682, and decides in favour of Charles d'Orleans. His reasons can be summarized as follows:

(1) The Duke claims authorship in four lines.

(2) Harley MS. 682 has similarities to the Paris autograph MS.

(3) Ballade 113 is based on the Ballade of the Duke of Burgundy who was in secret correspondence with Orleans.

(4) The vocabulary is Chaucerian with a few Northern forms, learned by Charles at Pontefract and Fotheringay.

Hammond, on the other hand, takes an opposing view, writing (p. 214): 'There is very little English verse in the fifteenth century worthy of comparison with these faithful, vigorous, and often graceful translations. . . . He [some future editor] will note, of course, the easy command of English in them, as compared with the stiff insecurity of the English bits preserved in the French volumes; and he will have to consider the possibility either that lapse of years brought Charles to mastery of his gaolers' language, or that in the French MSS. the French scribe has garbled a fairly good English text. He will have to reckon with the fact that the personality behind the English recension is a more forceful and buoyant one than is the personality of the mass of the French poems; and he will have to note the presence in the translations of an occasional Chaucerian trace not in Charles' French.' Hammond's view is also that of Bullrich, Sauerstein, and Saintsbury. Champion (*Le MS. Autographe de Poésies de Charles d'Orléans*, Paris 1907) believes that the English poems of the Paris MS. were written by an English scribe.

Charles d'Orleans was taken prisoner at Agincourt at the age of twenty-one in 1415, lived in London until 1417, then at Pontefract, Fotheringay, and Bolingbroke to 1429, and in various other houses until his release in 1440.

## 183. *The Service of His Mistress*

*Index*, No. 922. Previously printed by Champion, *Charles d'Orléans*, ii. 570; and by Steele, EETS, 215. 220. Occurs also in the Grenoble MS., printed by Champollion-Figeac, *Poésies*, pp. 265–6; and by MacCracken, *PMLA*, xxvi. 175; and in Royal MS. 16. F. ii, printed (with Paris MS.) by Hammond, *Eng. Verse Chaucer–Surrey*, pp. 221–2.

Steele (p. xxv) comments on this poem: 'In accepting his authorship of the English poems, students of Charles are relieved of the necessity of accounting for a number of English copies of verses found in his personal manuscript (two of them in his own handwriting). Up to now French critics have regarded them as the work of some English or Scots visitor to Blois, Charles's manuscript being used as an album. A single instance shows this explanation to be unlikely. The form "quippe" (v. 6) for "keep" could not arise from a Scotticism; nor could it conceivably be an error of the Prince's secretary when copying from an English original. It must have been due to a French author writing English phonetically, since only at this stage in the history of the poem could the error have been introduced. The presence of the þ in the two poems written in Charles's own handwriting points to a confirmed habit of writing English, and these particular poems are undoubtedly his in sentiment. . . . It may be noted that the poems in Charles's personal manuscript which he did not compose, other than these, have the names of the authors attached to them.'

Steele also notes (p. xviii) that in Harley MS. 682 the roundels are written 'on the lower part of the page, a blank space being left for the insertion of music later on'.

For other instances of foreign phonetic spelling of English words, see No. 157.

4–5. Royal. That ye gette her oftyme pryuely.
  6. R. kepe.
 11. R. dwel. Hammond reads do wel.

### 184. *The Beauty of His Mistress*

*Index*, No. 3465. Previously printed by Steele, EETS, 215. 139 (Roundel No. 69).

### 185. *A Confession of Love*

*Index*, No. 2243. Previously printed by Chambers & Sidgwick, *Early Eng. Lyrics*, p. 31; and by Steele, EETS, 215, 133 (Roundel No. 57).

## 186. *A Place in His Mistress' Heart*

*Index*, No. 1240. Previously printed by Steele, EETS, 215. 209–10 (Ballade No. 111).

## 187. *A Lover's Plaint Against Fortune*

*Index*, No. 2567. Previously printed by MacCracken, *PMLA*, xxvi. 160–1. Occurs also in the Paris MS., printed by Champion, *Charles d'Orléans*, ii. 571–2; by Hammond, *Eng. Verse Chaucer-Surrey*, pp. 222–3; and by Steele, EETS, 215. 223; and in Grenoble MS., printed by Champollion-Figeac, *Poésies*, pp. 268–9.

This poem was copied from the Bodl. MS. into the Paris MS. at a date later than the autograph. The author of the Bodl. Fairfax poems, MacCracken believes, was not Charles d'Orleans, but the Duke of Suffolk, William de la Pole: see 'An English Friend of Charles d'Orleans' in *PMLA*, xxvi. 142–51. This poem is not a translation. See Crow, *Speculum*, xvii. 89. Nos. 187–9 come from a series of ballades, letters, and complaints, usually of three or four stanzas each, nineteen items in all, on fols. 318ʳ to 329ʳ of the Fairfax MS.

## 188. *In Praise of Margaret the Queen*

*Index*, No. 2178. Previously printed by MacCracken, *PMLA*, xxvi. 168–71; by Hammond, *MLN*, xxvi. 75–6; and *Eng. Verse Chaucer–Surrey*, pp. 200–1.

MacCracken comments (pp. 149–50) on this poem: 'Still more interesting is the *Praise of the Flower*, a poem which may have been written to please that Margaret (marguerite) whom Suffolk brought to Henry VI, and for whom Lydgate is said to have devised the pageants of welcome in London in 1445. After a light-hearted praise of the Flower, the poet, in words more sincere than any save Hoccleve's, laments the death of Chaucer, who had known so well how to praise this flower in days gone by. Then he turns to Lydgate, and after telling him he is the only worthy successor of Chaucer, takes him jokingly roundly to task for making light of women in his various works, and bids him, if he would have pardon, to seek it at the next Love's Parliament. The whole tone of this latter portion, it will be observed, is that of a patron, not of a humble imitator of the Monk of Bury. Here, then, we find five points: a lordly patron's tone, familiar with parliaments, an intimacy with Lydgate, a praise of the marguerite, an affectionate regret for Chaucer, and a friendship with Orleans implied by his preservation of one of these poems; and these five attributes taken together can be filled by Suffolk alone among the personalities of the time.'

### 189. *A Letter to His Heart's Joy*

*Index*, No. 2182. Previously printed by MacCracken, *PMLA*, xxvi. 165. For a reworking of this text into a poem in eight-line stanzas, see *Index*, No. 2247 (printed by Furnivall, EETS, 15. 68). St. 1 adds a final line, 'vnto you, the floure of goodely-hede'. St. 2 inserts a line before the last, 'And schall be youre Deffence in all aduersite'. St. 3 follows ll. 1–5, then adds three lines and a concluding quatrain:

> This same day at myne vp-Ryssinge,
> Where that y be-sought god of merci
> Tho to haue my souerein in his kepeing.

> As wyssely god me save,
>  As y am onely yours,
>  what payne so euer y haue,
>  And will be at all owres.

The vogue of epistles reached its height in the fifteenth century, but some earlier texts are to be found, e.g. *Index*, Nos. 16 and 19, two macaronic poems in English, Latin, and French, the one 'De Amico ad Amicam' and the other the 'Responcio' (printed by Chambers & Sidgwick, *Early Eng. Lyrics*, pp. 15–19). Other epistles, classified here under other groupings, which belong to this section, include Nos. 129, 130, 131, 146, 149, 161, 188, 189, 207, 208, and 209. Without doubt, the love epistle is the main conventional form during the fifteenth century.

### 190. *To His Mistress, Flower of Womanhood*

*Index*, No. 3291. Previously printed by Furnivall, EETS, 15. 71–2; and by Chaytor, *Troubadours and England*, pp. 137–8.

Chaytor comments (p. 138): 'This poem is of somewhat late date (about 1450) but it is interesting for the number of troubadour commonplaces which it contains; in particular, it repeats ideas from the love letter of Folquet de Romans. The rime-scheme, ababbcc, was used by Aimeric de Pegulham, Folquet de Marseille, Pons de Capduelh.' Chaytor gives many illustrations (pp. 138–40) in support of this statement. However, of these parallelisms, Chaytor remarks (p. 120): 'It may also be assumed that many of them are obvious commonplaces which would occur to any lyric poet.' It might further be remarked that, by 1450, rhyme royal was thoroughly indigenous with English poets.

## 191. *A Letter to His Heart's Sovereign*

*Index*, No. 1238. Not heretofore printed.

## 192. *A Letter Protesting His Devotion*

*Index*, No. 1510. Not heretofore printed.

The stylized treatment of 'epistles' by lovers has been carried over to other uses, e.g. *Index*, No. 4232, a letter to a 'worshepfulle brother' in six quatrains; *Index*, No. 866, five stanzas rhyme royal sent by John Pympe to Sir John Paston; and *Index*, No. 1360, 22 lines from John Pympe to Margaret. In the Paston Letters is also *Index*, No. 303.

## 193. *To His Mistress 'M'*

*Index*, No. 1344. Printed by Robbins, *PMLA*, lxv. 268–9.

## 194. *A Letter to His Truelove*

*Index*, No. 926. Printed by Robbins, *PMLA*, lxv. 271.

## 195. *A Letter to His Mistress*

*Index*, No. 1241. Not heretofore printed.

## 196. *From a Caitiff Bound and Thrall*

*Index*, No. 2478. Not heretofore printed. Occurs in an early-sixteenth-century hand on the flyleaf of a Chaucer (including *Troilus* and *Parlement of Foules*).

18. colours savyn] The seven perfect colours (cf. Peacham, *Compleat Gentleman*, Oxford, 1906, p. 156).

## 197. *From a Departing Lover*

*Index*, No. 3785. Printed by Jordan, *Eng. St.* xli. 265–6.
27. Tr. 'Were it not that there were hope, etc.'

### 198. *To His Mistress, Root of Gentleness*

*Index*, No. 751. Not heretofore printed. Followed in the MS. by No. 128. In sts. 2 and 4 the basic rhyme royal pattern is defective. In st. 2, l. 8 appears as written in the MS., although, since *wys* rhymes with *seruyse*, 'þat euer y can or may' might have been originally part of another line (to rhyme with *nature, endure*), so making the stanza regular. In st. 4, the copyist may have conceivably omitted two lines at the bottom or top of the page.

### 199. *To His Mistress, Fairest of Fair*

*Index*, No. 754. Not heretofore printed. The first four lines of each stanza are written in the MS. as two long lines.

### 200. *To His Mistress, Delectable Daisy*

*Index*, No. 366. Previously printed by Padelford and Benham, *Anglia*, xxxi. 371–2.

### 201. *An Envoy to His Mistress*

*Index*, No. 2386. Not heretofore printed. Written in a late-fifteenth-century hand on a vellum page, bound up with French poems (in a different hand). Followed by *Index*, No. 823:

> ffor he is true
> And will pursue ⎱ in hyr seruice
> Attendaunce due⎰

> . . . hym not rue
> his seruice true ⎱ . . . . . ce
> Do that exchue ⎰

### 202. *A Farewell to His Mistress, I*

*Index*, No. 766. Not heretofore printed. Added in a sixteenth-century hand to a fifteenth-century MS. of Lydgate's *Life of Our Lady* and other poems. Preceded by *Index*, No. 511, a Prayer to the B.V., in the same hand.

### 203. *A Farewell to His Mistress, II*

*Index*, No. 763. Not heretofore printed.

### 204. *A Farewell to His Mistress, III*

*Index*, No. 767. Previously printed by Padelford and Benham, *Anglia*, xxxi. 369. Occurs also in Advocates MS. 1. 1. 6, f. 225, printed by Ritchie, *STS*, n.s. xxvi. 284–5.

12. Cf. *Digby Myst.* iii. 958: Beryl brytest of bewte; and No. 205, l. 88.

### 205. *A Lover's Farewell to His Mistress*

*Index*, No. 752. Previously printed by Warton, *History* 1824, iii. 392; and by Strutt, *Manners and Customs*, iii. 152. In Douce's list of contents at the beginning of the MS. the poem is entitled 'A Love Poem of ye Duke of York'.

### 206. *Love Longing*

*Index*, No. 1018. Previously printed by Furnivall, *Ballad Soc.* vii, p. clvi; by Ritson, *Anc. Songs*, 1829, ii. 27–31; and in *Reliquiae Antiquae*, i. 70–3. Furnivall notes that this poem is 'godliefied' in the *Godlie Ballates*, p. 132. Although the majority of references indicate a woman's point of view (e.g. ll. 51, 52, 66–8, 84), other lines might refer to a man (e.g. ll. 9, 97—unless this is a warning from one woman to another).

### 207. *To Her Lover*

*Index*, No. 2547. Previously printed by Padelford and Benham, *Anglia*, xxxi. 370–1.

20. Whether or not this letter is a translation from the French, it indicates some French connexion with formal love poetry; cf. No. 172.

### 208. *A Mocking Letter to Her Lover*

*Index*, No. 3832. Previously printed by Cords, *Archiv*, cxxxv. 296; and by Robbins, *MLR*, xxxvii. 416.

### 209. *The Lover's Mocking Reply*

*Index*, No. 2437. Previously printed by Cords, *Archiv*, cxxxv. 297; and by Robbins, *MLR*, xxxvii. 417–18. For other and longer satirical descriptions of a mistress, see *Index*, No. 2237 (with refrain, 'When she hath on her hood of grene'); *Index*, No. 1957, a burlesque love song with

refrain, 'When I sleep I may not wake'; *Index*, No. 2524;
*Index*, No. 1300; and here, No. 37, and No. 210 (by Hoccleve).

44. lowcray] A nonce-word: may have some connexion
with Luke(s) = made at Liège, said especially of velvet, and
ray = (striped) cloth.

## 210. *Praise of His Lady*

*Index*, No. 2640. Previously printed many times, among
others, by Furnivall, EETS, lxi, p. xxxviii; by Gollancz,
EETS, lxxiii. 37–8; by Hammond, *Eng. Verse Chaucer–
Surrey*, p. 68; and by Robbins, *MLR*, xxxvii. 419.

## 211. *Scorn of Women* ·

*Index*, No. 1944. Previously printed by Skeat, *Oxford
Chaucer*, vii. 295–6. Occurs also in Trinity Coll. Camb. MS.
1450 and Harley MS. 2251 (where it is headed: Do not
Reade thys but hyde your eye). Delete from *Index*, ref. to
Bodl. 10234, fol. 38ʳ. Printed from Stowe's *Chaucer* 1561 by
Chalmers, *Eng. Poets*, i. 564. At side of the text is written
'Chaucer'. Trinity Coll. Camb. MS. 1450, fol. 28ʳ re-
arranges the order of stanzas (1, 2, 4, 3, 6, 5) and adds a
seventh (fol. 28ᵛ):

> What thyng than eyr is lyȝter and meveabyll?
> The lyȝt, men say, þat passyth, yn A trowth,
> All yff the lyȝt be not so waryabyll
> As ys the Wynde that euery weye blowth.
> And yut, of reson, sum men deme & trowe
> Wymmen be lyȝtyst of thes company.
> lett passe ouer yn ese, & let þe wynd blow.
> Beware! the blynde ettyth many A flye.

33. and all ys as teyte] Even though all is cheerful.
36. See Irving Linn, 'If All the Sky were Parchment',
*PMLA*, liii. 951–70; and *Oxford Dictionary of Nursery
Rhymes*, pp. 436–8.

## 212. *Abuse of Women*

*Index*, No. 2580. Previously printed by Ritchie, *STS*, n.s.
xxvi. 35–6.

# GLOSSARY

This Glossary includes all words which might present some difficulty to the reader, including, as well as those words no longer current in Modern English, those words whose meaning or orthography has changed. In most cases, only a single reference is recorded, generally the earliest occurrence of a given form in these Texts.

**a,** *conj.*; *and* 171. 8.

**a,** *interj.*; *ah* 1. 5.

**a,** *prep.*; *in, by* 41. 16; *on* 28. 1; 29. 26.

**abate,** *v.*; *to do away with* (a condition), *back out* 40. 2.

**abone,** *adv.*; *above* 132. 23.

**abye,** *v. pr.* 1 *pl.*; *pay for* 116. 19.

**acord,** *n.*; *agreement* 4. 12.

**a-dere,** *v.*; *to injure* 120. 32.

**aduertyse,** *v.*; *to consider* 120. 80; (*imp.*) 177. 31.

**ae,** *adv.*; *ever* 203. 5.

**a-ferde,** *pp.*; *frightened* 48. 6.

**affiance,** *n.*; *religion* (fig.) 123. 2; **affyaunce,** *pledge* 166. 7.

**afforce,** *n.*; *endeavour* 123. 15.

**affray,** *n.*; *disturbance* 49. 34.

**after,** *prep.*; *in accordance with* 130. 26.

**agagement,** *n.*; *agreement* 116. 23.

**aȝen,** *prep.*; *in preparation for* 29. 4.

**aȝens,** *prep.*; *against* 41. 6; **agaynys** 181. 51; **agein** 172. 26; **ageyn** 113. 2; **ageyne** 96. 37; **ageynst** 51. 5; **ayen** 205. 44; **ogaines** 58. 20; *upon* 48. 1.

**akynge,** *n.*; *aching* 81. 18.

**alayn,** *adv.*; *alone* 73. 38.

**ale,** *adj.*; *all* 33. 21.

**ale,** *n.*; *ale* 1. 35; **alle** 56. 21.

**ale-hows,** *n.*; *tavern* 38. 34.

**ale-schoth,** *n.*; *scotale* (festival with levies for ale) 29. 26.

**alhaill,** *adv.*; *entirely* 133. 17.

**allegeaunce,** *n.*; *alleviation* 173. 35; **allygaunce** 164. 13.

**allewys,** *adv. phr.*; **on allewys,** *in every way* 146. 6.

**allmayn,** *n.*; *almond* 56. 19.

**allonly,** *adv.*; *solely* 187. 22.

**als,** *conj.*; *as* 58. 2; *also* 101. 16.

**al-ther-best,** *adv.*; *best of all* 22. 1.

**al-ther-most,** *adv.*; *most of all* 62. 2.

**amable,** *adj.*; *lovable* 177. 89.

**amende,** *v.*; *to improve* 165. 6; 171. 30.

**a-meved,** *pp.*; *stirred up, aroused* 53. 6.

**amit,** *v.*; *to admit* 178. 69.

**among,** *adv.*; *from time to time* 120. 72; **euer among,** *continually* 138. 15.

**amyable,** *adj.*; *lovable* 170. 1; **ameable** 130. 7.

**amytest,** *n.*; *amethyst* 205. 95.

**and,** *conj.*; *and* 3. 8; **an** 18. 23; 180. 30; **ant** 17. 4; *if* 32. 39; 44. 3; 136. 13; 138. 22.

**angers,** *n.*; *troubles, afflictions* 58. 50.

**anne,** *see* **ony.**

**anowȝe,** *adv.*; *enough* 72. 15.

**antioche,** *n.*; *medicinal herbal drink* 103. 15.

**aparans,** *n.*; *appearance in court to answer charge* 178. 61.

**apele**, *v.*; *to challenge someone to defend himself* 176. 1.

**appayre**, *v.*; *to deride* 208. 4.

**appert**, *adj.*; *frank* 131. 2; 190. 8.

**applied**, *pp.*; *disposed, determined* (to) 106. 11.

**appose**, *v.*; *to examine* 1. 11.

**apropred**, *pp.*; *assigned* 209. 25.

**aquyte**, *v.*; *to requite* 138. 46.

**ar**, *conj.*; *or* 164. 6.

**areche**, *see* rech.

**arnde**, *n.*; *petition* 19. 9.

**arrerages**, *n.*; *debts* 106. 6.

**arvyst-gos**, *n.*; *goose eaten at feast at end of harvest* 42. 5.

**arwe**, *n.*; *arrow* 103. 7.

**asent**, *n.*; *agreement* 116. 22.

**asor**, *n.*; *azure* 46. 13; **aȝwr**, *adj.* 196. 21.

**assay**, *n.*; *assay, trial* 108. 3.

**assay**, *v.*; *to examine* 26. 18; (*pp.*) **assayd** 198. 15; **asayid**, *made trial of* 7. 7.

**assent**, *v. pr. subj.* 3 *s.*; *agree* 139. 20.

**assise**, *n.*; *judgement, sentencing* 58. 108.

**assoyled**, *v. pt.* 3 *s.*; *absolved* (from sin) 49. 14.

**a-sterte**, *v.*; *to happen* (to one) 167. 11; *to escape* 199. 59.

**astrapotent**, *n.*; *God* 121. 1.

**at**, *prep. with inf.*; *to* 58. 81.

**atast**, *v.*; *to attest* 178. 59.

**ataynt**, *pp.*; *condemned* 128. 3.

**atcheued**, *pp.*; *achieved* 177. 40.

**avale**, *v. imp.*; *wreathe* 11. 4.

**auaunce**, *v.*; *to cause to prosper* 173. 39; 177. 97.

**avaunt**, *n.*; *boast* 178. 26.

**auayll**, *v.*; *to avail* 99. 2; **avayle** 120. 21.

**auctor**, *n.*; *the Creator* 121. 1; **aucthour**, *author* 177. 24.

**auenture**, *v.*; *to take a chance* 101. 15.

**aventure**, *n.*; *chance* 188. 35.

**avisance**, *n.*; *consideration* 152. 5.

**avisynes**, *n.*; *deliberation* 131. 3; 185. 5; 187. 6.

**auld**, *adj.*; *old* 132. 14.

**avys**, *n.*; *advice* 4. 12; **avis** 88. 75.

**avysament**, *n.*; *consideration* 209. 25.

**avyse**, *v. imp.*; *reflect* 40. 4; 181. 25; **awyse** 134. 15; (*pp.*) **auiset**, *purposed* 193. 5; **avy-syd**, *thoughtful* 198. 35.

**avysyoun**, *n.*; *vision* 96. 30.

**a-went**, *pp.*; *thought* 36. 9.

**a-wreke**, *pp.*; *avenged* 9. 9.

**awstern**, *adj.*; *harsh*, 212. 10.

**axe**, *v. pr.* 1 *s.*; *ask* 185. 12; **haske** 134. 7.

**ayene**, *adv.*; *again* 49. 29; 190. 34; **ogayne** 58. 15.

**babyr**, *adj.*; *thick, protruding* 209. 29.

**bace**, *n.*; *bass* 1. 34.

**bale**, *n.*; *misery* 37. 5; **baill** 132. 11; **balles** 128. 35; **balus** 148. 15; **balyes** 158. 2.

**ball**, *n.*; *stool-ball* (in phr. **ren-nyng at þe ball**) 8. 7.

**ballid**, *adj.*; *bald* 124. 2.

**band**, *n.*; *bond* (of love) 133. 21.

**bandoun**, *n.*; *power* 116. 6.

**bare**, *adj.*; *complete* 199. 25.

**barm-fellys**, *n.*; *leather aprons* 118. 11.

**barn**, *n.*; *man* (no barn, *nobody*) 158. 2.

**bat**, *see* bede.

**bating**, *pres. p.*; *beating* 96. 46.

**be**, *prep.*; *by* 61. 6; 73. 31; 188. 57; 189. 17; 194. 3; *in* 65. 12.

**bede**, *v.*; *to make known* 19. 9; (*pt.* 3 *s.*) **bat**, *ordered* 30. 2; **bad** 45. 11; **bade** 30. 26.

**be-gone**, *pp.*; so well ys me be-gone, *so fortunate am I* 35 bur.

begyle, *v.*; *beguile* 78. 62; (*pp.*)
begyld 20. 4; begyled 25. 12.

bell, *n.*; *bell* 36. 4; belle 28. 31;
be bel & boke, *oath used in
excommunication* 25. 3.

bellewys, *n.*; *bellows* 118. 6.

benignitee, *n.*; *kindly feeling*
106. 11; 126. 5; benyngnyte
205. 3; 207. 22.

benome, *pp.*; *taken away from*
205. 12.

bente, *adj.*; *arched* (of eyebrows)
129. 15; y-benth 143. 10.

benynge, *adj.*; *kindly* 76. 8;
benyngne 131. 33.

beo, *v.*; *to be* 96. 69; boe 16. 5;
(*pres. p.*) beand 73. 83; (*pp.*)
bene 24. 14; byn 198. 43; (*pr.
3 s.*) byth 198. 31; es 58. 1;
(*neg.*) nis 8. 1; nys 150. 2;
179. 31; (*pr. 1 pl.*) arn 4. 10;
er 58. 11; 73. 4; 144. 10; ben
46. 13; (*pr. 2 pl.*) beon 131.
30; by 136. 16; (*pr. 3 pl.*) bin
177. 12; buþ 33. 21; byth 128.
25; bytt 143. 5; er 73. 6; (*pt.
3 s. neg.*) nas 203. 7.

ber, *n.*; *beer* 12. 4.

bere, *n.*; *bier* (death) 205. 43.

bere, *v.*; *to carry* 49. 4; beyre
25. 16; (*pr. 1 s.*) ber 28. 42;
(*pr. 1 pl.*) bern 7. 1; (*pr. 3 pl.*)
bere 114. 1; (*pt. 1 s.*) bar 17. 4;
(*pt. 3 s.*) beryt 27. 16; bere þe
bell, *to be the best* 59. 26; beryth
the name, *has the reputation*
34. 3.

beshrewe, *v. · pr.* 1 *s.*; *curse*
14. 17; (*pp.*) be-shrewyd 208.
13.

best, *n.*; *animal* 119. 57; bestes,
*farm animals* 72. 54; 136. 25;
beestis 100. 4.

be-stad, *pp.*; *harassed* 163.19.

bet, *adv. comp.*; *better* 41. 3; go
bet, *go quicker* 57. bur.

bete, *pp.*; *beaten* 199. 37.

bete, *v.*; *to relieve* 127. 5.

be-tyme, *adv.*; *early* 78. 43.

be-vayle, *v. pr.* 3 *pl.*; *lament*
206. 50.

beyne, *pro.*; *both* 19. 5.

bidene, *adv.*; *completely* 58.
101.

bird, see bryd.

biteche, *v. pr.* 1 *s.*; *commit* 9: 17.

blac, *adj.*; *black* 33. 7; 52. 13;
blak 47. 9; blake 78. 42; (*comp.*)
blakkyr 211. 39; *melancholy*
127. 7; *dark-complexioned* 33.
1.

blame, *n.*; *culpability* 112. 4;
*condemnation* 134. 43.

blasterand, *adj.*; *raging* 212. 17.

blee, *n.*; *hue* 204. 12.

blered, *pp.*; *afflicted with in-
flammation of eyes* 81. 24.

blethly, *adv.*; *gladly* 172. 16;
blythly 180. 2.

blin, *v.*; *to stop* 58. 66; blyne
99. 2.

bliŏ-ful, *adj.*; *kindly* 147. 3.

blosmen, *n.*; *flowers* 141. 2.

blwet, *n.*; *browet, soup* 56. 19.

blysse, *n.*; *happiness* 128. 30;
147. 12; *cause of happiness*
52. 6; 133. 19; *joy of heaven*
52. 14; 150. 4.

blyve, *adv.*; *quickly* 78. 34; 119.
26.

bogeler, *n.*; *buckler* 30. 5.

bogges, *n.*; *movements?* 31. 7.

bolde, *adj.*; *self-willed* 41. 5;
*immodest* 136. 39.

bole, *n.*; *bull* 118. 11.

boll, *n.*; *drinking-vessel* 14 bur.

bolwerkys, *n.*; *breastworks* (fig.)
209. 46.

bon-ayre, *n., courtesy* 198. 3.

bond, *adj.*; *encumbered* 74. 7.

bord, *n. in phr.* with-in bord,
*within* 178. 87.

borgh, *n.*; *security* 58. 41; boro,
*deliverance* 206. 106.

bosshelle, *n.*; *vessel used as a bushel measure* 30. 29.

bot, *adv.*; *only* 34. 12; butt 159. 4.

bote, *n.*; *profit* 58. 19; *remedy* 150. 2; 172. 8.

botelere, *n.*; *butler* 3. 18; butler 14 bur.; butlar 14. 8.

boun, *n.*; *petition* 205. 31.

bounte, *n.*; *virtue* 131. 11; 198. 33; bountee 131. 26; bontie 133. 19.

bour, *n.*; *abode* 18. 21; *boudoir* 36. 1; bowre 180. 74.

bowe, *n.*; *bow* (in archery) 114. 11.

bowe, *n.*; *bough* 67. 5; bowys 69. 1.

bowgy, *adj.*; *bulgy* 210. 5.

bownes, *v. pr. 2 s.*; *go* 97. 17.

brakes *n.*; *bracken, ferns* 20. 12.

brane, *n.*; *bran* 13. 1.

brane, *n.*; *brawn* 54 bur.

brant, *adj.*; *unwrinkled* 144. 7.

bred, *n.*; *bread* 43. 9; 53. 15.

bred, *n.*; *breadth* 119. 65.

bred, *v.*; *to spread out* 29. 18.

brek, *v.*; *to break* 158. 6; oure hertes breke, *to disclose what is on our minds* 193. 26; (*pr. 3 s.*) breke3, *bursts into flower* 141. 2.

brenne, *v.*; *to burn* 5. 9; 128. 6; (*pres. p.*) brennynge 61. 6.

brer, *n.*; *briar* 45. 9; 130. 17; 196. 28.

brist, *v.*; *to break* 132. 32; birst 133. 15; bruste 136. 30; (*pp.*) berst 180. 59; to-brest 138. 8; (*pr. 3 s.*) brestes, *bursts* 118. 6.

brodde, *adv.*; *with eyes wide open* 39. 2.

brode, *adj.*; *broad* 30. 5.

bromes, *n.*; *broom* (shrubs) 114. 3.

brotylle, *adj.*; *fickle* 108. 3.

brout, *pp.*; *brought* 37. 5; brocht 132. 24; broth 143. 4.

browes, *n.*; *eye-brows* 129. 15; 210. 3; bruys 143. 10.

brows, *n.*; *brows, forehead* 144. 7.

bryd, *n.*; *mistress* 147. 1; bird 127. 4; 136. 5; biryd 147. 3; brid 147. 1.

bryde, *n.*; *bird* 200. 5; bird 205. 58; bridde 96. 1; bryddis 5. 2; 69. 3; byrdes 55. 2.

bryghte, *adj.*; *beautiful* 198. 47; brith 174. 4; britht 196. 3; bryhit 147. 5; (*sup.*) bryghtest 204. 12.

bryme, *adj.*; *fierce* 53. 4; 212. 17.

brymly, *adj.*; *fierce* 53. 7.

brynston, *n.*; *sulphur* 113. 8.

bugge, *v.*; *to buy* 9. 3; (*pt. 3 s.*) bought, *redeemed* 130. 33.

bundin, *pp.*; *bound* 133. 21.

burde, *n.*; *table* 58. 57.

burdus, *n.*; *frivolities* 28. 34.

burne, *n.*; *well* 25. 6.

but, *conj.*; *unless* 128. 29; 156. 8; bot 73. 21; but þat 180. 62; but yf 162. 11.

but, *prep.*; *except* 127. 5; *without* 133. 3; 212. 9.

butyr, *adj.*; *bitter* 128. 35.

by and by, *adv. phr.*; *one by one* 14. 3; 49. 6; *in due order* 180. 69.

byd, *v.*; *to remain* 132. 32.

byddyn, *v.*; *to invite* 57. 14; (*pt. 3 s.*) bed 28. 14.

byes, *n.*; *rings* (fig. testicles) 31. 24.

byhette, *v. pr. 1 s.*; *promised* 28. 22; (*pt. 2 pl.*) byhy3t 197. 36.

byhte, *n.*; *bend* 81. 49.

byldus, *v. pr. 3 s.*; *builds* (a nest) 148. 3.

byll, *n.*; *letter* 130. 61; 188. 32; bill 196. 6; *written document* 66 rub.

byrall, *n.*; *beryl* 204. 12; **burell** 205. 88.

bysynesse, *n.*; *diligence* 98. 8; 183. 2; *occupation* 120. 73.

bytteris, *n.*; *bitterns* 56. 14.

by-tuyxt, *prep.*; *between* 22 bur.

cache, *v.*; *to take* 116. 8; (*pr.* 2 *pl.*) **cacche** 106. 19.

cammede, *adj.*; *snub-nosed* (v. notes) 118. 5.

camusyd, *adj.*; *snub* (-nosed) 209. 22.

cappons, *n.*; *capons* 56. 25.

care, *n.*; *sorrow* 128. 14; 134. 50; **car** 171. 22; **cares** 150. 1.

case, *n. in phr.* **I put case that** ; *I supposed* 188. 57.

cast, *v.*; *to throw* 171. 22; **cayste**, *to cast out* 136. 46; **kest her ee**, *to look* 194. 18; (*pr.* 3 *s.*) **caste**, *takes away* 136. 12; (*pr.* 2 *pl.*) 138. 28; (*pr.* 3 *pl.*) *spread out* (in hunting) 119. 20.

catel, *n.*; *goods* 60. 4.

catife, *n.*; *prisoner* 196. 8.

cawtelus, *adj.*; *wily* 212. 19.

certen, *n.*; *certainty* 20. 9.

certente, *n.*; *certainty* 191. 4.

cete, *n.*; *city* 58. 95.

cewre, *v. pr. subj.* 3 *s.*; *relieve* 128. 38.

chalonus, *n.*; *blankets* 28. 26.

chambur, *n.*; *private room* 28. 23; 149. 4; **chaumbyr**, *bedroom* 46. 20; **chaumbr**, *city* (v. notes) 122. 2.

chapmen, *n.*; *pedlars* 7 bur.

chappynd, *v. pt.* 3 *s.*; *fastened, laced* 115. 9 (Latin laquitissinauit).

chapyn, *pp.*; *formed* 144. 9.

chaumbys, *n.*; *legs* 208. 26.

chaunce, *n.*; *fortune* 28 bur.; 173. 37; 188. 11; **chawnce** 163. 10.

chayse, *n.*; *hunting* 137. 31.

che, see she.

cheertee, *n.*; *affection* 106. 20.

chefe, *adj.*; *foremost* 52 bur.; **chef** 78. 53; **cheff** 55. 6.

chefe, *n.*; *chief* 169. 8.

cheke, *n.*; *chicken* 49. 30.

chelde, *adj.*; *cold* 18. 16.

chere, *n.*; *countenance* 3. 1; 130. 17; **chiere** 77. 2; **cherys** 211. 15; *gaiety* 12. 3; 200. 7; **cheres** 211. 8; *kindly welcome* 1. 2; 3. 17; 54. 6.

cherrus, *n.*; *chores, tasks* 29. 14.

cherubud, *n.*; *a kind of beetle* 115. 4 (Latin scarabius).

cherye, *n.*; *cherry* 45. 5; 129. 13; **cheris** 114. 4.

chese, *v.*; *to choose* 42. 4; (*pr.* 1 *s.*) 134. 17; 135. 30; (*pr.* 3 *s.*) **chesse** 136. 19; **I-chese** 208. 34.

chesone, *n.*; *reason* (for the **chesone** of me, *because of me* 28. 7).

cheve, *v.*; *to prosper* 78. 43.

chide, *v.*; *to dispute with* 58. 28.

child, *n.*; *young man* 23. 1.

chorle, *n.*; *fellow* 36. 15; **charll**, *villain* 44. 14.

cith, *n.*; *sight* 171. 6; **sight** 170. 3.

clater, *v.*; *to talk idly* 38. 26.

clayme, *n.*; *title, right* 121. 2.

clene, *adj.*; *pure* 13. 11; *free from phlegm* 1. 27; *undefiled* 96. 60.

clene, *adv.*; *clean* 81. 67.

clennesse, *n.*; *purity* 205. 111.

clepe, *v.*; *to call* 119. 41; (*pp.*) **clepid** 101. 3.

cler, *adj.*; *clear* 96. 38; (of complexion) 130. 25; *illustrious* 73. 73; 130. 34; *honest* 111. 1; *unencumbered* 74. 3.

clerke, *n.*; *one connected with*

the Church 24. 1; *cleric* 98. 2; 179. 17; *clerk* 106. 18; (*pl.*) *scholars* 96. 22; 129. 50; 188. 60.

**clernesse**, *n.*; *beauty* 153. 2.

**clogges**, *n.*; *blocks of wood* (fig. testicles) 31. 4.

**cloke**, *n.*; *claw* (of the devil) 116. 13.

**clooe**, *v.*; *to staunch the* (menstrual) *flow* [cf. cloyen] 80. 10.

**clos**, *n.*; *yard* 42. 7.

**clot**, *n.*; *heavy blow* 28. 41.

**cloþemerys**, *n.*; *mare-clothers, horse armourers* 118. 21.

**clovʒt**, *v.*; *to hit* 44. 7.

**clymates**, *n.*; *climes, regions* 121. 2.

**coarte**, *v.*; *to compress* 88. 32.

**coccioun**, *n.*; *boiling* 88. 56.

**cok**, *n.*; *vane* 208 rub.; **by cokkes sovle**, *God's* 119. 39; **cook**, *cock* 46. 1.

**colde**, *adj.*; *gloomy* 41. 7; *cold* (i.e. dead) 89. 4; *calm* 38. 12.

**cole**, *n.*; *cold* 59. 18; **colde** 78. 58.

**cole**, *n.*; *live coal* 48. 3; 178. 81; **col** 118. 5.

**collaig**, *n.*; *religious establishment* 125 rub.

**colour**, *n.*; *disguise, deceit* 177. 20; *figure of speech* 190. 9; **colours** 98. 14.

**comand**, *v. pr.* 1 *s.*; *commend* 128. 17; (*imp.*) **command** 194. 1.

**comelyhede**, *n.*; *comeliness* 199. 30.

**cominalte**, *n.*; *corporation* 122. d.

**comynycacion**, *n.*; *conversation* 181. 3.

**conceyte**, *n.*; *understanding* 77. 18; **conseyt** 188. 63.

**conciste**, *v. pr.* 3 *pl.*; *exist* 121. 2.

**condite**, *n.*; *fountain* 122. p.

**confecon**, *n.*; *mixing, compounding* 73. 78.

**conning**, *n.*; *studying* 177. 4; *intelligence* 188. 15; *capacity* 188. 27.

**continwans**, *n.*; *perserverance* 132. 1.

**conttray**, *n.*; *country* 119. 20; **cuntre** 57. 4; **contre**, *neighbourhood* 149. 5.

**cooffer**, *n.*; *coffer* 130. 19.

**cook**, see **cok**.

**copious**, *adj.*; *furnished plentifully* (with gifts) 25. 14.

**coppud**, *adj.*; *bad-tempered* 28. 37.

**corage**, *n.*; *spirit* 188. 38; *confidence* 211. 5.

**corel**, *n.*; *red coral* 46. 7; **coral** 210. 3.

**coriouse**, *adj.*; *beautifully fashioned* 205. 94; 209. 6.

**cornes**, *n.*; *grain, corn crops* 72. 90; 120. 23.

**corrans**, *n.*; *Corinth* (only in phr. **reysons of corrans**, *currants* 56. 26).

**cors**, *n.*; *body* 128. 19.

**cosse**, *n.*; *kiss* 185. 4.

**cossyng**, *n.*; *kissing* 179. 84.

**coueityse**, *n.*; *avarice* 58. 111; **covetise** 77. 23; 111. 2.

**couerd barine**, *n.*; *covert-baron* (i.e. married woman under authority of her husband) 74. 16.

**couert**, *n.*; *thicket* 119. 11.

**couieiture**, *n.*; *covetousness* 121. 10.

**coulpable**, *adj.*; *guilty* 188. 55.

**countenaunce**, *n.*; *behaviour* 128. 14; **continaunce** 196. 4; *appearance* 136. 7; 177. 44; 201. 8; **contnaunc** 76. 3.

**countirpayse**, *v.*; *to counterbalance, measure up to* 188. 18.

**covenable**, *adj.*; *appropriate* 107. 5.

**covert**, *adj.*; *deceitful* 121. 10.

**cowde**, *adj.*; *known* 180. 21.

**cowet**, *v.*; *to covet* 76. 10; **couete** 192. 6.

**cowght**, *pp.*; *coughed* 1. 23.

**cowpe**, *n.*; *coop* 49. 15.

**cowpully3t**, *v. pr. 3 pl.*; *fasten* (dogs) *together in pairs* 119. 15.

**coyntyse**, *n.*; *cunning, cleverness* 116. 1.

**crabbed**, *adj.*; *disagreeable* 38. 8.

**craft**, *n.*; *deceit* 20. 7; *occupation* 184. 5; *science* 79. 1; *branch of learning* 116. 5; **craftes**, *learning* 73. 1.

**crake**, *v.*; *to utter* 4. 3; (*pt. 3 s.*) **crakit** 27. 10.

**crannis**, *n.*; *cranes* 56. 14.

**creator**, *n.*; (human) *creature* 110. 2; **creature** 153. 1; **crayator** 209. 16.

**cred**, *n.*; *creed* 44. 18.

**croked**, *adj.*; *perverse* 38. 8.

**croofte**, *n.*; *enclosed ground* 48. 9; **croft** 49. 1.

**crooke**, *n.*; *hook* 89. 2; **croke**, *crooked staff* 25. 2.

**crope**, *v. pr. 1 s.*; *eat* 119. 37.

**croppis**, *n.*; *tops of trees* 114. 4.

**cumbers**, *adj.*; *troublesome* 38. 9.

**cumlye**, *adj.*; *decorous* 130. 4; *pretty* 128. 14; **comelich** 205. 42; **comly** 208. 5; (*sup.*) **comliest** 127. 69; **cumlyst** 204. 7.

**cun**, *v. pr. 3 pl.*; *are able, can, know* 41. 10; (*pr. 1 s.*) **can** 205. 44; **kan** 144. 3; **kane** 181. 2; (*pr. 3 s.*) **con** 3. 11; **kan** 96. 19; (*pr. 3 pl.*) **can** 38. 23; (*pt. 1 s.*) **cothe** 148. 5; **couthe** 188. 12; **cowde** 28 bur.; **cowth** 181. 1; **kuwthe** 88. 67; (*pt. 3 s.*) **cowd** 24. 5; **cowthe** 88. 48;

**kuothe** 88. 44; (*pt. 2 pl.*) **cowthe** 178. 12.

**cure**, *n.*; *cur* 119. 41.

**cure**, *n.*; *care* 110. 4; 139. 11; 173. 17; *cure* 164. 12; 198. 31; *medical treatment* 102. 8; (*adv. phr.*) **besy cure**, *attentively, diligently* 196. 1; 211. 22; *level best* 96. 67.

**curlews**, *n.*; *curlews* 114. 17.

**curtes**, *adj.*; *polite* 38. 6; **curteys** 77. 7; 78. 20; **curteysse** 129. 5.

**custumed**, *adj.*; *habitual* 98. 8.

**dagged**, *adj.*; *slashed* (of garment) 209. 45.

**dairt**, *n.*; *dart* 132. 43.

**daliaunce**, *n.*; *conversation* 78. 22; 131. 4; *flirtation* 202. 7.

**dame**, *n.*; *mistress of a household* 28. 37; 29. 39; **damme** 28. 41; *madam* (form of address) 6. 1; *mother* 34. 2.

**dar**, *v. pr. 3 s.*; *it is needful* (for) (= þar) 103. 16.

**dare**, *n.*; *injury* 64. 3.

**darf**, *v. pt. 1 s.*; *dared* (confusion between tharf and dare) 17. 3.

**darst**, see **durn**.

**daswed**, *pp.*; *dimmed* 98. 9.

**daunger**, *n.*; *stand-offishness, refusal* (of love) 127. 59; 131. 36; 132. 9; 205. 34; **daynger**, *liability* (to loss) 74. 5; **danger**, *peril* 133. 4.

**daunted**, *pp.*; *overcome* 121. 46.

**dawnce**, *n.*; *course of action, game* (in *phr.*) **louers dawnce** 163. 9; **leyd the dance**, *take the lead* 136. 31.

**de**, *v. to die* 132. 29; 196. 10; **dey** 158. 8; (*pr. 1 s.*) **day** 184. 12; (*pt. 1 s.*) **dyd** 138. 37.

**debonayre**, *adj.*; *gracious* 131. 33; **deboner** 199. 17.

**dede**, *n.*; *death* 58. 109; **det** 142. 3.

**dede**, *n.*; *deed* 58. 77.

**defende**, *v. pr. subj.* 3 *s.*; in phr. **god defende**, *God forbid* 188. 59.

**degre**, *n.*; *condition* 78. 15; 205. 92; *social position* 59. 2.

**dele**, *n. in phr.*; **a thowsan dele**, *a thousandfold* 199. 46.

**dele**, *v.*; *to participate* 38. 28; *to act* 199. 26.

**deley**, *v.*; *to assuage* 200. 11.

**delfe**, *v. pr.* 1 *s.*; *dig* 67. 2.

**delitable**, *adj.*; *delightful* 205. 123.

**delyberall**, *adj.*; *liberal* 76. 5. [Cf. 77. 1.]

**delysyn**, *n.*; *deception* 181. 43.

**demaeyne**, *n.*; *possession* 95. 2.

**deme**, *v. pr.* 1 *s.*; *consider* 6. 2.

**demene**, *v.*; *to regulate* 187. 3; (*pp.*) **demenid**, *conducted* 131. 3; **dymeynet** 182. 2.

**demenyng**, *n.*; *behaviour* 139. 31; **demeaninge** 177. 19.

**demure**, *adj.*; *reserved* 131. 2; *serious* 190. 8; *sober* 77. 7.

**den**, *n.*; *noise* 118. 2.

**denty**, *adj.*; *scarce* 206. 99.

**depairt**, *v.*; *to separate* (something *from*) 132. 21; (*pr. subj.* 3 *pl.*) **depart** 177. 10.

**depreue**, *v.*; *calumniate* 181. 36.

**dere**, *adj.*; *expensive* 32. 25; (*comp.*) **der** 193. 16; *beloved* 58. 48; **deir** 71. 4; **der** 127. 36; **dyere** 198. 4.

**derectyon**, *n.*; *orderly arrangement* 130. 26.

**dereyne**, *v.*; *to claim possession of* 94. 7.

**deris**, *v. pr.* 3 *s.*; *injures* 162. 3.

**derne**, *adj.*; *out-of-the-way* 119. 10.

**derworth**, *adj.*; *beloved* 205. 23; **dyrward**, *precious* 22. 14.

**descrye**, *v.*; *to declare* 177. 47.

**dese**, *n.*; *seat, throne* 58. 55; 144. 1.

**despite**, *n.*; *contempt* 78. 27.

**dette**, *n.*; *debt* 6. 5; **deute** 128. 15.

**devise**, *n.*; *counsel* 108. 7; **at youre dewys**, *to your liking* 134. 34.

**devisioun**, *n.*; *disagreement* 78. 29.

**devys**, *n.*; *aspect* 205. 4.

**devyse**, *v.*; *to recount* 209. 43.

**dew**, *adj.*; *fitting* 166. 1.

**dew**, *adv.*; *rightly* 161. 2.

**dieutye**, *n.*; *duty* 178. 58.

**disable**, *adj.*; *incapable* 177. 88.

**discouer**, *v. imper.*; *give away* 178. 42.

**discryue**, *v.*; *to describe* 177. 2; (*pp.*) **discriuede**, 72. 2.

**displesaunce**, *n.*; *displeasure* 173. 38.

**disportt**, *n.*; *entertainment* 159. 3; 202. 7.

**dispytfull**, *adj.*; *malicious* 212. 3.

**dissavaunce**, *n.*; *deceit, treachery* 123. 18.

**dissemble**, *n.*; *dissimulation* 120. 55.

**dissent**, *n.*; *descent* 122. 16.

**disservyd**, *pp.*; *deserved* 178. 42.

**dissese**, *n.*; *discomfort* 164. 2.

**diuers**, *n.*; *several, many* 122. d.

**dome**, *n.*; *judgement* 58. 46.

**domes-men**, *n.*; *judges* 58. 43.

**don**, *v.*; *to transact* 57. 9; **do**, *to take* (pains) 178. 9; *to put* 58. 14; **done**, *to do* 72. 43; 131. 48; 164. 12; **doo** 201. 14; **a-doo** 78. 5; **doo**, *to fare* (**well for to doo**, *to prosper*) 129. 42; **doe** (*pr.* 2 *s.*) 180. 11; (*pr.* 3 *s.*) **do̧p**, *causes* 43. 11; **dooth**, *does* 91. 3; (*pr. subj.* 3 *s.*) **do**, *give* 44. 19; 99. 3; (*pt.* 2 *s.*) **dest** 29. 35;

dedyst 39. 1; (*pt.* 3 *s.*) **dede**
21. 16; (*pp.*) **do,** *ended* 211. 25.

donne, *adj.*; *dark* 96. 11.

doubill, *adj.*; *deceitful* 78. 25;
**doble** 209. 26; **dowbull** 181.
29; **duble** 108. 2.

dour, *adj.*; *sullen* 212. 3.

dow, *n.*; *doe, deer* 56. 24; **dowe**
119. 58.

dow, *n.*; *dough* 29. 19.

dowbylnesse, *n.*; *deceitfulness*
211. 25.

dowe, *n.*; *dove* 45. 7; **doyff** 136.
17.

dowe, see **dow.**

dowel, *v.*; *to dwell, continue*
183. 11.

dower, *n.*; *portion of deceased
husband's estate belonging to
widow during her life* 74. 6.

dowge, *adj.*; *useful* 29. 16.

dowghty, *adj.*; *valiant* 72. 82;
**du3ty** 115. 3.

dowgit, *adj.*; *obstinate* 212. 3.

dowsemeris, *n.*; *dulcimers* 122. 1.

dowt, *v.*; *to fear* 136. 35.

dowtevous, *adj.*; *dreadful* 72. 68.

drages, *n.*; *drugs* 79. 5.

drede, *n.*; *reverence* 189. 6; but
**dreid,** *assuredly* 132. 20.

dreme, *n.*; *noise* 118. 16.

dress, *v.*; *to make ready* 196. 1;
(*pp.*) **dreste** 206. 52.

dronkelawe, *n.*; *drunken* (persons) 78. 54.

drow, *v. pt.* 3 *s.*; *pulled* 29. 33.

drowryis, *n.*; *love-tokens* 45. 3.

drynk, *n.*; *drink* 14. 23; **drynke**
20. 16; **dryng** 18. 14.

dur, *n.*; *door* 6. 3; **dore** 36. 1.

dure, *v.*; *endure* 166. 4.

durn, *v. pr.* 3 *pl.*; *dare* 41. 6;
(*pr.* 1 *s.*) **dare** 55. 9; (*pr.* 2 *s.*)
**darst** 180. 18; (*pt.* 1 *s.*) **durst**
29. 39; 184. 9.

dwer, *n.*; *doubt* 57. 11.

dych, *n.*; *dish* 43. 6.

dyche, *n.*; *ditch* 3. 15.

dyd, see **de.**

dy3ght, *pp.*; *arrayed for battle*
115. 2; **dyght,** *ordained* 138. 51.

dygne, *adj.*; *honorable* 120. 5.

dynke, see **thyng.**

dyntes, *n.*; *strokes* 118. 2.

dyre, *n.*; *darling* 22. 14.

dyrlyng, *n.*; *darling* 128. 15;
**derlyng** 204. 9.

dysgreuyt, *pp.*; *aggrieved* 181.
45.

dysseuabyll, *adj.*; *deceitful* 76.
13; **dissavable** 212. 3.

dysseuyde, *pp.*; *deceived* 198. 16.

e, see **eyen.**

easy, *adj.*; *unhurried* 178. 57.

effeir, *n.*; *appearance* 132. 26.

efte, *adv.*; *again* 130. 70.

eires, *n.*; *heirs* 94. 22.

eke, *adv.*; (in phr.) **to eke in**
*addition* 48. 22; **heyke,** *also*
119. 36; **yke** 201. 10.

electuaries, *n.*; *medicinal paste*
79. 5.

ell, *adv.*; *else* 66 rub.; 88. 76;
**ellis** 185. 12.

elleccion, *n.*; *choice* 136. 19.

elther, *adj.*; *older* 120. 43.

e-mange, *prep.*; *among* 48. 20.

emeraudes, *n.*; *haemorrhoids*
81. 80.

emperre, *v.*; *to damage* 128. 22.

emprice, *n.*; *empress* 178. 44.

enameryd, *pp.*; *fascinated* 211.
3.

encheson, *n.*; *reason* 205. 24.

encresce, *n.*; *increase* 96. 6.

endite, *v.*; *to compose* 177.
7; 199. 12; (*pp.*) **endyghted**
209. 6.

enlonged, *v. pt.* 3 *s.*; *made distant* 121. 9.

ennewyd, *pp.*; *shaded, coloured*
188. 7.

ensue, *v.*; *to follow* 190. 3.

**ensure**, *v. pr.* 1 *s.*; *assure* 140. 21; 173. 22.

**entencion**, *n.*; *purpose* 177. 22.

**entende**, *v.*; *to be directed to* 139. 7; (*pr.* 3 *s.*) **entendeth**, *purposes* 139. 11.

**entenderd**, *pp.*; *melted* (of heart) 190. 32.

**entent**, *n.*; *meaning* 209. 26; *mind* 196. 23; *purport* 154. 2; 162. 20; *purpose* 104. 13; 177. 25; 188. 1.

**entirmet**, *pp.*; *mixed* 190. 22.

**enþer**, *adj.*; *latter*; (in phr.) þis enþer dai, *a day or two ago* 24. 1; thys enderȝ nyght 200. 1.

**eonde**, *v.*; *to end* 170. 8.

**er**, *adv.*; *formerly* 5. 10; 40. 3; ar 143. 20; are 58. 38; or 40. 1; 48. 8; 106. 9; 137. 6.

**erand**, *n.*; *errand* 73. 19.

**erbe**, *n.*; *plant* 62. 9.

**erdlie**, *adj.*; *earthly* 132. 23; yearthly 177. 95; urthely 94. 10; erly 167. 19.

**ere**, *n.*; *ear* 28. 16; 81. 13; eris, 127. 22; eyr 80. 5.

**eresy**, *n.*; *heresy* 188. 63.

**ermor**, *adv.*; *evermore* 60. 2.

**erne**, *v. pr.* 1 *s.*; *obtain, earn* 67. 9.

**es**, see beo.

**ese**, *n.*; *contentment* 168. 6; 189. 13.

**esperaunce**, *n.*; *hope* 196. 5.

**ete**, *v.*; *to eat* 80. 12; eytte 195. 14; (*pr.* 3 *s.*) ettes 73. 59; (*imp.*) ete 78. 2; (*pp.*) eette 119. 75.

**euelles**, see ivell.

**euell-turnynge**, *n.*; *dizziness, vertigo* 81. 15.

**evyl**, *adj.*; *bad* 80. 2.

**euensong**, *n.*; *time of evensong, sunset* 28. 21.

**euerychon**, *pro.*; *each one* 1. 9; 38. 6.

**euerykune**, *adj.*; *every kind of* 16. 1.

**euyre**, *adv.*; *at all times* 134. 47.

**excedent**, *adj.*; *surpassing* 122. 23.

**excesse**, *n.*; *outrageous conduct* 78. 30.

**exemplayre**, *n.*; *perfect specimen* 131. 30; **exemplary** 139. 33.

**experiens**, *n.*; *Experience* (personified) 176. 7.

**exspence**, *n.*; *cost* 120. 36; *wasteful expenditure* 76. 14.

**extendeth**, *v. pr.* 3 *s.*; *strains the capacity of* 177. 1.

**ey**, *n.*; *egg* 45. 23.

**eyder**, *conj.*; *or* 94. 12; eiþer 101. 9.

**eyen**, *n.*; *eyes* 81. 23; E 132. 4; ee 194. 18; een 144. 8; eeyn 72. 106; eyeghen 131. 6; eynyn 46. 17; hye 116. 20; iye 177. 44; yee 201. 9; at eye, *at first hand* 176. 7; by þe eye, *immediately* 14. 2; 48. 13.

**eyȝe**, *n.*; *awe*; (in phr.) stant me non eyȝe, *I am not afraid of* 29. 23.

**eyre**, *n.*; *year* 94. 5; ȝeir 97. 4; yeris, *New Year* 96 rub.; yeeris 96. 5.

**eyre**, *n.*; *air* 78. 42; **ayre** 78. 66.

**fabulle**, *n.*; *fabrication* 181. 33.

**fair**, *v.*; *to go* 132. 34; (*pr. subj.* 3 *s.*) *prosper* 132. 40.

**famyliarly**, *adv.*; *intimately* 137. 7.

**fand**, *v. pt.* 1 *s.*; *obtained* 133. 23.

**fane**, *n.*; *vane* 178. 97.

**far**, *adv.*; *a long way distant* 23. 4; **farre** 200. 12; fer 45. 2; ferr 6. 5; for 171. 6; fore 88. 32.

**fare,** *n.*; *food* 54. 7; *fuss, commotion* 179. 86.

**fare,** *n.*; *welfare* 199. 29; *success* (in phr.) **fare you be-fall** 205. 116.

**fase,** see **fon.**

**fassit,** *pp.*; *pledged* 132. 25.

**fast,** *adv.*; *firmly* 49. 17; 100. 10; *quickly* 54. 11; 148. 7.

**faull,** *v.*; *to fall* 134. 23.

**fause,** *v.*; *to give way* 94. 12.

**favtt,** *n.*; *defect* 206. 28; **faut,** *lack, want of* 88. 73.

**faye,** *n.*; (in phr.) **in faye,** *in faith* 81. 42.

**fayn,** *adj.*; *worthless* 24 bur.

**fayne,** *adv.*; *gladly* 171. 1; **feyne** 130. 37.

**fayne,** *v.*; *to dissemble* 139. 36; (*pr.* 2 *pl.*) **feyneth** 138. 24; (*pr.* 3 *pl.*) **feyne** 211. 12; (*pres. p.*) **fayning** 167. 23.

**fayr,** *adv.*; *well* 27. 7.

**fayre,** *adj.*; *beautiful* (of persons) 28. 11; (of animals) 47. 1; *bright* 76. 7.

**fedderit,** *pp.*; *feathered* 132. 44.

**federes,** *n.*; *feathers* 5. 5; 49. 38.

**fedyrfoy,** *n.*; *feverfew* 209. 2.

**fee,** *n.*; *perquisite* 110. 6; *reward* 200. 40; *wealth* 136. 10.

**fefee,** *n.*; *trustee holding an estate* 74. 8.

**feinte,** *v.*; *to become discouraged* 177. 70.

**fekyl,** *adj.*; *inconstant* 41. 14; **fekoll** 134. 27.

**fele,** *adj.*; *many* 176. 3.

**fell,** *adj.*; *fierce* 58. 38; 73. 46; 212. 2.

**fell,** *n.*; *moorland* 58. 75.

**felowing,** *pres. p.*; *following* 123 rub.

**felychype,** *n.*; *fellowship* 181. 11.

**fend,** see **fonde.**

**fenჳeing,** *n.*; *feigning* 133. 18; **feynyng** 188. 4.

**fer,** *n.*; *fear* 20. 10; 206. 99; **fere** 20. 3.

**fere,** *adj.*; *fierce* 73. 30.

**fere,** *n.*; *companion* 3. 19; 10. 4; 200. 2; **ffeer** 172. 12.

**fere-flunderys,** *n.*; *fiery sparks* 118. 12.

**ferly,** *n.*; *wonder, miracle* 128. 33.

**fers,** *adj.*,; *fierce* 73. 30; **fiers** 96. 3.

**ferthe,** *adv.*; *out* (of) 204. 20.

**fervence,** *n.*; *intensity* 77. 12.

**feschun,** *v.*; *to fetch* 29. 9.

**fetis,** see **fyt.**

**fett,** *v.*; *to take away, steal* 63. 6.

**feuerჳere,** *n.*; *February* 73. 29.

**feyn,** (in phr.) **yn feyn,** *ineffectual* 197. 31.

**feynt,** *adj.*; *false* 109. 2.

**figurat,** *adj.*; *ornamented* 132. 43.

**flawres,** see **flour.**

**flayne,** *pp.*; *having the skin rubbed off* 81. 34.

**flece,** *v.*; *to fleece* 119. 36.

**flee,** *v.*; *to fly* 96. 62; 163. 10; 180. 12; (*pr.* 3 *s.*) **fflys** 148. 7; (*pt.* 1 *s.*) **ffloghe** 178. 86.

**flewmatyke,** *adj.*; *phlegmatic* 76. 4; 77. 15.

**fleych,** *n.*; *meat* 43. 13; **fleche** 73. 59; **flesche,** *human flesh* 103. 18.

**flore,** *n.*; *floor* 49. 12.

**flour,** *n.*; *flower* 17. 4; 18. 26; 127. 37; 172. 30; (fig.) *mistress* 138. 1; 204. 2; **flur** 147. 8; **flowr** (fig.), *Christ* 61. 2; **flawres,** *menses* 81. 78.

**flussh,** *v.*; *to fly up* 205. 59.

**flyt,** *v.*; *to drive away* 80. 8.

**fode,** *n.*; *beguiler* 180. 17.

**foison,** see **fusoun.**

**fold,** *v.*; *to falter* 191. 17; **foyld,** *to turn away* 136. 36.

fon, *n.*; *foes* 61. 3; **fase** 58. 52.

fonde, *adj.*; *foolish* 179. 76.

fonde, *v.*; *to try* 4. 11; *to prove* 180. 14; *to have knowledge of* 128. 28; (*pt.* 3 *s.*) **fonde**, *practised* 79. 1.

fondyst, *v. pr.* 2 *s.*; *foundest* 181. 35; (*pp.*) **fonde** 55. 7.

foole, see foull.

foo-men, *n.*; *adversaries* 179. 52.

for, see far.

for-do, *v.*; *to remove* 81. 80; *to put an end to* 195. 18.

fore, *prep.*; *for* 134. 21.

forewrityng, *n.*; *claim* [cf. L. praescriptio, prescription] 178. 60.

forfeture, *n.*; *liability* 139. 12.

forfure, *v. pr.* 1 *s.*; *come to grief* 133. 7.

for-geit, *pp.*; *forgotten* 171. 17.

forgit, *pp.*; *fashioned* 132. 44.

forme, *n.*; *lair of hare* 119. 62.

forme-fadres, *n.*; *forefathers* 72. 7.

forryd, *pp.*; *trimmed with fur* 135. 28.

fors, *n.*; *violence* 65. 4; 123. 13; *strength* 123. b; (in phr.) **holdyn but lytil fors**, *pay no attention to* 57. 19.

forsake, *v.*; *to refuse* 73. 51; (*pp.*) *forsaken* 134. 33.

for-svering, *pres. p.*; *renouncing* ⸥57. 7.

force, *prep.*; *for to* 9. 6; 19. 10.

for-powȝt, *v. pt.* 3 *s.*; (in phr.) **me for-powȝt**, *I was grieved that* 135. 11.

foull, *n.*, *domestic fowls* 71. 8; *birds* 141. 3; **foole** 96. 1; **foule** 208. 7; **fowle** 179. 3.

fourthe, *adv.*; *forth* 64. 1.

foyld, see fold.

fra, *adv.*; *from the time that* 132. 34.

fransy, *n.*; *delirium* 81. 22.

fraunce crownes, *n.*; *French crowns, ecus* 97. 18.

frayed, *pp.*; *frightened* 48. 11; 179. 52.

fre, *adj.*; *honourable* 136. 47; 205. 90; *of good breeding* 19. 1; 144. 2; *freehold* 74. 7; *unrestricted* 137. 31.

freefull, *adj.*; *very honourable* 205. 87.

fres, *adj.*; *bright* (coloured) 22. 18; **frece**, *gay* 50. 4; **fresche**, *healthy looking* 132. 26; (*sup.*) **fresshest** 205. 90.

fretyng, *adj.*; *gnawing* 77. 24.

frith, *n.*; *wooded country* (in phr.) **frith and fell** 58. 75; **frith or felde** 58. 98.

frothe, *n.*; *foam* 134. 22.

ffrov, *prep.*; *from* 119. 7; **fra** 132. 5; **fro** 119. 12.

froward, *adj.*; *perverse* 78. 67; 208. 1; *ugly* 209. 39.

fructuous, *adj.*; *productive* 98. 11.

frynd, *n.*; *friend* 57 bur.; **frend** 59. 27; 109. 2.

fulgent, *adj.*; *shining* 130. 45.

furmante, *n.*; *frumenty* (wheat boiled in milk) 56. 23.

fusoun, *n.*; *abundance* 78. 31; **foison**, *nourishment* 205. 124.

fylle, *n.*; (in phr.) **to speke my fylle**, *to one's heart's content* 197. 30.

fynde, *v.*; *to provide* 72. 84; (*pr. subj.* 3 *s.*) 25. 19.

fynde, *v.*; *to discover* 111. 7; (*pr. subj.* 3 *s.*) 92. 1; (*pp.*) **founde** 72. 111.

fyne, *n.*; *purpose* 139. 7.

fyne, *v.*; *to cease* 104. 6.

fyre, *n.*; *fire* 3. 17; **fer** 5. 9; **fier** 88. 17; **fyer** 59. 10.

fyt, *n.*; *feet* 7. 10; **fot** 27. 17; **fetis** 184. 4.

gabbust, *v. pr.* 2 *s.*; *tell lies* 179.
34; gabste 181. 23.

gabbyng, *n.*; *arguing* 180. 20.

gagil, *n.*; *cackling, chattering*
42. 6.

galow-claper, *n.*; *gallows-bird*
14. 22.

game, *n.*; *amusement* 13. 2;
*game* 179. 67; *happiness* 179.
48; *object of hunting* 119. 61;
*proceedings* 101. 8; *victory* 41.
8; gamin 58. 91; gamyn 162.
22; gomyn 3. 2.

ganekalling, *n.*; (in phr.) but
ganekalling, *irrevocably* 132.
17.

garison, *n.*; *treasure-store* 127.
56.

gaunte, *adj.*; *slender* 129. 20.

gay, *adj.*; *sportive* 28. 4; 143. 1;
*bright-coloured* 55. 2; 56. 2.

gay, *adv.*; *joyously* 1. 8; *brightly*
56 bur.

geason, *adj.*; *barren* 211. 9.

geitt, *adj.*; *jet* 35. 11; get 46. 8;
Ieet 210. 4.

gelyfloure, *n.*; *gillyflower* 130.
18.

genstand, *v.*; *to resist* 133. 18.

gent, *adj.*; *noble, courteous* 51. 1.

gentil, *adj.*; *well-bred* (of birds)
46. 1; *courteous* 130. 4; 144. 2;
geintil, *soft* 46. 14; Ientyl, *kind*
50. 11.

gentilnesse, *n.*; *courtesy* 151. 3;
gentylnes 198. 1.

gentylesse, *n.*; *good breeding*
131. 1.

ger, *v.*; *to cause one to do some-*
*thing* 58. 29; (*pr.* 3 *s.*) gers,
*makes* 73. 34; (*pt.* 3 *s.*) gewrt
167. 4.

gerdonlesse, *adv.*; *without re-*
*ward* 170. 8.

gese, *n.*; *geese* 49. 2; geys 48. 6.

gèwrt, see ger.

geyne, *v.*; *to avail, serve* 19. 7.

glade, *v.*; *to make glad* 4. 6;
(*imp.*) *rejoice* 78. 7.

gladly, *adj.*; *joyful* 1. 9.

glasyn, *adj.*; *made of glass* 180.
81. (See Notes.)

gle, *n.*; *sport* 141. 4; 162. 22;
glee 179. 67.

glistren, *v. pr.* 3 *pl.*; *glitter* 210.
4.

glose, *n.*; *flattery* 138. 23; *gloss*
209. 14.

glouus, *n.*; *gloves* 28. 18.

gnacchen, *v. pr.* 3 *pl.*; *gnash the*
*teeth* 118. 9.

god, *n.*; *God* 58. 64; gode 181.
50.

god, (in phr.) truly and god (=
in good truly), *truly* 191. 34.

goodlyhed, *n.*; *beauty* 127. 14;
168. 10.

goodman, *n.*; *husband* 49. 25;
*good man* (vague term of address) 91. 1.

good-wyfe, *n.*; *mistress* (of a
home) 49. 19.

gore, *n.*; *skirt* 180. 48.

gornardes, *n.*; *gurnards* 114. 11.

goslynges, *n.*; *goslings* 114. 20.

gouernall, *n.*; *control* 196. 14.

gouernance, *n.*; *self-control* 129.
37; *behaviour* 190. 8.

gowlis, *adj.*; *gules, red* 196. 20.

grace, *n.*; *fortune, luck* 28. 12;
73. 21.

graif, *n.*; *grave* 132. 33.

gramery, *n.*; *magic* 24. 5.

grante, *v. imp.*; *give* 28. 17;
(*pr. subj.* 3 *s.*) graunt 121. 7.

grauen, *v. pr.* 3 *pl.*; *grieve* 118.
9.

gre, *n.*; *pre-eminence* 58. 94; in
gre, *favourably* 192. 20.

greffe, *n.*; *grief* 158. 1; gref 164.
6; 190. 32; greuys 168. 7.

greid, *v. pr.* 2 *s.*; *make ready*
147. 4; greyð 147. 4.

gremercy, *interj.*; *thanks* 28. 19.

**grene**, *n.*; *grassy spot* 141. 4.

**grengese**, *n.*; *goslings* 114. 12.

**greshope**, *n.*; *grasshopper* 115. 1.

**gret**, *adj.*; *stout* 8. 6; *big* 49. 14; **greth**, *large* 29. 38; **grete**, *severe* 72. 48.

**gret**, *n.*; *distinguished lineage* 46. 6.

**grete**, *v. pr.* 1 *s.*; *greet* 22. 11; (*imp.*) **gret** 195. 21; (*pres. p.*) **greting** 196. 4.

**grettyng**, *n.*; *greeting* 129. 56.

**grevaunce**, *n.*; *suffering* 152. 4; 182. 11.

**greyð**, see **greid**.

**griffons**, *n.*; *vultures* 114. 20.

**gripyng**, *pres. p.*; *clasping* 190. 20.

**grome**, *n.*; *man-servant* 2. 2.

**gronde**, *n.*; *ground* 198. 10; *base* 139. 35; *foundation* 156. 1; **on the ground**, *on earth* 127. 69.

**gronys**, *v. pr.* 3 *pl.*; *complain* 118. 9.

**grose**, *adv. phr.*, **in grose**, *generally* 177. 75.

**grounder**, *n.*; *establisher* 122. 8.

**grucchyng**, *pres. p.*; *complaining* 78. 15.

**grundin**, *adj.*; *sharpened* 132. 47.

**gryf**, *n.*; *a shoot inserted in another stock* 21. 11.

**gryffyn**, *v.*; *to insert* (a shoot of one tree) *into a different stock* 21. 11; (*pt.* 1 *s.*) 21. 17; (*pp.*) **gryffid** 21. 13.

**gryll**, *adj.*; *severe* 73. 56.

**Gryzell**, *n.*; *Griselda* 38. 19.

**guerdone**, *n.*; *requital* 107. 5; *reward* 177. 95; 211. 16.

**gurdul**, *n.*; *girdle* 28. 43.

**gy**, *v.*; *to conduct* (oneself) 99. 7.

**gyle**, *n.*; *deceit* 28 bur.; 180. 5.

**gynnyng**, *n.*; *beginning* 104. 16.

**gynt**, *n.*; *measure* 6. 7.

**gyue**, *v. pr. subj.* 3 *s.*; *may give* 118. 21; **ȝeue**, *grant* 149. 6; (*pr.* 3 *s.*) **gyffis**, *cares* 148. 13; (*imp.*) **gif** 196. 17; (*pt.* 3 *s.*) **yafe** 94. 15; (*pres. p.*) **yevyng** 122. h; (*pp.*) **yeve** 198. 6.

**ȝat**, *conj.*; (= þat) *that* 161. 4.

**ȝeme**, *n.*; *heed* 102. 9.

**ȝeme**, *v.*; *to care for, guard* 102. 10.

**ȝeorne**, *adv.*; *eagerly* 119. 35.

**ȝern**, *n.*; *yarn, thread* 28. 44.

**ȝernid**, *pp.*; *desired* 58. 59.

**ȝeth**, *adv.*; *yet, still* 29. 7; **ȝett** 134. 46; **ȝut** 29. 19.

**ȝole**, *n.*; *Yule* 3. 1; **ȝol** 27. 1.

**ȝyf**, *conj.*; *if* 40. 2; **gif** 71. 3; **giff** 71. 1; **gef** 184. 9; **ȝeyfe** 119. 61; 134. 45.

**haburyone**, *n.*; *coat-of-mail* 115. 2.

**haȝt**, see **haue**.

**hakkyt**, *v. pt.* 3 *s.*; *mangled* 27. 14.

**halle**, *n.*; *large room* (in contrast to bower) 31. 1; 49. 13; 149. 4; 180. 74; *residence* 51. 4.

**halse**, *v.*; *to embrace* 41. 10.

**hammes**, *n.*; *thighs* 81. 77; 208. 25.

**handled**, *pp.*; *wielded* 118. 13.

**hansell**, *n.*; *auspicious gift* 97. 4.

**happ**, *n.*; *good fortune* 58. 112; *fortune* 96. 68; *mishap* 119. 56; 206. 27.

**happyly**, *adv.*; *by chance* 138. 14.

**hardy**, *adj.*; *presumptuous* 9. 5; *sturdy* 57. 1; 77. 5; 96. 1.

**hare-pipe**, *n.*; *trap for catching hares* 119. 47.

**harmus**, *n.*; *arms* 143. 6.

**harnes**, *n.*; *armour* 114. 13.

hart, *n.*; *heart* 196. 6; (*pl.*) 38. 35; ert 180. 79; hert 58. 67; hairt 132. 6; harth 143. 15; herte, *sweetheart* 134. 9, 47; 166. 7.

hartes, *n.*; *male deer* 114. 8.

hasadours, *n.*; *dice-players* 78. 56.

haske, see axe.

hast, *v. imp.*; *hasten* 99. 2.

haue, *v.*; *to have* 23. 10; (*pr.* 1 *s.*) ha 28. 18; han 29. 1; haue 45. 1; (*pr.* 2 *s.*) hastu 28. 38; (*pr.* 3 *s.*) hase 6. 7; haȝt 5. 5; 7. 11; 45. 24; hath 111. 2; hatt 143. 4; (*pt.* 3 *pl.*) haddun 28. 33; (*imp.*) hawe 135. 7; havfe 135. 16.

haunt, *v.*; *to practise* 77. 19.

hauntyng, *adj.*; *familiar* 180. 1.

haylsed, *v. pt.* 1 *s.*; *greeted* 194. 20.

he, *pro.*; *they* 5. 3; ham, *them* 42. 7; hem 27. 14; 62. 1; hom 100. 2; hym 138. 11; þam 58. 53.

hed, *n.*; *head* 53. 11; 81. 47; hede 65. 8.

hede, *n.*; *care* 190. 6.

hedewark, *n.*; *headache* 80. 6.

hedous, *adj.*; *terrible* 72. 76.

hele, *n.*; *good health* 189. 9; 199. 47; heylle, *prosperity* 195. 1.

helme, *n.*; *helmet* 115. 2.

heltre, *n.*; *halter* 41. 4.

hend, *n.*; *end* 73. 22; ende 104. 4.

hende, *adj.*; *gracious* 179. 66; 180. 16.

hende, *n.*; *gracious one* 147. 6.

henne, *adv.*; *from here* 5. 10.

hente, *v. pt.* 3 *s.*; *grasped* 48. 13; (*pp.*) hent 205. 14.

here, see hyr.

here, *n.*; *hair* 114. 24; 130. 13; heer 127. 19; herys 13. 16.

here, *v.*; *to hear* 103. 1; 197. 6;

heyre 119. 13; (*pt.* 1 *s.*) hard 119. 3; (*pp.*) harde 72. 1; 129. 38.

herke, *v.*; *to listen* 24. 3.

herne, *n.*; *hiding place* 119. 12.

herynges, *n.*; *herrings* 114. 9.

herys, see here.

heste, *n.*; *commandment* 104. 9.

hete, *n.*; *heat* 59. 18; 199. 36; *fever* 120. 54.

hete, see hyght.

hete, *v.*; *to eat* 54. 2; (*imp.*) etes 53. 13; etys 53. 14.

hette, *v.*; *to strike* 119. 44; (*pr. subj.* 3 *s.*) hit, *meet with* 167. 17.

heve, *adj.*; *serious* 3. 13; heuy 166. 3.

hevynes, *n.*; *dejection, grief* 127. 71.

hew, *n.*; *appearance* 204. 2; *colour* 209. 27.

hew, *v. pr.* 1 *s.*; *sever* 53. 11.

heye, see eyen. (Notes 48. 13.)

heye, *v.*; *to hasten* 48. 15; (*imp.*) hey 54. 11; hy 59. 15.

heyke, see eke.

heyled, *v. pt.* 3 *s.*; *healed* 193. 10.

heyrrons, *n.*; *herons* 56. 14.

heyvy, see ivy.

hic, see isch.

ho, see wo.

hoare, *adj.*; *venerable* 63. 18.

hode, *n.*; *hood* 58. 14; hod 44. 7.

hokyd, *pp.*; *bandy* 208. 25.

hold, *n.*; *custody, imprisonment* 136. 37; 160. 5.

hole, *adj.*; *cured* 103. 10; *complete* 189. 1.

hole, *n.*; *private parts* 208. 35.

holly, *adj.*; *holy* 64. 6; holy 178. 41.

holvyr, *n.*; *holly* 50. 1; holly 51. 5.

hombuls, *n.*; *edible entrails* 56. 24.

home, *n.*; *membrane* 21. 18.
home, *pro.*; *whom* 162. 6.
honde, *n.*; *hand* 7. 11; 55. 1.
hondert, *adj.*; *hundred* 146. 2.
hondes, *n.*; *dogs* 119. 66.
hoot, *adj.*; *hot* 56. 17; **hoyt** 136. 34.
horde, *n.*; *store of money* 58. 60.
houly, *adj.*; *troublous* 73. 53.
hull, *n.*; *hill* 115. 18.
humblis, *n.*; *humbleness* 190. 36.
hus, *n.*; *nest* (fig.) 148. 14.
huscher, *n.*; *usher, assistant teacher* 116. 1.
hwmyll, *adj.*; *humble* 196. 4; humble 199. 7.
hyet, *pro.*; *it* 195. 16; **ytt** 200. 18.
hyght, *v. pr.* 1 *s.*; *am called* 76. 8; (*pr.* 3 *s.*) het 203. 10; (*pr.* 2 *pl.*) hete, *promise* 199. 38; (*pp.*) hy3t 135. 18; hy3te, *commanded* 135. 25.
hy3e, *adj.*; *principal* 29. 4; hie 197. 1; hy 29. 8; hye, *high* 51. 8; heye 99. 8; hie 97. 19.
hyll, *v. imp.*; *cover* 113. 9.
hyr, *pro.*; *her* 44. 5; 52. 7; hire 9. 17; hur 129. 12; (*gen. s.*) here, *hers* 128. 23.
hyr, *pro.*; *their* 8. 11.

i-drevfe, *pp.*; *driven* 119. 7.
ilche, *pro.*; *each* 116. 5.
ilk, *adj.*; *each* 58. 10; iche, 116. 2; ilche 141. 4; ilka 58. 32; ylk 180. 39; *that* ylke, *that same* 95. 1.
ill-usyde, *pp.*; *ill-treated* 130. 63.
importabyl, *adj.*; *unendurable* 139. 3.
inbraste, *pp.*; *embraced* 136. 6.
inde, *n.*; *indigo* 46. 12.
i-nought, *n.*; *enough* 13. 8; y-nough 120. 67.
i-now, *adv.*; *enough* 67. 6; i-nough 77. 5; y-noghe 76. 14.

insipience, *n.*; *foolishness* 98. 17.
insolens, *n.*; *inexperience* 181. 10.
intere, *adj.*; *entire* 78. 45.
interiall, *adj.*; *inward, innermost* 196. 6.
into, *prep.*; *in* 196. 10.
invennomit, *pp.*; *envenomed* 132. 43.
invenons, *n.*; *poisons* 77. 17.
ipocras, *n.*; *hippocras, sweet wine* 1. 35.
irous, *adj.*; *hot-tempered* 77. 9; 177. 37.
is, see sal.
isch, *pro.*; *I* 9. 3; hic 147. 9; I 37. 1; ic 29. 1; ich 15 bur.; y 28. 1; yc 28. 5.
i-slawe, *pp.*; *slain* 57. 5.
ivell, *n.*; *disease* 65. 1; euelles 81. 6.
I-vonded, *pp.*; *wounded* 196. 19.
ivy, *n.*; *ivy* 52 bur.; heyvy 50. 1.
i-ware, *adj.*; *wary* 180. 5.
iwis, *adv.*; *certainly* 1. 42; i-wovs 44. 14; y-wis 33. 18; 205. 27.

iapry, *adj.*; *jesting* 178. 85.
ielyf, *n.*; *jelly* 7. 9.
ienet, *adj.*; *early* (fruit) 21. 8.
ientyll, *adj.*; *gentle* 38. 6; *courteous* 50. 11.
ioy, *v. imp.*; *rejoice* (with) 53. 16.
iowes, *n.*; *jaws* 210. 6.
iugeit, *condemned* 212. 14.
iull, *n.*; *July* 88. 19.
iust, *v.*; *to joust* (fig.) 30. 9.

karchos, *n.*; *carcass* 32. 19.
keep, *n.*; *heed* 103. 14; 178. 8.
kell, *n.*; *maidenhead* 25. 8.
kend, *v. pt.* 1 *s.*; *became acquainted with* 133. 14.

kendly, *adj.*; *natural* 205. 12.

kene, *adj.*; *hardy* 72. 56; *sharp* 75. 1; *harsh* 28. 37; **kyn** 73. 27.

kepe, *v.*; *to guard, preserve* 38. 14; **keape** 91. 6; (*pr.* 3 *s.*) **kepyth** 167. 15; *to prevent* 81. 15; *to be careful to* 169. 19; (*pr.* 1 *s.*) **kep,** *care, wish* 28. 34.

khyn, *n.*; *chin* 29. 10.

knad, *v. pt.* 1 *s.*; *kneaded* 29. 20.

knappes, *n.*; *knobs* (fig. testicles) 31. 13; *buttons* 115. 10.

knaue, *n.*; *servant* 180. 34; *gen. pl.* **knauene,** *assistants* 118. 4.

knockes, *n.*; *blows* 118. 4.

knokeilles, *n.*; *ends of the bone at any joint* 81. 69.

knot, *n.*; *knot* (of marriage) 40. 4; **on a knot,** *at a time* 27. 13.

knyt, *v.*; *to bind, heal* 80. 7; (*pr.* 2 *s.*) *unite* (in marriage) 40. 2; (*pp.*) **knet** 41. 2; 88. 33; (*pr.* 2 *pl.*) *embrace* 138. 11; (*pr.* 2 *s.*) **knet vp,** *hang up* 41. 4.

kongons, *n.*; *changelings* (general term of abuse) 118. 5.

koueryng, *n.*; *covering* (*of book*) 94. 12.

kowrs, *n.*; *course* (of a meal) 56. 13.

kovle, *n.*; *kale* 119. 37.

kyn, *n.*; *family* 36. 11; 116. 12.

kyn, see kene.

kynd, *adj.*; *typical* 181. 22; *friendly* 161. 6; *charitable* 197. 18; *natural* 72. 41.

kynde, *n.*; (good) *lineage, kin* 46. 10; *nature* 77. 4; 96. 10; 129. 48; 181. 51.

kyndenesse, *n.*; *devotion* 131. 18.

kyndly, *adv.*; *by nature* 187. 2.

kyrchers, *n.*; *kerchiefs, headdresses* 38. 39; **kerchef** 29. 10.

kys, *v.*; *to kiss* 26. 1; (*pt.* 3 *s.*) **kyst** 36. 27; (*n. part*) **cussynge** 28. 14.

lac, *n.*; *defect* 33. 3; 35. 23.

lace, *n.*; *snare* 140. 11; 177. 82.

lace, *v.*; *to involve* 59. 29.

lafte, see leue.

laitis, *n.*; *manners* 212. 5.

lak, *n.*; *pond* 47. 10.

lakke, *v.*; *to blame* 4. 1; *to be without* 6. 2; 52. 15; 78. 16.

lape, *n.*; *pudenda muliebra* 26. 15; **lappes** 31. 17.

large, *adj.*; *liberal* 77. 1; *considerable* 120. 36; *broad* 129. 17.

lat, see let.

lath, *adj.*; *reluctant* 58. 46.

laye, *n.*; *lea, open ground* 119. 69.

layne, *v.*; *to conceal* 24.4; **leyn,** *to be concealed* 94. 21.

leche, *v.*; *to cure* 103. 4.

lechecrafte, *n.*; *the art of healing* 103. 1.

leches, *n.*; *physicians* 78. 9; 102. 1.

lechours, *n.*; *lechers* 78. 54.

lede, *v.*; *to deal with* 44. 17; (*pt.* 1 *s.*) **ladd,** *led* 28. 1.

leef, *n.*; *leaf* (of a book) 94. 8.

lef, *n.*; *loved one* 9. 6; 147. 4; **lefe** 160. 1; **leffe** 158. 3.

lefe, *adj.*: *dear, pleasing* 134. 8; **leefe** 134. 16; (*comp.*) 134. 45; (*sup.*) 22. 5.

legge, *v.*; *to lay* 29. 30.

leill, *adv.*; *faithfully* 132. 28; **lele** 199. 48; **lelyly** 134. 12.

leke-worttes, *n.*; *herbs* 119. 75.

lele, *adj.*; *faithful* 144. 4.

lemmon, *n.*; *lover* 9. 4; **leman** 36. 31; **lemman** 9. 10; 45. 11.

lemys, *n.*; *rays of light* 198. 49.

lende, *v.*; *to stay, dwell* 58. 51; 205. 79; (*pp.*) **lend,** *set* 143. 18; **lent,** *abiding* 58. 3.

lene, *adj.*; *thin* 1. 25; *containing little fat* 13. 10.

lene, *v.*; *to lend* 58. 73; (*pt.* I *s.*)
lent 87. 2; (*pp.*) lent 104. 15.

lenkithes, *v. pr.* 3 *s.*; *lengthens*
58. 109.

lepe, (in phr.) in a lepe, *straight-
way* 51. 8.

lepre, *n.*; *leprosy* 81. 20.

lere, *v.*; *to teach* 3. 11; *to learn*
103. 2; 205. 73; leir 132. 2;
(*pp.*) lerde, *learned* 9. 14.

leris, *n.*; *cheeks* 127. 27.

les, *n.*; *falsehood* 43 bur.; lese
135. 3; 144. 3.

lese, see lowse.

lese, *v.*; *to lose* 113. 12; (*pr.* 2 *s.*)
lesythe 72. 69; (*pr.* 3 *s.*) leset
9. 13.

lesynge, *n.*; *lying* 81. 16; 179.
44.

let, *v.*; *to give up, abandon* 142.
4; 128. 12; 180. 20; (*pr.* 3 *pl.*)
58. 68; lete, *to permit* 24. 15;
lat, *to let* (blood) 73. 52; lat
go, *to forget* 33. 19; (*pr.* 3 *pl.*)
lat ly3t be, *think little of* 8. 9;
(*pr.* I *s.*) late, *let* 101. 14;
(*imp.*) let 117. 12; 175. 3;
(*pt.* I *s.*) lete, *allowed* 24. 10;
(*pt.* 3 *s.*) leete 96. 23.

letheryn, *adj.*; *leathern* (of skin
of living animals) 31. 13.

lett, *v.*; *to hinder* 63. 4; lete, *to
prevent* 134. 12; (*pr.* 3 *s.*) lettes
73. 82.

lette, *n.*; *hindrance* 104. 14;
129. 29.

leue, *v.*; *to leave* 116. 10; 129.
45; 179. 94; *allow* 119. 65;
(*pp.*) lafte 129. 35.

leue, *v.*; *to live* 171. 23; lif 58.
74; (*pr.* I *s.*) leyffe 136. 15;
lywe 163. 11; leve 119. 5; lyfe
139. 19; (*pr.* 3 *s.*) 171. 14.

leuer, *adv.*; *rather* 38. 15; leuur
116. 4.

leve, *n.*; *leave* (in phr.) taketh
his leve 55. 11; 197. 56; leif

132. 34; leyfe 56. 10; lyve, *permission* 62. 16.

leve, *v.*; *to believe* 179. 96.

lewdenesse, *n.*; *ignorance* 98. 5.

ley, *v. pr.* I *s.*; *present, put forward* 33. 12; (*pr.* 3 *s.*) lyeth,
*lies* 48. 21; lyyt 143. 2; (*pr.*
3 *pl.*) ley, *lay down* 48. 24;
(*pt.* I *s.*) *placed* (one's limbs)
in certain position 30. 5.

leyd, *v. pr.* I *s.*; *lead* 119. 6.

leyke, *n.*; *leek* 119. 34.

leyn, see layne.

leysier, *n.*; *opportunity* 131. 47;
leyser 197. 42.

liche, see lyk.

licherous, *adj.*; *lecherous* 72.
110; 212. 5.

lif, see leue.

lime, *n.*; *limb* 147. 7.

lite, *adj.*; *small* 186. 13; 192. 10;
*insignificant* 199. 14.

locces, *n.*; *locks* 134. 13.

locched, *pp.*; *lodged* 209. 42.

loke, *v. pr.* 3 *s.*; *look* 44. 6;
(*imp.*) 6. 3; *look for* 70. 2;
brodde to loke, *to keep your
eyes wide open* 39. 2.

lokyn, *pp.*; *set* 46. 18.

lokyng, *n.*; *appearance* 179. 82.

long, *adv.*; *over a long stretch*
116. 6; 120. 76.

longe, *v. pr.* 3 *s.*; *belongs* 128.
26; longet 33. 8; longeth 120.
13.

longgyng, *n.*; *yearning desire*
45. 12.

longith, *v. pr.* 3 *s.*; *lengthens*
118. 17. (See Note.)

lordynges, *n.*; *gentlemen* 72. 33.

lore, *n.*; *learning* 179. 37.

lorelles, *n.*; *laurels* 114. 4.

lorne, *pp.*; *lost, doomed* 61. 8;
lore 128. 4; for-lorn 73. 12.

lothe, *adj.*; *unpleasant* 134. 8;
178. 28; *reluctant* 138 rub.;
148. 11.

**louelynesse,** *n.*; *humility* 151. 2; **lowlynes** 183. 3.

**love,** *adv.*; *low, quietly* 119. 22.

**lowcray.** See Notes 209. 44.

**lowe,** *n.*; *love* 20. 20; 143. 18; **loue** 82. 1; **lovfe** 135. 6; **lowfe** 195. 13; **luf** 132. 36.

**lowe,** *v.*; *to love* 163. 21; (*pr.* 1 *s.*) **loue** 26. 5; **low** 143. 14; **lowfe** 135. 2; (*pr.* 3 *s.*) **louit** 45. 27; (*pr.* 2 *pl.*) **lowe** 32. 10; **luf** 58. 110; (*pt.* 1 *s.*) **lowet** 195. 11; (*pres. p.*) **lowynge** 76. 5.

**lowse,** *v.*; *to untie* (a knot) 40. 5; **lese,** *to release* 58. 34.

**lure,** *n.*; *falconer's lure for recalling hawks* 178. 78.

**lussom,** *adj.*; *beautiful* 205. 106.

**lust,** *n.*; *desire, wish* 106. 19; 110. 3; *pleasure* 59. 29; *sinful longing* 73. 82; **list** 177. 56; **lustes,** *sexual desires* 211. 2.

**lust,** *v. pr.* 3 *s.*; *wishes* 93. 1; **list** 177. 53; 38. 38; **lustyth** 198. 25; (*pr.* 2 *s.*) **lyst** 187. 4; (*pr.* 2 *pl.*) 131. 38; (*pr.* 3 *pl.*) 38. 25; (*pp.*) **lyst** 164. 12; (*pr.* 3 *impers.*) 32. 3; **liste** 37. 8; 154. 6.

**lusty,** *adj.*; *cheerful* 78. 63; *pleasing, beautiful* 131. 1; 198. 41.

**lustynes,** *n.*; *delight* 198. 34.

**lutel,** *adv.*; *little* 117. 11; **lityl** 118. 17.

**lutyng,** *n.*; *playing on the lute* 136. 2.

**lyberall,** *adj.*; *licentious* 38. 3; *generous* 120. 66.

**lycory,** *n.*; *licorice* 143. 7; **lycoresse** 130. 5.

**lycyvs,** *adj.*; *luscious* (of food) 56. 18.

**lyde,** *n.*; *person* 162. 15.

**lyght,** *adj.*; *bright* 198. 49.

**lyght,** *adj.*; *cheerful* 67. 5; 138.

26; *digestible* 78. 3; *nimble* 72. 82.

**lyȝt,** *n.*; (in phr.) **lat lyȝt be,** *think little of* 8. 9.

**lyk,** *prep.*; *like* 35. 25; **liche** 186. 21; **liik** 203. 9; **lyche** 96. 66.

**lykes,** *v. impers.*; *is pleasing to* 144. 4.

**lykke,** *v.*; *to lick* 32. 38.

**lykur,** *n.*; *beverage* 6. 4.

**lykyng,** *n.*; *delight* 19. 3; 127. 2; 179. 4; *bodily condition* 129. 4.

**lynd,** *n.*; *linden tree* 148. 14.

**lynne,** *v.*; *to cease* 28. 28.

**lysse,** *v.*; *to relieve* 19. 6.

**lyte,** *adv.*; *a little* 29. 15.

**lyte,** *v.*; *to grow cheerful* 167. 4.

**lyth,** *n.*; *joint, limb* 53. 9.

**lythe,** *adj.*; *easy* 73. 25.

**macke,** *v.*; *to make* 48. 7; (*pt.* 3 *s.*) **mase** 58. 43; (*pt.* 3 *pl.*) **mad** 50. 1.

**made,** *adj.*; *insane* 162. 9.

**magrie,** *prep.*; *in spite of* 190. 6.

**make,** *n.*; *mate* 208. 34.

**making,** *n.*; *composing* 177. 86.

**man,** *n.*; *lover* 139. 23; 171. 7; **mone,** *servant* 194. 6.

**marshall,** *n.*; *official at ceremonial banquet* 2. 2.

**mat,** see **mot.**

**matyins,** *n.*; *early morning service* 46. 4.

**mawe,** *v. pr.* 1 *s.*; *cut* (grass) 67. 7.

**may,** *n.*; *maiden* 198. 41; 209. 47.

**mayn,** *n.*; *strength* 24. 8.

**maystre,** *n.*; *victory* 50. 2; 58. 92.

**maystur,** *n.*; *teacher* 116. 21; **masster,** *lord, employer* 95. 7; 98. 10; 118. 17; **maysters,** *scholars* 73. 1; 81. 1.

me, *pro.*; *my* 29. 18; 128. 10; 198. 45.

measure, *n.*; *moderation* 177. 71.

mede, *n.*; *meadow* 47. 14.

mede, *n.*; *reward* 58. 122; med 44. 19.

medyll, *n.*; *waist* 129. 20; 143. 12.

medyll, *v.*; *to associate with* 137. 28; *to contend* 209. 4.

mell, *v.*; *to mingle in combat* 53. 3; *to interfere* 58. 37; *(pp.)* mellyd *mixed* 80. 4; mellit 212. 21.

memery, *n.*; *memorandum* 99. 6.

memorall, *adj.*; *remembering* 190. 23.

mene, *n.*; *middle voice in a song* 1. 26.

mene, *v. pr.* 1 *pl.*; *declare* (to) 96. 53; *(pp.)* mente 99. 10; 188. 3; *(pr.* 1 *s.)* mean 211. 8; *(pr.* 3 *pl.)* by-meenen 100. 7.

mensworne, *pp.*; *perjured* 212. 21.

mer, *n.*; *mere, pond* 13. 23.

mercylese, *adj.*; *without having received mercy* 191. 35.

mere, *adj.*; *merry* 3 bur.; merie 27 bur.; mery 25. 11; myrie *pleasant* (of weather) 141. 1; *(comp.)* 8. 1; *(sup.)* murgust 28. 29.

merth, *n.*; *joy, mirth* 42. 2; merthis 171. 1; murþus 19 bur.; myrthes 204. 26.

meruell, *n.*; (in phr.) I haue grete meruell, *I am struck with astonishment* 148. 1.

meruolse, *adj.*; *marvellous* 181. 3; mervelous, *astonishing* 72. 25.

merwell, *v. pr.* 1 *s.*; *wonder* 163. 6.

mes, *n.*; *course* (of food) 56. 7; mese 58. 56.

mestres, *n.*; *mistress* 137. 1; mestrys 161. 1.

mesurable, *adj.*; *moderate* 178. 66.

mete, *adj.*; *becoming, proper* 79. 6.

mete, *n.*; *food* 18. 7; mett 35. 5; *meat* 78. 2; *feast* 54. 1.

mete, *v.*; *to encounter* 129. 40; met 24. 11; *(pr.* 1 *s.)* meth 28. 37; *(pt.* 3 *s.)* mette 28. 21; *(pres. p.)* methyng 177. 35.

meve, *v. pr. subj.* 3 *s.*; *belong to* 74. 15.

meynt, *pp.*; *mingled* 77. 3.

misfare, *n.*; *misfortune* 199. 23.

mo, *pro.*; *more, others* 22. 12. 143. 14; moo 163. 7.

mode, *n.*; *mood, temper* 58. 13; 179. 12.

mold, *n.*; *earth* 59. 1.

mone, see man.

mone, *n.*; *complaint* 162. 17; mowne 206. 4.

mone, *n.*; *month* 73. 23; *moon* 113. 10.

moo, *adv.*; *more* 38. 34; mair 132. 35; moir 132. 46.

mor, *n.*; *moor* 18. 1.

mot, *v. pr.* 1 *s.*; *may* 48. 17; *(pr.* 2 *s.)* mat 57 bur.; *(pr.* 3 *s.)* mote 5. 9; 81. 89; *(pt.* 1 *s.)* moste, *must* 29. 9; *(pt.* 3 *s.)* mouste 167. 14; *(pt.* 3 *impers.)* me must 44. 10; 53. 3.

mote, *n.*; *mood* 179. 103.

mote, *v.*; *to argue* 58. 20.

moth, *n.*; *mouth* 195. 22; mouþe 197. 48.

mow, *v. pr.* 1 *s.*; *may* 32. 13; 185. 10; *(pr.* 2 *s.)* 41. 3; *(pr.* 1 *pl.)* 122. 4; *(pr.* 1 *s.)* mun 193. 22; *(pr.* 3 *s.)* mon 140. 15; *(pt.* 1 *s.)* mikte, *might* 147. 9; mouth 28. 42; myth 150. 6; mytte 28. 24; *(pt.* 2 *s.)* myst

19. 6; (*pt.* 3 *s.*) **mouth** 127. 24;
**myght** 49. 25; (*pt.* 1 *pl.*) **myth**
116. 7.

**mowrnarus**, *n.*; *mourners* 206.
75.

**mulne**, *n.*; *mill* 116. 8.

**mun**, see **mow**.

**mutable**, *adj.*; *changeable* 109. 4.

**myche**, *adj.*; *much* 1. 39; **mekell**
58. 17; **mekill** 58. 21; **mekyl**
57. 2; **mekyll** 134. 25; **moche**
42. 6; **muche** 37. 4; **muiche**
76. 1; **mych** 188. 58; **mykel**
100. 5; **mykyll** 12. 2; (*sup.*)
**muste** 198. 5.

**myddis**, *n.*; *middle* 21. 5.

**myght**, *n.*; *power* 58. 21.

**mylner**, *n.*; *miller* 115. 18.

**mynd**, *n.*; *opinion* 6. 1; *judgement* 136. 20; *mind* 205. 107;
*recollection* 209. 40.

**mynder**, *n.*; *keeper* 205. 107.

**mynon**, *adv.*; *elegantly* 35. 3.

**mynstralsy**, *n.*; *music* 122. ee.

**myny**, *adj.*; *many* 5. 2.

**myscheuyt**, *pp.*; *harmed* 181.
44.

**mys-doe**, *v. imp.*; *wrong* 180.
68.

**mys-fenyng**, *adj.*; *tendentious*
181. 33.

**mysse**, *n.*; (in *phr.*) **with-owten
mysse**, *undoubtedly* 204. 26.

**mysse-went**, *pp.*; *gone astray*
179. 97.

**myssomur**, *adj.*; *midsummer*
28. 1.

**na**, *adv.*; *not* 133. 6.

**nakyn**, *adj.*; *no kind of* 73. 75.

**narw**, *adj.*; *narrow* 28. 13.

**nede**, *n.*; *personal business* 19.
11; *service* 33. 9; *necessity* 110.
6.

**neghe**, *adv.*; *near* 170. 5; (*comp.*)
**ner** 28. 9; **nere** 134. 14; **neir**
133. 3.

**ner**, *conj.*; *if . . . not* 197. 27.

**neven**, *v.*; *to name* 96. 19.

**newere**, *adv.*; *never* 195. 20.

**nis**, see **beo**.

**nist**, see **nyght**.

**noblesse**, *n.*; *nobility* (form of
address) 106. 4.

**nobleye**, *n.*; *nobility of nature*
98. 26.

**nocke**, *n.*; *cleft in buttocks* 32. 19.

**noise**, *n.*; *nose* 80. 5; **nose** 81.
21.

**noll**, *n.*; *head* 14. 17.

**nolde**, see **wele**.

**non**, *adj.*; *no* 45. 22.

**non**, *pro.*; *none* 43. 2; 57. 17.

**non**, *n.*; *noon-time* 43. 5; **none**
29. 13.

**nonys**, *adv. phr.*; *for þe nonys*,
*for the nonce* 7. 5.

**norice**, *n.*; *nurse* 205. 103.

**nose-thryllys**, *n.*; *nostrils* 209.
22.

**not**, *v. pr.* 1 *s.*; *know not* 119. 8.

**noþir**, *pro.*; *neither* 42. 2;
**neyther** 110. 6; **nowþer** 58. 69.

**noust**, *adv.*; *nought, not* 17. 3;
**nawht** 42. 4; **nocht** 132. 31;
**noght** 58. 28; **noȝt** 22. 7; **nout**
28. 34; **nowght** 36. 15; **nowt**
27. 17; **nowte** 99. 2.

**novelry**, *n.*; *what is new* 175. 8.

**nowte**, *n.*; *cattle* 71. 8.

**noxiall**, *adj.*; *nocturnal* 190. 15.

**noyus**, *adj.*; *vexatious* 212. 13.

**nu**, *adj.*; *new* 3. 6.

**nurter**, *n.*; *that which nourishes*
204. 23.

**nyce**, *adj.*; *foolish* 209. 3.

**nye**, *v.*; *to annoy* 135. 17; (*pr.*
3 *s.*) **noyth**, *grieves* 159. 7.

**nyght**, *n.*; *night* 34. 10; **nist** 17.
2; **nycht** 133. 9; **nyȝth** 66. 2;
**nyȝt** 28. 32; **nyt** 28. 29.

**nyȝthe-mare**, *n.*; *female gob-
lin afflicting horses by night* 66
rub.

nylle, see wele.

nything, *adj.*; *niggardly* 58. 114.

obeysaunȝ, *n.*; *homage* 139. 4; 182. 6.

obles, *n.*; *thin pastry cakes* 122. bb.

occianne, *n.*; *ocean* 211. 38.

oder, *adj.*; *other* 2. 6; odyr 56. 26; vddir 132. 16; wthir 196. 15; þe todyr 90. 4.

off, *prep.*; *of* 20. 9.

offende, *v.*; *to cause to go wrong* 104. 14.

offys, *n.*; *church service* 27. 3.

ogaines, see aȝens.

oghte, *v. pr. impers.*; *owe, am bound to* 98. 7.

on, *pro.*; *one* 1. 11; 209. 41; ane 132. 36; o 180. 33; oon 68. 3; the ton 90. 3; won 115. 12; yn one, *without ceasing* 166. 1; 199. 5.

on-bred, *pp.*; *unborn* (of seed) 45. 25.

on-loft, *adv.*; *high up* 71. 5.

onpreyse, *v.*; *to dispraise* 34. 1.

onsar, *n.*; *answer* 32. 23; an-swere 28. 19.

ony, *adj.*; *any* 44. 17; 45. 6; anne 195. 12.

onys, *adv.*; *once* 5. 10; anis 133. 23; ones 22. 7; onis 163. 21; ons 134. 16.

onys, *pro.*; *one's* 41. 11.

oowte, *adv.*; *out* 48. 15; oute 167. 14; outht 112. 2; ovth 174. 9; owt 112. 4.

ordeyn, *v.*; *to establish* 94. 20.

oreant, *adj.*; *orient, brilliant* 130. 3.

Orient, *n.*; *God* 121. 32.

or-passand, *adj.*; *surpassing* 139. 14.

os, *conj.*; *as* 35. 11; 136. 21; 144. 6.

osyde, *adv.*; *aside, away* 182. 12.

oþur, *adj.*; (in phr.) þe oþur day, *the following day* 28. 36; þis oþer yere, *the year before* 193. 5.

ouer-all, *adv.*; *everywhere* 177. 79.

our, *n.*; *hour* 188. 10; oure 209. 41.

ourperte, *adj.*; *over-pert* 212. 18.

out, *prep.*; *without* 185. 5.

oute, see oowte.

ouþer, *conj.*; *either* 9. 1; other 73. 60; owþer 58. 97.

out-rage, *n.*; *intemperance* 103. 16.

ovȝt, *n.*; *ought, anything* 44. 5; 72. 44; out 59. 33.

ovth, see oowte.

ow, see ye.

owre, *v. pr. subj.* 3 *s.*; *destine* 167. 17.

owtrage, *adj.*; *extravagant* 76. 14; 177. 71.

page, *n.*; *servant* 2. 2; *young man* 24. 13.

pagiont, *n.*; *movable platform* 122. v.

pake, *n.*; *pack* 8. 14; pak 49. 24.

pape-iay, *n.*; *popinjay* 210. 20.

pappis, *n.*; *breasts* 127. 43; 129. 18; 209. 21.

party, *n.*; *dispute, contest* 50. 1.

parvis, *n.*; *church-porch* (of St. Paul's) 59. 34.

pastaunce, *n.*; *recreation* 137. 8.

patente, *n.*; *patent* (document conferring privilege) 106. 5.

pauyer, *n.*; *pavement* 122. cc.

pay, *n.*; (in phr.) to pay, *to* (her) *satisfaction* 148. 5; vnto my paye 200. 6.

payid, *v. pt.* 1 *s.*; *suffered for* 27. 11.

pax-brede, *n.*; *tablet kissed during mass* 27. 16.

**peckel**, *n.*; *vessel used as a peck measure* (by analogy with bushel) 30. 17.

**pectorellys**, *n.*; *breast ornaments* 209. 46.

**peersande**, *pres. p.*; *penetrating* 96. 36.

**peise**, *v. pr. subj.* 3 *s.*; *deliberate* 98. 23.

**pentice**, *n.*; *over-hanging roof* 210. 11.

**per**, *n.*; *pear* 21. 7.

**peraile**, *n.*; *peril* 72. 120; *loss* 72. 62.

**percase**, *adv.*; *by chance* 137. 29.

**perchis**, *n.*; *perch* (fish) 114. 24.

**pere**, *n.*; *equal* 129. 11; **peer** 172. 10.

**peressh**, *v.*; *to pierce* (the heart) 205. 46; (*pr.* 3 *pl.*) **perse** 201. 9; (*pp.*) **pershid** 156. 6; **peryschid** 168. 10.

**perseueraunce**, *n.*; *constancy* 131. 15.

**person**, *n.*; *parson* 56. 6; 58. 9.

**pertrychys**, *n.*; *partridges* 56. 15.

**pery**, *n.*; *pear-tree* 21. 12.

**peryr**, *n.*; *pear-tree* 21. 6.

**peryth**, *v. pr.* 3 *s.*; *appears* 181. 28.

**pese**, *n.*; *pea* (in phr.) **half a pese**, *valueless* 43. 19.

**pese**, *n.*; *peace* 58. 49; **pease** 78. 32; **pees** 84. 1; **pes** 43 bur.; **peyce** 135. 16; **peys** 135. 1; **peyse** 135. 8.

**pese**, *v.*; *to pacify* 168. 7.

**pesys**, *n.*; *pieces* 56. 25; **pecis** 197. 28.

**peyn**, *n.*; *suffering* (of love) 154. 5; **paine** 196. 12; **payn** 198. 40; **payne** 168. 4; **peane** 200. 22; **peynes** 205. 26.

**peyre**, *n.*; *pair* 28. 18.

**pight**, *pp.*; *planted* 205. 21.

**pilion**, *n.*; *cap* (especially of doctor of divinity) 59. 18.

**piter-pater**, *v.*; *to pitter-patter, whisper* 194. 15.

**plane**, *adj.*; *guileless* 132. 13; 173. 25; **playn**, *straightforward* 169. 20.

**plase**, *n.*; *place* 81. 4; (*pl.*) **place** 101. 18.

**plee**, *n.*; *law suit* 84. 4.

**plente**, *adj.*; *abundant* 58. 58.

**plesaunce**, *n.*; *lawn, fine gauze* 122. i.

**plesaunce**, *n.*; *pleasure* 127. 56; **plasauns** 198. 20.

**plete**, *v.*; *to plead, litigate* 59. 33; (*pr.* 3 *pl.*) **pletyn** 178. 1.

**pley**, *v.*; *to frolic amorously* 24. 16; 25. 9; 26. 2; **pley3e** 29. 22; **pleie**, *to play* 101. 15.

**pleyne**, *n.*; *complaint* 157. 8.

**pli3t**, *v. pr.* 1 *s.*; *promise* 81. 10.

**plowers**, *n.*; *plovers* 56. 15.

**pociouns**, see **potacyon**.

**podynges**, *n.*; *sausages* 13. 19.

**port**, *n.*; *bearing* 139. 26.

**portresse**, *n.*; *female door-keeper* 78. 53.

**porttoryng**, *n.*; *carrying* 56. 2.

**pose**, *n.*; *rheum* 209. 52.

**potacyon**, *n.*; *drink* 73. 77; **pociouns**, *medicinal drinks* 79. 5.

**potdtage**, *n.*; *pottage* 56. 23.

**pouert**, *n.*; *poverty* 84. 4.

**poues**, *n.*; *pulse* 79. 2.

**poured**, *pp.*; *impoverished* 140. 26.

**ppoke**, *n.*; *puck, familiar spirit* 116. 14.

**pransede**, *v. pt.* 3 *s.*; *pranced* 28. 28.

**praty**, *adj.*; *pleasing* 26. 18; *pretty* 32 bur.; *nice* 47. 4.

**pray**, *n.*; *prey*, 197. 38.

**prease**, *v.*; *to praise* 130. 41.

**prees**, *n.*; *crowd* 205. 66; (in phr.) **putten hem in pres**, *exert themselves* 88. 59; **putt me yn**

preace, *press my claims home* 129. 32.

preisable, *adj.*; *praiseworthy* 205. 93.

prengnavnt, *adj.*; *significant* 190. 9.

prepotent, *adj.*; *pre-eminent* 123. 1.

prese, *v. imp.*; *press* 175. 7.

prest, *pp.*; *ready, prepared* 180. 61; 197. 37.

pretens, *n.*; *pretext* 20. 7.

preue, *v.*; *to prove, establish* 120. 57; pryve 197. 47; (*pr.* 3 *s.*) preuys 175. 4; (*pp.*) 205. 2; (*imp.*) prove, *test, find out* 40. 1; preveþ 205. 50.

preyse, *v. pr.* 2 *s.*; *appraise* 40. 1.

prime, *n.*; *early morning* 28. 36; *new moon* 70. 2.

primerole, *n.*; *primrose* 18. 9; prymerose 205. 136.

prise, *n.*; *value* 130. 2; pris 205. 2; pryse 209. 1.

priuey, *adj.*; *secret* 28. 17; *intimate* 177. 48; prive 205. 102.

priuey, *adv.*; *privately* 28. 42.

priyede, *v. pt.* 3 *s.*; *pried* 28. 11.

probeyt, *n.*; *evidence* 116. 10.

profondyd, *pp.*; *deep-seated* 198. 5.

promyssioun, *n.*; *promise* (in phr.) provynce of promyssioun 121. 24.

prow, *n.*; *advantage* 33. 2.

pryck, *v.*; *to have intercourse* 32. 39; (*pt.* 3 *s.*) prikede 28. 28; (*pr.* 2 *s.*) prekyst, *ride fast on horseback* 59. 22.

prynte, *v. imp.*; *imprint* 207. 1.

puere, *n.*; *power* 198. 12; pore 26. 16.

pult, *v. pt.* 3 *s.*; *thrust* 29. 33.

purce, *n.*; *bag* 119. 47.

purchase, *v.*; *to bring about* 163. 25.

pured, *pp.*; *very fine* 205. 119.

purpasse, *n.*; *purpose* 129. 28.

pursieu, *v.*; *to carry on legal action* 178. 5, 57.

pye, *n.*; *magpie* 5. 5.

pyk, *v.*; *to pick at* (food) 56. 17.

pyn, *n.*; *ornamental brooch* 29. 11; pynnis 7. 2; *door latch* 36. 3; *hook* 119. 74.

pyne, *n.*; *grief, suffering* 37. 6.

pyp, *n.*; *catarrh* 209. 52.

pypis, *n.*; *water pipes* 122. bb; *musical instrument* 122. ee.

pystyl, *n.*; *epistle* (in mass) 27. 7.

quan, *conj.*; *when* 21. 13; wan 28. 23; 180. 51; wanne 37. 3; wen 22. 8.

quarel, *n.*; *bolt or arrow* 103. 9.

quarteyne, *n.*; *quartan fever* 81. 82.

quat, *pro.*; *what* 7. 12; wat 18. 8; quhat, *whatever* 132. 14.

quaylys, *n.*; *quails* 208 rub.

queare, *n.*; *poem* 207. 15.

qued, *n.*; *bodily ill* 81. 48.

quek, *v.*; *to quack* (as a duck) 49. 18.

queynt, *adj.*; *crafty* 211. 8.

quhay, *pro.*; *who* 133. 6.

quhill, see wyle.

quhois, *pro.*; *whose* 132. 47.

quhome, *pro.*; *whom* 196. 13.

qui, *adv.*; *why* 148. 9.

quippe, *v. pr. subj.* 3 *s.*; *keep* 183. 6.

quit, see whyt.

quite, *v.*; *to requite* 177. 63; 199. 39; (*pp.*) quyt 132. 46; qwyt, *done with* 4. 4.

quod, *v. pt.* 3 *s.*; *said* 48 bur.

quyt, *adj.*; *equal with* (in retaliation) 107. 5.

quyt-rent, *n.*; *token rent* 74. 14.

qwat, *interj.*; *how* 24 bur.

qwer, see ware.

qwert, *n.*; *health* 189. 8.
qwylk, *pro.*; *which* 73. 75; quhilk 132. 17; weche 164. 8; wheche 140. 25; wheeche 96. 32.

race, *v.*; *to root out* 140. 5.
rad, *pp.*; *afraid* 58. 53.
rage, *n.*; *sexual passion* 24. 15.
ragius, *adj.*; *full of passion* 206. 11.
rapere, *adv.*; *sooner* 7. 8.
rayne, *v.*; *to stream with tears* 168. 12.
reaggeth, *adj.*; *shaggy* 28. 33.
reame, *n.*; *realm* 120. 19; royme 122. 30.
rech, *v.*; *to attain* 52. 7; a-reche, *reach* 180. 45.
recke, *v. pr.* 1 *s.*; *care* 124. 4; (*pt.* 3 *s.*) roght 124. 4.
recure, *v. pr.* 1 *s.*; *regain health* 138. 45.
recurles. See Notes 169. 11.
rede, *adj.*; *red* 18. 23; redde 67. 12; reede 101. 1; *golden* 67. 10.
rede, *n.*; *advice* 180. 53; reed 101. 21.
rede, *v.*; *to advise* 197. 19; (*pr.* 1 *s.*) 4. 7; *to read* 93. 2; redde 99. 1; (*pt.* 3 *s.*) 27. 7; (*pr. subj.* 3 *s.*) 103. 2; (*imp.*) ryd, *guess* 7. 12.
redowtid, *pp.*; *feared* 123. 2.
redres, *n.*; *remedy, relief* 129. 33.
redres, *v.*; *to restore* 162. 7.
refrayn, *v.*; *to abstain* 78. 70; refreyne, *to restrain* 168. 5; (*pp.*) 88. 29.
reft, *v. pt.* 1 *s.*; *took away* 53. 9.
refute, *n.*; *refuge* 121. 19.
regement, *n.*; *control* 120. 62.
rehete, *v.*; *to attack, pester* 59. 34.
rele, *v.*; *to wind* (thread) 29 bur.
relese, *v.*; *to relieve* 58. 50; release 121. 6; relesse 201. 7.

releue, *v.*; *to raise oneself* 120. 47.
releve, *v.*; *to relieve* 196. 12; (*pp.*) releuyd 164. 14; 181. 47.
reluys, *adj.*; *glittering* 26. 17.
remewe, *v.*; *to remove* 78. 76.
reneye, *v.*; *to abjure* 140. 13.
rennyn, *v.*; *to run* 43. 11; rene 119. 66; (*pr.* 3 *s.*) 190. 10; (*pr.* 3 *pl.*) 119. 17.
rente, *n.*; *income* 78. 60; 186. 14.
replete, *adj.*; *abundantly filled* 130. 46; 198. 36.
rere-soupers, *n.*; *midnight feasts* 78. 50.
reserthe, *n.*; *resort for aid* 198. 38.
rest, *n.*; *peace of mind* 157. 3.
retorucion, *n.*; *rhetorician* 209. 4.
retournable, *adj.*; *returnable* 107. 4.
reuen, *pp.*; *cracked* 43. 6.
reuth, *n.*; *pity* 100. 6; ruthe 205. 72; routh 131. 41.
rewe, *v.*; *to have pity* 205. 27; *do penance* 193. 22.
rewen, *n.*; *ruin* 120. 20.
reych, see ruschen.
reyne, *n.*; *rain* 205. 16.
reyne, *v.*; *to rain* 210. 12; rayne, *to shed tears* 168. 12.
reysons, *n.*; *raisins* (in phr.) reysons of corrans 56. 26.
rialte, *n.*; *regal state* 136. 15.
ring, *n.*; *circular group of persons* (in dance) 28. 7.
robbe, *n.*; *robe* 180. 41.
rochis, *n.*; *dogs* 119. 17.
rode, *n.*; *complexion* 143. 11.
rode, *n.*; *cross* 65. 10.
rode, *n.*; *rod* (measure of length) 66. 8.
rofe, see ryfe.
rok, *n.*; *distaff* 49. 20.
rokkes, *n. gen. s.*; *tunic* 180. 48.

rollyng, *adj.*; *moving to and fro* (of eyes) 130. 14.

rolyons, *n.*; *fish* [O. Fr. rouillon] 114. 11.

romnay, *n.*; *sweet wine* 56. 19.

roow, *n.*; *roe, deer* 56. 25.

rope, *v.*; *to water* (of eyes) 113. 7.

rouffully, *adv.*; *piteously* 119. 4.

rowe, *n.*; *row* (in phr.) be rowe, *in turn* 118. 15.

rowght, *v.*; *to move round* 14 bur.

rown, *adj.*; *round* 143. 6.

rowne, *v.*; *to whisper* 28. 16.

rowners, *n.*; *tale-bearers* 78. 28.

rowtyn, *v. pr.* 3 *pl.*; *crash* 118. 15.

rubycounde, *adj.*; *red* 130. 42.

rudy, *n.*; *complexion* 127. 26.

ruschen, *n.*; *rushes* (for floors) 29. 7; **not wor3t a reych,** *worthless* 43. 15.

rut, *n.*; *root* (of heart) 132. 19; rote, *foundation* 139. 32.

rwe, *v.*; *to have pity for* 116. 12; rewe 140. 1; (*pr.* 2 *pl.*) ruwen 19. 2; (*pt.* 2 *pl.*) rued 199. 56.

ryal, *adj.*; *royal* 96. 5; rial 98. 1; ryall 205. 120.

ryd, *v.*; *to ride* 44. 9.

ryd, see rede.

ryfe, *v. pr.* 3 *s.*; *rend* 132. 19; (*pt.* 3 *s.*) rofe 25. 8.

rynde, *n.*; *branch* 45. 10.

rysse, *n.*; *small branch* 129. 7; rys 205. 120.

rythe, *adj.*; *right, very* 37. 11; ryth 54. 6; rigth 77. 7; (*adv.*) 146. 1.

sad, *adj.*; *dignified* 78. 63; *steadfast* 58. 52; *serious* 139. 31; *melancholy* 76. 6; shadde 171. 12.

sal, *v. pr.* 3 *s.*; *shall* 71. 4; (*pr.*

1 *s.*) ichulle 117. 6; Is, *I shall* 6. 1; xall 24. 6; (*pr.* 3 *s.*) sall 71. 6; ssal 16. 5; (*pr.* 1 *pl.*) xul 4. 11; xal 54. 3; (*pr.* 3 *pl.*) shull 72. 32; (*pt.* 1 *s.*) icholde 9. 9; (*pt.* 2 *s.*) schust 116. 15; (*pt.* 3 *s.*) schold 22. 5; (*pt.* 2 *pl.*) xuld 7. 8; (*pt.* 3 *pl.*) suld 116. 12.

sale, *n.*; *prosperity, joy* 11. 3.

salyfe, *n.*; *ointment* 136. 41.

sane3, *prep.*; *without* 73. 64; sauns 190. 9.

sapher, *n.*; *sapphire* 204. 3; saphir 205. 89.

saue, *n.*; *sage* 103. 15.

sauke, *n.*; *sake* (in phr.) al for þi sauke 119. 48.

sausfleme, *n.*; *swelling of face* 81. 20.

savyn, *adj.*; *seven* 196. 18.

sawe, *v. pr.* 1 *s.*; *sow* 67. 10.

sawus, *n.*; *promises* 23. 9; 58. 77.

sayssyde, *pp.*; *endowed* 207. 9.

scall, *n.*; *eczema* 81. 16.

scape, *v.*; *to escape* 138. 39; (*pr.* 1 *s.*) schape 119. 28.

schakeled, *pp.*; *protected with greaves* 118. 12.

schanginge, *pres. p.*; *changing* 190. 42.

schankes, *n.*; *legs* 118. 12; shankys 208. 22.

schappes, *n.*; *shapes* 128. 17.

schayl, *n.*; *bowl* 29. 18.

schelde, *n.*; *shield* 58. 97.

schend, *v.*; *to blame* 180. 18; (*pp.*) shente, *punished* 72. 98; *disgraced* 179. 99; schent 168. 14.

schetus, *n.*; *sheets* 28. 26; schett 143. 13.

schew, see she.

schew, *interj.*; *shoo* 115. 20.

schone, *n.*; *shoes* 29. 15.

schortithe, *v. pr.* 3 *s.*; *shortens* 190. 28.

schow. See Notes 56. 17.

schrew, *v. pr.* 1 *s.*; *curse* 25. 18.

schylde, *n.*; *child* 27. 20.

schylde, *v. pr. subj.* 3 *s.*; *preserve* 27. 19.

schyle, see skyll.

science, *n.*; *knowledge* 109. 3.

scoth, *n.*; *contribution* 29. 25.

scripture, *n.*; *handwriting* 94. 1; *the Bible* 96. 4.

scrowe, *n.*; *scolding woman* 119. 51.

scrybabyll, *adj.*; *suitable for being written on* 211. 37.

se, *v.*; *to see* 100. 12; sse 158. 3; (*pt.* 1 *s.*) say 138. 10; (*pt.* 3 *s.*) saughe 96. 30; (*pr. subj.* 3 *s.*) se 113. 10; (*imp.*) sethe, *look* (to) 182. 11; (*pp.*) seyne 184. 10.

seche, *v.*; *to seek* 119. 30; seke 129. 43.

secree, *adj.*; *discreet* 131. 23.

secree, *n.*; (in phr.) in secree, *privately* 38. 3.

see, *n.*; *royal throne* 96. 48; 121. 3.

seemlynesse, *n.*; *dignity of bearing* 131. 25.

seke, *adj.*; *sick* 48. 21; sek 193. 9.

sel, *n.*; *good fortune* 27. 8.

selcouth, *adj.*; *strange, wonderful* 69. 5; 73. 4.

sell (in phr.) to sell, *on sale* 130. 24.

semblable, *adj.*; *like* 188. 56.

semely, *adj.*; *pleasing* 130. 1; semle 144. 10; (*comp.*) semelokyr 138. 14.

semelynes, *n.*; *pleasing appearance* 139. 27.

semewes, *n.*; *sea-mews* 114. 18.

sen, see sythe.

ser, *adj.*; *diverse* 73. 87; sers 73. 1.

sertayn, *adv.*; *certainly* 174. 10.

serttes, *adv.*; *certainly* 134. 41; in serttes 134. 19; certes 177. 1.

seruiture, *n.*; *lover* 191. 24.

seruyse, *n.*; *professed love* 179. 60; seruyce, *course, dish* 55. 6.

sese, *v.*; *to cease* 135. 6; seyse 135. 14; sease, *to cause to cease* 207. 4.

set, *v. pr.* 1 *s.*; *evaluate* 136. 9; (*pr.* 3 *s.*) 176. 2; (*pp.*) *determined* 188. 1.

sethe, see se.

setithe, *v. pr.* 3 *s.*; *sits* 190. 35; (*impers.*) it sittyth, *it is proper* 140. 20.

seuenyst, *n.*; *week* 18. 3.

sewe, *v.*; *to serve* (as lover) 140. 3; sieu 178. 23; sew, *to plead* (a cause) 188. 80; sew, *to follow* 188. 40; (*pr.* 3 *s.*) 140. 22.

sewre, see shewre.

seyn, *v.*; *to say* 174. 14; sey 49. 36; seyȝ 43 bur.; sayne 199. 58; (*pr.* 1 *s.*) 44. 3; (*pr.* 3 *s.*) seyth 52. 2; seyȝt 43 bur.; (*imp.*) 50. 11; (*pp.*) seyde 62. 8.

seynsyng, *pres. p.*; *censing* 122. z.

seyte, *n.*; *sight* 167. 3.

shadde, see sad.

shame, *n.*; (in phr.) taketh shame, *are disgraced* 138. 20.

she, *pro.*; *she* 148. 7; che 21. 16; sche 48. 18; schew 119. 4; scho 144. 12; schoe 181. 51; schowe 119. 39; sho 148. 8; sse 16. 5; yhe 147. 7.

sheene, *adj.*; *bright* 96. 37; schen 144. 6.

sheete, *v.*; *to strive* (after) 106. 15; (*pr.* 3 *pl.*) shote, *shoot* 114. 11.

shere, *v. pr.* 1 *s.*; *cut* (crops) 67. 8.

sherys, *n.*; *scissors* 211. 17.

shett, *pp.*; *shut* 113. 6.

**shewre,** *adj.*; *sure* 32. 29; **sewre**
186. 7; **sure** 191. 22; **sewer,**
*reliable* 110. 5.

**shrewd,** *adj.*; *malicious* 114. 27.

**shryll,** *adj.*; *high-pitched* 204.
22.

**siccurly,** *adv.*; *surely* 24. 7;
**securly** 193. 17; **sekurly** 145.
3; **sekyrly** 57. 16; **sikerli** 142.
3; **sykerly** 197. 42.

**siching,** *n.*; *sighing* 157. 4.

**sidis,** *n.*; *sides* (of body) 127.
46; 144. 9.

**similacion,** *n.*; *simulation* 111.
4.

**sire,** *n.*; *lord, ruler* 58. 55.

**sit,** *v.*; *to sit* (in seat of honour)
58. 81.

**sithe,** *n.*; *times* 127. 67; **syiss**
132. 36.

**sittyth,** *v. impers.*; *it is* (not)
*proper for* 140. 20.

**skaithful,** *adj.*; *harmful* 212. 11.

**skarste,** *n.*; *inadequacy, lack*
178. 89.

**skyers,** *n.*; *squires* (next in rank
to knights) 56. 5; **squyer** 59.
9.

**skyll,** *n.*; *reason* 24. 6; 72. 41;
**schyle,** *one's cause* 33. 16; **can
no skill,** *have no knowledge*
38. 23.

**sla,** *v.*; *to murder, kill* 58. 74;
**sley** 72. 116; **sclon** 62. 12;
(*pp.*) **slane** 132. 42; **slayne**
140. 28; **slo,** *to cure* 80. 6.

**slake,** *v.*; *to diminish* 200. 14;
205. 40.

**sleyght,** *n.*; *trickery* 77. 10;
**slycht** 132. 25.

**slo,** see **sla.**

**slough,** *n.*; *sloth* 78. 52.

**slowe,** *adj.*; *dull* 76. 1; 77. 15.

**sluggy,** *adj.*; *indolent* 76. 1.

**sly,** *adj.*; *clever* 72. 83.

**smac,** *n.*; *distinctive flavour* 33.
19.

**smal,** *adv.*; *finely* 80. 4.

**smale,** *adj.*; *low* 4. 3; *fine* 7. 3;
*little* 49. 14; *unimportant* 28.
34; *slender* 8. 6.

**smater,** *v.*; *to chatter* 38. 25.

**smateryd,** *pp.*; *begrimed* 118. 1.

**smekyd,** *pp.*; *smoke-blackened*
118. 1.

**smeþes,** *n.*; *smiths* 118. 1.

**snove,** *n.*; *snow* 119. 29.

**snyt,** *n.*; *snipe* 56. 15.

**so,** *adv.*; *as* 63. 17.

**sodenly,** *adv.*; *without delay*
143. 17; **sodeynly** 170. 6.

**softe,** *adj.*; *gentle* 52. 5.

**softe,** *adv.*; *in a low voice* 1. 19;
*quietly* 48. 10.

**soget,** *n.*; *subject, inferior* 78.
38.

**soȝne,** *n.*; *sun* 113. 3.

**solas,** *v.*; *to polish* 29. 15 (cf.
solace (n.) *cleaning material*).

**soleynge,** *adj.*; *sullen* 76. 9.

**sompnelent,** *adj.*; *sleepy* 77. 15.

**son,** *adv.*; *soon* 56. 11; **sone** 89.
4; (*comp.*) **sonner** 199. 47.

**sonde,** *n.*; *gift* 122. 20; **of godes
sonde,** *sent from God* 7. 9.

**sone,** *adv.*; *speedily* 164. 7.

**soore,** *adv.*; *deeply* 139. 24; **sair**
133. 21; (*sup.*) **soryst** 180. 9.

**soore,** *v.*; *to soar* 96. 8; (*pres. p.*)
**soryng** 96. 11.

**soþe,** *adj.*; *truthful* 146. 8.

**souffyse,** *v.*; *satisfy* 98. 9; **suffysse** 198. 46.

**sownyth,** *v. pr.* 3 *s.*; *conduces*
192. 2, 21.

**sowse,** *v.*; *to drench* 29. 27.

**space,** *n.*; *opportunity* 131. 47.

**spare,** *v.*; *to show mercy* 197. 22;
*to abstain* 116. 18; *to shun* 101.
16; (*imp.*) *hoard* 60. 2; (*pt.* 3 *s.*)
*desisted* 28. 9.

**spede,** *v.*; *to prosper* 58. 83;
(*pp.*) **sped** *satisfied* 58. 40.

**spellyn,** *v. pr.* 3 *pl.*; *tell* 118. 8.

spende, (*pp.*) *expressed* 134. 29.

sper-hauk, *n.*; *sparrow hawk* 194. 5.

sperlynges, *n.*; *smelts* 114. 13.

splendant, *adj.*; *resplendent* 130. 43.

splene, *n.*; (in phr.) on þe splene *in jest* 159. 5. (See Notes.)

spon, *n.*; *spoon* 43. 7.

spores, *n.*; *spurs* (back-claws of bird) 46. 15.

sport, *n.*; *entertainment* 2. 3.

spraulyn, *v. pr.* 3 *pl.*; *sprawl* 118. 8.

sprynge, *v.*; *to grow* (of vegetation) 67. 3.

spurne, *n.*; *stroke* 25. 7.

spute, *v.*; *to dispute* 180. 84.

spyll, *v.*; *to kill* 204. 14; spille 205. 78; *to meet with bad fortune* 130. 36; (*pt.* 3 *s.*) *destroyed* 178. 52.

spynne, *v.*; *to spin* 29 bur.; (*pp.*) y-spunne 28. 44.

sqynsye, *n.*; *quinsy* 81. 36.

stable, *adj.*; *trustworthy* 72. 28; 109. 2; stabyll, *constant* 136. 13.

stabulnesse, *n.*; *constancy* 131. 19.

stake, *n.*; *ale stake* (in front of tavern) 11. 4.

stalworthest, *adj.*; *most valiant* 58. 99.

standfra, *adj.*; *aloof, refractory* 212. 8.

stant, *v. pr.* 3 *s.*; *stands* 205. 81.

star, *v. pr. subj.* 3 *s.*; *look about with eyes wide open* (in madness or fury) 39. 4.

stark, *adj.*; *hard* 118. 14.

stave, *n. staff* 119. 43; stavfe 119. 72.

stayne, *v.*; *to lose colour* 140. 30; steyne, *to paint* 139. 14.

sted, *pp.*; *beset* 58. 82.

stede, *n.*; *place* 148. 3; in stede and stall, *everywhere* 58. 86; 135. 31.

stedfaste, *adj.*; *constant* 146. 6; stidfast 193. 15; stydfast 129. 6.

stedfastnesse, *n.*; *constancy* 131. 16.

stele, *n.*; *steel* 205. 128; stel 33. 22; stylle 195. 12.

stelle, *v.*; *to steal* 89. 3; (*pr.* 3 *s.*) stelys 89. 1; sstellyth 90. 3; (*pt.* 1 *s.*) stale 185. 4.

stelyd, *pp.*; *made of steel* 118. 14.

sterue, *v. pr.* 1 *s.*; *die* 188. 13.

steuyn, *n.*; *voice* 58. 104.

steyne, *see* stayne.

steyppes, *n.*; *footprints* 119. 31.

stille, *adv.*; *quietly* 101. 10; *without movement* 62. 13; 117. 7; style 119. 22.

stoken, *pp.*; *fastened* 100. 10.

stokke, *n.*; *anvil* 118. 14; stok, *stock* 198. 2.

stoppynge, *n.*; *stoppage* (of bodily organ) 81. 18, 68.

stound, *n.*; *thrill* (of delight) 132. 40; *time* (in phr.) at this stounde 81. 12; þat ilke stownde 180. 56.

stowpe, *v.*; *to bow down* (to superior power) 49. 16.

stowre, *n.*; *conflict, battle* 58. 99.

stowte, *adj.*; *obstinate* 41. 5; *menacing* 73. 56.

strange, *adj.*; *strong* 58. 26; stronge, *severe* 72. 75; 205. 48; strang, *arduous* 73. 19.

strange, *adj.*; *unusual* 76. 3; 136. 33.

strayte, *adj.*; *difficult* (in phr.) strayte breth, *shortness of breath* 81. 28.

strecche, *v.*; *to extend* 104. 13.

stremys, *n.*; *rays* (of light) 96. 37.

strete, *n.*; (in phr.) in the strete, *out of doors* 149. 4.

streyne, *v.*; *to clasp, encircle* 95. 5.

stripes, *n.*; *blows* 116. 17.

strumpeth, *n.*; *prostitute* 28. 38.

stycke, *v.*; *to hesitate* 32. 37.

stye, *n.*; *enclosure for animals* 49. 5.

stynte, *v.*; *to cease* 106. 10; (*pres. p.*) styntyng, *causing to cease* 184. 6.

suche, see swych.

suehte, *n.*; *sweeting* 95. 1.

sueit, see sweth.

suffisaunce, *n.*; *sufficiency* 78. 14.

suffereigne, *n.*; *sovereign* 130. 1; souerane 198. 42; soueraine 205. 1.

sugryd, *adj.*; *alluring* 211. 19.

sulphur viv, *n.*; *virgin sulphur* 88. 3.

superfluens, *n.*; *superabundance* 114. 6.

supportatyon, *n.*; *assistance* 207. 22.

surfetis, *n.*; *excessive eating* 78. 49; *morbid condition from excesses* 78. 76.

surfetrie, *n.*; *immoderate eating or drinking* 103. 12; 120. 53.

surplusage, *n.*; *superabundance* 131. 34.

surrance, *n.*; *grievance* 136. 45.

suster, *n.*; *sister* 45. 1.

suth, *n.*; *truth* 58. 45.

suttyll, *adj.*; *crafty* 76. 11; *abstruse* 77. 19.

suye, *v.*; *to petition* 130. 58.

suyes, *n.*; *sways, movements* 31. 25.

swaine, *n.*; *boy* 58. 18.

swappes, *n.*; *blows, strokes* 31. 16.

swarte, *adj.*; *black* 118. 1.

sweir, *adj.*; *indolent* 97. 19.

swete, *v.*; *to exude, sweat* 59. 35.

swete, *n.*; *beloved one* 134. 3.

sweth, *adj.*; *sweet* 143. 7; swyt 135. 20; swett, *dear* 26. 7; sqwete 144. 14; sueit 133. 11; (*sup.*) suotes, *most fragrant* 16. 3.

swett, *adv.*; *pleasing* 26. 1.

swetyng, *n.*; *beloved* 172. 6.

swych, *adj.*; *such* 21. 3; seche 164. 3; sic 132. 41; swech 118. 3; suche 37. 5; svch 44. 17; (*pro.*) swych 4. 7.

swynk, *v.*; *to labour* 44. 1.

swyuyd, *pp.*; *swived* 180. 2.

syde, *adv.*; *to the ground* 58. 29.

syes, *n.*; *sighs* 146. 2; syghys 163. 2.

syght, *v.*; *to sigh* 206. 10; syth 145. 4.

sykernesse, *n.*; *assurance* 187. 20.

sykke, *v. pr.* 1 *s.*; *sigh* 23. 7; sigh 172. 32.

syldom, *adv.*; *seldom* 13. 11; seld 76. 6; seldyn 171. 17; syldyn 135. 15.

sylly, *adj.*; *deserving of sympathy* 119. 60.

symplesse, *n.*; *simplicity* 106. 12; *innocence* 189. 6.

syphyr, *n.*; *cipher, person of no importance* 138. 12.

syth, see syght.

sythe, *conj.*; *since* 168. 11; san 196. 11; sen 133. 2; sethe 190. 5; seyne 136. 25; sithen 193. 25; syn 186. 17; sythyn 198. 38.

taberd, *n.*; *short coat* 59. 18.

tacched, *pp.*; *fastened* 94. 2.

taiclit, *pp.*; *entangled* (in) 212. 6.

tak to, *v.*; *to have recourse to* 59. 4; (*pr.* 3 *pl.*) tak, *capture* 114. 22.

tale, *v. pr.* 1 *s.*; *speak* 157. 3.

talent, *n.*; *inclination* 106. 19.

tappster, *n.*; *keeper of tavern*
11. 1.

taste, *v.*; *to have knowledge of*
136. 22.

tayil, *n.*; *tail* (of bird) 46. 8; 49.
22; tayl, *pudenda muliebra*
41. 15.

tayle, *n.*; *limitation of inheritors of an estate* 74. 11.

te, *def. art.*; *the* 18. 23; 48. 6.

tekyl, *adj.*; *excitable* 41. 15.

tempereth, *v. pr.* 3 *s.*; *tunes,
makes ready* 1. 19.

templers, *n.*; *templets, forehead
ornaments* 209. 44.

tender, *adj.*; *mild* 73. 44...

tene, *n.*; *misery* 119. 59.

tent, *n.*; *surgical probe* (fig.
penis) 31. 3.

terne, *adj.*; *fierce* 212. 15.

terrestreall, *adv.*; *in a worldly
way* 29. 23.

teyte, *adj.*; *cheerful* 211. 33.

than, see þo.

þar, *v. pr.* 3 *impers.*; *it is needful* (for) 58. 53; 103. 14.

þaut, *conj.*; *although* 9. 7.

the, *pro.*; *thee* 65. 2; 95. 5; 128.
4.

thee, see theyn.

þei, *conj.*; *although* 19 bur.

þen, *adv.*; *than* 197. 46.

þer, *adv.*; *where* 33. 15.

þer, *pro.*; *these* 73. 11.

theyn, *v.*; *to prosper* 72. 94; soo
mot I the 48. 17; thee 135. 19;
thye 135. 21.

þi, *pro.*; *they* 135. 19.

tho, *adv.*; *then* 9. 11; thoo 49.
24; þan 45. 22; than, *when*
190. 24.

tho, *pro.*; *those* 94. 13; 187. 5.

thow, *conj.*; *although* 22. 4;
thocht 132. 29; þough 205. 28;
thouh 107. 3; thovght 206. 69.

þredele, *v.*; *to tie* (with thread)
29. 10.

thrope, *n.*; *village* 93. 3.

þroth, *n.*; *throat* 29. 27.

throw, *n.*; *brief space of time*
36. 21; 180. 20.

thryfte, *n.*; *fortune* 208. 28.

thurght, *prep.*; *through* 73. 90;
thorw 103. 20; thurgh 120. 53;
thru3 179. 99; trught 136. 29.

thye, see theyn.

thyes, *n.*; *thighs* 31. 26.

thyke, *adj.*; *lowering* 72. 88.

thyng, *v.*; *to think* 192. 2; (*pr.
1 s.*) 162. 8; 168. 13; *remember*
20. 19; (*imp.*) dynke 146. 7;
(*pr.* 3 *impers.*) me þynkyt 27.
5; me-thynke 129. 19.

thynge, *n.*; *seeds* (pl.) 67. 3;
(fig.) *woman* 176. 2; þinke,
*matter* 135. 17.

thys, *adv.*; *thus, in this way* 119.
53; 129. 35; 162. 9; 169. 2.

till, *prep.*; *to* 133. 1.

till, *v.*; *to entice, win over* 58.
25.

tirtyll, *n.*; *turtle-dove* 38. 2;
turtill 205. 112.

to, *adv.*; *too* 78. 59; 176. 3.

to, *n.*; *toe* 28. 8; 49. 38; at my
too, *near me* 174. 5.

to, *prep.*; *for* 9. 4; *until* 35. 31;
189. 11; *as* 56. 23.

to, *pro.*; *two* 19. 5; too 22 bur.;
80. 3.

todryue, *v. pr. subj.* 3 *s.*; *dispel*
118. 16.

todyr, see oder.

tokynnynge, *n.*; *token* 194. 3.

ton, see on.

ton, *n.*; *tone, voice* 27. 2.

too, see to.

toth, *adj.*; *firm* 143. 6.

toth, *n.*; *thought* 143. 8; tho3th
143. 2.

toune, *n.*; *tun, barrel* 209. 38.

towght, *adj.*; *taut, congested* 1.
22.

toyn, *n.*; *tune* 4. 5.

travers, *n.*; *formal denial in law court* 178. 87.

traveyle, *n.*; *labour* 78. 68; 99. 4.

tray, *n.*; *grief* 144. 15.

trayl, *v.*; *to walk with trailing garments* 58. 29.

treble, *n.*; *a treble note* 118. 18.

trende, *v.*; *to turn round, rotate* 205. 82.

trew, *adj.*; *true, faithful* 33. 22; treu 33. 11; trw 195. 3; trwe 179. 31; trywe 22. 12.

trewe, *v. pr.* 1 *s.*; *suppose* 28. 33.

triable, *adj.*; *proved* 205. 112.

trill, *v.*; *to tirl, make rattling noise by moving something up and down* 36. 4; (*pt.* 3 *s.*) 36. 3.

trippede, *v. pt.* 3 *s.*; *trod lightly* 28. 8; (*pr.* 2 *pl.*) tryp, *dance* 209. 48; (*noun p.*) trippyng, *dancing* 28. 39.

trippus, *n.*; *steps in dancing* 28. 2.

triste, *n.*; *loyalty* 151. 3.

Troiles, *n.*; *Troilus* 190. 38.

trouble, *adj.*; *turbulent* 78. 27.

trouth, *n.*; *pledge* 173. 25; truthe 199. 10; trueth 123. 15; *honesty* 175. 6.

trow, *v. pr.* 1 *s.*; *believe* 1. 8; (*pr.* 2 *pl.*) 38. 25.

trught, see thurght.

trumpyt, *v. pt.* 3 *s.*; *blew a trumpet* 115. 4.

trym, *adj.*; *elegant* 35. 3.

trym, *adv.*; *properly, nicely* 26. 7.

trypys, *n.*; *tripe* 13. 11.

tufft, *n.*; *clump* 20. 12.

tumland, *pres. p.*; *tossing* 133. 10.

tuycioun, *n.*; *protection* 121. 22.

tweylffyt, *adj.*; *twelfth* 56. 11.

twylmouth, *n.*; *twelve month* 73. 3.

twyne, *v.*; *to separate* 134. 42.

twyneth, *v. pr.* 3 *s.*; *joins* 118. 18.

twynkelid, *v. pt.* 3 *s.*; *winked* 27. 17.

twynkelyng, *n.*; *winking* 28. 8; 116. 20.

tyde, *v. pr. subj.* 3 *s.*; *betide* 63. 13.

ty3t, *adv.*; *quickly* 59. 15; ty3tt 81. 54.

tyll, *prep.*; *to, toward* 115. 19.

tyll, *v.*; *to till, cultivate* 72. 91.

tymbris, *n.*; *timbers* 61. 1.

tyre, *v.*; *to draw* (breath) 199. 35.

vddir, see oder.

un, *prep.*; *on* 24. 9.

vnable, *adj.*; *incapable* 188. 73.

vnbeth, *pp.*; *not built up* 29. 6.

vnbynde, *v.*; *to untie* 134. 53; onbynde, *to cure* (sorrow) 158. 2.

vnchest, *adj.*; *impure* 212. 20.

un-colde, *adj.*; *vigorous, stinging* 116. 17.

vnconnyngly, *adv.*; *ignorantly* 98. 12.

vndo, *pp.*; *undone* 23 bur.; *opened* 81. 8.

vndyt, *pp.*; *unclosed* 88. 34.

vnfayn, *adj.*; *displeased* 162. 5.

vnfeynyngly, *adv.*; *sincerely* 169. 19.

unhance, *v.*; *to bring down, depress* 136. 29.

vnkothe, *pp.*; *unknown* 134. 28.

vnleill, *adj.*; *unfaithful* 212. 5.

vn-loke, *v. imp.*; *unlock* 6. 3.

vnneth, *adv.*; *with difficulty* 109. 8.

vnrepe, *pp.*; *uncut* 29. 7.

unryd, *adj.*; *violent* 53. 7.

vnsward, *v. pt.* 3 *s.*; *answered* 181. 49.

vnswope, *pp.*; *unswept* 29. 5.

vntill, *prep.*; *unto* 58. 6.

vpryst, *n.*; *arising* (out of bed) 189. 21.

vre, *n.*; *fortune, luck* 186. 2;
188. 34.

vre, *n.*; *custom* 173. 21; *use,
performance* 32. 30.

urthely, see erdlie.

vsaunce, *n.*; *custom* 192. 3.

vtterly, *adv.*; *emphatically* 59. 2;
137. 3; weterly 73. 47.

valeys, *n.*; *valleys* 88. 43; wallay 119. 10.

variant, *adj.*; *inconstant* 209
rub.

varyaunce, *n.*; *inconstancy* 131.
17.

veleny, *n.*; *insult* (in phr.) sey
me no veleny, *do not defame
me* 50. 11.

vemous, *adj.*; *venemous* 121. 30.

veyllabyl, *adj.*; *profitable* 99. 8.

visage, *n.*; *face* 127. 35.

vitaile, *n.*; *produce* 72. 53.

vith, *prep.*; *with* 1 bur.

vleth, *n.*; *floor* 29. 5.

vowchasafe, *v. imp.*; *vouchsafe*
198. 37; 199. 26.

voyde, *adj.*; *ineffective* 77. 18.

wafeyyng, *pres. p.*; *waving* 114.
25.

waik, *adj.*; *weak* 58. 39.

wake, *v.*; *to pass the night* (by a
well) 25 bur.; (*pt.* 1 *s.*) woke
25. 1.

walaway, *n.*; *lamentation* 73.
34.

walkyn, *v. pr.* 1 *s.*; *awaken* 133.
12.

wallay, see valeys.

wame, *n.*; *scar* 132. 45.

wan, see quan.

war, *adj.*; *vigilant* 87. 6; waere
179. 25.

war, *v. pr.* 3 *pl.*; *know* 73. 1.

warant, *n.*; *evidence of authori-
zation* 106. 7.

wardly, see worldly.

ware, *adv.*; *where* 28. 38; whare
58. 36; quhair 97. 17; qwer
50. 6.

ware, *n.*; *merchandise* 7. 4;
*watchful care* 60. 3; *target*
(pudenda muliebra) 30. 5.

ware, *v. imp.*; *avoid* 78. 50.

wariabull, *adj.*; *variable* 181. 35.

wariat, *adj.*; *varied in nature*
181. 41.

warne, *v.*; *to refuse* 24. 8; (*pr.*
1 *s.*) *inform* 43. 1.

warrantyse, *n.*; *warranty of
security of title to estate* 74. 18.

wary, *v. pr.* 1 *s.*; *curse* 133. 14.

washe, *n.*; *washing* 34. 6.

wast, *v. pr.* 2 *pl.*; *consume* 1. 39;
wast wynd, *speak to no pur-
pose* 1. 43.

wat, *n.*; *hare* 119. 60; watte
119. 26.

water-bowge, *n.*; *skin water-
bottle* 209. 21.

wayle, *v. pr.* 1 *s.*; *choose, seek*
106. 21.

waytes, *n.*; *musicians* 122. m.

waytnas, *v. imp.*; *witness* 100. 8.

web, *n.*; *cataract* 81. 25.

wedde, *n.*; *pledge* 33. 12; wed
58. 41.

wede, *n.*; *garment* 58. 88.

wede, *v. pr.* 1 *s.*; *remove weeds*
67. 6.

wedowis, *n.*; *widows* 41. 9.

wele, *v. pr.* 3 *s.*; *will* 21. 7; 107.
7; welethe 190. 35; wel 80. 6;
(*pr.* 2 *pl.*) wald 133. 7; (*pt.* 3 *s.*)
wowld 115. 11; (*pt. subj.* 3 *s.*)
wilde 190. 13; (*pr.* 3 *s.*) nylle
179. 32; (*pt.* 3 *s.*) nolde 28. 28;
(*pr.* 2 *s.*) wyltow 187. 7.

well, see wiel.

well, *n.*; *well* 25 bur.; 204. 18.

welle, *adj.*; *good* 18. 7; *fortunate*
52. 7; 127. 24.

welle, *adv.*; *very* 9. 5; 127. 18;
wyll 12. 4; wol 41. 9; wel 180.

21; *satisfactory* 19. 11; *fully*
28. 39; *certainly* 22. 20; **weill**
132. 22; **wyl,** *well* 5. 9; **weel** 96.
17; **wele** 104. 2.

**welle-spring,** *n.*; *spring* 18. 20.

**wend,** *v.*; *to go* 119. 14; (*pr.*.2
*pl.*) 205. 84; (*pr.* 3 *pl.*) 179. 68;
(*pp.*) **went,** *turned from* 148. 2.

**wennissun,** *n.*; *venison* 56. 23.

**wenyn,** *v.*; *to think* 4. 2; (*pr.*
1 *s.*) 28. 36; (*pr.* 2 *s.*) **wenest**
44. 15; **wenis** 181. 27; (*pt.* 1 *s.*)
**wende** 23. 2; (in phr.) **I wene**
72. 55; 73. 49.

**were,** *n.*; *doubt* 178. 54.

**were,** *n.*; *wearing* 28. 18.

**werre,** *adv.*; *worse* 116. 15.

**werrour,** *n.*; *defender* 204. 21.

**werue,** *n.*; *reel, whorl of a spindle*
29. 2.

**wete,** *v.*; *to dip, steep* (in) 54. 3.

**wey,** *adv.*; *away* 180. 11.

**wey,** *v. pr.* 3 *s.*; *weigh* 179. 104.

**wher-as,** *adv.*; *wherever* 32. 10;
129. 10.

**where,** *adv.*; *whether* 80. 5.

**wheris,** *v. pr.* 1 *s.*; *wears* 135.
28.

**whityng,** *n.*; *whiting* 114. 8.

**whoo,** see **wo** (adv.).

**whyt,** *adj.*; *white* 13. 2; **quit**
147. 7; 196. 20; **qwyt** 46. 15;
**qwyte** 5. 5; **whight** 47. 5; **wyth**
28. 18; **wyte** 33. 4.

**wiel,** *n.*; *happiness* 145. 1; **well**
167. 9.

**will,** see **wyle.**

**wille,** *n.*; *pleasure* 23. 10; *wil-
fulness* 38. 22; **wyll,** *wish* 24. 8;
207. 12; *sexual desire* 24. 10;
180. 4.

**wit,** *v.*; *to know* 1. 4; **wete** 73. 3;
**wette** 200. 10; **wyett** 195. 15;
**wyt** 188. 47; (*pr.* 1 *s.*) **wait** 133.
22; **wat** 127. 61; **wet** 132. 22;
**wot** 69. 1; 158. 8; **wott** 134. 4;
**wyst** 138. 22; (*pr.* 2 *s.*) **wytt**

188. 5; **wyst** 135. 4; (*pr.* 3 *s.*)
**wot** 38. 35; (*imp.*) **wite** 102. 1;
**wote** 173. 11; (*pt.* 1 *s.*) **wot**
25. 17; (*pt.* 3 *s.*) **wist** 36. 25;
(in phr.) **had y wyst** 40. 5.

**with-all,** *adv.*; *in addition* 2. 3;
*therewith* 4. 6.

**without,** *conj.*; *unless* 1. 27; 25.
19.

**witt,** see **wyt.**

**witty,** *adj.*; *crafty, knowledge-
able* 58. 22.

**wnther,** *prep.*; *under* 48. 19.

**wo,** *adv.*; *cursed* (with **welle**)
9. 5; **whoo** (in phr. **whoo be
the whyle**) 129. 33.

**wo,** *n.*; *woe* 128. 37; **woo** 34. 8;
**wo worth,** *it shall be ill for* 206.
25.

**wo,** *pro.*; *who* 109. 1; **ho** 50. 2;
164. 5.

**wod,** *adj.*; *mad* 44. 6; **wode** 73.
70.

**woddowes,** *n.*; *wood-pigeons*
114. 19.

**wodknyffes,** *n.*; *hunting knives*
114. 19.

**wol,** see **welle.**

**wond,** see **wynde.**

**wonder,** *adj.*; *curious* 179. 7.

**wonder,** *adv.*; *exceedingly* 25.
14; **wonderly** 38. 14.

**wonyt,** *pp.*; *accustomed* 150. 5.

**woo,** *adj.*; *woeful* 22. 4; **wa**
145. 1.

**worchith,** *v. pr.* 3 *s.*; *works* 77.
10; (*pr.* 3 *s.*) **wyrkyth** 179. 77;
(*pr.* 3 *pl.*) **worchen** 211. 12.

**worchype,** *n.*; *source of honour*
198. 34; **wershype** 204. 25;
**wirchepe** 203. 1.

**word,** *n.*; *world* 119. 57.

**worldly,** *adj.*; *worldly* 140. 1;
**wardly** 136. 10.

**worly,** *adj.*; *attractive* 28. 12.

**worshipped,** *pp.*; *conferred
honour upon* 36. 11.

worȝt, *adj.*; *worth* 43. 15.

wortes, *n.*; *herbs* 27. 14; **worton** 29. 9.

worte-wale, *n.*; *root of a cock's spur* 46. 16.

wow, *v.*; *to make love to* 29. 35; (*pr.* 2 *s.*) wowe 41. 2; (*pres. p.*) wowyng 41 bur.

wowkes, *n.*; *weeks* 21. 19.

woyde, *v. imp.*; *avoid* 78. 54; (*pr.* 2 *s.*) voyde 81. 82.

writhe, *v. imp.*; *write* 66 rub.; wryte 66 end rub.

wroght, *pp.*; *fashioned* 128. 20; wrocht 132. 22; wrout 127. 51; wroȝte, *laboured* 134. 18.

wroth, *adj.*; *angry* 38. 23; wrath 58. 47; wrathe 134. 6.

wroþe, *adv.*; *badly* 42. 8.

wrye, *v. imp.*; *accuse* 205. 33.

wryng, *v.*; *to wring* (one's hands) 51. 11; (*pr.* 1 *s.*) *wring out* (from eyes) 205. 67.

wrynge, *n.*; *wringing* (of clothes) 34. 6.

wy, *v.*; *to weigh, consider* 24. 6.

wybbe, *v.*; *to weave* 29 bur.

wycars, *n.*; *vicars* (priests acting for rectors) 56. 6.

wyf, *n.*; *wife* 48. 21; wif 88. 7; wyve, *woman* 127. 68; wyffys 119. 49.

wyght, *n.*; *creature, person* 34. 9; wicht 132. 3; wight 178. 3; wyȝt 135. 20; wyȝth 66. 3.

wyked, *n.*; *wretched person* 198. 24.

wyl, see welle.

wyle, *adv.*; *while* 28. 42; quhill 97. 11; qwyll 181. 39; whylle 198. 11; whylys 166. 4; *will, until* 48. 24; quhill 132. 19.

wyle, *n.*; *time, occasion* 28 bur.; wile 194. 10.

wyll, *n.*; *testament* 206. 57.

wylly, *adj.*; *crafty* 24. 2.

wyltow, see wele.

wympeles, *n.*; *veils, head-dresses* 7. 3.

wyn, *v.*; *to acquire* 58. 63.

wynd, *n.*; *scent* (of animal in hunting) 119. 20.

wynde, *v.*; *to wind, roll* 134. 52; (*pt.* 1 *s.*) wond, *wound* (thread) 29. 2.

wyne, *n.*; *wine* 6. 6; wyin 56. 19; wyn 21. 15.

wynk, *v.*; *to close one's eyes* 39. 1; 192. 12; *to have one's eyes shut* 170. 4.

wynne, *n.*; *delight* 179. 62.

wys, *adj.*; *wise* 99. 12; wisse 72. 83; wysse 74. 21.

wys, *adv.*; *certainly* 33. 14; wysse 198. 22; *wisely* 73. 9; see i-wis.

wyssyng, *pres. p.*; *wishing* 173. 7.

wyt, *prep.*; *with* 15. 3; witt 56. 3; 134. 6; 195. 1.

wyt, *n.*; *mind, wits* 4. 2; wette 190. 28; *knowledge* 102. 4.

wyth, see whyt.

wythstand, *v.*; *to prevent* 187. 7.

xul, see sal.

yafe, see gyue.

yarde, *n.*; *barn-yard* 48. 5.

y-benth, see bente.

y-brent, *pp.*; *consumed* 162. 18.

y-closyd, *pp.*; (in phr.) **y-closyd aboue**, *covered in* 82. 3.

ye, *pro.*; *you* 1. 5; ȝe 4. 1; yie 136. 13; ow 19. 2; ȝou 43. 1; ȝow 19. 4; you 1. 11; yw 6. 1.

yede, *v. pt.* 3 *s.*; *went* (in phr.) **yede to**, *went about his work* 48. 2.

yeris, see eyre.

yfere, *adv.*; *together* 146. 4.

yhe, see she.

yholde, *pp.*; *obliged* 33. 16; halden 58. 60.

ying, *adj.*; *young* 127. 74; **yong**
176. 2.

y-low, *adv.*; *on the ground* 29.
34.

ymagerie, *n.*; *pictures* (in phr.)
**boke of ymagerie,** *finely illus-*
*trated manuscript* 100. 1.

yng, *n.*; *ink* 192. 9; **inke** 197.
46; **hynke** 195. 10.

y-noghe, see i-now.

ynvyws, *adj.*; *envious* 76. 13.

yoie, *n.*; *joy* 198. 20.

yoore, *adv.*; (in phr.) **ful yoore**
**agoon,** *a long time ago* 96.
30.

you-ward, *adv.*; (in phr.) **to**
**youward,** *towards you* 205. 84.

your, *pro.*; *yours* 138. 40.

yowes, *v.*; *to use* 85. 1.

y-wys, see i-wis.

# INDEX OF FIRST LINES

PRINTED IN GREAT BRITAIN
AT THE UNIVERSITY PRESS, OXFORD
BY VIVIAN RIDLER
PRINTER TO THE UNIVERSITY